D0903535

Principles
of
ANIMAL
BIOLOGY

Principles of ANIMAL BIOLOGY

LAWRENCE S. DILLON

Professor of Biology, Texas A & M University

In collaboration with
ELIZABETH S. DILLON

The Macmillan Company, New York
Collier-Macmillan Limited, London

First Printing

Portions of this book previously appeared under the title *The Science of Life,* © copyright 1964 by Lawrence S. Dillon.

Library of Congress catalog card number: 65-12478

The Macmillan Company,
New York

Collier-Macmillan Canada, Ltd.,
Toronto, Ontario

Printed in the United States of America

Designed by Andrew P. Zutis

The imaginative and original mind need not be overawed by the imposing body of present knowledge or by the complex and costly paraphernalia which today surround much of scientific activity. The great shortage in science now is not opportunity, manpower, money, or laboratory space. What is really needed is more of that healthy skepticism which generates the key idea—the liberating concept.

P. H. ABELSON

Preface

Among the thousands of higher educational institutions of the world, virtually all of which offer courses in zoology, there must certainly exist scores of widely different approaches to the teaching of the subject. Particularly is this diversification true of one-semester (or one- or two-quarter) courses in which, because of the limitations of time, all aspects of the science cannot possibly be covered; consequently, the topics included therein must be selected to meet the peculiar requirements of the students. Although details vary from campus to campus, such abbreviated courses appear to fall into three major categories: In the first, stress is placed upon acquainting the students with the major types of animal life, with the result that principles and the vertebrates receive only minimal attention. At the opposite end of the scale, no (or almost no) consideration is given to systematic aspects —principles and vertebrate physiology being the chief items of concern. And, finally, the third approach to course content attempts to follow a middle path, with the inclusion of a quick survey of animal types along with some detailed study of cellular and vertebrate physiology and the major zoological concepts. To provide for the latter two types of introductory zoology courses this textbook has been particularly designed, with subdivision of content into sections and chapters carefully made to permit the requisite flexibility.

Flexibility, however, is a matter of arrangement of convenience, not a major goal. Were one principal objective in preparing this text to be selected, probably that of up-dating the whole content of introductory zoology would be chosen. While a few books at this same level have modernized one or two aspects of the science, other fields are frequently treated like so many old court records, in which nothing new could possibly take place. Doubtlessly the so-called molecular facets of zoology have produced some striking—and often highly publicized—results, but progress has been made even in such old disciplines as morphology and systematics. To avoid slighting any major field, so far as time considerations permitted, each has been treated as a research project during the preparation of the manuscript, and the literature in every case searched accordingly.

If modernity of contents ranks first, avoidance of dogma must follow closely in second place among the author's objectives. Far too often in the teaching of this subject the student is presented with but a single set of ideas, so that he gains the impression that all in zoology is already cut and dried, with few discoveries left for new investigators to make. For example, to the present writer it is incomprehensible why, when two major theories of muscle contraction exist, and both of these imperfectly substantiated, only one should be presented, and this as though it has been demonstrated true beyond doubt. Moreover, even though the instructor must of necessity follow a single scheme of classification, should not the beginning zoologist at least be fully aware of the existence of others? All is not "old shoe," even in systematics. Is progress in science simply a matter of picking up new facts or concepts, like so many precut diamonds, and presenting them in the literature, or is strife sometimes involved with argument, not always entirely objective in its nature, occasionally developing? Even freshmen in college or university are sufficiently mature to comprehend the humanity of scientists and to appreciate the struggle through which lasting progress is made. Of still greater importance, the presentation of differing views implies a need for selection on the part of the reader, and choice in turn demands thoughtful consideration; the value of the processes involved requires no discussion here.

Other objectives also were in mind as this textbook was prepared. But if an appreciation of the nature of the organic world, an understanding of the differences and likenesses that exist between animals, a comprehension of man's true position in the scheme of living things, and an awareness of the threadwork of unity that ties all of life together are not achieved by reading the following pages, a detailed outlining of these goals here would be meaningless indeed.

As in the case of most books, the assistance of many persons has been required during its preparation. First of all, by carefully reading and criticizing the entire manuscript, Dr. Norman S. Kerr, of the University of Minnesota, has aided materially with his constructive suggestions. Furthermore, innumerable scientists and organizations have contributed to the clarity of the contents by generously supplying illustrative materials, but their assistance is more appropriately acknowledged individually with the reproductions. However, one source of such aid is deserving of special mention here. Through Dr. K. A. Siegesmund and his associates, the Bob Quinn Memorial Electron Microscope Laboratory at Marquette University has supplied numerous electron micrographs of unusual quality, and for the generous gift of prints the author is indeed grateful.

LAWRENCE S. DILLON

Contents

ix

PART VI

The Consequences of Genetic Changes

PART I

Basic Principles

So UNIQUE are the typical animals as a group that at first glance they seemingly form a world separate and distinct from the realm of the plants. For instance, little difficulty is experienced in distinguishing either caterpillars or deer from the leaves on which they feed or, for that matter, in differentiating them from the bacteria and fungi which frequently attack their bodies. Yet upon closer comparison of even these highly diverse types, there are found many fundamental characteristics which serve to unify them as well as all other living things. Regardless of whether an organism is a tree or a bear, a mushroom or an amoeba, a microorganism or a whale, each shares with all the rest an abundance of identical chemical processes and characteristics, as well as numerous features of structure. In this first portion of the text, it is these similarities and general principles common to the whole of life that will occupy our attention.

It is the great destiny of human science, not to ease man's labor or to prolong his life, noble as those ends may be, nor to serve the ends of power, but to enable man to walk upright without fear in a world he at length will understand and which is his home.

PAUL B. SEARS

The Science of Zoology

As you probably already know, zoology is one of the principal subdivisions of biology, which in turn is one of the natural sciences. All the natural sciences, such as physics, chemistry, and astronomy, together form that major segment of human knowledge which is concerned with objects in nature. Their functions are those of gathering facts and arranging them systematically in such a fashion that the general laws of nature may be disclosed. In the processes of collecting facts and setting them in order, theories or hypotheses are usually proposed; these assist the scientists either in the devising of further experiments or by directing their observations. There is nothing imposing or awesome about theories, nor is there, contrary to certain views currently circulating, anything mysterious or supernatural about any of the sciences—the former

are guides, the latter highly organized bodies of facts, and that is all. Nor can science alone, as some appear to believe, solve every single human problem; many of the most perplexing require the aid of the social sciences as well as liberal applications of high moral values and the great virtues.

The Facts of Science

First a few words are necessary about the nature of the facts with which science deals. Since the word "fact," mistakenly but frequently nevertheless, is taken to be synonymous with "truth," its usage is often avoided in scientific writings by substituting the term *datum* (plural *data*). Actually both terms, facts and data, apply equally to observations of reality; hence, they denote truths in a

3

restricted sense, but certainly not truths of universal implication. For example, let us suppose that last night, being exceptionally exhausted, you went to bed at 9:30 P.M. This is a set of facts that are demonstrably true, and so in a limited sense are a body of truths. Yet no one would consider them absolute truths that are universally established and applicable; otherwise not only you but everyone else would have to retire simultaneously every night! And even if such were in reality the case, the data would be a universal truth only for the present time and would not necessarily appertain to past or future generations. Truths with a capital T, as it were, are philosophical concepts, not observable details.

Nor are observed details always clear and distinct; more usually there is a broad range of variability into which the facts fall. One can scarcely state, by way of illustration, that in a certain kind of rodent the heart beats 155 times per minute. This statement might be true as an average or *mean* when hundreds of examples are studied, but more than likely many specimens would have a faster rate of beating and numerous others a slower one. Moreover, even these rates would depend on the conditions. A rodent that had been rapidly running or digging would obviously have a more actively beating heart than one that had been sleeping. So the heart rate for the rodent would in actuality have a range of 92 to 207, for instance, with a mean of 155 under resting conditions at 20°C. Thus each set of data is true only as mean values and solely under the conditions specified. Moreover, the data only approach reality. To illustrate, it might be suggested that the foregoing data had been obtained through a study on 1,000 specimens of the rodent. If 10,000 are studied, perhaps the mean may be found to be 156.1, and if 100,000, maybe 155.803.

While no one is ever likely to carry such a project further, it is conceivable that future studies based on a larger number under better controlled conditions might still more refine the mean and hence even more closely approximate the actual, or "true," value.

Furthermore, it must be borne in mind that actual observations may not always be entirely dependable; what one sees, in other words, should not necessarily be believed. To realize the truth of this statement, one need only gaze out the window for a few minutes. Then to anyone with two eyes the world appears flat and the sun seemingly moves across the skies. As the student knows, these observations were accepted as representing the actual facts for countless centuries; only after astronomical data had been obtained by exacting procedures were the earlier data shown to be superficial and fallacious. And only then could the current concepts regarding the earth's shape and its interrelationships with the sun and stars be formulated. In the interest of both objectivity and accuracy, scientists devise and perfect instruments as far as possible to obtain their data, rather than depend solely on their sense organs. Perhaps the "facts" of the matter will become even clearer if you follow the instructions under Figure 1–1 and determine the reliability of your own color observations.

The Methods of Science

Since science deals with facts, it has been necessary for scientists to devise means of objectively determining what is really reliable and what is not. One criterion that has been established in connection with experimentation is that of *repeatability*. Under a given set of conditions, an experiment should always pro-

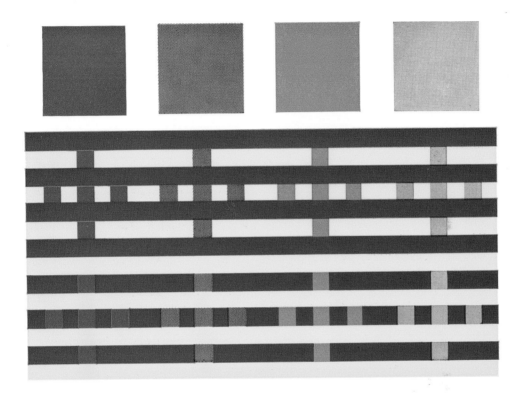

Figure 1–1. The subjective nature of observed facts. First, holding the book as for ordinary reading, compare corresponding sets of small color blocks. Perhaps you will find the upper ones placed within yellow stripes very slightly darker than those below located in the blue ones, despite the fact that both sets are printed with exactly the same inks as in the large squares along the top. This, however, is not especially striking. But now, hold the book at arm's length and tilt it away from you, or place it open on the table and stand back from it, and again compare the colors of corresponding blocks. The lower the angle of view, the better. Can you now understand why scientists often pay hundreds or thousands of dollars for instruments which measure actual wave lengths of light rather than making visual color comparisons? (Courtesy of Prof. W. D. Wright and the *Ciba Review*.)

TABLE 2-1

RELATIVE ABUNDANCE OF THE 12 CHIEF CHEMICAL ELEMENTS IN PROTOPLASM

| Element | | | Relative Abundance per 10,000 Atoms | | | |
Symbol	Name	Atomic weight	In whole protoplasm	Organic portion	Inorganic portion Water	Inorganic portion Salts
H	Hydrogen	1	6140	1360	4778	2
O	Oxygen	16	2655	262	2389	4
C	Carbon	12	965	963		2
N	Nitrogen	14	141	140		1
Ca	Calcium	40	37	34		3
K	Potassium	39	25	23		2
P	Phosphorus	31	19	16		3
Na	Sodium	23	6.2	2		4.2
Cl	Chlorine	35	5.6			5.6
S	Sulfur	32	4.3	4.2		0.1
Mg	Magnesium	24	1.2	1.19		0.01
Fe	Iron	56	0.1	0.1		
—	Others	—	0.6	0.5		0.1
	Totals		10,000	2805.99	7167	27.01

THE INORGANIC PORTION

Among the inorganic constituents of protoplasm, water, salts, and gases are represented; the first of these is the most abundant single substance present, comprising from 60 to 95 per cent by weight of the whole. In living matter this compound serves to dissolve or suspend within itself most of the remaining material. Moreover, through its fluidity, water undoubtedly assists in the movement of chemicals throughout the mass of protoplasm, and through its property of breaking many compounds into ions, it aids in bringing about numerous chemical reactions, often entering directly into these reactions itself. In fact there are few activities in living matter in which water does not actively participate.

The remainder of the inorganic fraction is small indeed, being less as a rule than 0.3 per cent of protoplasm and largely in the form of salts. Although minor in concentration, these salts, es-pecially those of calcium, potassium, and sodium, are exceedingly important in assisting in bringing about many of life's activities. Moreover, many are involved in the maintenance of the proper degree of acidity or alkalinity by their buffering effects; particularly are the carbonates and phosphates active in this manner. By the term *buffer* is meant a substance that is able to stabilize the degree of acidity in the medium in which it is present. The acidity of a solution depends on the relative number of hydrogen ions (H^+) free within it, a number usually stated in terms of pH, in which the "p" is the exponent (i.e., the power) of 10. This or any number raised to the power of 0 is, as you know, equal to 1, and in measuring pH, this exponent is used to designate a solution that is as acid as possible, that is, has the maximum number of free hydrogen ions (Table 2–2). Since the exponents are negative, a pH of 1 implies that the solution is only one-tenth as acid as possible, of 2, one-hundredth,

TABLE 2-2

HYDROGEN AND HYDROXYL ION CONCENTRATION AND THE QUALITY OF THE RESULTING SOLUTIONS

pH	Mathematical Expression	Relative Hydrogen (H^+) Ion Concentration	pOH	Relative Hydroxyl (^-OH) Ion Concentration	Mathematical Expression	Quality
0	10^0	1.0	14	0.00000000000001	10^{-14}	Acid
1	10^{-1}	0.1	13	0.0000000000001	10^{-13}	"
2	10^{-2}	0.01	12	0.000000000001	10^{-12}	"
3	10^{-3}	0.001	11	0.00000000001	10^{-11}	"
4	10^{-4}	0.0001	10	0.0000000001	10^{-10}	"
5	10^{-5}	0.00001	9	0.000000001	10^{-9}	"
6	10^{-6}	0.000001	8	0.00000001	10^{-8}	"
7	10^{-7}	0.0000001	7	0.0000001	10^{-7}	Neutral
8	10^{-8}	0.00000001	6	0.000001	10^{-6}	Alkaline
9	10^{-9}	0.000000001	5	0.00001	10^{-5}	"
10	10^{-10}	0.0000000001	4	0.0001	10^{-4}	"
11	10^{-11}	0.00000000001	3	0.001	10^{-3}	"
12	10^{-12}	0.000000000001	2	0.01	10^{-2}	"
13	10^{-13}	0.0000000000001	1	0.1	10^{-1}	"
14	10^{-14}	0.00000000000001	0	1.0	10^0	"

and so on. Similarly alkalinity is the result of the relative abundance of hydroxyl ions (^-OH) free in a solution, and one could measure pOH equally as well as pH. However, as the two concentrations are codependent, a measurement of one also supplies the concentration of the other, so as a rule it is customary to determine just the hydrogen ion concentration.

Buffers maintain the pH, at least within certain limitations, by combining with any acids or bases (alkalies) that may be added to a solution containing them, reacting in such a manner that the added substance is neutralized. For example, if hydrochloric acid (HCl) is added to a solution containing sodium bicarbonate, the following reaction occurs:

$$NaHCO_3 + HCl \rightarrow$$
$$NaCl + H_2O + CO_2 \uparrow$$

In this case, the acid combines with the sodium bicarbonate to form a salt, water, and carbon dioxide, the last being given off as a gas; thus no hydrogen ions from the acid are added to the solution, and the acidity remains unchanged. Similarly if a base, such as sodium hydroxide (NaOH), is added to a bicarbonate solution, the following reaction takes place:

$$NaHCO_3 + NaOH \rightarrow Na_2CO_3 + H_2O$$

Here the hydroxyl ions are removed by combination with the hydrogen in the bicarbonate to form water; so once more the concentration of free ions remains unchanged.

In addition to water and salts, a third sort of inorganic matter, *gases,* may be present in protoplasm. Largely these consist of oxygen, nitrogen, carbon dioxide, and ammonia, the latter two being by-products of the protoplasm's chemical processes and the first two being absorbed from the environment. In most organisms, nitrogen as a gas is almost always entirely inert, the sole exception being in the bacteria, which can "fix" this element directly. Oxygen is, of course, vital to metabolic activities; in addition, it may be a by-product of photosynthesis.

duce similar results, no matter whether it is performed in Maine or California, in Germany or South America, or whether it is carried out by one worker or another. Briefly the procedure works out much in this manner: Upon satisfying himself that a series of experiments yields results which are repeatable and which contain pertinent new facts, a scientist will publish his results, along with a description of his material and procedures, in a suitable scientific journal. When this "paper," as scientific articles are called, appears in print, other scientists interested in the same area of investigation may attempt to repeat the experiments in their own laboratories, duplicating the original conditions and techniques as closely as possible. The results of these confirmatory experiments, whether positive or negative, are published subsequently as parts of other papers or as brief notes. In this way the original facts become incorporated into, or excluded from, the total body of knowledge. Sciences advance primarily through the publication of articles, each of which is subject to the critical study of all scientists interested in its content, both those living at the time and those of the future. Every effort is made to weed out all unreliable statements and theories, although sometimes in practice the weeding-out process is exceedingly slow.

Theories are of many sorts, differing primarily in the extent of the material covered. Some are minor working *hypotheses,* preliminary guesses, as it were, about cause, relationships, and so on. For instance, were one working on digestion, using the rat as the experimental animal and noting that it appeared able to digest fats, one might hypothesize, "The liver secretes a substance that digests fats." Accordingly one would devise experiments using the liver to see whether or not such was the case. If nothing in liver secretions could be found that appeared to break down fats, a new theory would be set up; perhaps, "The pancreas secrets a fat-digesting substance." If success were not met with, the stomach secretions could be tried, or the intestinal, or various combinations, until a fat-digesting secretion were encountered. These hypotheses would never be published as such; only the results of the experiments based upon them would warrant publication. As knowledge of the digestive functions increased widely through the processes of data collecting illustrated above, a second sort of theory might be proposed, one that encompasses a much larger area of the science. On the basis of preliminary observations and broad experience with the subject, one scientist might reach the theory, "All mammals have precisely the same fat-digesting substance in their pancreatic juices." When he had gathered all available data dealing with many diverse mammals, had made exhaustive chemical analyses, and had found them in agreement with the supposition, he would be more than justified in publishing his *theory,* along with the supporting evidence, for theories such as this serve to organize and integrate a considerable segment of knowledge. Still other theories are even broader and attempt to aid in the organization of all the knowledge included in one of the sciences. In this category of broadly inclusive concepts can be listed the relativity theories of physics and astronomy, the atomic theory of matter, and the evolutionary theory of biology. None of this type are clearly demonstrable, nor, at this early stage of scientific development, is any likely to be found perfect as originally conceived. All will probably be seen to need revision as knowledge increases and as more and more exceptions to their generalizations accumulate. Theories that prove to be essentially correct and of broad application generally become accepted after considerable time as *principles*. Only after a theory has been demonstrated beyond doubt to be universally true is it accepted as a *law*, although this term is frequently used also in other senses.

It must be remembered, too, that not all natural objects lend themselves to experimentation; some natural bodies or certain of their aspects are studied primarily by observation. Just as with data collected through experimentation, results obtained using this second method of approach are made meaningful and are organized by means of theories of the various types discussed above. To distinguish between fact and fancy on an objective basis, observations are made in accordance with firmly established terminology, each term, ideally at least, being clearly and sharply defined. Such definitions serve as measuring sticks so that precise descriptions of the object in hand and its attributes can be made. For example, body organs are universally accepted today as being composed of varied layers of like cells that work together. Such layers of cells are called "tissues." Hence, if in some organism a group of cells is encountered and if these cells are found to be alike and appear to work together, they may be referred to by this term; if one or more of these attributes is lacking, some other term would need to be applied. While the foregoing process of creating and applying definitions appears simple enough, many objects and concepts are not readily definable. Nevertheless, if a science is to strive for exactitude, all its terms must eventually be sharply defined. In fact, if a precise definition of any given concept or term proves to be an impossibility, such concepts or terms should be open to serious doubt as to their validity, and new ones

that can be sharply delimited should be substituted for them. In this book the attempt will be made to scrutinize all terms to ascertain whether they can be rigidly defined or not. We shall begin by defining the particular natural science with which we are concerned.

Zoology as a Science

Since zoology, as has already been stated, is a major subdivision of that natural science called biology, the latter term must be defined first, possibly as that natural science concerned with the study of life and of things that possess life, including their relationships both to one another and to their environment. Now according to the statements made above, if this definition is to be meaningful, all its terms must be found clear and sharply limited. When examined, the terms "natural science" and "life" are seen to be employed, the first of which, but not the second, has already been defined. Although the precise import of the second term is difficult to set into words, until we have done so we really shall be unable to know with what biology is concerned as a science. Therefore the following definition of the obscure term is proposed here: *Life* is the term applied to the sum of the manifestations of the peculiar chemical processes known as metabolism. While the word "manifestations" and the phrase "peculiar chemical processes" are vague at present, the former will be enlarged upon in the next chapter and the latter in Chapter 4, after which this definition will be found clear and sharply delimited. Only then will our statement concerning the nature of biology be completely meaningful.

Similarly even the simple definition of *zoology* as that branch of biology concerned with the study of animals cannot be entirely lucid until the word animal has been defined. On the proper limits of this term no general agreement has as yet been reached, but the matter will receive closer attention later (page 94). Because of the uncertainties that exist, however, especially in regard to the proper assignment of the unicellular forms, the term *organism,* referring to a living thing in general, finds occasional use in subsequent sections.

THE BRANCHES OF ZOOLOGY

Among natural objects, organisms are unique in their seemingly endless ability to vary, a ceaseless variation that is displayed both individually and as a group. On one hand, virtually no two individuals of any single type of organism are precisely identical in all respects; on the other, collectively the variability has resulted in the formation of an estimated 10 million *species* (i.e., distinct kinds) of things living on our earth today, each of which differs as a unit from all the others at least in several distinct traits. Although this interminable variation adds to the difficulties of zoology as a science and causes it to lack the precision of the mathematically based sciences of physics and astronomy, at the same time it adds fascination to the subject through its introduction of an element of unpredictability along with a continual newness.

Because of the large number of organisms it embraces and their complexity of organization and activities, zoology has been subdivided into numerous branches or subsciences, which can be classified under three headings—observational (or descriptive), quantitative (or experimental), and synthetic.

Among the *observational* aspects is included a number of subsciences (usually

TABLE 1-1
SOME BRANCHES OF ZOOLOGY

Major Subdivision	Discipline	Area of Interest
Descriptive:		Principally describes objects, conditions, or activities
	1. Morphology	The structure and form of animals
	A. Anatomy	The structure of whole animals and their major parts
	B. Histology	The study of tissues
	C. Cytology	The study of cells
	2. Physiology	The functions of the various structures and processes involved
	3. Embryology	Development of the individual from an egg
	4. Pathology	Abnormal structures and diseases
	5. Genetics	The passing of traits from one generation to another
	6. Systematics	Description, classification, and relationships of animals
	7. Zoogeography	The distribution of animals on the earth
	8. Ecology	The relationships of organisms to their environment
Quantitative:		The measurement of the life processes
	1. Radiation zoology	The effects of rays on animals
	2. Biochemistry	The chemistry of life processes
	3. Biophysics	The physics of life processes
	4. Biomathematics	The application of mathematics to organic processes
Synthetic:		The interpretation of data and lesser theories and their synthesis into more meaningful wholes

Figure 1–2. Some effects of irradiation on mice. These two mice are exactly the same age (14 months), are identical as to strain, and have been raised on the same diet, but the one on the right is from a set that has been subjected to irradiation, whereas that on the left is from an untreated lot (the "control" group; see p. 9). The irradiated mice in this experiment are thinner, much grayer, and are otherwise prematurely senile. (Courtesy of Dr. P. Alexander, Chester Beatty Research Institute, and *Discovery*, London, June 1962.)

referred to as sciences) which mainly observe and describe conditions as they occur in nature, or at least did so originally. The oldest branch, *morphology,* is concerned with the structure of living things and is itself subdivided into three principal facets: Under the term *anatomy* is placed the study of the structure of the whole animal and its large parts, under *histology* the study of tissues (for a definition of which see page 146) that compose the animal's organs, and under *cytology* the study of its cells. Closely allied to morphology is *physiology,* the science concerned with the functions of the vari-

ous structures and with the processes involved therein. *Embryology* and *pathology* are similarly closely related to morphology. The first of these is involved with the study of the individual's growth from the egg and the origin and formation of the body parts, whereas the second is concerned with abnormal structures and conditions. Under the term *genetics* is included the science concerned with the mechanisms by means of which individual traits are passed from one generation to another. A science nearly as old as morphology, *systematics,* is involved with the description, classification, and interrelationships of species and is closely allied to *zoogeography,* in which investigations are made of the distribution of animals over the face of the earth. And finally, in *ecology,* a study is made of the relationship of living things to their external environment, both physical and biological (Table 1–1).

Today it is the vogue to classify under the term *quantitative* zoology all those aspects in which an attempt is made to measure physiological activities by mathematical, physical, and chemical means. Under this heading are included *radiation zoology* (Figure 1–2), in which organisms are exposed to various doses of rays, such as those from radioactive substances, X rays, and cosmic rays, as well as *biophysics* and *biochemistry,* respectively concerned with the physics and chemistry of living things.

While distinctive names are applied to these various fields, in both quantitative and observational branches, it must not be supposed that the lines between them are always sharply drawn. For example, morphologists, embryologists, and physiologists draw freely on one another's findings for their own usage and equally as freely utilize quantitative methods where applicable. Similarly systematists base their work on morphology, zoogeography, ecology, genetics, physiology, and experimental procedures as the occasion demands. In reality, it is the respective goals of these subsciences that form their chief distinctions; methodologies and the resulting data often overlap. In final analysis all zoologists are working toward the same ends, those of accumulating more and more reliable information regarding animals and of formulating general laws that govern them.

In addition there is a third major aspect of zoology, which can be designated *interpretive,* or *synthetic.* Contrary to the foregoing subsciences, which function chiefly in collecting and organizing factual information, synthetic zoology attempts to show the meaning and interrelationships of the data that have been garnered. Pertinent information sifted from many subsciences, and from other sciences too in some instances, is brought together and compounded into a single meaningful account. In this manner light has been thrown on the temperature, rainfall, and biological conditions existing during the Ice Age, the manner in which life may have arisen, and so on. As may be readily understood, a particularly broad background of experience is requisite for successful ventures in this field.

THE EXPERIMENT IN ZOOLOGY

Because living things are so variable, in running scientific experiments in zoology it is necessary to take precautions to ensure that the observed results are really due to the experimental procedures and not just to chance or some unsuspected factor. Were one interested in determining the effect of a certain diet on the rabbit, by way of illustration, it would not suffice to feed one or two rabbits the special food and note the increase or loss in weight at the end of a stated period of time in contrast to the gain or loss in

an earlier or later period. The results would be meaningless, no matter how long the procedure is carried out or how often it is repeated, because there is no evidence that some other factor is not involved. Perhaps it is actually the condition of the cages, an unsuspected parasite or disease, or even normal individual variation that produces the observed results and not the special diet.

In order that the results be reliable, it is necessary for zoological experiments to be *controlled.* The *controls* in all cases are not restrictions or supervisory activities but merely the use of untreated specimens. In the rabbit-feeding experiment suggested above, reliable observations could be made if a number of rabbits from the same lot or of the same breed, age, and sex as the animals experimented on (called the *experimental* rabbits) were to be reared in the same place under similar conditions but fed a normal diet. Even then it would usually be necessary to run *replications* of the experiment; i.e., the entire experiment including controls and experimentals would be repeated in exactly the same manner. However, it is possible to run three or four replications of the experimentals with just one set of controls providing all are performed simultaneously under identical conditions. Let us say that in the original set 10 rabbits had been fed the special diet and 10 others had been used as controls. Assuming that this first run had shown promising results, three replicates of 10 experimentals each and one set of 10 control rabbits could be set up and run off under conditions, including rations, as closely identical with the original as possible. After sufficient *data* (the observed facts) had been collected, results would as a rule be tested by statistical methods to see whether or not they were *significant.* Should statistical significance be found, the conclusion could be safely drawn that the results probably were not due solely to chance individual differ- ences in the rabbits but most likely arose as a result of the experimental diet.

Questions for Review and Thought

1. State precisely some of the functions, objectives, and procedures of the natural sciences in general.

2. What sorts of problems facing mankind can the natural sciences solve? Name some that might be more readily solved by the social sciences. Cite examples of types that might better be treated with high moral standards and by the great virtues.

3. Why is experimentation more characteristic of the natural than the social sciences? In which natural science is experimentation almost impossible?

4. Death has been defined as the absence of life. Write a more precise definition in terms of the information supplied in this chapter.

5. There are many zoological subsciences not listed in this text; from your own general knowledge, the dictionary, or other source, define each of the following in your own words:

(a) entomology
(b) parasitology
(c) myology
(d) conchology
(e) helminthology
(f) limnology
(g) protozoology
(h) endocrinology
(i) cytochemistry
(j) neurology

6. Examine the definitions you have written for question 5 and evaluate them objectively as to which are entirely precise and which are not, placing a plus mark before the former, a zero before the latter.

7. Animal morphology has been studied scientifically for more than 400 years whereas radiation zoology came into existence about 30 years ago. In which of these subsciences would important discoveries be most readily made? Why do you think so? Do you think more attention should accordingly be devoted to the more productive one to the detriment of the other? Why or why not?

8. Re-examine the definitions of certain subsciences you wrote in answer to question 5. Each is in reality a particular aspect of one of the major zoological branches; name the specific branch of which each of these is a subdivision.

9. Is it correct to refer to laboratory exercises in which you dissect a frog as an experiment? Would an exercise in which you were to feed a number of a single-celled organism a dye while you watched the reaction through a microscope be properly classed as an experiment? In each case state why or why not.

Supplementary References

Beckner, M. *The Biological Way of Thought*. New York, Columbia Univ. Press, 1959.
Butterfield, H. "The Scientific Revolution." *Sci. Amer.*, September 1960.
Cassidy, H. G. *The Sciences and the Arts*. New York, Harper, 1962.
Conant, J. B. *Modern Science and Modern Man*. New York, Columbia Univ. Press, 1962.
Gillespie, C. C. *The Edge of Objectivity*. Princeton, N. J., Princeton Univ. Press, 1960.
Hull, L. W. H. *History and Philosophy of Science*. New York, Longmans, 1959.
Kuhn, T. S. *The Structure of Scientific Revolutions*. Chicago, Univ. Chicago Press, 1962.
MacIver, R. M. *Life; Its Dimensions and Its Bounds*. New York, Harper, 1960.
Madden, E. H. *The Structure of Scientific Thought*. Boston, Houghton, 1960.

Mausner, B., and Mausner, Judith. "A Study of the Anti-Scientific Attitude." *Sci. Amer.,* February 1955.
Oppenheimer, J. R. *The Open Mind.* New York, Simon and Schuster, 1955.
Singer, C. J. *A History of Biology.* New York, Schuman, 1950.
Sinnott, E. W. *Matter, Mind, and Man.* New York, Harper, 1957.
Terman, L. M. "Are Scientists Different?" *Sci. Amer.,* January 1955.
Wald, G. "Innovation in Biology." *Sci. Amer.,* September 1958.

CHAPTER 2

The Substance
of Life

ANIMALS, like all living things, are composed of a peculiar mixture of chemical compounds called *protoplasm*. This mixture, then, is the "life substance," for it is the material that carries on metabolism and accordingly displays all those attributes together referred to as life. As stated above, it is not a definite compound but a mixture (in the chemical sense of the term) that differs greatly from one organism to another and in the various parts of the body. In fact, some evidence points to rhythmic changes occurring daily in its composition even within a single cell! But that is part of a later discussion. Here it can be emphasized that the protoplasm of a turkey is different from that of a chicken and quite distinct from that of a deer or a fish, while the protoplasm of a kidney differs from that of the liver or a muscle and so on. Yet in spite of this great variability in details of composition, it possesses chemical, physical, and biological properties which are universal in occurrence among living things.

The Chemical Composition
of Protoplasm

Chemically protoplasm consists of a number of complex organic compounds suspended or dissolved in water along with a few inorganic substances. While components and proportionate amounts are variable, almost all protoplasm is composed of only 12 of the 92 known chemical elements. In Table 2–1 is shown the relative abundance of these 12 in a sample of protoplasm containing approximately 10,000 atoms as well as their distribution between the organic and inorganic fractions.

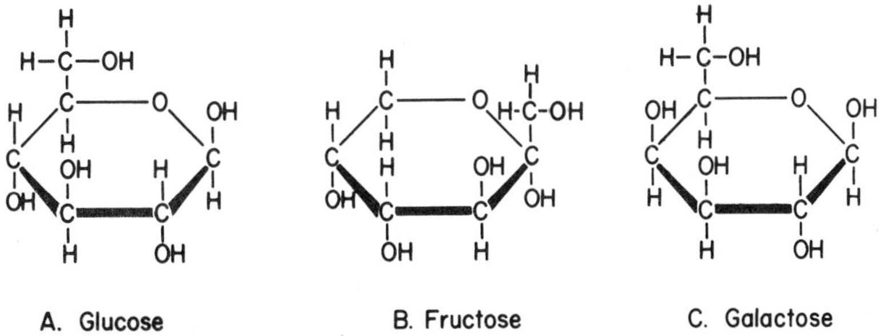

A. Glucose   **B. Fructose**   **C. Galactose**

Figure 2–1. Representative simple sugars (hexoses). The molecule in each instance is essentially a hexagonal or pentagonal plate composed of one oxygen atom and of either four or five carbon atoms, usually the latter. From this plate one carbon (or sometimes two) projects upwards and hydrogen and hydroxyl (OH) units are attached to each of the carbons.

THE ORGANIC PORTION

Much more numerous in protoplasm than the inorganic are the types of organic material, for among them are included carbohydrates, fats and other lipids, proteins, nucleic acids and their components, and enzymes, to mention only the more important. As these substances are often of considerable complexity and diversified in composition, as well as involved in more than one later discussion, each type must be described in some detail.

Carbohydrates. The members of this class of organic materials, in which sugars, starches, and certain complex compounds are included, consist of carbon, hydrogen, and oxygen. The simpler ones, the sugars, are employed solely for energy purposes; the complex ones, like cellulose and chitin, have supportive functions, whereas glycogen and other starches provide a means of storage for the sugars. In animals approximately 1 to 2 per cent of protoplasm consists of carbohydrates.

Under the term *sugars* are grouped a number of substances which for the greater part can be classed in two major subdivisions, single (simple) sugars (*monosaccharides*) and double sugars (*disaccharides*). All the single sugars have their molecules composed of the same proportionate amounts of carbon, hydrogen, and oxygen in a ratio that may be expressed as $(CH_2O)_n$. The *n* may be any number from 2 to 6 inclusive, but only those with $3n$ (3-carbon or trioses), $5n$ (5-carbon or pentoses), or $6n$ (6-carbon or hexoses) are of universal importance biologically. The *hexoses* are of particular significance and participate, directly or indirectly, in most of the chemical processes of the animal. Although the sugars of this type are often pictured in the form of chains, they do not occur in that arrangement in living things; instead in all organisms, five of the six carbon atoms are linked together with one oxygen to form a flat polyhedral disk. Above and below this platelet, then, the sixth carbon and the other atoms and radicals * project in a fashion characteristic for each variety of sugar (Figure 2–1). As a result of the differences in internal organization, each hexose has distinctive chemical properties not possessed by the others; hence, they are not freely interchangeable one for another

---

* A radical is a short combination of atoms that acts as a single unit, such as the hydroxyl radical (⁻OH) or methyl radical (CH₃ +).

within the protoplasm. Of all the 6-carbon sugars, *glucose* is probably the most important and widely distributed; for it is an essential ingredient in the basic chemical activities within the protoplasm and is found in a free state in the blood of animals and in the sap of the plants used for food. *Fructose* is a close second to the foregoing in importance as it too enters into the fundamental chemistry of life; one common variety has two side chains and only four carbons in the plate. While a third hexose, *galactose*, is not found as such in either animals or plants, it is an ingredient essential in the formation of certain more complex carbohydrates. Structurally *pentoses* are similar to hexoses but lack the carbon-containing side chain or otherwise possess one less carbon atom. Among these 5-carbon sugars only *ribose* and *deoxyribose* are important in animals and occur solely in complex compounds, never in a pure state (Figure 2–2). The complicated substances (nucleotides) in which they are a significant ingredient are indispensable, however, for life and will be discussed in more detail below.

The protoplasm of all animals possesses the ability to combine two monosaccharide molecules to form a double sugar, or *disaccharide*, by processes called *dehydrolysis* which subtract the elements of one water molecule. The reverse of these processes, that is, the restoration of water to the compound, or *hydrolysis*, results in the release of the two original simple sugars. Of the three important disaccharides, *sucrose*, ordinary cane or beet sugar, is by far the most abundant, for it occurs in the leaves, stems, flowers, roots, and sap of all the plants consumed by animals. It is a combination of one molecule of glucose with one of fructose (Figure 2–3). In addition, *lactose*, which composes about 5 per cent of milk, and *maltose*, one derivative of starch breakdown, are representatives of this class of carbohydrates.

By repetition of the processes of dehydrolysis over and over again, many molecules of simple sugars may be united to form one extremely large *complex carbohydrate* molecule. Such *polysaccharides* are of frequent occurrence throughout the living world and serve two diverse types of functions of major importance. One of these principal functions is that of support, as exemplified by *chitin*, in the skeletons of crabs, lobsters, insects, and related forms, and by cellulose, in the body covering of a few creatures like the sea squirts (page 213). In animals the second function, storage, is largely provided by so-called animal starch, or *glycogen*. This substance differs from the

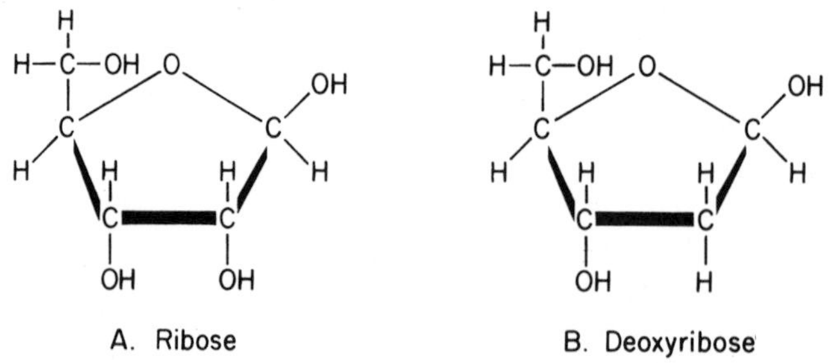

A. Ribose   B. Deoxyribose

Figure 2–2. Two important pentoses. In pentoses there is always a pentagonal plate comprised of one oxygen and four carbon atoms, while a fifth carbon projects upwards. To each carbon are attached hydrogens and hydroxyl units in definite patterns.

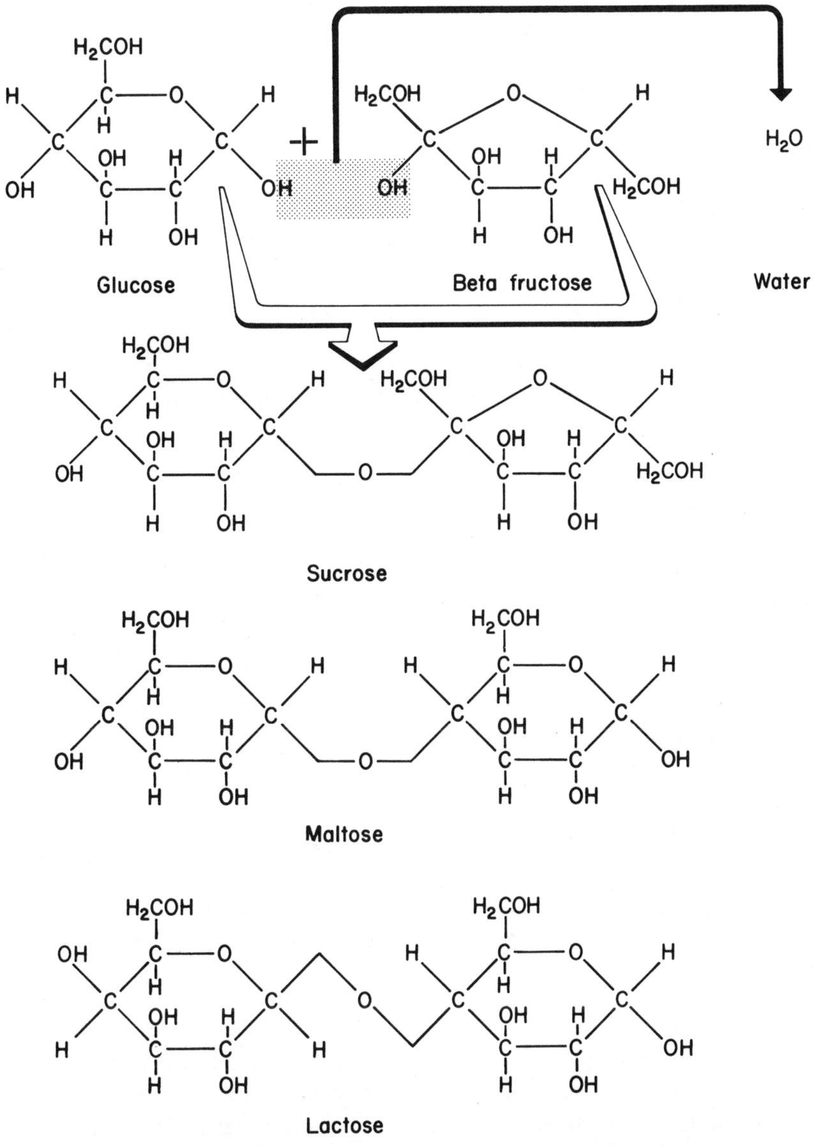

Figure 2–3. A few disaccharides. Disaccharides are formed by the chemical union of two simple sugars. One means by which the coupling is accomplished is by removal of water as shown in glucose formation. In that reaction glucose is united to a special form of fructose called beta-fructose; alpha-fructose is illustrated in Figure 2–1.

true starch of plants in having its molecules more densely branched (Figure 2–4); both these compounds are nearly insoluble and can therefore be stored directly in the protoplasm and thus held in reserve. When needed as a source of energy, hydrolytic steps break them into their components, thus restoring their solubility and making them ready for use.

Lipids.   On the average, protoplasm contains about 3 to 7 per cent lipids by

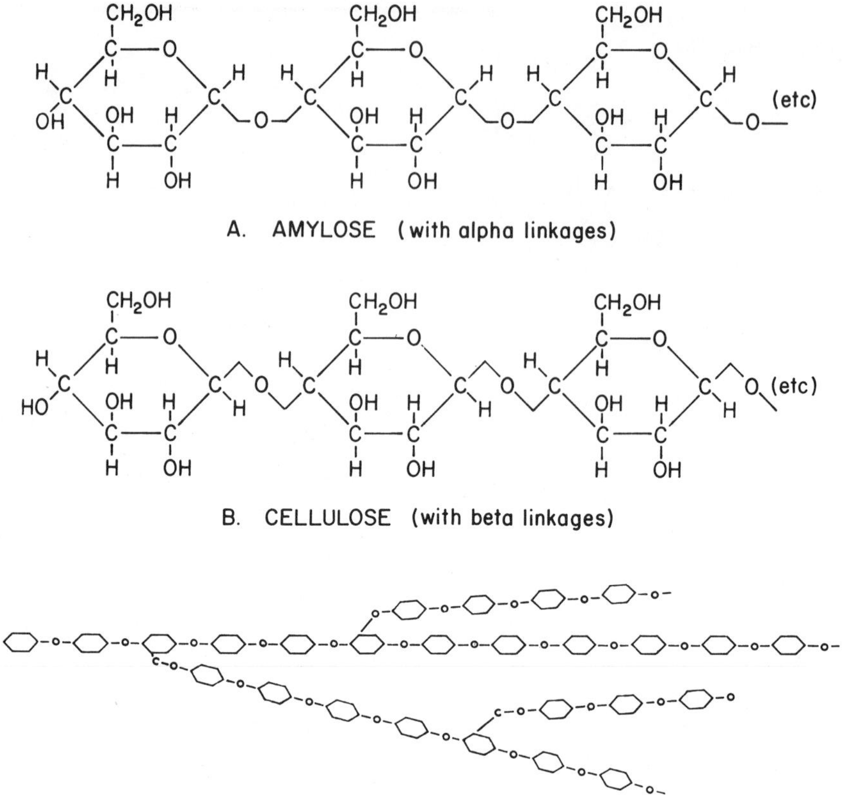

A. AMYLOSE (with alpha linkages)

B. CELLULOSE (with beta linkages)

C. Portion of a branched molecule (Amylopectin)

Figure 2–4. Polysaccharides. Most common polysaccharides consist of numerous glucose units joined together by removal of a phosphate unit, a process called *dephosphorylation*. Ordinary starch consists of a mixture of long chains and shorter branched ones (amylopectin C). On the other hand, glycogen (animal starch) consists entirely of shorter molecules branched in a somewhat different pattern from the one illustrated.

weight. Among these substances are included fats, waxes, steroids, the four fat-soluble vitamins (A, D, E, and K), and many others of less general occurrence. Most of them resemble the carbohydrates in being composed solely of carbon, hydrogen, and oxygen atoms; a few of the more complex types may contain phosphorus or nitrogen as well. Particularly distinctive is their lack of solubility in water.

Under the term *fats* are also included those in the liquid state, called oils in popular usage. These substances are composed of fatty acids (Figure 2–5) combined with glycerine by a process of dehydrolysis like that found in the carbohydrates (Figure 2–6). As the number of fatty acids is large and as they can be linked together by glycerol in nearly any combination, the actual composition of most fats varies widely. Especially is this true for animal fats, in which a greater variety of fatty acids occurs than in those from green plants; in almost all cases they may be looked upon as mixtures rather than as pure and consistent compounds (Table 2–3). In many organisms fats may be formed from excess carbohydrates and stored for future use. While

TABLE 2-3

FATTY ACID CONTENT OF HUMAN FAT
BY WEIGHT

Fatty Acid	Formula	Mean Per Cent
Lauric	$CH_3(CH_2)_{10}COOH$	0.3
Myristic	$CH_3(CH_2)_{12}COOH$	4.1
Palmitic	$CH_3(CH_2)_{14}COOH$	24.9
Stearic	$CH_3(CH_2)_{16}COOH$	7.0
Other 14-carbon	—	0.4
Other 16-carbon	—	6.4
Other 18-carbon	—	55.5
Other	—	1.4

fats are used mainly as concentrated sources of energy, they are employed in other ways as well. Many warm-blooded vertebrates in colder regions have extensive deposits of these substances beneath the skin, where they serve as insulation against heat loss. In this fashion, the fatty layers of polar bears and the blubber of whales appear to be essential for the survival of these mammals. In numerous animals adipose (fatty) tissue surrounds many of the internal vital organs, such as kidneys and reproductive

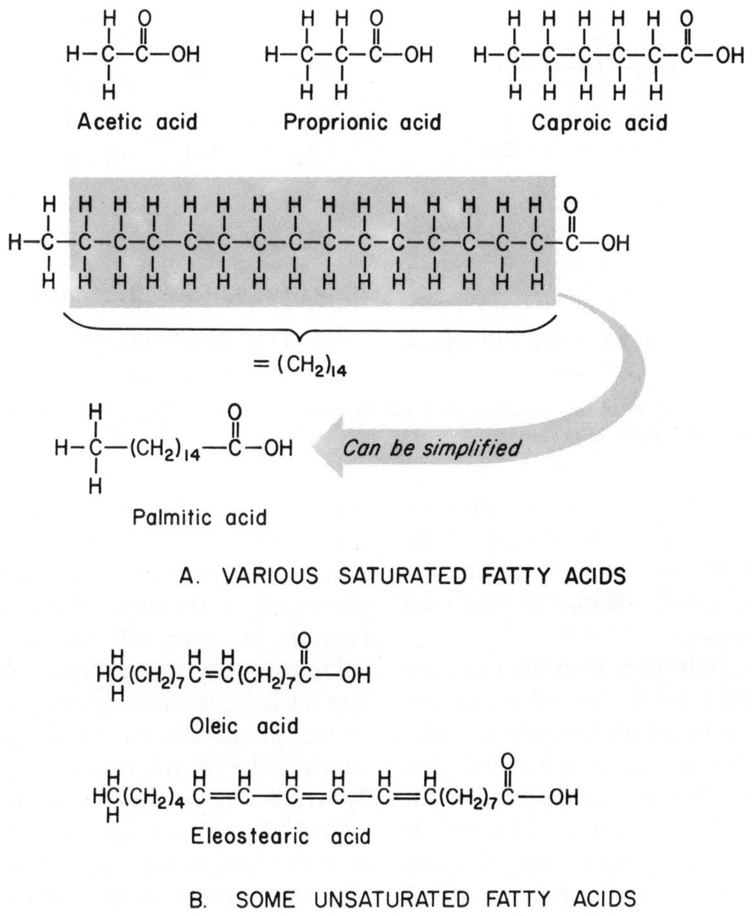

Figure 2–5. The molecular structure of several fatty acids. Fatty acids have series of carbon atoms connected in chains, some of which may be many times longer than any example shown here. Unsaturated fatty acids differ in having one or more sets of double bonds between carbons.

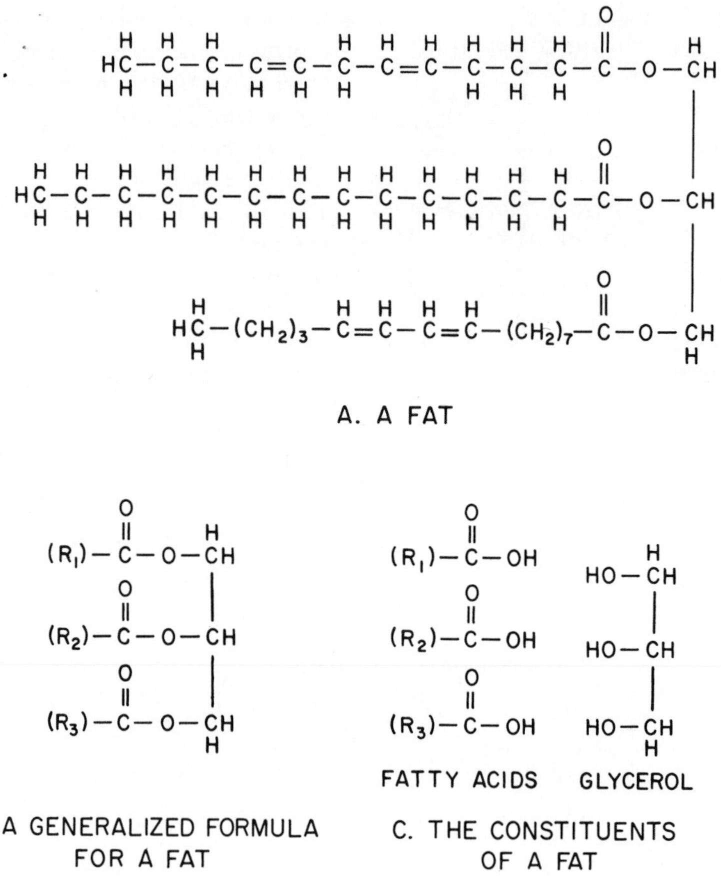

$$
\begin{array}{c}
\text{H H H}\qquad\qquad\text{H H H H H H}\quad\ \ \text{O}\\[-2pt]
\qquad\qquad\qquad\qquad\qquad\qquad\qquad\qquad\qquad\ \parallel\\[-2pt]
\text{HC}-\text{C}-\text{C}-\text{C}=\text{C}-\text{C}-\text{C}=\text{C}-\text{C}-\text{C}-\text{C}-\text{C}-\text{O}-\text{CH}\\[-2pt]
\text{H H H H H H}\qquad\qquad\quad\text{H H H}\qquad\ \ \ \big|
\end{array}
$$

$$
\begin{array}{c}
\text{H H H H H H H H H H H H H}\quad\ \ \text{O}\\[-2pt]
\qquad\qquad\qquad\qquad\qquad\qquad\qquad\qquad\qquad\qquad\qquad\ \parallel\\[-2pt]
\text{HC}-\text{C}-\text{C}-\text{C}-\text{C}-\text{C}-\text{C}-\text{C}-\text{C}-\text{C}-\text{C}-\text{C}-\text{C}-\text{C}-\text{O}-\text{CH}\\[-2pt]
\text{H H H H H H H H H H H H H}\qquad\qquad\quad\big|
\end{array}
$$

$$
\begin{array}{c}
\text{H}\qquad\qquad\text{H H H H}\qquad\ \ \text{O}\qquad\ \big|\\[-2pt]
\text{HC}-(\text{CH}_2)_3-\text{C}=\text{C}-\text{C}=\text{C}-(\text{CH}_2)_7-\text{C}-\text{O}-\text{CH}\\[-2pt]
\text{H}\qquad\qquad\qquad\qquad\qquad\qquad\qquad\qquad\qquad\text{H}
\end{array}
$$

A. A FAT

$$
\begin{array}{cc}
\text{O}\qquad\qquad\quad & \text{O}\\
\parallel\qquad\quad\text{H} & \parallel\\
(\text{R}_1)-\text{C}-\text{O}-\text{CH} & (\text{R}_1)-\text{C}-\text{OH}\qquad\quad\text{H}\\
\text{O}\qquad\quad\big| & \qquad\qquad\qquad\text{HO}-\text{CH}\\
\parallel\qquad\quad\big| & \text{O}\\
(\text{R}_2)-\text{C}-\text{O}-\text{CH} & (\text{R}_2)-\text{C}-\text{OH}\qquad\quad\big|\\
\text{O}\qquad\quad\big| & \qquad\qquad\qquad\text{HO}-\text{CH}\\
\parallel\qquad\quad\big| & \text{O}\\
(\text{R}_3)-\text{C}-\text{O}-\text{CH} & (\text{R}_3)-\text{C}-\text{OH}\qquad\quad\big|\\
\qquad\qquad\quad\text{H} & \qquad\qquad\qquad\text{HO}-\text{CH}\\
& \qquad\qquad\qquad\qquad\qquad\text{H}
\end{array}
$$

FATTY ACIDS   GLYCEROL

B. A GENERALIZED FORMULA
FOR A FAT

C. THE CONSTITUENTS
OF A FAT

Figure 2–6. The structure of fat molecules. As a rule fats consist of several fatty acids, alike or different, joined together by means of glycerol.

organs, where it serves as protection against shocks and other mechanical injuries. In marine animals, particularly those that actively swim, fats also seem to add buoyancy.

Certain lipids other than the fats, such as the waxes, are of limited occurrence in nature and need not be discussed here; others, however, are of great biological significance. Possibly the most important of all types are the steroids, which include many diverse compounds, some of which belong to a group of substances called "hormones" and will be described in more detail in a later section of this book. In addition to these, a sterol called cho-

lesterol (Figure 2–7) is extremely important in the protoplasm of animals. It is particularly abundant in the sheaths of nerves and in the walls of the heart; its function, however, still remains obscure.

Proteins. By far the most abundant class of organic substance in protoplasm is the group known as the *proteins,* which make up from 10 to 30 per cent by weight. In fact, protoplasm may well be looked upon as a solution of proteins in water containing small amounts of salts and of other organic substances. In addition to carbon, hydrogen, and oxygen, which compose all the organic substances discussed above, this class of ma-

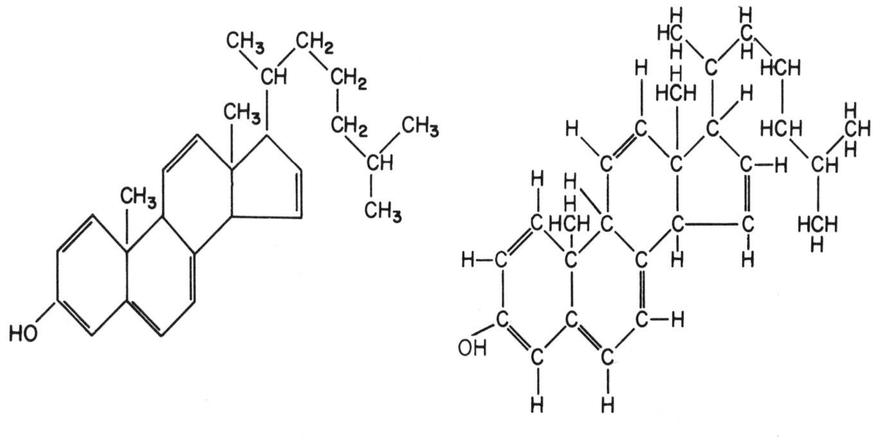

A.   Simplified Diagram   B.   Detailed Diagram

CHOLESTEROL

Figure 2–7. Cholesterol. A typical representative of the group of lipids called steroids, cholesterol is notorious as playing a role in atherosclerosis. Much debate now is current over the part diet plays in the deposition of this compound in the walls of the larger arteries, the chief feature of the disease.

terials consists of nitrogen to the extent of approximately 16 per cent by weight and of sulfur in small quantities. Some contain traces of other chemical elements, such as phosphorus, zinc, and iodine.

The molecules of protein are extremely large and complex, being composed of innumerable links, known as *amino acids,* joined together. Basically these amino acids are alike in containing the chemical unit

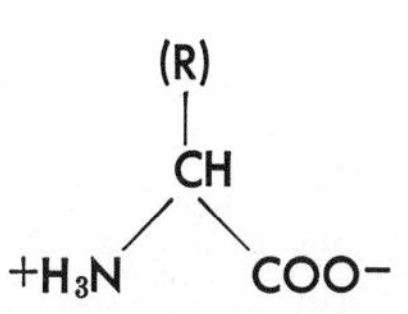

$$\begin{array}{c} (R) \\ | \\ CH \\ \diagup \quad \diagdown \\ ^{+}H_3N \qquad COO^{-} \end{array}$$

with various chemical combinations (radicals) attached at R (Figure 2–8). On this stem compound the positive and negative signs indicate that amino acids are ionized, and on this fact depends one of the important features of proteins—namely, their ability to serve as buffers. In solutions to which an alkali has been added, the hydrogen ion (H^{+}) is freed

and neutralizes the excess alkalinity caused by the hydroxyl ion (^{-}OH), becoming

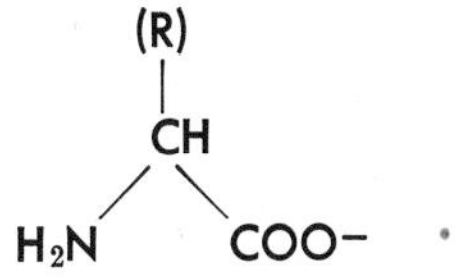

$$\begin{array}{c} (R) \\ | \\ CH \\ \diagup \quad \diagdown \\ H_2N \qquad COO^{-} \end{array}$$

On the other hand, in solutions to which acid is added, the additional hydrogen ions combine with the COO^{-}, changing the amino acid thus

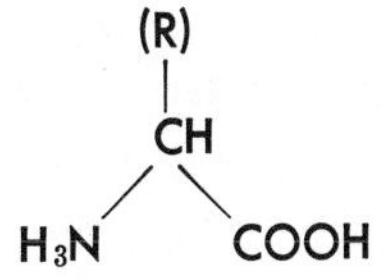

$$\begin{array}{c} (R) \\ | \\ CH \\ \diagup \quad \diagdown \\ H_3N \qquad COOH \end{array}$$

In this fashion proteins assist in maintaining a constant balance of acidity and alkalinity in the protoplasm.

In forming proteins the amino acids join together by a process of dehydrolysis, similar to that seen above in the formation of the more complex carbohydrates

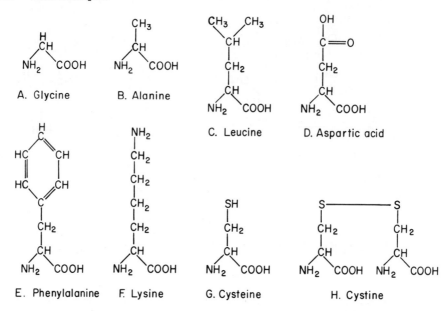

Figure 2–8. Several important amino acids. Some of the numerous variations in amino acid molecular structure are diagrammed here. Two cysteine molecules can combine by union of the sulfur atoms (after loss of the hydrogens) to form the amino acid cystine; this reaction is of frequent occurrence in protein formation (see Figure 15–4).

and lipids. In the present case the "bond" where two amino acids join is referred to as a *peptide linkage,* as in the following equation:

The linkage of two amino acids results in what is known as a *dipeptide,* of three, a *tripeptide,* of many, a *polypeptide;* usually, however, such compounds are simply referred to as *peptides.* Occasionally unusually large peptides may be referred to as *peptones.* In turn, *proteins* are series of peptones or polypeptides and are formed through combination of many peptides by the same sort of linkage and are very large molecules. How large these are may best be visualized by examination of Table 2–4.

Proteins basically are of two types, the fibrous and the globular, depending on the shape of the molecule. As these two types differ extensively in certain of their traits, they need to be discussed separately. Of the two, the *fibrous* is probably the simpler and will be described first. These proteins possess two properties that make them especially adapted as structural material—namely, those of relative insolubility in water and of extensibility and contractility. Among them are included such substances as the tough

TABLE 2-4

RELATIVE WEIGHTS AND COMPLEXITY OF AMINO ACIDS,
PEPTIDES, AND PROTEINS

Type of Substance	Example	Empirical Formula	Molecular Weight
Amino acids	Glycine	$C_2H_5O_2N$	75
	Serine	$C_3H_7O_3N$	106
	Cysteine	$C_3H_7O_2NS$	121
	Leucine	$C_6H_{13}O_2N$	131
	Tyrosine	$C_9H_{12}O_3N$	181
Dipeptides	Glycylglycine	$C_4H_8O_3N_2$	132
	Alanylvaline	$C_8H_{16}O_3N_2$	188
Tripeptides	Alanylglycylvaline	$C_{10}H_{19}O_4N_3$	245
	Glutathione	$C_{10}H_{17}O_6N_3S$	315
Polypeptides	Penicillin	$C_{14}H_{20}O_4N_2S$	320
	Gramicidin s	$(C_{30}H_{47}O_5N_6)_2$	1142
Proteins	Cytochrome c	—	15,600
	Egg albumen	—	44,000
	Hemoglobin of horse	—	68,000
	Antitoxin (diphtheria)	—	150,000
	Myosin	—	850,000
	Nucleohistone	—	2,300,000
	Tobacco mosaic virus	—	60,000,000
	Influenza virus	—	340,000,000

material (*collagen*) in cartilage, tendons, and fish scales, a chief contractile constituent (*myosin*) of muscle, and the horny material (*keratin*) found in hair, horns, claws, feathers, and the like. In addition the fibers in blood clots (*fibrin*) and in silk (*fibroin*) are representatives, as well as innumerable other examples. In the fibrous proteins, it is believed that the polypeptides of many molecules together arrange themselves side by side to form ribbons; furthermore, these ribbons appear to be pleated (Figure 2–9), with the "radicals" projecting perpendicularly from the surface. Some fold, as shown, across the length of the fiber, and others fold between the molecules, parallel to their length. These ribbons of molecules are wound spirally to form strands, and the strands, in turn, are wound together in groups, usually three or seven to a group, to form fibers (Figure 2–9). In the contractible members, contractility results, it is believed, through the pleated nature of the peptides.

Globular proteins differ from the above in being soluble in water, in being crystallizable as a rule, and in lacking contractility (Figure 2–10). A large number of the most abundant proteins belong in this category. Among them are the *albumen* of eggs, the *hemoglobin* of the blood cells, the *globulins,* often useful in disease resistance, most of the *enzymes* of cells and of the body, and the largest portion of those substances called "hor-

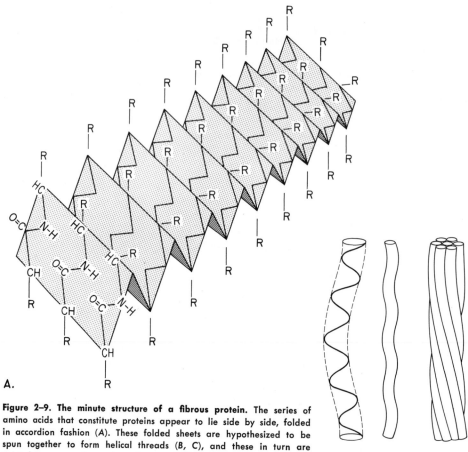

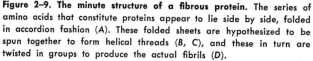

A.

Figure 2–9. The minute structure of a fibrous protein. The series of amino acids that constitute proteins appear to lie side by side, folded in accordion fashion (A). These folded sheets are hypothesized to be spun together to form helical threads (B, C), and these in turn are twisted in groups to produce the actual fibrils (D).

B.   **C.**   **D.**

mones" mentioned above under lipids. *Toxins,* those poisons secreted by bacteria, and the *antibodies* formed by cells against toxins, bacteria, and other foreign bodies are also examples of globular proteins, as are the *venoms* of snakes, bees, and wasps.

A distinctive feature of proteins regardless of their type is their *specificity.* By this term is meant that in each species of organism, whether bacterium, seed plant, animal, or any other type of life,

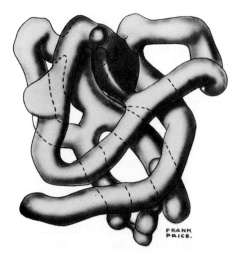

Figure 2–10. A model of a globular protein molecule. In this model of a myoglobin molecule, the long chain of amino acids is seen to be much coiled about itself so that it assumes a shape approximating a sphere. (Courtesy of Dr. J. C. Kendrew and *Nature,* Vol. 185, 1960.)

many of the proteins present are found in it and in no other living thing. Closely related, i.e., very similar, organisms share a large number of proteins with one another, whereas unlike or distantly related ones share few. Nevertheless, even in a group of closely related species, each sort possesses some proteins not shared by the remaining ones.

Another unique trait of the proteins is their ability to combine, or "conjugate," with other chemical compounds. Among such conjugated proteins are the lipoproteins, phosphoproteins, glucoproteins, metalloproteins, and nucleoproteins; respectively, these are combinations of proteins with lipids, phosphorus compounds, sugars, metals, and nucleic acids. Of these the nucleoproteins are of such importance that they need to be discussed in some detail, after some of their essential ingredients have first been described.

Pyrimidines, Purines, and Nucleic

Acids. These rather complex compounds are generally unfamiliar to most persons who are not biologists or biochemists. Yet they are among the most important and most active substances in the cell; without them, life, as we know it at least, would not exist. *Pyrimidines* basically consist of four carbon and two nitrogen atoms arranged in a hexagonal "ring"; *purines* are constructed of this pyrimidine ring plus a side ring of one carbon and two nitrogen atoms (Figure 2–11). Although occasionally purines and pyrimidines occur in a free state, such as in the case of theobromine and caffeine, for the most part they are combined with certain sugars and with phosphoric acid in the form of *nucleotides*. Within the protoplasm these nucleotides occur most frequently as the *nucleic acids* and as certain *coenzymes*. In the nucleic acids they are linked together to form large complex molecules and are believed to be

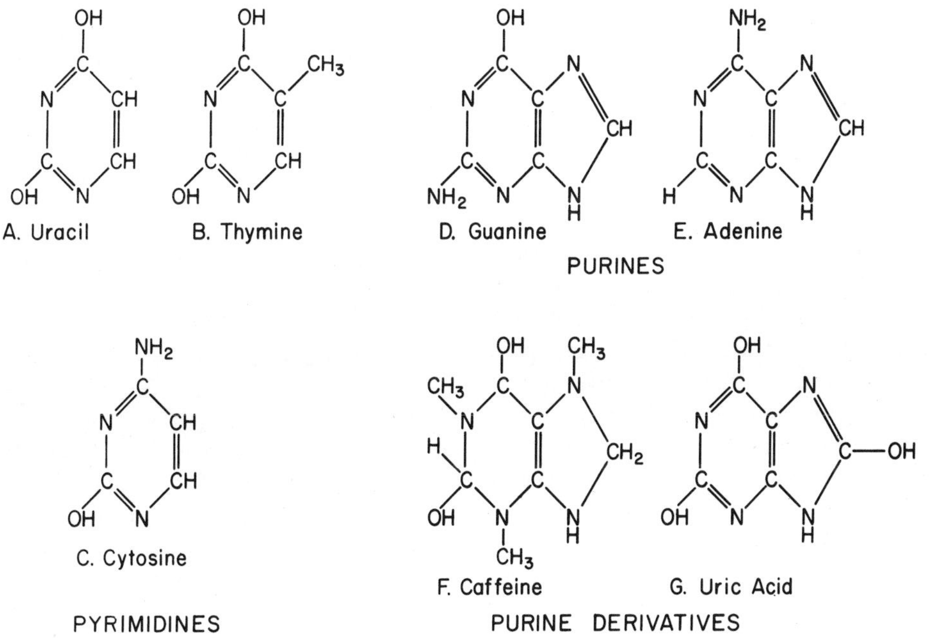

A. Uracil B. Thymine D. Guanine E. Adenine

PURINES

C. Cytosine

PYRIMIDINES

F. Caffeine G. Uric Acid

PURINE DERIVATIVES

Figure 2–11. Pyrimidines, purines, and some derivatives. These substances are important ingredients in DNA and RNA, which complex substances are among the most distinctive constituents of living matter. Later, in connection with the study of inheritance, they will receive more detailed attention.

able to reproduce themselves either directly or when they are combined with proteins.

Two nucleic acids are known: *ribonucleic acid*, in which the sugar ribose has been united with the purine or pyrimidine base, and *deoxyribonucleic acid*, in which deoxyribose is the sugar involved. Usually the names of these acids are reduced to RNA and DNA, respectively. It is these nucleic acids with which proteins conjugate to form the nucleoproteins mentioned above. These latter compounds compose the chromosomes, which appear to be involved in carrying the hereditary material of organisms.

Enzymes. In protoplasm are many chemical compounds which serve as catalysts—i.e., they aid in bringing about reactions without entering directly into the chemical processes. In other words, they are not themselves altered by the reaction they induce. Catalysts in the protoplasm and in the bodies of organisms are referred to as *enzymes*. Numerous kinds are known, most of which are proteins and each of which normally has a specific function. Some are able to bring about dehydrolysis of the simple carbohydrates, thus building them into starches or cellulose, or to break down the latter substances by hydrolysis and convert them into their simple constituents. Similarly others act on lipids or on proteinaceous compounds. Although often enzymes act on whole groups of compounds, for example those that act on the peptide bonds, others are able to induce reactions only between a certain few compounds, as in the case of some of the carbohydrate-reactive enzymes like sucrase. Sucrase can break down sucrose into fructose and glucose or unite these two simpler sugars to form sucrose, depending on the concentration of the various substances present. Usually reactions involving enzymes are *reversible*, as in the preceding example. They may be written as follows:

$$C_6H_{12}O_6 + C_6H_{12}O_6 \underset{}{\overset{sucrase}{\rightleftarrows}}$$

Glucose   Fructose

$$C_{12}H_{22}O_{11} + H_2O$$

Sucrose

Often in addition to enzymes biological reactions require the presence of substances called *coenzymes*, which assist by temporarily combining with, or "accepting," one of the chemicals produced. Particularly important is the nucleotide called *adenosine triphosphate*, usually abbreviated ATP. This compound will be found to enter into the discussion of more than one topic in later chapters, for it is a principal source of energy for many activities of protoplasm. Many other coenzymes are known, but only two are of sufficient general importance to mention here. These two are *DPN* (*diphosphopyridine nucleotide*),* the hydrogen-transporting coenzyme, also known as coenzyme I, and CoA (*coenzyme A*), which is responsible for the transfer of the acetyl (CH_3CO—) group. In subsequent chapters the actions of these substances will be outlined in greater detail.

Physical Properties of Protoplasm

Since protoplasm varies so widely from organism to organism and from part to part within the same individual, it is difficult to make many generalizations on the physical nature of this life substance that would be universally true. Essentially it is a colloidal suspension of protein in a watery solution of salts and

---

* Currently, in some quarters this compound is being referred to as *NAD* (nicotinamide diphosphate).

sugars. Colloids differ from true solutions in the fact that the "dissolved" (really suspended) particles, while very fine, will settle out if the suspension is permitted to stand sufficiently long or if centrifuged. Much of the protoplasm in organisms is of the fluid type of colloid known as a *sol;* other portions of it are of a solid or semisolid nature and represent the *gel* type of colloid. Gels and sols are readily convertible from one type to the other by physical or chemical factors, such as temperature, degree of acidity, and salt content; thus gelatin desserts are gels when cool and sols when warm. Some of the constituents of protoplasm, like the fats, are in the form of *emulsions,* a term applied to colloids in which one liquid is suspended in another, with mayonnaise a familiar example.

The Biological Properties of Protoplasm

While protoplasm may be distinguished from nonliving substances by its chemical composition, it is most readily recognized by its activities. These activities, or biological properties, together make up the *manifestations of life* of which mention was made in the first chapter. Of all these attributes probably the most unique is that of *self-reproduction;* only living things are capable of making duplicates of themselves. Furthermore, protoplasm is capable of *growth.* Although lakes and crystals may indeed grow, the process in living things differs tremendously. For in the case of lakes or crystals, the increase in size is due to the addition of material exactly the same as in the original, whereas organisms take in materials vastly different from themselves and convert it into their own substance. A third distinctive feature of protoplasm is its *responsiveness* to changes in its surroundings. Inorganic matter may respond to environmental changes by boiling, solidifying, or evaporating, by breaking down into its chemical constituents, or by uniting chemically —in short, it responds through changes in its own physical or chemical composition. In contrast, protoplasm responds through the use of either of two other unique attributes, by *movement* or by *secretion.* Movement in organisms is autonomous—that is, it comes from within themselves. Secretions are substances produced by protoplasm and consist of chemicals differing in kind from those of the protoplasm. While lifeless objects sometimes can move, the movement receives its energy entirely through the force of gravity or, in the case of automobiles and airplanes, through material placed in them by man; none can move autonomously nor can any inanimate thing secrete.

Living things are, of course, physical objects composed of chemicals. But the chemicals that compose them and the activities resulting from their reactions are so unique as to warrant studying them in a distinct natural science.

Questions for Review and Thought

1. It is sometimes stated that the salts of the body or those in protoplasm are very similar in concentration to those in sea water. How would one investigate the truth of this statement? Conduct your own investigation and briefly state your findings.

2. In what way do certain salts and a certain type of organic compound function similarly?

3. Summarize briefly the chemical composition of protoplasm.

4. In what ways are all the organic constituents of protoplasm alike? Which, if any, major type could be eliminated without seriously affecting a large group of living things?

5. List the reactions and activities occurring within protoplasm in which water is directly involved.

6. Name the principal uses of sugars, lipids, and proteins in protoplasm.

7. In what essential way do fats differ from both the complex carbohydrates and proteins? In what way is the process of formation of the complex carbohydrates and the fats identical with that of the proteins?

8. Which two large classes of organic substances are not only interchangeable but also intertransmutable?

9. Which large class of organic substances may sometimes be as harmful as it is beneficial?

10. Define the term *enzyme* completely and clearly. To what class of organic compounds do most enzymes belong? List some of the most generally important representatives.

11. Which biological features of life are the most unique? Name some inorganic things besides lakes and crystals that can grow and some that can move. Can you name any other features of living things that distinguish them from nonliving?

Supplementary References

Avery, G. S. *Survey of Biological Progress,* Vol. 2. New York, Academic Press, 1952.

Baldwin, E. *Dynamic Aspects of Biochemistry,* 3rd ed. Cambridge, Cambridge Univ. Press, 1957.

DeRobertis, E. D. P., W. W. Nowinski, and F. A. Saez. *General Cytology,* 3rd ed. Philadelphia, Saunders, 1960.

Doty, P. "Proteins." *Sci. Amer.,* September 1957.

Fieser, L. F. "Steroids." *Sci. Amer.,* January 1955.

Heilbrunner, L. V. *The Dynamics of Living Protoplasm.* New York, Academic Press, 1956.

Kendrew, J. C. "The Three-dimensional Structure of a Protein Molecule." *Sci. Amer.,* December 1961.

Laidler, K. J. *Introduction to the Chemistry of Enzymes.* New York, McGraw-Hill, 1954.

Pauling, L., R. B. Corey, and R. Hayward. "The Structure of Protein Molecules." *Sci. Amer.,* July 1954.

Swanson, C. P. *The Cell.* Englewood Cliffs, N. J., Prentice-Hall, 1960.

Wasserman, E. "Chemical Topology." *Sci. Amer.,* November 1962.

The Unit Structure of Life

Wᴵᴛʜɪɴ the bodies of all organisms, whether they be great or microscopic, the protoplasm does not occur merely as larger or smaller masses but is arranged into minute, compact units named *cells*. Similarly within the cell, the protoplasm is highly organized into smaller bodies called *organelles,* which are themselves proving to be surprisingly complex in organization. However, these organelles are parts of the whole cell specialized for particular roles and incapable of an independent existence. Hence protoplasm may be considered the basic material of living things, whereas the cell is the fundamental unit. All organisms consist of at least one cell.

The Cell Principle

These facts, now so simply stated, required many years of effort to establish.

Since most cells are usually extremely small, their existence was entirely unsuspected until after the advent of the microscope; they were first seen in a thin slice of cork by an Englishman named Robert Hooke in the year 1665. After many decades of study by early microscopists, in the first half of the nineteenth century Schleiden, a botanist, and Schwann, a zoologist, separately advanced the cell theory, which states that all organisms are composed of cells. Still many more decades later, we now recognize this concept, in a slightly modified form, to be universally true and, hence, accept it no longer as a theory, but as a proven principle. The *cell principle,* as modified from the original, states that all organisms are composed of cells and their products. For example, nails, hair, and certain structures of our bodies are not cellular but are secreted by organs that are. In this connection, the student will recall that secretion is one of the universal properties of protoplasm and, hence, of the cell.

Not only is the cell the unit of structure of an organism, it is the unit of function as well. Reproduction, growth, reaction to changes in the environment, digestion—in short, all the activities of even the most complex body—in final analysis result from the activities of the cells that form it.

Cells are extremely varied in their form, as may be seen by examining Figure 3–1. Likewise they are highly diversified in size, for although they are typically very minute, in the range of 1/2,500 to 1/250 of an inch, many are much larger. For example, certain single-celled organisms, like the paramecium, are large enough to be visible to the unaided eye. Furthermore, a few are relatively gigantic; the yolk of a hen's egg, like that of an ostrich, is actually a single cell— a highly modified cell it is true, but a single one nonetheless. Still others, though fine in diameter, are exceedingly long— e.g., some nerve cells may be more than 3 ft in length although less than 1/1,000 of an inch in diameter. However, these are exceptional cases; the vast majority of cells are too minute to be discernible except with special equipment and techniques.

Methods of Studying Cells

As already pointed out, the first instrument invented that assisted in studying the cell was the *light microscope*. Since its origin, many modifications have occurred perfecting its functioning and ease of use, so that the modern research micro-

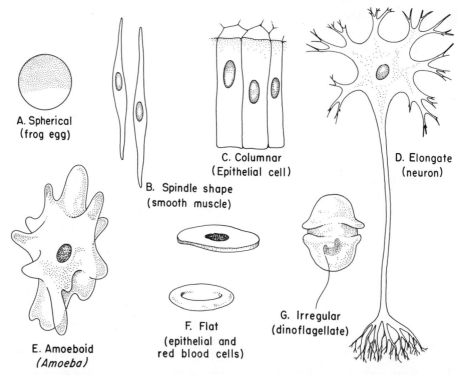

Figure 3–1. A few shapes assumed by cells. The forms acquired by cells in becoming adapted for particular environments or functions are nearly as numerous as the species of organisms which they comprise.

scope (Figure 3–2) is a highly precise instrument. Along with the development of this implement, methods in preparing material for study with it have advanced. Cells must first be "fixed" with reagents to maintain the protoplasm in its natural form, dehydrated, and embedded in wax or collodion. Following this treatment, they are sliced on a special machine, called the *microtome,* usually in "sections" about 1/2,500 of an inch thick. After sectioning, the cells are mounted on microscope slides, dewaxed, and stained. In all these operations special solutions and procedures are employed, each of which has required much experimentation and years of time to develop.

parts of the object under examination become distinguished in tones of black and gray. With the addition of time-lapse photography, motion pictures can be made through the phase-contrast microscope, and the activities of the live cells can be observed greatly accelerated.

Another recent invention extremely useful in studying the structure of cells is the *electron microscope* (Figure 3–4). In many ways this instrument is comparable to the light microscope but employs a stream of electrons, in place of light, and electromagnets, instead of glass lenses. With it magnification as great as 600,000$\times$ have been attained, whereas 3,000$\times$ is the absolute limit of enlargement with the light microscope. Unfortunately the electron microscope has

Figure 3–3. A stereoscopic microscope. In contrast to ordinary light microscopes, the stereoscopic variety, by providing depth, is particularly valuable in studying larger objects and in making exacting dissections. (Courtesy of The American Optical Company.)

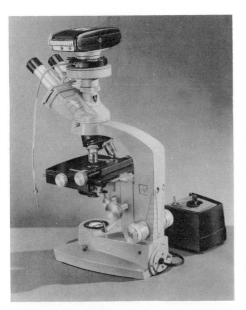

Figure 3–2. A modern research microscope. (Courtesy of the American Optical Company.)

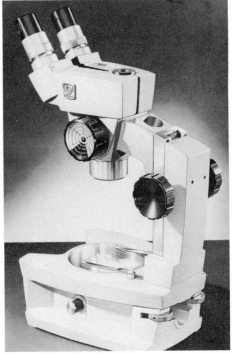

A recent advancement in light microscopy is the *phase-contrast microscope,* which facilitates the study of actually living cells. With this modification light passes through layers of different optical density (i.e., differing in the speed with which light penetrates them), so that its rays become out of phase; as a result, the

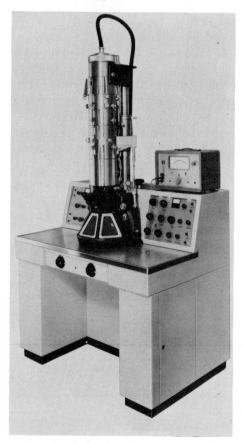

Figure 3–4. An electron microscope. With the aid of such instruments as this, magnifications as high as 600,000× can be obtained. By its use, the cell has been found to be far more complex than formerly conceived. (Model Norelco EM-200, courtesy of Phillips Electronic Instruments.)

some features that thus far have restricted its use to nonliving material, the chief disadvantage stemming from the nearly absolute vacuums needed for the electron beam. Another centers around the relatively poor penetrating power of the electrons with the consequence that material to be studied must be cut extremely thin. For best results sections must not be more than 1/1,250,000 of an inch (0.02 μ, i.e., *micron*, which unit is equivalent to 1/1,000 mm). To cut such thin sections an *ultramicrotome* is needed, which uses glass or

diamond as the cutting blade, the material being first embedded in a plastic. Instead of being dyed, materials for study are now "electronically stained" by treatment with solutions of heavy metals, such as osmium, tungsten, and gold, before being sectioned.

Other methods of studying cells do not involve means of observing their structure but are concerned with their functions, growth, and related activities. For these purposes cells are grown as *cultures* on or within a nutritive medium (Figure 3–5). Media are usually complex mixtures of proteins and amino acids, vitamins, and inorganic chemicals dissolved in water; sometimes extracts of embryonic tissues, particularly from developing chicks, and the plasma of blood are used too. The medium is thoroughly sterilized and placed in sterile glass con-

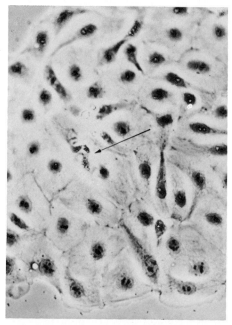

Figure 3–5. A culture of human cells. These cells, taken from an epithelial lining of an oviduct, are growing in a fluid medium carefully maintained at a constant temperature under sterile conditions. The arrow points to a cell preparing to divide. (Courtesy of Dr. Carlos Valenti, *Zeitschr. Zellforsch. Mikro. Anat.*, **60**:850–890, 1963, Springer Verlag, Berlin.)

tainers of various sizes and shapes, depending on the type of cell to be cultured. Into the medium are placed small pieces of living tissue, clumps of live cells, or single cells, and the containers are covered and kept at constant temperatures. Under these conditions the cells grow and multiply, continuing to do so as long as the culture medium is replenished and oxygen is supplied. Much has been learned and is being learned through tissue culture methods about the activities of individual cells and their influence on one another in groups.

One use currently being made of culture methods assists in the study of the manner in which cells use nutritives in building up new protoplasm; this employs radioactive chemicals instead of the normal type. For example, if one were interested in learning where phosphates are utilized in a cell, in place of an ordinary calcium phosphate, a *labeled* phosphate would be used—i.e., one made with radioactive phosphorus, P^{32}. At carefully timed intervals, cells grown in this medium would be removed, mounted on a special type of photographic film, and placed in a lighttight compartment for a period of time. When the film is developed and an enlargement made, it is possible to find where the phosphate had been concentrated or distributed within the cell, for the radioactivity affects a film in a manner quite like that of light. Such an *autoradiographic* study is only one of many types employing both radioactive chemicals and tissue culture procedures.

Cultures of cells are also valuable in providing the large quantities of materials needed for still other cytological techniques, one of which involves fragmenting a quantity of the cells so as to liberate their component parts. To carry out the fragmentation process various procedures have been devised, including the use of very high-frequency sound waves (*ultrasonics*). After the cells have been broken into bits, the remains are centrifuged at extremely high speeds, often refrigerated to reduce the heat produced by the friction of the containers against the air. In such *ultracentrifuges* speeds of 50,000 rpm are sometimes produced. Under the influence of the resulting forces, the various constituents of the cells become arranged in definite strata, in the sequence of their respective specific weights, the heaviest ones outermost, of course. The strata can then be carefully pipetted out and segregated for biochemical or cytological studies on any desired portion of the cell.

The Structure of Animal Cells

As has already been stated, the protoplasm in a cell is not homogeneous but is arranged as those discrete parts called organelles. Among the various types of organisms in general the presence and actual construction of a given organelle vary extensively from one major group to another. In a later section it will be seen that some groups have an extremely simple cellular construction and others a highly complicated one, each type reflecting the degree of complexity of its possessor. For the present, however, attention will be confined to one of the most highly involved representatives, that of the true animals or Metazoa.

To begin with, the protoplasm of animal and most other cells is considered to consist of two major parts, a smaller, usually centrally located portion called the *nucleus* and the remainder, the *cytoplasm* (Figure 3–6). In the living cell, both these subdivisions are of equal importance, for the nucleus quickly perishes when removed from the cytoplasm, whereas the latter portion alone,

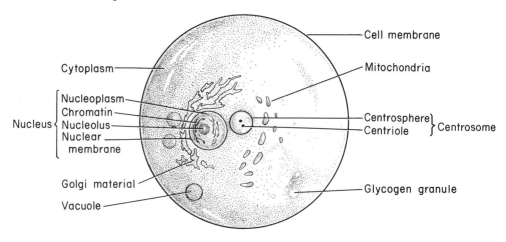

Cell membrane

Cytoplasm

Mitochondria

Nucleoplasm
Chromatin
Nucleolus
Nuclear membrane

Nucleus

Centrosphere
Centriole

Centrosome

Golgi material

Vacuole

Glycogen granule

Figure 3–6. Diagram of a typical animal cell. For the sake of clarity, only a few examples of granules, mitochondria, and Golgi bodies are shown, although these are normally present in large numbers.

although capable of surviving often for several months, is unable as a rule to increase its size or to reproduce. In intact cells, the nucleus seems to be concerned especially in inheritance and in guiding the formation of proteins, while the cytoplasm carries out the chemical activities of the cell. Each subdivision in turn acts through the varied organelles they respectively contain, some of which, as will be seen below, are permanently present whereas others appear only when a cell is reproducing itself.

The Nucleus. Insofar as structure is

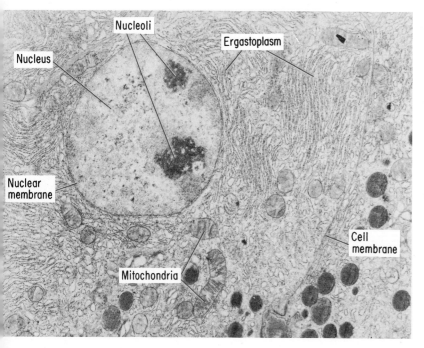

Nucleoli

Ergastoplasm

Nucleus

Nuclear membrane

Cell membrane

Mitochondria

Figure 3–7. An electronmicrograph of a mouse pancreas cell. The dark bodies are zymogen bodies—that is, bodies that secrete an enzyme. Magnified 10,000×. (Courtesy of Dr. S. Bradbury, Dept. of Human Anatomy, Oxford University.)

concerned, the nucleus is relatively simple and includes only a few types of organelles. Basically in animals it consists of a spherical mass of protoplasm, called the *nucleoplasm,* over the surface of which lies a protective covering, the *nuclear membrane.* Under the electron microscope this membrane is seen to be a double structure penetrated by many pores through which, it is believed, chemical products may be interchanged between the nucleus and cytoplasm (Figure 3–7). Within the nucleoplasm, when proper stains have been applied or under the phase-contrast microscope, irregular strands and granules may be seen just beneath the nuclear membrane. These strands and seemingly scattered granules are together known as the *chromatin* material; the name is in reference to their chromatic properties, that is, the ability to take a stain readily. Composed of the complex *deoxyribonucleic acid* (*DNA*) and proteins discussed in the preceding chapter, the chromatin matter becomes more compact during cell reproduction and is then known as the *chromosomes.* One additional body is located in the nucleus, a large, darkly staining mass called the *nucleolus* (Figure 3–7). Although the function of this structure has not been clearly established, it is known to consist largely of *ribonucleic acid* (*RNA*) and, in some organisms at least, to aid in the formation of the chromosomes.

The Cytoplasm. Within and around the cytoplasmic portion of the cell are a number of organelles which carry out many highly diversified activities. Covering the cytoplasm and, hence, the entire cell is the *cell membrane* or *plasma membrane,* far more complex in activities than its simple dual layer construction might suggest (Figure 3–8). By no means should it be viewed as comparable to our skin, for through it must be actively

taken (not just passively absorbed) all the foodstuffs and oxygen, hormones and vitamins, and other chemicals which the cell requires for survival, growth, and reproduction, and out through it must be transported all the waste products and secretions.

Throughout the cytoplasm are a number of organelles which for the greater part are not at all visible under the ordinary microscope or which can be detected only by means of special stains. Among the latter group are small granules or rodlike bodies, the *mitochondria,* which carry out many of the chemical activities of the cell, mainly those of respiration. In electronmicrographs the animal mitochondrion (Figures 3–7, 3–9) is seen internally to be partially subdivided by a number of cross-walls called

Figure 3–8. Boundaries of two adjacent liver cells. Where two different cells meet, the cytoplasmic membranes may lie simply in direct contact or may be intricately folded in the form of minute projections, called "microvilli," which greatly increase the surface area. Magnified 35,000×. (Courtesy of Drs. K. A. Siegesmund and C. A. Fox.)

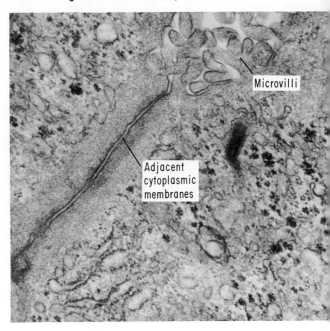

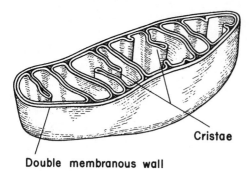

Cristae

Double membranous wall

Figure 3–9. Diagram of an animal mitochondrion. The cross-walls, or cristae, are suspected to bear the enzymes active in the processes of breaking down sugars.

cristae; upon these the molecules of the numerous types of enzymes concerned with the chemical activities are assumed to be located. Another type of organelle is important in the chemical processes of the cell, one whose existence was not even suspected before the advent of the electron microscope. These structures called the *endoplasmic reticulum* or, better, the *ergastoplasm* (Figure 3–10) are now known to be active in combining amino acids to proteins, seemingly guided by RNA received from the nucleus. Typically ergastoplasm consists of a network

Figure 3–10. An electronmicrograph of ergastoplasm. Ergastoplasm may consist of granules (ribosomes or microsomes) placed along a network (reticulum) of membranes, or the granules alone may be present as at the left of the figure. It is because of the occasional lack of these membranes that many workers are currently employing the term "ergastoplasm" rather than its synonym "endoplasmic reticulum." Mouse pancreas. Magnified 61,500×. (Courtesy of Dr. S. Bradbury, Dept. of Human Anatomy, Oxford University.)

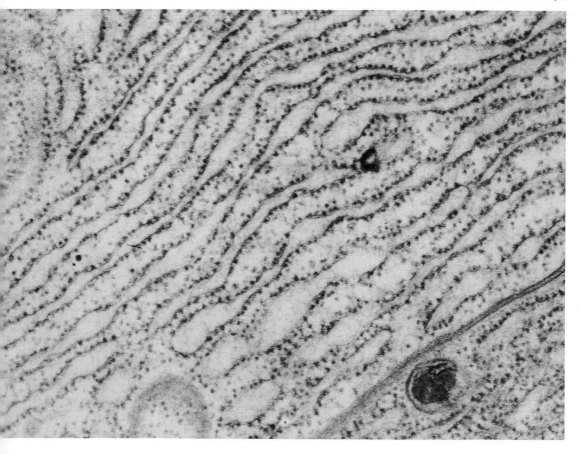

of membranes, often complexly folded, on which are rows of grains called *microsomes,* in allusion to their size, or *ribosomes,* because of the ribonucleic acid that composes them. These granules are the portion of the cytoplasm actually concerned with protein synthesis and are always present, scattered in the cytoplasm when distinct membranes are absent, as is sometimes the case. In some quarters it is suspected that the membranous portion is responsible for the secreting of steroids, but this has as yet not been clearly established. Moreover, both the cell and the nuclear membranes appear to be extensions of these membranes, so that a continuum may exist from the outside to the very interior of the cell (Figure 3–11).

An organelle that as such is confined almost solely to the metazoans is the *centrosome,* a structure that is really dual in its composition (Figure 3–6). Since few studies under the electron microscope have been made of this organelle, only one of which is normally present in any given cell, its grosser features alone can be described. Characteristically found in close proximity to the nucleus, it appears to be active mostly during the processes of cell reproduction. When properly stained, it can be seen to consist of an outer shell, the *centrosphere,* enclosed in which are two rounded dotlike parts, the *centrioles.* The respective roles of these two constituents will be made clear when cell division is discussed in the next chapter.

A group of organelles that resembles ergastoplasm in being composed partly of membranes is that referred to as the *Golgi complex;* ever since its discovery this complex has been the subject of much debate. First, many cytologists were doubtful as to its actual existence, some believing it an artifact, others a different aspect of another organelle, such as the

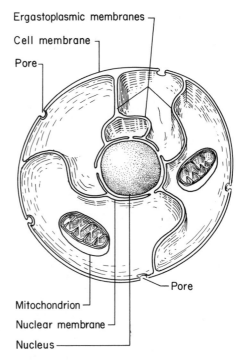

Ergastoplasmic membranes
Cell membrane
Pore
Pore
Mitochondrion
Nuclear membrane
Nucleus

Figure 3–11. Diagram of possible relations of the ergastoplasmic membranes. There is some evidence derived from electron microscope studies that the nuclear and cell membranes may be extensions of the ergastoplasmic membranes; however, there is no general agreement as yet that such may be actually the case.

mitochondrion. Now that the electron microscope has clearly demonstrated its actuality, disagreement centers around its function and precise limitations, for this complex is highly varied in its construction. However, most frequently in the metazoans it consists of a group of membranes, devoid of granules but often closely associated with small vacuoles or vesicles, in which some fluid material appears to be stored (Figure 3–12). Hence, evidence is accumulating that indicates its involvement in storage of secreted products or possibly in transport of various substances from area to area within the cell. Furthermore, there exists a possibility that it may serve in the modification of certain compounds, particularly lipoids, and may play a role in

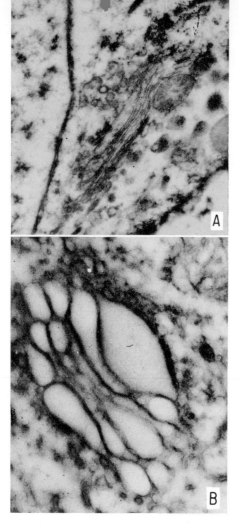

Figure 3–12. The Golgi complex. In these electron-micrographs of intestinal gland cells, two aspects of Golgi material are presented. A. Here the vacuoles ("cisternae") are empty, so that the membranes between which they lie are closely appressed and parallel. Magnified 50,000×. B. Here the vacuoles are filled, with the membranes highly distorted as a consequence. Magnified 40,000×. (Courtesy of Dr. S. W. Strunk, *Jour. Biophys. Biochem. Cytol.*, Vol. 5, Figures 3 and 5, 1959.)

The minute Golgi vacuoles should not be confused with the larger ones which occasionally are characteristic of certain cells. Most frequently encountered among unicellular forms are *food vacuoles,* rather small temporary sacs in which digestion of food particles takes place, and *contractile vacuoles,* which are similar but contain water and waste products.

The cell thus is seen to be an exceedingly complex structure made of many parts, each of which is intricately constructed in turn. While these parts have specialized activities, they are beautifully coordinated into a functional whole. As M. A. Ruderman and A. H. Rosenfeld have said of studies on the nature of matter, explorers into the structure of the cell can also state: "We are peeling an onion layer by layer, each layer uncovering in a sense another universe, unexpected, complicated, and—as we understand more—strangely beautiful."

maintaining a proper concentration of water in the protoplasm. By some researchers, the membranous portions are considered another aspect of the ergastoplastic system.

Questions for Review and Thought

1. What is the chief distinction between the concepts of *protoplasm* and *cell?*

2. Which major subdivision of the cell is more important to the daily life of the cell as a whole, the nucleus or the cytoplasm? Why do you think so?

3. Which of the nuclear structures were not discernible in your laboratory materials? Which cytoplasmic organelles were not visible in the laboratory?

4. List the organelles of the cytoplasm that are, and those that are not, distinctly involved in some sort of chemical activity.

5. What factors would you say are involved in limiting the size of the cell? How would you account for the large size of the cell in the hen or ostrich egg?

6. What instruments or procedures do you suppose would be most useful to a cytologist who is interested in some chemical activity of the cell—for example, how amino acids are absorbed and converted into proteins? Which to one who is interested in learning the structure of a particular type of cell?

Supplementary References

Borek, E. *The Atoms within Us.* New York, Columbia Univ. Press., 1961.

Butler, J. A. V. *Inside the Living Cell.* New York, Basic Books, 1959.

Cantarow, A. *Biochemistry,* 3rd ed. Philadelphia, Saunders, 1962.

Chambers, R. W., and A. S. Payne. *From Cell to Test Tube.* New York, Scribner's, 1960.

———, and E. L. Chambers. *Explorations into the Nature of the Living Cell.* Cambridge, Mass., Harvard Univ. Press, 1961.

DeRobertis, E. D. P., W. W. Nowinski, and F. A. Saez. *General Cytology,* 3rd ed. Philadelphia, Saunders, 1960.

Green, D. E. "The Synthesis of Fat." *Sci. Amer.,* February 1960.

Holter, H. "How Things Get into Cells." *Sci. Amer.,* September 1961.

Langley, L. L. *Cell Function.* New York, Reinhold, 1961.

Lehninger, A. L. "Energy Transformation in the Cell." *Sci. Amer.,* May 1960.

Mazia, D. "How Cells Divide." *Sci. Amer.,* September 1961.

Solomon, A. K. "Pumps in the Living Cell." *Sci. Amer.,* August 1962.

Stumpf, P. K. "ATP." *Sci. Amer.,* April 1953.

Swanson, C. P. *Cytology and Cytogenetics.* Englewood Cliffs, N. J., Prentice-Hall, 1957.

The Activities of Cells

Aᴌᴛʜᴏᴜɢʜ a knowledge of the morphological and chemical constitution of cells is of great importance to the proper understanding of living things, in the final analysis it is the activities of their cells that distinguish organisms from all the other objects in the world. While many of these activities differ greatly among the various types of living things, some of the most basic sorts are shared by all, at least in their essentials. It is these fundamental actions with which we shall be concerned here. They fall into two major groups—those which are characteristics of the cell in the *steady state,* i.e., in the normally functioning cell not engaged in reproducing itself, and those which occur during the processes of *cellular reproduction.*

Activities in the Steady State

In its customary condition, the cell is a veritable bundle of activity. Some of its occupations, such as locomotion and reactions to stimuli, are readily discernible and are best studied at first hand through the observation of living cells and through the medium of time-lapse motion pictures; it is to be hoped that the student will be enabled to gain an appreciation of the cell through contact with both these sources of information. However, there are others within the cell, which, being basically chemical or physical in their nature, are not externally manifest and which need to be studied by means other than direct observation.

Cʜᴇᴍɪᴄᴀʟ Aᴄᴛɪᴠɪᴛɪᴇꜱ

The term *metabolism* is applied to all the chemical activities of the cell together. As will be recalled, it has been suggested that the visible manifestations of life result from these chemical processes, processes that are peculiar to living things alone. Within these activities are included those which break down compounds into simpler substances, referred to as *catabolism,* as well as those which build complex molecules out of simpler ones (*anabolism*), thus breaking down or recreating protoplasm. All reactions involve energy in one way or another, either in requiring it for their completion or in releasing it. Were this energy released directly, as it is in ordinary chemical processes, cells would literally burn themselves out and disappear in a flash of fire and a puff of smoke. Since cells do not incinerate themselves in this fashion, it is obvious that a means of control over the release and utilization of energy has been devised. In fact it is around the control over energy that the unique characteristics of metabolism center.

Enzymes and Coenzymes. As has already been seen in a preceding chapter, *enzymes* are proteins that serve as catalysts, each being specific in its actions. That is to say, as will be recalled, that any one enzyme is capable of inducing reactions only between two or three compounds or within a particular class of substances; the chemicals affected by any one of them are referred to as its *substrate.* Further it will be remembered that enzymatic reactions are almost always reversible, so one that is able to bring about the union of two substances to form a more complex compound can also effect the latter's dissociation. The direction of the reaction is not controlled by the enzyme, however, but results from an interplay of many factors, such as the relative concentration of the substrate constituents and the availability of energy, factors that will be further discussed below. In many reactions the assistance of one or more coenzymes or other "cofactors" is required. The former term is applied to compounds of various types that act in the same manner as, but always in association with, true enzymes.

An extremely large number of enzymes and coenzymes has been isolated, and new ones are being found constantly (Table 4–1). To simplify their study, an extensive terminology has been developed. Many are named, on one hand, on the basis of the substrate acted on, using the suffix *-ase.* For example, that which acts on peptides to form amino acids is referred to as a peptidase. Second, they may be named according to their action, using the same suffix. Thus those which are involved in hydrolyzing reactions (or dehydrolyzing ones) are called hydrolases; most digestive enzymes of the body are of this type.

While this second method provides a convenient means of naming enzymes, it fails to furnish a satisfactory means of classifying them to form a basis for simplifying their study. However, many systems of classification exist. In one scheme currently in favor, five groups are employed. In addition to the *hydrolyzing* group, the *hydrolases* defined above, there are the *splitting* ones, which divide compounds into their components; one of this type (carbonic anhydrase) splits carbonic acid (H_2CO_3) into carbon dioxide and water. Another important group includes the *transferring* kind, which have the property of transferring one chemical group constituent (*radical*) of a compound to another. For example, transaminase can transfer the amino group from an amino acid to certain other organic compounds and convert the latter into an amino acid. Another very important series belonging to this class is the phosphorylases, which are involved in the processes of phosphorylation, to be described very shortly. *Oxidizing* enzymes are in reality a type of the transferring group, but they are of such importance that a separate class is provided for them. Specifically their action is that of transferring hydrogen atoms from one substance to another. In chemical parlance

TABLE 4-1
SOME TYPES OF ENZYMES

Type	Subtype	Example	Action
Hydrolyzing			Add or subtract water (hydrolysis and dehydrolysis)
	Esterase		Hydrolyze products of alcohols and acids
		Lipase	Converts fats to fatty acid and glycerol
		Phosphatase	Acts on organic phosphates
		Nuclease	Breaks down nucleic acids
		Nucleotidase	Hydrolyzes nucleotides
	Carbohydrase		Hydrolyze carbohydrates
		Maltase	Acts on maltose
		Sucrase	Acts on sucrose
		Polysaccharidase	Breaks down or builds up complex carbohydrates
		Cellulase	Acts on cellulose
	Protease		Hydrolyze proteins and peptides
		Dipeptidase	Acts only on certain dipeptides
		Pepsin	Breaks proteins into polypeptides
		Trypsin	Breaks down proteins
		Papain	Acts on proteins; present in papaya fruit
Phosphorylizing			Add or subtract phosphoric acid units
		Sucrose phosphorylase	Converts sucrose to glucose phosphate and fructose
Oxidizing			Active in oxidation-reduction processes
	Dehydrogenase		Remove hydrogen from organic compounds; work with acceptor coenzymes
	Aerobic oxidase		Utilize oxygen directly to oxidize substances
		Tyrosinase	Oxidizes tyrosine, the product of which subsequently forms melanin
		Catalase	Breaks hydrogen peroxide into oxygen and water
Transferring			Transfer radicals from one substance to another
	Transaminase		Transfer amino (NH) groups
	Phosphokinase		Transfer phosphate radicals
		Adenylic kinase	Transfers phosphate of ADP to another ADP to form ATP and AMP
Isomerizing (mutases)			Alter the internal arrangements of molecules
		Phospho-glucomutase	Converts glucose-1-phosphate to glucose-6-phosphate
Splitting			Split compounds into their constituents
		Carbonic anhydrase	Breaks carbonic acid (H_2CO_3) into water and carbon dioxide

a compound that loses one or more electrons (such as would be involved in the loss of hydrogen atoms) is said to be *oxidized,* and that which gains electrons (such as the substance that receives the hydrogen atoms) is said to be *reduced.*

Since this is so, the members of this class might just as logically be called reducing enzymes. However, since oxidation is always accompanied by reduction, with the reverse of this equally true, one term here is quite as good as the other. The fifth class is also of considerable importance. This group is formally referred to as the *isomerizing* enzymes, but it is much more convenient to call them *mutases*. Their function is that of rearranging the constituents of a molecule; usually the rearrangement consists of the shifting of a radical from one position in the molecule to another.

The Cytochrome Series. In the cell there exists an important group of enzymes and coenzymes which will provide the student with both an understanding of how enzymes work and an appreciation of the uniqueness of metabolism. This series is located in large measure within the mitochondria and is vital to all activities in which hydrogen atoms are directly involved, such as cellular respiration. In it are included seven substances, DPN (diphosphopyridine nucleotide), FM (flavin mononucleotide), four cytochromes (cytochrome *a, b, c,* and c_1), and cytochrome oxidase (also known as cytochrome a_3). All the cytochromes are proteins in which iron is an important ingredient, and it is believed that it is this element which gives them their catalytic properties.

Respiration in cells involves not only the intake of oxygen and the liberation of carbon dioxide through the cell membrane but also both the process in which oxygen is combined with hydrogen and that in which carbon dioxide is produced. For example, in the utilization of carbohydrates for the production of energy, one sequence of changes that can occur involves the production of lactic acid by a series of steps that will be explained later; subsequently, this substance may

be broken down into pyruvic acid. This occurs only in the presence of the cytochrome series of enzymes, DPN bringing about the initial reaction, namely that of receiving two hydrogen atoms from the lactic acid; as a result, DPN itself is temporarily reduced, as in the following equation:

$$C_3H_6O_3 + DPN \rightleftarrows$$
$$C_3H_4O_3 + DPN H_2 + E$$

Lactic acid — Pyruvic acid — Energy

The hydrogen atoms are then passed along, in "bucket brigade" fashion, first to FM, then, in turn, to cytochrome *b,* cytochrome *c,* cytochrome c_1, and cytochrome *a,* and finally to cytochrome oxidase, where they are united with oxygen, forming water (Figure 4–1). In each step in this series of reactions a certain amount of energy is released. As will be noted, the cytochromes are not named in accordance with the sequence in which they react but on the basis of other chemical properties. Each member of this series is able to pass the hydrogen only to the substance normally following it. Thus if, for instance, cytochrome c_1 alone is destroyed, cytochrome *c* is unable to pass its hydrogen to cytochrome *a,* and all reactions of this sort cease, resulting in the death of the cell. Since the entire process of removing the hydrogen atoms from the lactic acid and transmitting them along the chain of enzymes requires but a minute fraction of a second to complete, only a small amount of DPN and the other substances need be present to oxidize large quantities of substrate and thus supply the cell with some of its required energy. Some evidence points to the possibility of electrons being transported by this chain of substances, instead of an actual hydrogen atom. Since there is an abundance of hydrogen ions in the water of protoplasm, the electrons

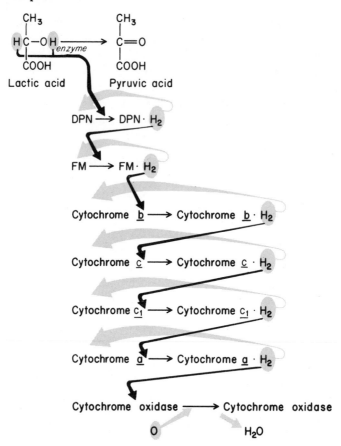

Figure 4–1. The activities of the cytochrome series. After a certain type of enzyme (a dehydrogenase) has removed two hydrogen atoms, they are passed first to a receiver (DPN as a rule) and thence through a whole series of substances until cytochrome oxidase unites them with oxygen to form water. Note that at each level, each receiver in turn unites with the hydrogens briefly until it passes them to the next member of the series. At several points small quantities of energy are released to be stored quickly in the form of ATP.

can be attached to one such ion at the end of the reaction.

From the foregoing illustration can be discerned the chief peculiarity of metabolism, that of utilizing whole series of catalysts to bring about reactions stepwise, so that energy is released gradually and thus controlled. The difference between metabolism and ordinary chemical reactions thus is comparable to that between going down the stairs and jumping out the window; in one case the energy is governed and in the other uncontrolled.

Phosphate Energy Storers. The energy released by the above and other oxidative reactions is not necessarily immediately employed by the protoplasm but can be stored for future use in several ways. Among the storage devices are those reactions which through dehydrolysis form the more complex organic substances; these later can then be broken down and the energy released by oxidative processes. These oxidative processes in the long run provide all the energy utilized by the cell, but they are relatively slow. At times, energy must be quickly available, and for a supply of this sort, it is stored in the form of certain organic *phosphates* ($^-H_2PO_3$). Two principal types occur. In one, the phosphate radical is attached to a nitrogen atom; in the second, the radical is attached to another phosphate group like itself, so that double or triple or even quadruple phosphates are built. In order to form such compounds, which are quite unstable, a large amount of energy is required; because of these facts, the bonds uniting phosphate with nitrogen or with another phosphate are referred to as *high-energy bonds* and

in formulas are indicated with the symbol ~.

Chief in importance among compounds with high-energy bonds in protoplasm is *adenosine triphosphate* (ATP), one of the nucleotides (page 25). This substance in the presence of an enzyme, such as myosin, breaks down to form adenosine diphosphate and phosphoric acid, releasing large quantities of energy in the process, as in the following:

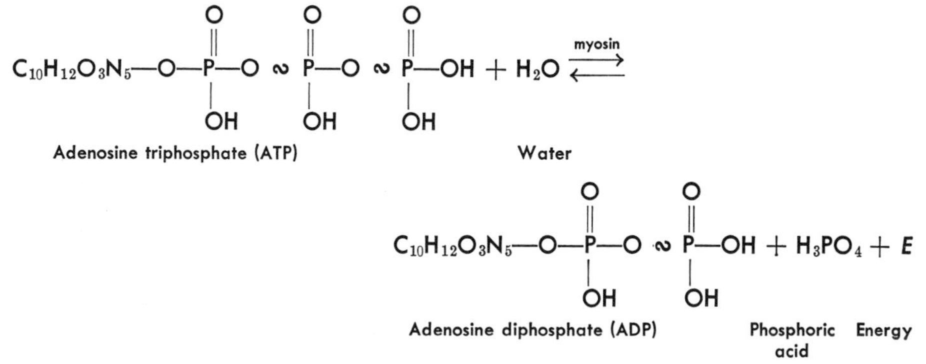

$$C_{10}H_{12}O_3N_5-O-\overset{\overset{\displaystyle O}{\|}}{\underset{\underset{\displaystyle OH}{|}}{P}}-O \sim \overset{\overset{\displaystyle O}{\|}}{\underset{\underset{\displaystyle OH}{|}}{P}}-O \sim \overset{\overset{\displaystyle O}{\|}}{\underset{\underset{\displaystyle OH}{|}}{P}}-OH + H_2O \underset{\longleftarrow}{\overset{myosin}{\longrightarrow}}$$

Adenosine triphosphate (ATP)   Water

$$C_{10}H_{12}O_3N_5-O-\overset{\overset{\displaystyle O}{\|}}{\underset{\underset{\displaystyle OH}{|}}{P}}-O \sim \overset{\overset{\displaystyle O}{\|}}{\underset{\underset{\displaystyle OH}{|}}{P}}-OH + H_3PO_4 + E$$

Adenosine diphosphate (ADP)   Phosphoric   Energy
                                               acid

This source of energy is employed in many cellular activities throughout all groups of living things. Other compounds are employed similarly, including guanosine triphosphate (GTP) and uridine triphosphate (UTP), but these are not known to be of such universal importance. Of the substances with the high-energy bond formed between a phosphate radical and a nitrogen atom, *phosphocreatine* is perhaps the most important (Figure 4–2), as it is involved in the contraction of muscles in vertebrates; it will be discussed more fully later in the book in connection with the subject of muscular action.

During the cytochrome series of reactions described in the preceding section, the energy released can form three high-energy phosphate bonds for every pair of hydrogen atoms removed; hence, three molecules of ADP can be converted to

ATP during the conversion of one molecule of lactic to pyruvic acid.

Glycolysis. The respiratory aspects of metabolism, like many others, are highly complex; so our discussion of this topic has thus far been imitating the metabolic processes in pursuing a stairlike approach rather than the more direct one. Now

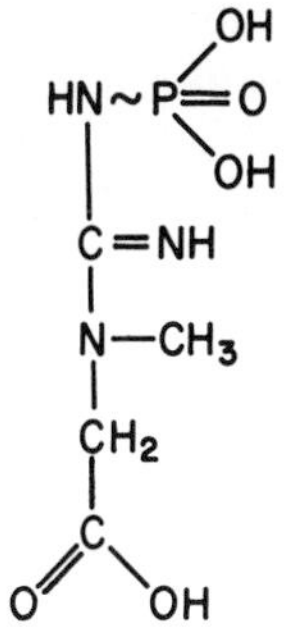

Figure 4–2. Phosphocreatine. A phosphate radical is attached by means of a high-energy bond directly to a nitrogen atom.

that several of the steps have been examined, treatment of the over-all process can be begun; in this, the first substrate may be any number of substances—fats, carbohydrates of many kinds, and other organic materials. With each type the initial reactions would vary in detail, but each eventually would lead to the same point, that of the production of pyruvic acid. So we shall choose the abundant sugar, glucose, to illustrate the processes;

the variations serve no useful purpose here. This first series of reactions in respiration is referred to as *glycolysis*.

Before glucose (or other substance) can be employed in respiration it first must be *phosphorylated*—i.e., combined with a phosphate radical. To do so requires energy, and the services of ATP are drawn upon, with *glucose phosphate* being formed as a result. This equation can be written:

Glucose   Phosphate   Energy   Glucose phosphate
           (from ATP) (from ATP)

The glucose phosphate is then converted into fructose phosphate through the agency of a mutase (see equation below).

This phosphorylated fructose then receives the same treatment as the glucose did originally—the addition of a second phosphate radical from ATP with the aid of energy from the same source, converting it into *fructose diphosphate* in the

presence of an enzyme (*phosphohexokinase*). Then in the presence of another enzyme (*aldolase*), fructose diphosphate is split into two, forming that number of molecules of a triose sugar called *phosphoglyceric aldehyde* (Figure 4-3). Now the cytochrome series enters the picture. While the DPN temporarily accepts two hydrogen atoms, another phosphate radi-

Glucose phosphate   Fructose phosphate

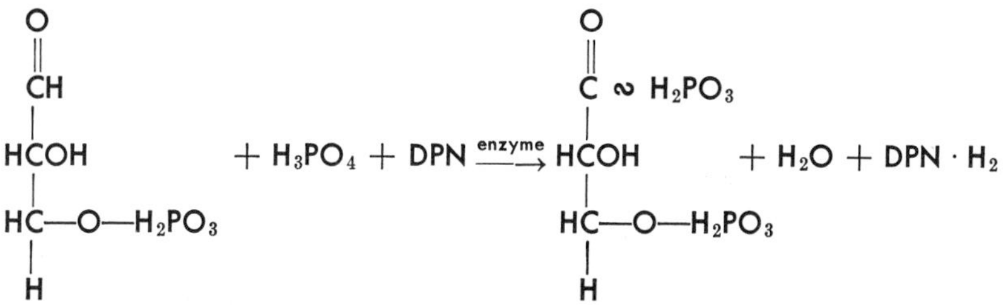

$$\begin{array}{c} O \\ \parallel \\ CH \\ | \\ HCOH \\ | \\ HC\!-\!O\!-\!H_2PO_3 \\ | \\ H \end{array} \;+\; H_3PO_4 \;+\; DPN \;\xrightarrow{\text{enzyme}}\; \begin{array}{c} O \\ \parallel \\ C \sim H_2PO_3 \\ | \\ HCOH \\ | \\ HC\!-\!O\!-\!H_2PO_3 \\ | \\ H \end{array} \;+\; H_2O \;+\; DPN\cdot H_2$$

| Phosphoglyceric aldehyde | Phosphoric acid | | Diphosphoglyceric acid | Reduced DPN |

cal from any source is added, with the result that a substance called *diphosphoglyceric acid* is formed, as in the equation above. In it the "enzyme" catalyzes the process of phosphorylation. The energy derived from this partial oxidation of the phosphoglyceric aldehyde is not released but is stored in the high-energy bond; that from the oxidation of the hydrogen via the cytochromes is available for other use. Next the high-energy phosphate of diphosphoglyceric acid is transferred to two units of ADP, thus restoring all the ATP utilized in the

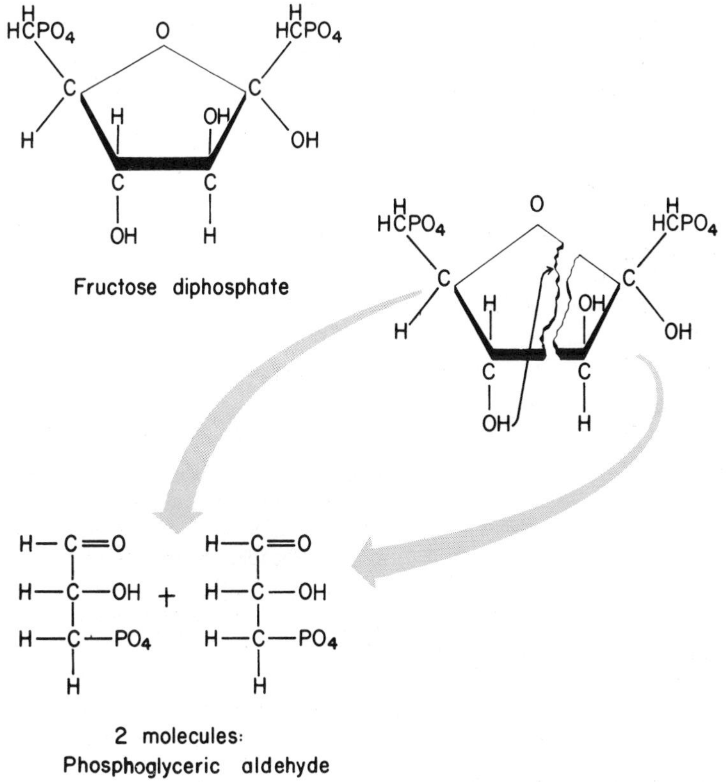

Fructose diphosphate

2 molecules:
Phosphoglyceric aldehyde

Figure 4–3. The formation of phosphoglyceric aldehyde. After fructose has received two phosphate units, the molecule is of such a form that it can be readily split into two identical parts, each with three carbon atoms. The two new molecules thus formed are in reality a triose sugar called, as noted, phosphoglyceric aldehyde.

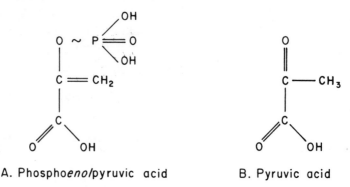

A. Phospho*enol*pyruvic acid   B. Pyruvic acid

Figure 4–4. Some products of glycolysis. The *enol* variety of pyruvic acid (A) can be seen to differ from the ordinary form (B) in possessing a double bond between two carbons rather than between a carbon and an oxygen atom.

earlier stages of the process and forming phosphoglyceric acid. This latter substance goes through several steps, ending in dehydrolysis, in which it is converted into *phosphoenolpyruvic acid,* a compound containing a high-energy bond (Figure 4–4*A*). As in the above case, this high-energy phosphate is transferred to two units of ADP, forming ATP and converting the phosphoenolpyruvic acid into simple *pyruvic acid* (Figure 4–4*B*). It is well for the student to keep this relatively unfamiliar substance in mind, for it is a very important one entering into numerous cellular activities and forming the common point shared by the oxida-

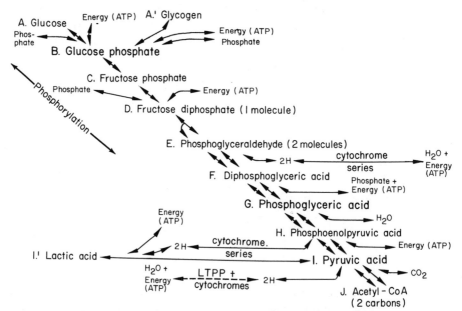

Figure 4–5. The glycolytic chain of reactions in cell respiration. In this diagram are outlined the principal events in the respiratory breakdown of sugars. For clarity's sake one or two minor intermediate reactions are omitted. As this sequence of events is of vital importance in the cell and, as such, is included in more than one process to be described later, a familiarity with its steps will be found to be of great value.

tion of many substrates pointed out earlier. The whole process of glycolysis may be summarized as in Figure 4–5.

One of the steps frequently taken after the formation of pyruvic acid is its hydrogenation (reduction) to lactic acid, through the cytochrome series of steps outlined previously, but in the opposite direction. In other words, hydrogen, presumably from water or other available source, and energy from three molecules of ATP may be added to pyruvic acid. Since this action is reversible, of course, the energy is readily available when the cell is ready to oxidize the lactic acid thus formed. And indeed, this function of temporarily storing energy may be the reason for the production of lactic acid at this stage, for during periods of active glycolysis, this substance is rapidly accumulated; in periods of rest or lessened activity, it gradually is broken down further. These additional steps in its breakdown represent the final respiratory processes, those involved in the *citric acid cycle,* also called the tricarboxylic acid cycle or Krebs cycle.

The Citric Acid Cycle. In this final series of reactions of cellular respiration, a deeper knowledge of organic chemistry is called for than the student, at this stage of his development, can reasonably be expected to possess. Hence, in the presentation that follows some simplification has been felt to be justifiable, in an effort not to obscure the essentials with too many less important details. The preliminaries to the cycle begin with the pyruvic acid formed by the glycolysis or any other metabolic process.

Through the agency of two coenzymes, LTPP (lipothiamide pyrophosphate) and CoA (coenzyme A), the pyruvic acid is reduced and condensed, the CoA removing an acetyl group (CH_3CO^-) and the LTPP removing two hydrogen atoms, with the liberation of *carbon dioxide* as a result. As the student may have noted, this is the first mention of the formation of this product thus far in respiration. The hydrogen atoms are passed to DPN and along the usual cytochromes as elsewhere; however, the acetyl radical along with water is added to a compound known as *oxaloacetic acid,* which is thereby converted into *citric acid* (Figure 4–6). The formation of this product can be taken as the point at which this cycle commences and ends.

For the details of the chemical changes

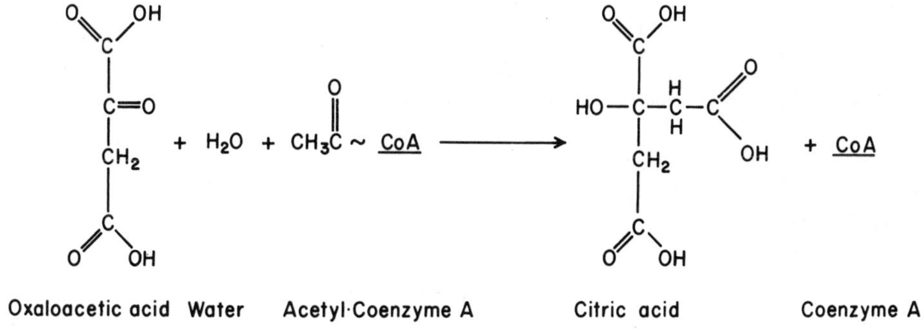

Oxaloacetic acid   Water   Acetyl·Coenzyme A   Citric acid   Coenzyme A

Figure 4–6. The formation of citric acid. The first step in the citric acid portion of the respiratory processes involves the formation of a six-carbon substance, citric acid. In the synthesis of this substance a two-carbon molecule ("acetyl" radical) from glycolysis is combined to a four-carbon compound (oxaloacetic acid). At the end of this reaction, the coenzyme A, which carried the acetyl radical from the glycolytic chain into this citric acid cycle, is released to repeat this function over again.

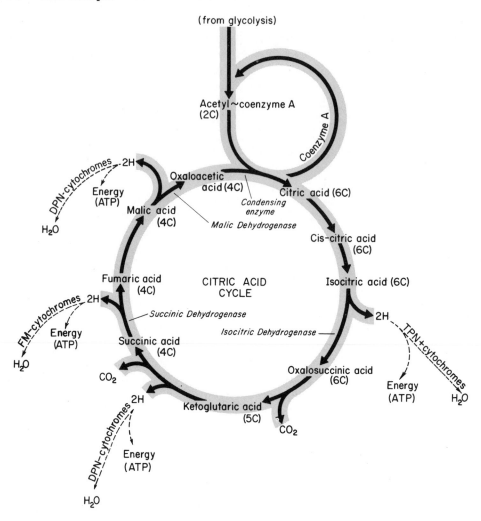

Figure 4–7. The citric acid cycle of reactions in cell respiration. Continuing the glycolytic reactions shown in Figure 4–5, a series of activities occurs in a cyclic pattern. It begins with the formation of citric acid (Figure 4–6) and continues by the familiar processes of hydrogen removal through the assistance of the cytochrome series and by a new set in which carbon dioxide units are broken off one by one. In the end, the four-carboned compound, oxaloacetic acid, is created, ready to receive an acetyl radical from glycolysis and thus to begin the cycle once more.

involved in the citric acid cycle, the interested student should refer to Figure 4–7. Basically the cycle includes a series of steps in which a substance containing six carbon atoms, citric acid, is gradually broken down to one containing only four, oxaloacetic acid. The latter then is converted into citric acid and so the cycle continues around and around. At each step wherever hydrogen is removed, the familiar DPN and cytochromes are to be found, with the resulting energy stored in the equally familiar ATP. As the number of carbon atoms is reduced, it will be noted that carbon dioxide is liberated. It will also be observed that oxidation of succinic acid to fumaric in this cycle is unique in that DPN is not involved, but

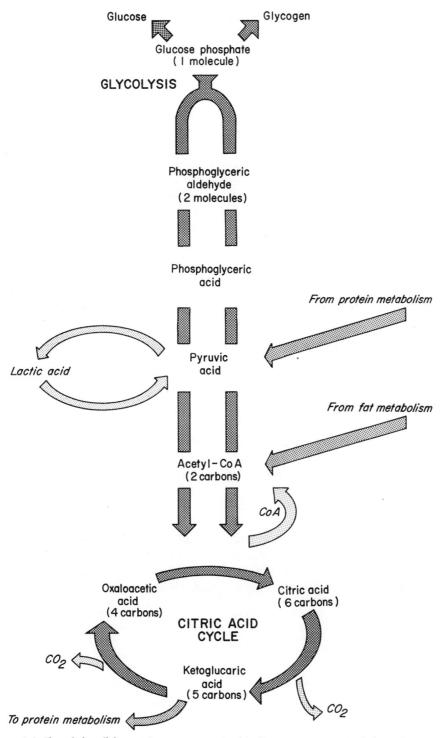

Figure 4–8. The whole cellular respiratory process. In this diagram are summarized the main events in cellular metabolism, without the confusion of enzyme names or less important reactions. In addition the places of entry of products from protein and lipid catabolism are indicated.

FM accepts the hydrogen atoms directly and passes them to the cytochromes. Only two molecules of ATP are produced as a result instead of the customary three.

From the two processes, glycolysis and the citric acid cycle (Figure 4–8), a total of 38 molecules of ATP is netted per molecule of glucose. In terms of calories, these contain only a little better than one fourth of the total energy released by the combustion of a like quantity of glucose by ordinary chemical reactions. Hence, metabolic processes are inefficient, as far as energy utilization is concerned. However, the fine control over the release and utilization of energy that metabolism makes possible more than justifies its employment. And it should be remembered, moreover, that most of man's own creations employ energy even less efficiently than does the cell; for example, an ordinary incandescent light bulb produces energy as light only to an extent of 15 per cent of the energy used in the form of electricity.

The Metabolism of Fats. In the cells and tissues, fats are not kept in "dead storage," as it were, but are continually being utilized and replaced, so that there is a steady turnover of the material. The glycerol constituent of fats (page 18) is readily phosphorylated and converted directly into glucose or glycogen; thus it can be used almost directly in the respiratory cycle. The fatty-acid portions, how-ever, need some preliminary treatment before they can be used for energy purposes. These preparatory steps, although somewhat more complicated, are not too different, except in certain details, from some steps of the respiratory reactions.

Essentially, the fatty acids are prepared for oxidation first by combining with CoA and going through a wheel-like series of steps, the net result of which is the peeling off of the carbon atoms in sets of two at each "revolution." Enzymes are, of course, required for catalysis, and three, each referred to as a *thiokinase,* are known to exist. As will be recalled (page 19), the fatty acids are in chains of various lengths, each link being represented by a carbon atom; each of the three thiokinases is specific for a certain range of chain length. One acts on those of 2 to 3, another on those of 4 to 11, and the third on fatty acids of 12 to 22 carbon atoms or links. In addition, energy is required, and as in carbohydrate metabolism, ATP is its source. In this case, however, the energy is supplied by the breakdown of this material to AMP (adenosine monophosphate, or adenylic acid), the break occurring at the first of the two high-energy bonds present instead of the second. In the presence of the thiokinase and energy source, water is removed from a fatty acid to form an *acyl* radical, which becomes attached to CoA, thus:

$$
\begin{array}{l}
CH_3 \\
| \\
CH_2 \\
| \\
CH_2 \\
| \\
CH_2 \\
| \\
C{=}O \\
| \\
OH
\end{array}
\;+\; ATP \;+\; CoA \;\xrightarrow{\;thiokinase\;}\;
\begin{array}{l}
CH_3 \\
| \\
CH_2 \\
| \\
CH_2 \\
| \\
CH_2 \\
| \\
C{-}O{-}CoA
\end{array}
\;+\; AMP \;+\; H_3P_2O_6{}^{-} \;+\; H_2O
$$

Fatty acid   Acyl-coenzyme A   Pyrophosphate

The acyl-coenzyme A first loses two hydrogen atoms by way of a coenzyme called FAD (flavin adenine dinucleotide), which probably passes it to the cytochromes, and then becomes hydrolyzed. In turn this is followed by the removal of two more hydrogen atoms, this time by the familiar DPN series, and the loss of an acetyl group (which contains two carbon atoms) to a second CoA molecule. The latter, converted by this action to acetyl-CoA, now can enter the citric acid cycle for further oxidation; the first CoA has been restored by this same step to acyl-CoA, with two carbon atoms fewer than originally, ready to go around the cycle just described again. As fewer atoms remain in the acyl-CoA, more can be added from other fatty acids as at the very onset of this series of reactions. Even-numbered and odd-numbered fatty acids receive somewhat different treatment to complete the processes of their oxidation, but these need not concern us here. Complete oxidation of a molecule of a 17-carbon fatty acid will convert 148 molecules of ADP to ATP.

The Metabolism of Proteins. Since the amino acids that compose the proteins are so extremely varied in their composition, many variations occur in the metabolism of this type of food. Nevertheless, some general principles are perceptible, and it is these that are of interest to the student. One of the most general procedures in amino acid breakdown involves the removal of the amino radical in the form of ammonia, converting the carbon chain into a keto acid first. This process consists of two steps as shown in the equation in the right column above.

The dehydrogenase can be associated with either the familiar DPN or, in some cases, the one involved in fat metabolism, FAD, or it may utilize any one of many others that serve in this capacity, some of

which are highly specific as to the amino acid acted on. Many avenues are open to the ammonia released by this process of *deamination,* but it must be rapidly removed or altered, for it is a very toxic substance. In many cases, it is simply excreted into the environment, particularly in unicellular organisms; in other cases, it is transformed into urea or uric acid and excreted in those forms. But many times, at least in small quantities, it is stored for future use. Mostly this is accomplished by uniting it to one of the amino acids, *glutamic acid,* converting it into another amino acid, *glutamine,* with energy supplied by ATP (top of page 54).

Probably more important in metabolism than deamination is a process called *transamination,* in which an amino group can be transferred from an amino acid

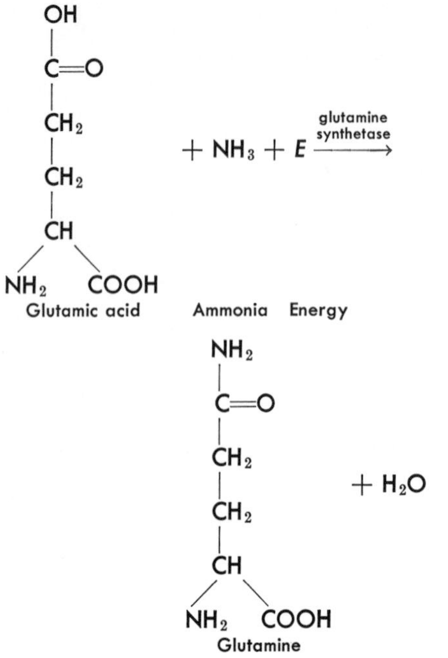

$$
\begin{array}{c}
\text{OH} \\
| \\
\text{C}=\text{O} \\
| \\
\text{CH}_2 \\
| \\
\text{CH}_2 \\
| \\
\text{CH} \\
\diagdown \diagup \\
\text{NH}_2 \quad \text{COOH}
\end{array}
\quad + \text{NH}_3 + \text{E} \xrightarrow{\substack{\text{glutamine} \\ \text{synthetase}}}
$$

Glutamic acid   Ammonia   Energy

$$
\begin{array}{c}
\text{NH}_2 \\
| \\
\text{C}=\text{O} \\
| \\
\text{CH}_2 \\
| \\
\text{CH}_2 \\
| \\
\text{CH} \\
\diagdown \diagup \\
\text{NH}_2 \quad \text{COOH}
\end{array}
\quad + \text{H}_2\text{O}
$$

Glutamine

to a keto acid. In the following example, the amino acid alanine is converted to pyruvic acid while its amino group is transferred to keto-glutaric acid, forming glutamic acid; all such reactions are catalyzed by a group of enzymes called *transaminases*.

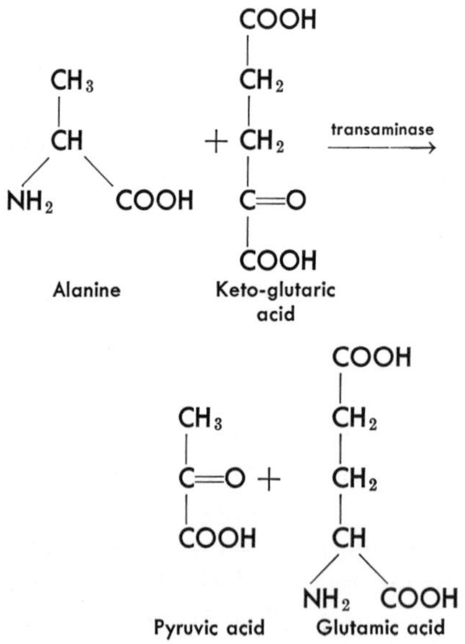

$$
\begin{array}{c}
\text{CH}_3 \\
| \\
\text{CH} \\
\diagdown \diagup \\
\text{NH}_2 \quad \text{COOH}
\end{array}
\quad + \quad
\begin{array}{c}
\text{COOH} \\
| \\
\text{CH}_2 \\
| \\
\text{CH}_2 \\
| \\
\text{C}=\text{O} \\
| \\
\text{COOH}
\end{array}
\quad \xrightarrow{\text{transaminase}}
$$

Alanine   Keto-glutaric acid

$$
\begin{array}{c}
\text{CH}_3 \\
| \\
\text{C}=\text{O} \\
| \\
\text{COOH}
\end{array}
\quad + \quad
\begin{array}{c}
\text{COOH} \\
| \\
\text{CH}_2 \\
| \\
\text{CH}_2 \\
| \\
\text{CH} \\
\diagdown \diagup \\
\text{NH}_2 \quad \text{COOH}
\end{array}
$$

Pyruvic acid   Glutamic acid

The importance of this type of reaction is that it enables the cell to synthesize amino acids needed to form specific proteins from whatever amino acids may be taken in as foods. Were this process of transamination not in existence, the protoplasm of any organism would of necessity vary in accordance with the foodstuffs available to it from day to day, and all specificity would be lost. By this process, too, carbohydrates can be converted into amino acids as long as a source of nitrogen in a suitable form is available. However, not all amino acids can be thus synthesized; there are eight in man that cannot. These eight (valine, leucine, isoleucine, threonine, methionine, phenylalanine, tryptophan, and lysine) must be taken into the body from external sources in vertebrates and are therefore referred to as the *dietarily essential* amino acids.

The above reactions are just a few of all types now known to occur within the protoplasm but are sufficient to provide a concept of how the cell operates, where it gets energy, and the manner in which this energy is controlled and used. Although much is known, the student should by no means believe that all details have now been worked out and that no important discoveries remain to be made. Precisely the opposite state of affairs prevails; far more remains obscure than has thus far been brought to light. Today we know what enzymes are involved in many of the cellular processes, but we still do not know exactly how any of them bring about their reactions —for example, how a mutase rearranges the atomic constituents of a molecule. Nor do we have the vaguest notion of how energy is applied to any chemical radical to make it attach to and become a part of a molecule. These and countless other basic problems await alert young minds for their solution—but the

minds need thorough training and acquisition of much knowledge before they
can be ready for such a task.

One of the problems confronting living cells is that of bringing in from the
environment needed substances, such as
water, salts, foodstuffs, and oxygen, without simultaneously taking in undesirable
or harmful compounds that may also be
present. Not always are cells entirely successful in avoiding noxious materials, but
they have solved the problem of selec-
tively absorbing chemicals to a fairly high
degree. This solution employs diverse
methods. In some cases use is made of
the process of *osmosis,* in others an activity called *active transport;* sometimes
"drinking" and "eating" procedures,
known respectively as *pinocytosis* and
phagocytosis, are employed. Still other
materials are taken in by as yet unknown
methods. The whole problem is referred
to as "transport through biological membranes" and consists of the aspects mentioned above of taking in materials
through the cell membrane and giving
off carbon dioxide and other substances,
including secretions of various sorts,
through membranes within the cell as
well as that on the surface.

Diffusion.   That all matter is made
of molecules, and the latter of atoms, and
that these particles are in constant motion is general information with which
almost all people are familiar. Similarly,
it is well known that the molecules of
gases move more freely than do those of
liquids, and those of the latter more
freely than the particles in a solid. These
facts supply an explanation of the phenomenon of *diffusion,* the scattering of
one substance in another by molecular
activity, and an understanding of the
greater speed at which this process takes
place in gases than in liquids and in the
latter than in solids. The movement
of the substance that is being diffused

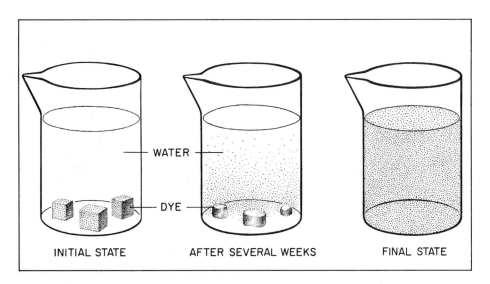

WATER

DYE

INITIAL STATE   AFTER SEVERAL WEEKS   FINAL STATE

Figure 4-9. Diffusion. When a soluble substance such as a dye is initially added to a container of
water, it soon commences to dissolve. If placed in a situation free from vibration or other disturbance,
the dissolved dye after several weeks is found concentrated largely in the lower portion of the container. If maintained vibration-free for an indefinite period, eventually the solution becomes uniform
in color from top to bottom as the dye molecules diffuse throughout the water.

(Figure 4–9) is always from the region of greatest concentration to that of the lesser and proceeds in time until equilibrium has been reached—that is, until the substance has become diffused equally throughout the medium.

Osmosis. In biology diffusion is of little importance except as it is represented in the process of *osmosis,* which is of fundamental significance in all living things. Osmosis can be defined as the diffusion of fluids and dissolved substances through a semipermeable membrane, the latter being a membrane that permits the passage of some molecules but not others. Thus, to use a simple example, in a case where an aqueous solution of sugar such as glucose is placed in an open sac made of a suitable membrane and the sac is suspended in pure water, the water on both sides of the membrane diffuses in and out freely, but the glucose molecules only to a negligible degree (Figure 4–10). If the concentration of the glucose solution is 15 per cent,

there are within the sac only 85 molecules of water against the interior of the membrane for every 100 molecules of water on its outer surface. Consequently more molecules tend to move into the sac than leave, 100 entering to every 85 leaving, so that the amount of water within the sac gradually increases at the expense of that in the outer container. This increase in the water content, if the sac is open, results in a raising of its water level, a rise that can be readily observed if a capillary tube is attached. Or, if the sac is sealed shut, the increased amount of water will build up pressure to such an extent that it will burst. This pressure exerted by a movement of fluid through a membrane is called *osmotic pressure.*

It should be borne in mind that any difference, no matter how slight, between the concentration of fluid enclosed within a membrane and that in its surroundings will cause a movement of fluid toward the area of lower concentration. In the above example, were the sac containing

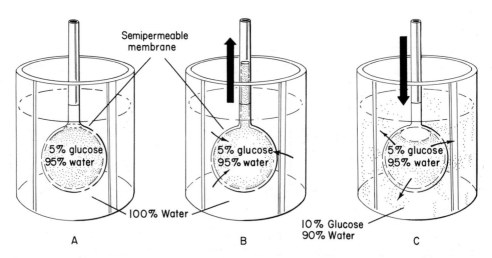

Figure 4–10. Osmosis. If a 5 per cent glucose solution, for example, is placed in a semipermeable membranous sac and immersed in water (A), more water molecules tend to enter the sac than leave as there are 100 molecules of this substance on the outside of the membrane for every 95 inside. Consequently, the increase in water content inside is indicated by the rise in the tube (B). When a similar sac is suspended in a 10 per cent glucose solution instead of in water (C), 95 water molecules then leave for every 90 that enter, with a decrease in the sac's contents as a result.

15 per cent glucose solution immersed in a vessel containing one of 12 per cent, the water would still move into the sac, but at a much slower rate than in the original instance. And movement would continue until equilibrium had been reached. Were it placed in a solution of greater concentration than that of its own contents, water would leave more rapidly than it entered and the level of the sac's contents would be lowered.

In living things similar reactions occur. As you will recall, of course, cells contain a certain percentage of salts and other substances dissolved in the water of their protoplasm, so that if they are placed in a *hypotonic solution*—i.e., one with a lower osmotic pressure—water will enter the cells by osmosis, causing them to swell. Depending on the amount of this *endosmosis*—i.e., osmotic movement of substances into the cell—the cells may become swollen until they are quite firm, or *turgid,* or even to the point where they rupture. The bursting of red blood cells from osmotic causes is referred to as *hemolysis.* On the other hand, if cells are placed in a *hypertonic solution,* one with a greater osmotic pressure than their protoplasm, water will leave by *exosmosis,* and *plasmolysis,* a shriveling effect, will occur. In studying cells, in giving blood transfusions, or in feeding glucose through blood vessels, care must be taken to maintain the media as *isotonic* as possible. In other words, the media must have the same osmotic pressure as the contents of the cells they will surround or contact.

Active Transport. Although particles as small as ions of potassium, sodium, chloride, and so on, normally would be expected to cross freely through a semipermeable membrane by ordinary osmosis, they appear to do so in cells only to a negligible extent. For one thing it has been found that certain ions can be taken into the cell against a concentration gradient—that is, when the concentration of the ions is greater within than on the outside. For another, it has become evident that energy is expended in the process of absorbing ions and that this energy is derived from ATP. Thus metabolism is directly involved. As an example of the type of evidence that has been gathered may be cited the uptake of phosphate ions in bacteria. As long as oxygen is available, the bacterial cells are able to absorb phosphate against at least a tenfold concentration gradient; without oxygen, however, absorption ceases. Moreover, when respiration is interrupted, the phosphate does not reenter the medium surrounding the cells, as would be anticipated were osmosis playing the principal role, but there occurs only an exchange of one phosphate ion for another, as detected by employment of labeled material. The rate of this exchange exactly equals the rate of uptake during respiration. Thus it would seem that an enzyme located in the cell membrane is involved. When oxygen is available and respiration is proceeding, the enzyme molecules pick up phosphate ions from the surrounding substrate and pass them to receptor compounds inside with the aid of the free energy then present. When oxygen is lacking, this free energy is absent, so the enzymes, while still capable of transporting phosphate ions into the cell, are unable to dispose of them; therefore, the ions are carried out as rapidly as they are carried in. In some other cases that have received study, ion movements have been found to be interdependent. One such case is that involving the movement of potassium and sodium ions through the membrane of the red blood cell. Here the carrier enzyme is able to move potassium ions solely into and solium ions only out of the cell; the absence of either ion halts the movement of the other. Here, too, energy is involved.

During the uptake of large molecules, such as those of sugars and amino acids, similar systems of enzymatic transport apparently are involved, but usually they are accompanied by chemical changes in the absorbed molecules. Sugars, for instance, are phosphorylated in the process of absorption. However, the basic principles are similar in all cases, regardless of whether the substance moved is an ion or a gigantic molecule.

Pinocytosis and Phagocytosis. Even prior to the advent of the phase-contrast microscope, Lewis in 1931 observed living cultures of cells taking in fluid through active movement of the cytoplasm near the cells' surfaces. In this "drinking" process, called *pinocytosis,* droplets of the fluid become surrounded by folds of the cytoplasm and are moved inward into the body of the cell. More recent observations have determined, with the assistance of labeled compounds, that the cell thus not only obtains its water but takes in and utilizes proteins, sugars, and other substances dissolved in the water. Electron microscope studies indicate that in the process of taking in fluids in this fashion, the cell membrane infolds deeply and actually conducts the liquid inward. Many cells are also able to take in solid substances in a comparable manner, an "eating" process called *phagocytosis.* By this means certain types of cells are able to engulf relatively large bits of organic matter or even other intact cells.

Cellular Reproduction

One of the distinctive features of living things, *growth* by conversion, is carried out by means of the metabolic processes described. Especially active toward this end are such anabolic phases as peptide formation and aminization, namely those concerned with building the proteins distinctive of the protoplasm for each species. Normally after a cell has grown to its maximum size, it then performs a second unique activity of life, that of *self-reproduction.* This it accomplishes simply by dividing itself into halves, each new part being a cell precisely like that of the original before division occurred. Although the result of the division is simple enough, the production of two cells from one, the actual processes of carrying it out are quite intricate, for the cell is, as the student now knows, an exceedingly complex object. The orderly processes of dividing the nucleus are together usually referred to as *mitosis,* those of splitting the cytoplasm as *cytokinesis.* In most animals two variations exist, one employed during routine or *vegetative* activities, the second when reproductive bodies or *gametes* are to be formed. In the latter variant, the term *meiosis* is applied to the processes of nuclear division.

MITOTIC CELL DIVISION

Mitosis. Since, as implied above, the processes of division of the nucleus involve a considerable degree of complexity, it has been found convenient for descriptive and comparative purposes to subdivide them arbitrarily into four stages called phases. The first of these, *prophase,* is concerned with preparing the nuclear components for actual division and, hence, is long and intricate; the same statement is true too for the last phase, *telophase,* in which, following division, the nuclear organelles are restored to their original condition. In contrast, the two intermediate stages, *metaphase* and *anaphase,* are brief and relatively simple. Actually, because telophase is virtually identical in reverse sequence to

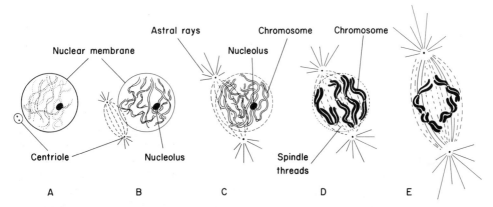

Figure 4–11. The first steps in nuclear reproduction. *A.* The nucleus in the normal active cell. *B.* When nuclear reproduction (i.e., mitosis) begins, the chromosomes first appear as fine threads while the centrioles commence to migrate around the nucleus after the centrosphere has disappeared. Astral rays often put in an appearance at this time also. *C.* As the preceding processes continue, the nuclear membrane begins to disintegrate. *D.* By the middle of this sequence of events, which characterizes prophase, the chromosomes are well-developed rods and the nucleolus has disappeared. *E.* At the end of prophase the nuclear membrane is no longer evident and the centrioles, along with the astral rays and spindle fibers, have attained the opposite poles.

prophase, only the latter requires close attention by the student.

In prophase (Figure 4–11), as has already been pointed out, the parts of the nucleus are prepared for division. Some of the preparatory steps occur before any trace of the mitotic processes can actually be detected, such as the raising of the level of DNA in the nucleus. However, it should also be borne in mind that some of the divisionary activities are carried out by the cytoplasm; the nucleus is absolutely unable to divide by itself. First the necessary energy comes through respiratory activities of the mitochondria, but in addition a certain cytoplasmic organelle, the *centrosome,* is even more directly involved. In fact, changes within this structure are the first that can be noted in the initiation of prophase; its outer shell, the *centrosphere,* disappears, setting free the two dotlike parts, the *centrioles,* into the cytoplasm. After their liberation, the centrioles begin to migrate around the nucleus away from each other toward opposite ends (*poles*) of the cell. As they travel, around each appears a set

of fibers (*astral rays*) radiating out into the cytoplasm and, together with the centriole, forming a starlike cluster called the *astral body* (Figure 4–11*B*). At the time these bodies are first formed, a change can also be noted within the nucleus. The chromatin matter, which normally appears as scattered granules and broken threads, begins to condense and is seen to consist of long, fine filaments, each of which is composed of two like *chromatids* closely entwined. With these developments the *early* part of prophase has become established. These changes continue along similar lines, the astral bodies becoming more widely separated while the chromatin strands shorten and thicken. Finally the latter attain the characteristic rodlike form of *chromosomes,* each composed of two identical chromatids. As stated in the preceding chapter, the nucleolus aids in forming the chromosomes; so by this stage in mitosis, it has exhausted its substance and no longer is visible. At the same time, the nuclear membrane begins to break down and disappear (Figure 4–11*C, D*); with

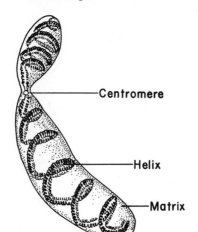

Figure 4–12. Chromosomal structure. A "half" chromosome (chromatid) is here greatly enlarged to show the structural details. The centromere holds two "sister" chromatids together until late in mitosis and also provides a point of attachment for the spindle fibers.

the initiation of its breakdown and the formation of chromosomes the *middle* portion of prophase closes. After the for-

mation of the chromosomes, a new set of fibers is seen to begin emanating from each centriole, running toward the nucleus. In the meantime the nuclear membrane continues to break down; after its disappearance, these newly formed *spindle threads* extend to the chromosomes and become attached at that part of the chromosome called the *centromere* (Figure 4–12). By the time all these processes have been completed, the astral bodies have reached opposite poles of the cells, with the chromosomes irregularly massed between them, bringing prophase to an end (Figure 4–11C). It is a long and complex phase indeed, and its completion actually consumes close to 40 per cent of the total time required for the cell to divide.

The next stage, *metaphase,* is short and simple, with only one new development. The chromosomes, which formed a disorderly clump at the end of prophase,

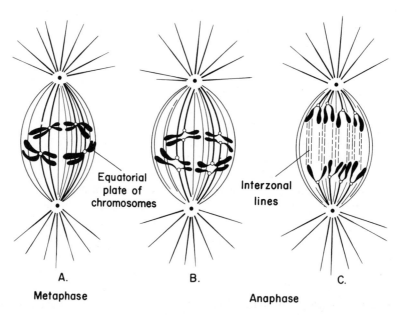

Figure 4–13. The intermediate phases of animal mitosis. A. Metaphase comes into existence when the chromosomes are arranged in an orderly fashion across the middle ("equator") of the cell; this arrangement results in a loose disklike configuration called the equatorial plate. B, C. Anaphase is marked by the division of the centromeres, followed almost immediately by the separation of sister chromatids. The movement apart of sister chromatids continues until each set has attained the opposite poles.

now arrange themselves evenly at the central plane of the cell, as though they were placed on a plate at the cell's "equator." Viewed from the side, this *equatorial plate,* as the arrangement of chromosomes is called, appears linear, with the arms of the chromosomes projecting irregularly toward the poles. The formation of this structure marks the beginning, end, and sum total of this second phase (Figure 4–13*A*).

The third stage, *anaphase,* is only slightly more complex, for it includes only one process and the establishment of one new organelle. Thus far in mitosis, it will be noted, no actual division of the cellular parts has occurred, unless one wishes to consider the movement of the centrioles to opposite ends as an instance of this nature. Here in anaphase, however, all the spindle threads appear to contract, and as they do so, the chromatids are separated from their respective mates and pulled toward opposite poles. Since each chromatid is an exact duplicate of its counterpart, the nuclear matter is thus precisely divided into identical halves. As the chromosomes split (Figure 4–13*B, C*), between the separating parts appears a new organelle, in the form of numerous fine threads extending from one chromatid to its former partner. These *interzonal lines,* as they are called, play a role as yet undeciphered but apparently of some considerable importance to the cell, for they are of nearly universal occurrence.

Now that the nuclear constituents have been exactly halved, all that remains are the events that will restore them to their normal condition. These occur during the final phase, *telophase* (Figure 4–14), and

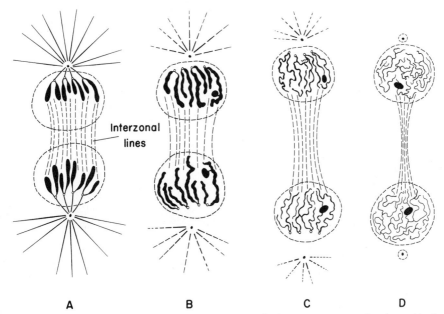

Interzonal lines

A   B   C   D

Figure 4–14. The last set of activities in nuclear division (telophase). As soon as the chromatids (hereafter considered chromosomes) have attained the poles, a sequence of events begins not unlike those of prophase except that it is reversed in direction. A, B. First a nuclear membrane is reformed, while the chromosomes begin to elongate and become threadlike. Then, as chromosomal elongation continues, a nucleolus again becomes visible (C, D); at the same time the astral rays slowly disappear, and a centrophere develops about each single centriole. After the interzonal lines have disintegrated, mitosis is considered to be completed.

proceed as in prophase but reversed in order and direction. That is to say, the chromosomes gradually elongate to become fibrous and slender, then later assume the appearance of granules and scattered threads characteristic of the undividing cell. Simultaneously the nuclear membrane slowly reforms and a nucleolus reappears. In the cytoplasm, the centriole becomes covered by a centrosphere and may in many cases divide now; frequently, however, its division seems to occur during the normal functioning of the cell, i.e., in *interphase*. The astral rays gradually disappear, and, finally, when the interzonal lines are no longer apparent, mitosis is considered to come to a close. The former nucleus has now been divided into two duplicates of the original.

Cytokinesis. When the nucleus enters telophase of mitosis, usually the processes of *cytokinesis,* or cytoplasmic division, commence immediately; exceptions are found in such cells as those of the liver and muscles in which two or more nuclei are normally found. In all animal cells, division of the cytoplasm is accomplished by the cell virtually pulling itself into two. At the onset of the processes, time-lapse motion pictures of actual living material show the cell becoming extremely active as it sends out and retracts numerous long cytoplasmic projections in rapid succession. Then around the entire cell on a plane midway between the already divided nucleus there appears a groove, called the *cleavage furrow,* as though a belt were being drawn tightly about it. This groove steadily deepens and finally penetrates through the whole cytoplasm, dividing it completely into halves and bringing into existence two *daughter cells,* each an exact replica of the original (Figure 4–15).

Insofar as the cytoplasmic organelles are concerned, some, such as the mitochondria, apparently divide into halves independent of the cytoplasm as cytokinesis progresses; whether this is true

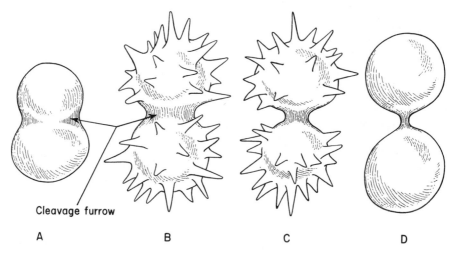

Cleavage furrow

A   B   C   D

Figure 4–15. Cytokinesis in an animal cell. A. During the first three stages the cytoplasm remains relatively inactive; with the onset of telophase, however, it begins to elongate and a constriction (cleavage furrow) begins to form. B. As the cleavage furrow deepens, the cytoplasm becomes extremely active, sending out processes in all directions which disappear as rapidly as they form. C. This "boiling" activity continues while the cleavage furrow increases in depth. D. Finally the deepening of this furrow separates the cytoplasm into two daughter cells, held together for a while until the interzonal lines disappear.

for all organelles or not remains to be discovered. Although the precise number of each type of organelle and the exact quantity of cytoplasm received may vary to a small degree between any two daughter cells, each possesses sufficient chemical identity with the mother cell to equalize quantitative differences of this sort later during subsequent growth.

Duration of Cell Division. As might be anticipated, the exact length of time required for completion of cell division varies with the species, the particular type of cell, and the temperature. In fact, there is considerable individual variation among the same kinds of cell even at a given temperature; nevertheless some approximations can be provided as illustrations. For instance, in cultures of mammalian tissues, mitosis extends over a period of between 16 and 40 minutes at 100°F and occurs about twice every 24 hours. However, at the same temperature, cell division in a developing grasshopper embryo requires 180 minutes, of which 102 are spent in prophase, 13 in metaphase, 9 in anaphase, and 56 in telophase. In this case interphase is quite short, being only 27 minutes in duration.

CELL DIVISION

IN SEXUAL

REPRODUCTION

In sexual reproduction, which is characterized by the union of a sperm cell with an egg, each of these elements carries its own nucleus, yet it is a well-known fact that the number of chromosomes present in each cell remains constant for any given species, generation after generation. Why does it not double with each one, so that if the original parents had two chromosomes each, their offspring would have four, the descendants of

which would possess eight, and so on? Were there not some device that avoids this doubling with each generation, by this time all sexually reproducing organisms would possess impossibly huge numbers of chromosomes, with extinction of the species having occurred eons ago as a result. The device that circumvents this dilemma is a simple one; it consists of a means by which the chromosome number in eggs and sperm is reduced to half. Hence, union of an egg and a sperm merely restores normality, and constancy of chromosome number is maintained. It is customary to phrase this state by referring to the reduced number of chromosomes as found in the *gametes* (i.e., the eggs and sperm) as the *haploid* (simple) number, designated as n, whereas the individual resulting from fertilization (that is, the union of the egg and the sperm) possesses the *diploid* (double) number, designated as $2n$ (Figure 4–16). In other words, the usual number of chromosomes in the cells of the higher organisms is the diploid number, whereas that of the egg or sperm is one-half as great and is called the haploid. Human beings, for example, have 46 chromosomes in most body cells and 23 in the gametes.

If, as implied above, the individual animal resulting from a fertilized egg has a set of *maternal* chromosomes derived from the female parent and a similar *paternal* set from the male, the diploid number is made up of duplicate sets. Thus its chromosomes occur in pairs, whereas those of the gametes include only one of each kind. To the members of a given pair the name *homologous chromosomes* is applied. The process of reducing the number in the gametes must occur in such a fashion that a complete complement of homologues exists when the total is halved, so that the *quality* as well as the *quantity* of chromatic matter supplied the eggs or sperm continues

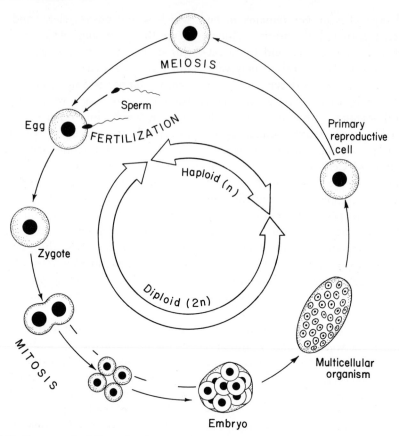

Figure 4–16. The generalized life cycle of a sexually reproducing animal. Many variations of the theme exist but the basic principle remains constant—the number of chromosomes is reduced in the gametes and is restored by fertilization to the full number in the embryo and resulting adult.

constant. For these purposes *meiosis,* a special type of mitosis in which the chromosome number is reduced, takes place.

Meiosis. Although the differences between meiosis and mitosis are confined chiefly to prophase, an additional one of importance lies in the fact that two complete cell divisions necessarily follow in close sequence, with only a short interphase between them. Thus four cells result from each original one. The events in prophase are of such significance and so complex that a distinctive way of arbitrarily subdividing it has had to be provided.

At first no differences from early prophase can be noted in the beginning

stages of meiosis; the movement of the centrioles and formation of the astral rays and the gradual condensation of the chromatin matter proceed quite normally. These preliminary steps are taken to constitute a subdivision of prophase called the *proleptonema* (Figure 4–17*A*). Beyond this point more and more distinctive features can be noted; the nucleolus and nuclear membrane persist until much later in the phase, and the chromatin strands behave entirely differently. However, the centrioles and astral rays migrate steadily toward the opposite poles, as in the usual type of cell division. The chromatin strands, tenuous in the early stages, finally become quite clear and

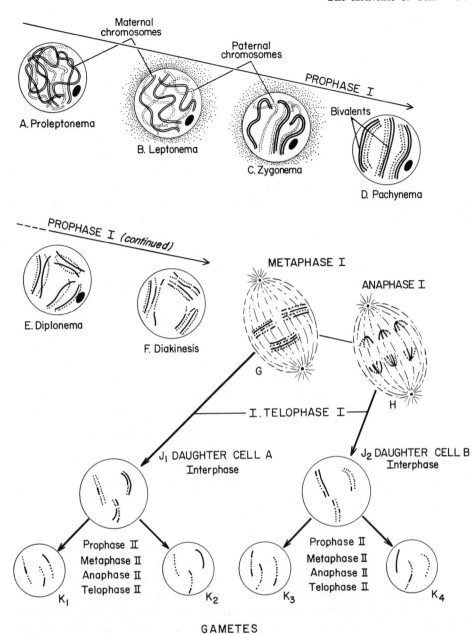

Figure 4–17. Meiosis. The maternal chromosomes (those received from the egg) are shown in stipple while the paternal (from the sperm) are in solid black. During the long prophase (*A–F*), corresponding (homologous) chromosomes from each set come to lie side by side; about half the chromatids then exchange segments (*E, F*). G. At metaphase pairs of chromosomes (bivalents), that is a total of four chromatids each, lie on the equatorial plate instead of single chromosomes of two chromatids each. H. Hence in anaphase combined with the complete second set of nuclear divisionary processes that follow, the total number of chromosomes is reduced to half that originally present. In the male, as a rule four sperm are produced from each original cell, whereas in females only one egg is produced from the same source. In the latter case, three additional minute cells, called polar bodies, are produced but these have no known function.

well-defined; their assumption of clarity is arbitrarily accepted as marking the beginning of the second subdivision, referred to as *leptonema* (Figure 4–17*B*). Only by the most refined techniques can these strands be seen to be actually double; the chromatids adhere much more tightly to one another than is the case in mitosis. Each dual filament remains well-separated from the others, and a strong tendency for these strands to assume a parallel arrangement is often apparent. Here and beyond this point, the chromatin strands are usually called chromosomes, although they are far more threadlike than under mitotic conditions. In the subdivision (the *zygonema,* Figure 4–17*C*) that follows the completion of the foregoing developments occur the first really distinctive features of meiosis. As the chromosomes move actively about, their ends now bend, and frequently those of neighboring ones overlap, forming U-shaped loops. These loops are formed and broken after a brief moment, until, after a number of such trials, homologous chromosomes (maternal ones and their paternal counterparts) come into contact. When encounters of this sort happen, the homologues break the loop but move so as to lie in close proximity to one another. This process of forming pairs is called *synapsis*. The pairing activity is carried out so thoroughly that not only corresponding chromosomes are brought together, but also their corresponding ends. In fact, each and every point on all the sets of two homologues (called *bivalents*) are placed so as to coincide precisely. When the synaptic processes are completed, the zygonema subphase is brought to a close and the next one, the *pachynema* (Figure 4–17*D*), is initiated. The bivalents, up to this point still threadlike, now contract longitudinally, becoming somewhat more rodlike as a result. Furthermore, each undergoes

a temporary change, the purpose of which is difficult to comprehend. First the two components appear to fuse so that their individuality is lost; then later, the homologues lose this fused nature, and each chromosome becomes distinct again, although still closely associated in pairs. Still later, the dissociation continues until the halves of each chromosome, named the *sister chromatids,* can be distinguished. An important act that now occurs involves corresponding sister chromatids of the homologous sets—i.e., one chromatid from each of the maternal and paternal components of the bivalents. Transverse breaks occur in the chromatids, at corresponding points in the homologues. In other words, if one maternal chromatid of a set breaks at a point one-tenth the distance from one end, a break in the matching paternal chromatid occurs at exactly the same level. The broken-off ends are then interchanged between the matching chromatids and attached to their respective remaining portions, so that the chromatids are no longer entirely maternal or paternal in composition but now include segments derived from each original gamete—in the above illustration, nine tenths are derived from one source and one tenth from the other. This exchange and recombination of parts, called *crossing over,* has important implications in the study of genetics and will be touched on again in the appropriate chapter. Its completion marks the close of the pachynema. The two remaining divisions of prophase are short and simple. First, in *diplotena* (Figure 4–17*E, F*), the homologous chromosomes *partially* separate and the chromatids become sharply indicated; and, second, in *diakinesis,* the chromosomes condense to their normal maximum extent and assume the typical rodlike form. Along with their reduction in length the nuclear membrane and nucleolus finally disappear. After the breakdown of the nuclear membrane, the spindle threads attach to the chromosomes, and the appearance of a normal late prophase is acquired.

Metaphase (Figure 4–17G) in meiosis is similar to that of ordinary cell division insofar that an equatorial plate is formed. Here, however, instead of individual chromosomes, composed of two chromatids each, lying on the plate, it is the bivalents that arrange themselves in like fashion. Thus groups of four chromatids compose the plate, with the essentially maternal chromosome facing toward one pole, the paternal homologue toward the opposite. The pole faced would be randomly selected in the case of each bivalent, so that there is little likelihood of all the essentially maternal chromosomes facing toward any one pole. Correspondingly in the anaphase that follows (Figure 4–17H), it is the component *chromosomes* of the bivalents that are pulled to opposite poles, not just *chromatids*. Hence, following telophase and cytokinesis, the resulting cells possess only half the number of chromosomes found in the original.

As stated earlier, almost without exception in the process of forming eggs and sperm, the above-described reductional division is followed by a second division after a very short interphase. This latter stage may sometimes be atypical in that the nuclear organelles may not all assume their usual interphasic condition in telophase; the chromosomes, for example, may still be visible. Nevertheless, the end result is the distribution of the original single cell into four new ones. Later these daughters are developed further into either eggs or sperm, depending on the sex of the individual in which they were produced, but the changes involved are a part of another story. For the present all that needs to concern us is the process that makes possible the maintenance of constancy in the quality and quantity of chromosomes in any given sexually reproducing species.

Although the activities of cells are thus perceived to be highly complex and extremely varied and to range from chemical and physical to strictly biological sorts, all are found to have one feature in common, that of a requirement for energy. This is true whether the activity is that of movement or secretion, absorption or ingestion, or even growth or reproduction. And since the source of and control over the energy lie in metabolic processes, the student can now see, as stated in the definition of life supplied in the first chapter, how that which we call "life" is in reality the aggregate of those activities made possible by metabolism. Even intangible attributes often given as properties of life by some biologists, such as individuality, organization, and adaptation, in the final analysis arise from the interplay of the more evident activities or, for the last-named property, out of reproduction over the long course of years. Life is not to be thought of as consisting of metabolism; it is the sum of the processes that the latter makes possible.

Questions for Review and Thought

1. Define the terms *metabolism, anabolism, catabolism, enzyme, coenzyme,* and *substrate.* In terms of chemical reactions what is the real distinction betweeen anabolism and catabolism?

2. List the end products of respiration for which the cell has further use, along with intermediate products that can be used cellularly in other activities.

3. What by-product of respiration results from the presence of oxygen? Is this the one that is generally thought of as being the end product? If not, what is?

4. List the chief reactions in the cell that provide energy.

5. Which chemical activities are principally anabolic and could result in growth?

6. What chemical compounds can you now list that provide for storage of energy in living things? Star those which are quickly available sources.

7. Which compound yields the greater amount of energy per carbon atom, a sugar or a fat?

8. In what ways do fat and protein metabolism tie into carbohydrate respiration? In what ways are each of these two unique?

9. In the two following combinations of substances, how much more rapidly does osmosis occur in one than in the other? Express your answer in percentage based on the slower.

a. Sac containing 20 per cent glucose, immersed in 15 per cent glucose.

b. Sac containing 3 per cent glucose, immersed in 2 per cent glucose.

10. By what methods can water be added to the cell's content? By what means are proteins taken into a cell?

11. What two processes comprise the whole of cell division?

12. List the phases of mitosis and the changes that occur in each.

13. Summarize the processes of cytokinesis.

14. List the major events of prophase in meiosis.

15. What explanation can you give for the fact that meiosis consists of two closely related divisions?

Supplementary References

Bourne, G. H. *Division of Labor in Cells.* New York, Academic Press, 1962.

Brachet, J. "The Living Cell." *Sci. Amer.,* September 1961.

Chambers, R., and E. L. Chambers. *Explorations into the Nature of the Living Cell.* Cambridge, Mass., Harvard Univ. Press, 1961.

DeRobertis, E. D. P., W. W. Nowinski, and F. A. Saez. *General Cytology,* 3rd ed. Philadelphia, Saunders, 1960.

Gerard, R. W. *Unresting Cells.* New York, Harper, 1949.

Hoffman, J. G. *The Life and Death of Cells.* New York, Hanover, 1957.

Hughes, A. *A History of Cytology.* New York, Abelard-Schuman, 1959.

Langley, L. L. *Cell Function; an Introduction to the Physiology of the Cell and Its Role in the Intact Organism.* New York, Reinhold, 1961.

Puck, T. T. "Single Human Cells *in Vitro."* *Sci. Amer.,* August 1957.

Siekevitz, P. "Powerhouse of the Cell." *Sci. Amer.,* July 1957.

Solomon, A. K. "Pores in the Cell Membrane." *Sci. Amer.,* December 1960.

Swanson, C. P. *Cytology and Cytogenetics.* Englewood Cliffs, N. J., Prentice-Hall, 1957.

Wilson, E. B. *The Cell in Development and Heredity,* 3rd ed., reprinted. New York, Macmillan, 1947.

Zamecnik, P. C. "The Microsome." *Sci. Amer.,* March 1958.

PART II

The Relationships of Animals

D IFFERENT IN OUTWARD appearance though the organisms themselves may be, few real distinctions between animals and other forms of life can be found insofar as the structure and activities of the cell are concerned. Particularly similar are the chemical functions and cellular reproductive processes studied in the preceding section. For this reason, at the unicellular level of organization there has been little general agreement among botanists and zoologists as to the proper limitations of the terms "plant" and "animal," so that many simpler forms are claimed by both groups of scientists as members of their respective areas of investigation. Since it is frequently difficult to differentiate clearly between these two major categories, a quick glance needs to be taken at the whole problem of animal relationships and at some suggested solutions.

There is nothing, Sir, too little for so little a creature as man. It is by studying little things that we attain the great art of having as little misery and as much happiness as possible.

SAMUEL JOHNSON

CHAPTER 5

The Types
of Relationships

ANIMALS may bear relationships to
one another and to other organisms in two distinct senses
of the term. By one implication, actual
kinship is suggested, as between the
members of a single species which are
all descendants of a common ancestral
stock countless generations past. In the
second sense, allusion is made to the
association of two different organisms
living together with a greater or lesser
degree of intimacy. A mammal dwelling
within a hollow log doubtlessly has occasional close contact with centipedes,
snakes, or other coinhabitants of the
fallen tree. And the bacteria that normally grow within human intestines
share much with the individuals they
occupy, including portions of meals! To
distinguish between the two meanings of
the word, the term "relationship" will be
reserved for cases of actual kinship, while

"interrelationship" will be employed to
designate close associations between and
within species.

The Principal Relationships
of Organisms

In Chapter 1 mention was made of the
diversification that exists among organisms; here it is to be pointed out that
these variations lie at different levels of
importance. For an illustration all one
has to do is to look around himself. No
two individuals seen are exactly alike,
even identical twins have some distinguishing traits. Yet each is recognizable
at once as a human being, and, in turn,
all humankind shares more likenesses
with other mammals than they do with
birds. And if the backbone and other
skeletal parts present in man and other

mammals as well as in birds are called to mind, a greater resemblance among these groups is to be noted than any of them exhibit when compared, for example, to an insect. These degrees of differences and similarities are the principal concern here. To express them, a *system of classification* has been devised, a scheme that in the long run is based on its smallest actual unit, the species.

THE SPECIES

Since the species forms the foundation for the whole outline of relationships, it is important enough to deserve careful consideration. Nor is it significant solely from this point of view, for often, too, it is looked upon as being the only unit of classification that actually exists in nature. Although the term has already been defined as "one kind of organism," this definition, useful for preliminary purposes, is far too loose to serve the present needs.

A Species Definition. In spite of the importance of the species, there is at present no general agreement regarding the exact manner in which it should be defined. For many years species were looked upon solely as units that differed from all others structurally, but while structural distinctions even today are considered valid species criteria, there are many reasons for not accepting them as the sole basis. In recent decades the so-called *biological species concept* was developed, in which the attempt was made to define the unit as an interbreeding group of populations which cannot interbreed with others. On various grounds, including its inapplicability to asexual forms and the fact that many perfectly good species do occasionally interbreed with others, this too has fallen into disfavor. Although there is still some basis for dissension, many taxonomists may

agree that the following definition is approximately what they have in mind when this term is employed: the *species* is a unit, consisting of groups of similar organisms (populations) capable of reproducing themselves, which differs sharply in several traits from all comparable units. Three or four clear-cut distinctions would usually be the minimal number acceptable for distinguishing a species, but all would not necessarily be structural in nature. Behavioral, physiological, and ecological peculiarities are just as acceptable as the morphological for this purpose.

The Number of Species. The infinite variation that exists among living things has already been pointed out, as has also the fact that this variation has resulted in the formation of an extremely large number of species. How large this number is in actuality can only be guessed at present, for only a small fraction of existing forms has as yet been described. On the assumption that the approximately 2 million known today represent only one tenth of the actual total, there presently exists on the earth some 20 million species of organisms. In this era when billions and even trillions are frequently spoken of, a million seems trivial indeed —yet it is still a figure of very respectable proportions. For instance, in this book there is a total of approximately one and one half million characters—letters, punctuation marks, numbers, and spaces between words—in the printed text. So if each organism's name were to be reduced to the size of a single character and then arranged as this book is printed, the list alone would fill nearly 15 volumes like this one. Furthermore, assuming just half of this number to be animals, had you decided at the age of five that you wanted to learn the names and characteristics of all the animals and if you were sufficiently brilliant that you could learn all about a species in just five minutes and were physically capable of working 24 hours every day, week after week and year after year without pause, you would have studied the last of the 10 million species just two months after your hundredth birthday and would then have been ready to go to work! As systematic zoology has been in existence now for only a little more than 200 years, it is readily understandable why only a portion of the task of making known the species of animals has been accomplished and that this branch of science still offers much to challenge young zoologists.

Natural Groups of Species—The Genus. If each species were entirely distinct from all others, the task of dealing with them would be quite overwhelming. Fortunately, almost all have relatives, and it is possible to work with groups of related forms. In systematic zoology closely allied species are placed together in a taxonomic unit (or *taxon*) called the *genus* (pl. genera). For example, dogs and dingos are quite like wolves and coyotes in appearance and in actual structure; consequently the various types of such animals are placed together in the genus *Canis*.

Quite frequently, since the various members of the same genus share so many traits, it is convenient to work with them as a unit rather than as individual species. For illustration, one might study the ecology of the genus *Turdus*, the Old World thrushes, or the reproductive habits of *Ursus*, the bears, or the distribution of *Papilio*, the swallowtail butterflies. Such studies provide a summary of the likenesses and differences of its members and, hence, form a convenient basis for comparison with other related forms. In short, as does also each taxon of all levels of relationship, the genus assists in the organization of zoological knowledge, much as theories do.

Scientific Names of Animals. Another area in which the genus is of value is in the provision of uniform names for each kind of animal. Names for living things in popular usage vary from locality to locality and from country to country; what is even more confusing, sometimes the same term may be applied to widely different species. The robin of America, for example, is in no way related to the robin of Europe; similarly, the blackbird of the United States is related to the orioles, whereas the European blackbird is a thrush. To provide world-wide standard names for all species, the Swedish naturalist Linné (in his writings he Latinized his surname to Linnaeus) devised a simple but effective method of constructing them. Prior to his time a brief descriptive sentence in Latin had been utilized for this purpose, the cumbersomeness of which the student can well imagine. In his treatment Linné condensed these phrases to just two words, the second of which is the name of the species, the first, that of the genus to which it belongs. Since only two words are employed for each species, his system is known as the *binomial scheme of classification*. As the term given each genus is distinctive and the specific names are not duplicated within any particular genus, the combination automatically becomes unique for every existing organism. To this scientific name is customarily added the surname of the author who first described and named the species in question. For instance, the scientific name of the cat is *Felis catus* Linné. In this term *Felis* designates the genus, *catus*, the specific kind of *Felis*, that is, the cat, and Linné, the author who first described and named it according to this system. No other group of species is called *Felis*, nor is any other species within the present genus named *catus;* however, *catus* could be used in any other genus, wherever it might be applicable.

Species as Populations. In the definition of species the term *population* is employed to designate a self-perpetuating group of organisms. In this connection the term can be used in several senses, as it can when applied to the human species. For example, one can discuss the population of the world as being more than 2 billion, referring to the total number of individuals constituting the whole of humanity, or one can speak of the population of this city or that country or of the urban population as opposed to the rural. In other words, the human species is, as are all others, a group of populations. In contrast to the human situation, in which political considerations often form the limiting boundaries, populations of other species are naturally occurring units, separated by nature from one another to a varying degree. For illustration, let us use a species of mouse which shall be called "mouse A" for the sake of convenience. When comparisons with mouse "species B" are being made, the entire population of each species is employed and their differences and resemblances noted. But similarly, both of these whole populations consist of smaller ones; mouse A, might be, for instance, looked upon as consisting of four major subpopulations—northern, eastern, western, and southern (Figure 5–1). Perhaps the individuals in the northern population are larger and darker in color than the rest, with tails of moderate length; perhaps those of the southern one are smallest and intermediate in color but with the longest tails proportionately. While the western one may be found to have its members pale and to be intermediate in tail and body length, the eastern one might be of mice intermediate in size and color but with the shortest tails. These populations thus differ slightly from one another, and it is the range of variation within the population differences that makes up the characteristics of the whole. Therefore the range of variation in species A must be employed when comparisons are made with species B, C, or any other. When inspected more closely, the northern, eastern, and other populations are seen themselves to be composed of smaller units, which in turn are divided into others still more minute, the smallest ones being designated as *demes*. If the mouse in question is a forest-dwelling form, each wood or forest contains a mouse A population of its own, separated by meadows, rivers, and fields from other such demes. Although each is somewhat isolated, occasional individuals, by leaving their native forests and successfully traversing the open areas in between, ultimately reach another woodland where they can reproduce with their own kind; by repetition of similar acts throughout the range the entire population becomes maintained as one natural self-reproducing unit.

The Subspecies. In many instances, especially in species with extensive ranges, the several major subpopulations, such as the four that constitute mouse species A, are considered sufficiently distinguished one from the other to be deserving of distinctive names. In cases of this sort, referred to as *polytypic species,* the major subdivisions are treated as *subspecies,* and, instead of the usual two-part scientific name, three (generic, specific, and subspecific) may be employed. As an example, the case of the lion (*Pardalis leo* Linné) might be cited, in which thirteen subspecies are recognized. Here only a few are given, for some of the remainder are based solely on characters of a technical nature. *Pardalis leo persica* is the small, whitish lion of Asia Minor, whose tail has a longer tassel than the others. *P. leo leo,* the Barbary

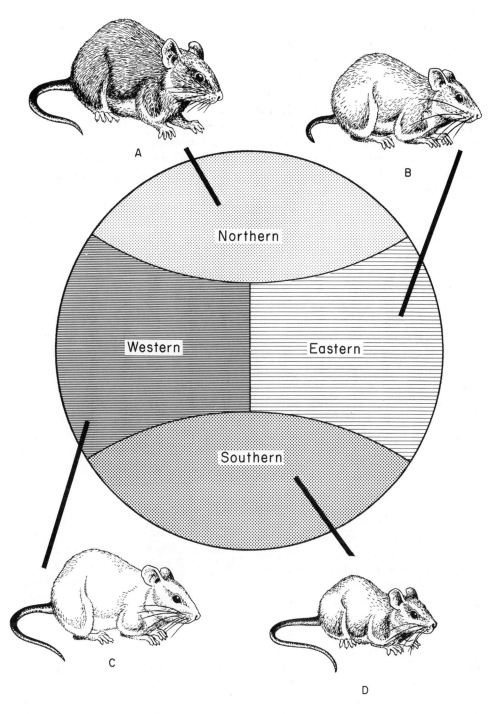

Figure 5–1. The major populations of "mouse species A." In this hypothetical species, the members of each major population are suggested to differ slightly from one another in several minor details, such as body size, coat color, and tail length.

lion of north Africa, is relatively small, reddish tawny and has a short mane of the same color. Both the east African subspecies *P. leo massaica* and the west African *P. leo gambianus* are somewhat larger bodied than the foregoing; while similar in color and size to one another, they differ in structure of the teeth. On the other hand, *P. leo melanochaitus* of South Africa, the largest of all, sometimes attains a total length of 12 feet; in addition, its mane is long and black.

Note that one subspecies name is identical with that of the specific. This treatment is accorded one subspecies in every polytypic species; it represents the population that happened to be the one originally described. Though *trinomials* can be employed where one is concerned with the smaller populations, the name of the species as a whole is still a binomial. Note, too, that the characters distinguishing subspecies are of minor importance, being confined to slight differences of color or size, of length of mane or tail tassel, or of comparable characteristics. Nor can sharp lines be drawn between them, as they intergrade into one another.

The Larger Units of Classification

To express relationships between organisms more remote than those shown by the genus, an entire hierarchy of categories exists. Closely related genera are grouped together to form *families;* the genus *Canis,* composed of various dogs and wolves, along with *Vulpes,* the red foxes, *Urocyon,* the gray foxes, and other doglike forms, constitute the family of dogs, called the Canidae. In similar fashion, families that show relationships in the sharing of pertinent traits are arranged together in a larger taxon called an *order.* The family of cats (Felidae) and those of the weasels (Mustelidae),

bears (Ursidae), raccoons (Procyonidae), and hyaenas (Hyaenidae), which possess the same type of teeth, show similar construction of the leg, form of claw, and other structural traits, are combined with the Canidae to form the Carnivora, the order of typical flesh-eating animals. In like fashion, orders that are closely allied are arranged into a *class.* Members of the order Carnivora have a body-covering of hair; they are warm-blooded, breathe with the aid of a diaphragm, and have milk glands, to mention only a few distinctive traits possessed by all other orders of the class Mammalia. Above the degree of relationship indicated by this taxon lies the *phylum.* In turn, phyla are grouped to form *subkingdoms,* which are combined into the greatest taxon of all, the *kingdom.*

Each species of organism then belongs not only to a particular genus but to one of every type of larger taxon. Indeed, often many more than the principal ones enumerated above are necessarily employed, for in a large majority of cases each taxon may be subdivided additionally by use of prefixes, such as *super-* and *sub-,* to indicate intermediate levels of relationship. *Superclasses* are larger than *classes,* which outrank *subclasses;* moreover, in some cases, especially in taxa containing great numbers of species, additional terms such as cohort, tribe, and section are employed as needed. But the chief point here is the fact that every organism has its relationships indicated at many levels by the various categories to which it belongs (Figure 5–2).

The Major Interrelationships of Organisms

The range of a given species is, however, not occupied solely by itself but is shared to a varying extent by numerous

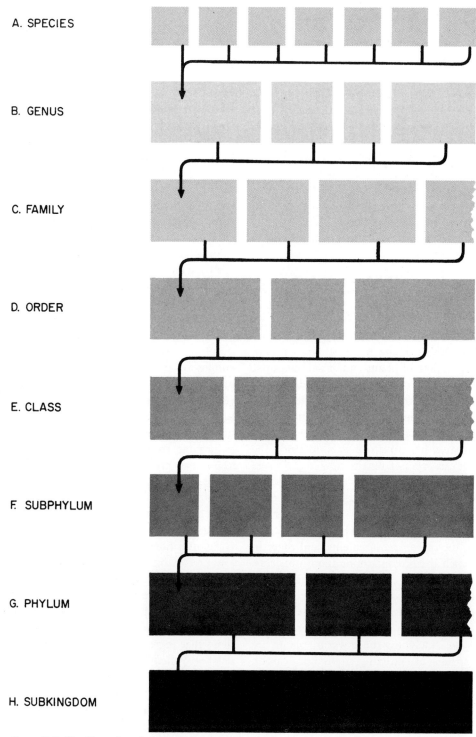

A. SPECIES

B. GENUS

C. FAMILY

D. ORDER

E. CLASS

F. SUBPHYLUM

G. PHYLUM

H. SUBKINGDOM

Figure 5–2. The hierarchy of systematic categories. Species are the basic unit from which all larger categories are built. Related species (A) are placed together in a "genus" (B); one or more closely similar genera are grouped into a family (C); similar families make up "orders" (D); and so forth. Accordingly, each successively higher level reflects a lesser degree of relationship (i.e., more distant) among its members.

others. As numbers of varied forms thus occupy every inch of the earth's surface, whether it be of land or of water, the diverse organisms which occupy the same region are not entirely independent of one another but bear close interrelationships, often of a most complex nature. In this fashion every wood plot, pond, lake, or reach of a river, each patch of grassland or barren soil, each inlet, bay, or coastline, has its own closely knit *community* of organisms. Here only the interrelationships of the organisms within communities are the topic of discussion.

ORGANIZATION OF COMMUNITIES

Within each community, the interrelationships of the many species composing it, both of plants and of animals, arise primarily from the diverse food requirements and the methods by which nutrients are obtained. In order to understand the organization of the biological community, it is first necessary to study the various types of nutrition.

Nutritional Types. The several kinds of nutrition are founded on two principal considerations—namely the state or states in which the energy-giving foodstuff, that is, the *carbon* requirements, and those in which the protoplasm-building nutrients, the *nitrogen* compounds, are obtained. From the standpoint of the carbon needs of the organism, the requirements can be met in three different ways. *Phototrophs,* including the flowering plants, are capable of utilizing inorganic carbon compounds, such as carbon dioxide or carbonates, and by photosynthesis of converting them into an organic condition. On the other hand, *heterotrophs* can make use only of carbon compounds that are already in organic form; as the student doubtlessly realizes, animals ultimately depend on the phototrophic plants

for their carbohydrates and fats. Moreover, many protozoa absorb their energy sources in the form of simple carbohydrates or organic acids dissolved in the water in which they live; since these chemicals are derived chiefly as decomposition products of other organisms, their final source is likewise the phototrophs. The third type, *chemotrophs,* use carbon dioxide directly but do not need energy from light to convert it into organic compounds, carrying out the process by oxidation of inorganic substances.

Similarly, there are four main methods by which the requirements for nitrogen are met. *Prototrophs,* for example, the nitrogen-fixing bacteria of peas and beans, are able to assimilate the free nitrogen of the atmosphere, whereas *autotrophs,* a term some writers mistakenly employ for phototrophs, can make use of nitrogen in the form of inorganic salts (nitrates and nitrites) or of ammonia, as in the seed plants. Many organisms, however, cannot utilize nitrogen except in organic compounds; these types are known as *mesotrophs* if their requirements, as in many protozoa, are met by amino acids, or as *metatrophs* if, as in most animals, proteins are required.

There is an additional means of classifying nutritional habits of organisms, a less precise method than the foregoing, but simple and quite useful, nevertheless. In this scheme photosynthetic organisms are described as *holophytic* (meaning entirely plantlike), whereas those that ingest (or swallow) food particles are called *holozoic* (entirely animallike). A third type, which does not photosynthesize or ingest particles but absorbs dissolved substances through the cell membrane, is known as *saprophytic* if it is a plant or *saprozoic* if it is an animal, the stem "sapro-" meaning rotten.

The Roles of the Various Nutritional Types. If any community is to survive independently of others, it first of all, obviously enough, must contain an adequate number of *producers* that can manufacture organic compounds out of the inorganic constituents of the air and soil. Equally apparent is the fact that only the phototrophs and chemotrophs can play this role. Both macroscopic and microscopic heterotrophs require the presence of the higher green plants, the various groups of algae, or the photosynthetic and chemotrophic bacteria as the original source of all their organic nutritional requirements. The nonproducers of the community obtain their foods in many ways. First of all there must be the plant-eating *herbivores,* a series of organisms that feeds directly on the producers. In size, herbivorous forms may range from microscopic protozoa or worms through insects to great animals such as the hippopotamus and elephant. In turn, the herbivorous species are fed upon by the flesh-eaters, the *carnivores,* likewise with a wide range of body sizes. Often there is a whole chain of carnivorous types in which secondary carnivores prey on the smaller primary ones and still larger tertiary forms eat the secondary sorts.

This chainlike series involves the organisms only as long as they are alive, for even the largest producers, such as giant trees, or the greatest carnivores, such as tigers and bears, do not live indefinitely. Sooner or later life ends for all, and the dead remains fall to the ground. In all communities there are *scavengers,* flies, beetles, birds, and other sorts that consume these remnants, and *decomposers,* principally bacteria, yeasts, and fungi, that do the final work of breaking down carcasses and fallen vegetation into simpler organic and inorganic products. The end results of these processes of *decay,* the inorganic compounds, such as carbon dioxide, nitrates, carbon-

ates, and others, are re-employed by the producers to build organic substances, and so the cycle is completed.

In strictly aquatic situations the same types of nutritional relationships exist but are represented by different sorts of organisms. Particularly striking is the contrast between the producers of the water and those of the land. Whereas the seed plants are the principal producers in terrestrial habitats, microscopic floating forms are the chief or sole food manufacturers in lakes and seas. Floating organisms and those capable because of their minute size of only limited movement are referred to as *plankton.* Phototrophic and chemotrophic producers constitute the *phytoplankton,* whereas the herbivores and primary carnivores are the *zooplankton.* Larger carnivores, such as fishes, are capable of moving about freely and are called *nekton.* In aquatic communities there is a much more marked graduation in size among the carnivorous types, in which the young fish and small species feed on the plankton, the medium-sized fish consume the smaller forms, and the large ones, the medium-sized—the larger the species, the larger, too, its normal prey, as a rule. There are exceptions, however, for the blue and some other whales, giants of the sea, feed directly upon plankton.

The Pyramid of Numbers in Communities. In every community the total number of individuals present must be distributed in certain proportions among the various nutritional roles. Of all the types, the producers must exist in greatest abundance (Figure 5–3), for it is essential that the number of this fundamental sort be sufficient, not just for the needs of the herbivores, but to supply this amount plus that required to perpetuate their own species. It is quite clear that if the demands of the herbivores were ever even to equal the output

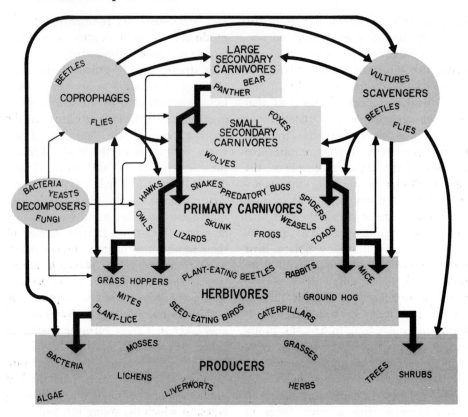

Figure 5–3. The pyramid of numbers in a terrestrial community. In every community, whether terrestrial or aquatic, the producers form the base upon which the life of the whole depends. Above these must come a smaller quantity of herbivores on which a still smaller number of primary carnivores depend, with still fewer secondary carnivores at the top of the whole. Off to the sides of the main pyramid, but intimately interwoven with it nevertheless, are organisms that make use of the dead remains and offal in one way or another.

of the producers for an entire season, the next year the community would be quite or nearly extinct. Similarly, the number of primary carnivores is necessarily smaller than that of the herbivorous species and that of secondary flesh-eaters still lower. Although the ratios of the various species within each type may alter radically from time to time, the proportion of the types is relatively constant.

For example, let us use a forest community in eastern North America under conditions that prevailed before white man made his appearance on the conti-

nent. In such a forest, it has been estimated that the common black bear requires an area of 3 sq mi to support each mature individual. But another large predator, the panther, also is present in these forests and probably requires a similar-sized territory for survival. So our community, if breeding pairs of both these species are to survive, must include an area of no less than 20 sq mi. Within this forested tract such smaller secondary carnivores as red and gray foxes and bobcats occur (Figure 5–4); as each of these species requires a far smaller amount of territory to reproduce itself, the total individuals of these forms present in the forest would far exceed that of the two largest ones. Living here, too, are primary carnivores such as skunks, weasels, snakes, lizards, hawks, owls, and many insect-eating birds, as well as spiders, predaceous insects, and others whose needs for self-maintenance can be met on a space measurable in hundreds of square feet. At the next level of the community, represented by the herbivores, the area required for successful survival ranges widely in extent. The smallest ones, the aphids, mites, and the like, are able to reproduce for many generations on the confines of a single leaf; and leaf-eating beetles and caterpillars may well complete their development on one or two small plants. Grasshoppers require a number of herbs during the process of their growth from an egg into adulthood, whereas mice and seed-eating birds cannot do with less than several hundred square feet of living room. Still larger are the requirements of groundhogs, and deer need many acres, suitably supplied with vegetation, to maintain themselves and rear their fawns each year. At the very lowest level of the series are placed the producers, the trees that together constitute the forest and the shrubs, herbs, grasses, mosses, liverworts, and others that fill in spaces between and beneath the canopy. Nor should one overlook the chemoprototrophs living within the soil, for they are producers, too, of real significance.

While the foregoing comprise one main pyramid in the community, there is another of equal importance lying to one side, but intimately interwoven with it—namely the interrelated organisms which thrive on the dead bodies and waste products of the constituents of the principal pyramid. While three major types exist that function in restoring the organic chemical components to

Figure 5–4. A north temperate deciduous forest and a member of that type of community. A. In the deciduous forests of North America, oaks, maples, and beeches are among the dominant tree species. B. Associated with this type of vegetation are found red foxes (like the one illustrated), gray foxes, squirrels of several sorts, woodpeckers, tanagers, bears, and many other characteristic forms. (Courtesy of the Wisconsin Department of Conservation.)

their original simpler and inorganic states, there are no close interconnections among them. In one type, the *scavengers,* there are forms which might readily be considered to be slightly modified carnivores—the turkey vulture, for example, which is closely related to the hawks. Moreover, foxes, mice, and others whose normal role is otherwise in the community feed on dead flesh on occasion and thus fit also into this category. But many scavenging forms, such as flesh flies and their maggots and scavenger beetles and their larvae, are confined solely to carcasses as a source of food. Other scavenging forms, including termites and ants, are concerned with dead plant rather than animal materials, and they, along with their own peculiar set of carnivores, are to be found in the dead trunks and branches of trees. A second role in the subcommunity is played by the *coprophages,* which function in utilizing the chemical substances in animal waste products. In addition, associated with both the scavengers and coprophagous types are the *decomposers,* mostly bacteria and yeasts, which in diverse ways break down the organic compounds and restore them to their original inorganic state. These, too, have a set of organisms preying on them, herbivores of sorts, including worms and many insects, which in turn are consumed by the carnivores of the principal pyramid. So it can be seen that even thus highly simplified, the interrelationships of the members of any community, as in the forest under discussion, are complexly interwoven into an intricate web.

Intimate Associations Between Species

The web of interrelationships is further complicated by the fact that each species inhabiting a major community forms a subcommunity with one or more other species with which it is intimately associated. Such close association of two species is called *symbiosis,* a word meaning "living together," three main types of which are known.

Mutualism. Sometimes symbiotic relations are of benefit to both species involved; actually, in many such cases, called *mutualism,* the interdependence of the two forms is so close that one cannot survive without the other. Termites are an interesting example. Although these insects feed exclusively on wood, they are unable to produce enzymes needed to digest the complex carbohydrates of which their woody food consists. In order to break down this material, they require the presence of complex protozoans in their digestive tract, which are able to do so (Figure 5–5). On their part, the microorganisms do not appear to have the ability of surviving outside the termites' intestines. Hence the very lives of each type of these organisms depend on the existence of the other.

Commensalism. The second type of symbiosis, named *commensalism* (meaning "to eat at the same table"), includes cases in which one of the species is benefited but the second is neither harmed nor aided. For instance, some marine crabs place sponges or peculiar animals called sea anemones on their shells and thus disguise themselves. In this way the crabs remain concealed from their enemies and receive benefit from the presence of the other species, whereas the sponges and sea anemones grow, quite unabetted and unharmed, no differently than in their usual location on the ocean floor.

Parasitism. There are animals, however, which live within bodies of other species and which derive their food from their victims (called the *hosts*). Often the latter are definitely harmed, at least by

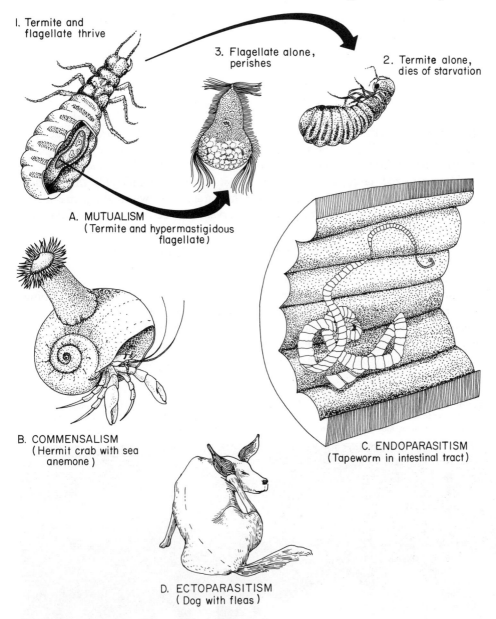

1. Termite and flagellate thrive

3. Flagellate alone, perishes

2. Termite alone, dies of starvation

A. MUTUALISM
(Termite and hypermastigidous flagellate)

B. COMMENSALISM
(Hermit crab with sea anemone)

C. ENDOPARASITISM
(Tapeworm in intestinal tract)

D. ECTOPARASITISM
(Dog with fleas)

Figure 5–5. Types of symbiosis. Many varied types and degrees of intimate interrelationships exist between members of different species. Sometimes, as in A, both species are benefitted; in others only one really is assisted by the association. In the latter types the second species may either be entirely unaffected, as in B, or may actually be harmed (C and D). These three varieties of associations are known, in the same sequence, as *mutualism, commensalism,* and *parasitism.*

heavy infestations, and sometimes may even be killed. This type of symbiosis in which one species is benefited and the other harmed is referred to as *parasitism,* a word meaning "an eating upon another." Perhaps among symbiotic relations this is the commonest; one need only think of all of the bacterial and protozoal diseases of mankind and his domesticated plants and animals for examples. In addition, there are the familiar tapeworms and other worms which occasionally grow in one part of the body or another; rarely are such parasites fatal, but they doubtlessly weaken the victim, sometimes quite seriously.

Not all parasites live, as the foregoing *endoparasites,* within the bodies of the species parasitized (Figure 5–6). Many types live on the outside of the host's body, and hence are called *ectoparasites.* Lice and fleas are perhaps the most familiar examples, but numerous mites, ticks, and others have similar habits.

Another form, designated as *social parasitism,* is frequently recognized. In such cases the symbiotic relationships between the two species are not nutritional but involve the use of the services of the host in carrying out reproductive functions of the parasite. The cuckoos of the Eastern Hemisphere and the cowbirds of the New World are good examples. In both groups of birds the females do not make nests of their own but lay their eggs in those of other species. When the eggs hatch, the rearing of the young is left entirely to the host, so that often its own progeny are neglected or underfed. Indeed, when the host species is considerably smaller than the parasite, its own nestlings may die of starvation or be crowded out of the nest.

INTIMATE ASSOCIATIONS WITHIN SPECIES

The interrelationships of living things within a community are woven not only by symbiosis of all types and by the differing nutritional habits of its inhabitants but also by occasional close associations

Figure 5–6. A case of endoparasitism. The white objects over the surface of this hawkmoth caterpillar are the cocoons of wasp grubs which had grown to maturity inside the caterpillar's body. The arrow points to a grub in the act of emerging from the host preparatory to spinning its cocoon.

Figure 5–7. A school of fish. In this aerial view of an Alaskan stream a shadowing effect along the left bank of the river can be seen. These "shadows" are actually the dark bodies of an immense school of sockeye salmon migrating upstream to spawn. (Fisheries Research Institute, University of Washington.)

among individuals of the same species. For the most part the members of species live as individuals—that is, they are *solitary*, dependent solely on their own devices for their existence except, in dioecious forms, for occasional contact for reproductive purposes. But some species form *aggregates* in which individuals bear some interdependence on others of their own kind. Such relationships may be loose and often temporary or close-knit, permanent, and frequently highly organized; based on the degree of intimacy and organization, two intergrading types are recognized.

Gregariousness. Many kinds of animals are *gregarious* to a greater or lesser degree; that is to say, they form groups of various sizes, composed of numerous individuals but having no real organiza-tion. For example, wolves for the most part live a solitary existence or in family units, except when hunting, particularly during the winter months. At such times they form packs and, by cooperating as a group, are much more successful in bringing down larger prey than they would be individually. Furthermore, fishes often form great schools, the members of which live together primarily during the breeding season (Figure 5–7). Many birds behave in a similar fashion but breed as isolated units and then come together in flocks during the fall and winter seasons. In these aggregates no organization of any sort is apparent. There is no chief individual to direct the activities of the whole mass nor any specialization in function on the part of any member of the group. All

Figure 5–8. Some colonial animals.   A. As this relative (*Cordylophora*) of the familiar *Hydra* matures, it sends out a stemlike shoot called a stolon; as the stolon elongates, buds are produced along its length which develop into adult forms. In this way a whole colony eventually is established. (Courtesy of Dr. C. Fulton, *Developmental Biol.*, Vol. 6, 1963, and the Academic Press.) B. Corals are colonies produced by much the same sorts of processes as those shown in A, but the bodies become embedded in a thick limy skeleton. Those shown are growing along the Great Barrier Reef of Australia.

are free to come and go as occasion demands.

Colonialism. In zoology the term *colony* is applied to aggregates of a species in which the association among the members is intimate and more or less permanent. In many kinds of unicellular organisms in which new individuals are formed by cell division the daughters remain attached to one another, and a colony results from a repetition of this act over and over again (Figure 5–8). Similarly, among many marine animals, notably the corals and related forms, large aggregates may be built up by asexual reproductive means, commencing with a single individual. In corals the same skeleton of lime binds all into one permanently fused mass. Both in unicellular forms and in the metazoans often a few individuals will be specialized for sexual reproductive purposes, whereas others are morphologically adapted solely for food collecting, defense, or other functions. In spite of such occasional specializations in individual activities, the colonies are considered *nonsocial*.

In truly *social* colonies the individuals carry out their activities independently, moving about freely in doing so, yet each plays a specialized role within the aggregate. Honey bees are among the most outstanding of social animals. Each colony (hive) includes three types of individuals, an egg-laying female (*queen*), sterile females (*workers*) that provide food and care for the queen and growing young, and males (*drones*) that live idly, except during the mating season and then serve to fertilize the queen. Some termites of tropical regions refine the worker caste by further adaptations. Often there are *soldiers* that defend the colony, *nurses* that care for the young, and *food-gatherers* that provision the nest. Ants, too, often have complex social organizations, sometimes even capturing smaller species or individuals from neighboring nests to perform the routine tasks of maintaining the colony.

Questions for Review and Thought

1. What is meant by a system of classification in zoology? In general, on what is it based?

2. Define the term *species*. Into what types of subdivisions may species be arranged? Into what may several related ones be grouped? Of what does a scientific name of an organism consist? Why is the scheme of naming organisms still considered to be binomial even though trinomials are frequently employed?

3. List all the basic features characteristic of any species in general.

4. In what diverse fashions is the term *population* employed? What distinguishes species from subspecies?

5. Define the word *taxon*. Starting with the largest taxon, list in sequence all with which you are familiar, breaking each down by using the prefixes *super-* and *sub-*.

6. Define the seven principal nutritional types.

7. Describe the structure of a biological community.

8. What large carnivores still survive in your native area? Which are now extinct? What large herbivores still persist there? What small carnivores abound even in and around large cities, despite upsets caused by man?

9. Define symbiosis and each of its three subdivisions.

10. What types of intraspecific relationships exist? Define each.

11. How do you classify webworms or tent caterpillars, as parasites or herbivores, and why? In what ways are humans occasionally social parasites?

Supplementary References

Allee, W. C. *Cooperation among Animals*. New York, Abelard-Schuman, 1951.

Allee, W. C., *et al.* *Principles of Animal Ecology*. Philadelphia, Saunders, 1949.

Caullery, M. *Parasitism and Symbiosis*. London, Macmillan, 1952.

Dice, L. R. *Natural Communities*. Ann Arbor, Mich., Univ. Michigan Press, 1952.

Gregg, J. R. *The Language of Taxonomy*. New York, Columbia Univ. Press, 1954.

Guhl, A. M. "The Social Order of Chickens." *Sci. Amer.,* February 1956.

Odum, E. P. *Fundamentals of Ecology,* 2nd ed. Philadelphia, Saunders, 1960.

Rogers, W. P. *Nature of Parasitism*. New York, Academic Press, 1962.

Simpson, G. G. *Principles of Animal Taxonomy*. New York, Columbia Univ. Press, 1961.

Tinbergen, N. *Social Behavior in Animals*. New York, Wiley, 1953.

The Origin and Kingdoms of Life

INCLUDED in the numerous taxa of living things are many highly diversified types, some readily recognizable as being plant or animal and others that could with equal logic be considered either. All these diverse groups are differentiated not only by their external morphology but internally by the structure of their cell organelles as well; even the nucleus is at times so highly modified as to be scarcely recognizable. Yet in spite of the variations, permeating all can be traced an interconnecting threadwork of basic identity, manifest both in structural similarities and in those intricate chemical processes and other cellular activities outlined in the preceding section of this book. To understand these seeming contradictions of great differences and close resemblances, it is best to start at the very beginning of the account by examining the existing concepts concerning the origin of life upon this planet of ours.

The Origin of Life

In all probability man has always been interested in his own origins and in those of the living things around him, for all existing peoples, from the most primitive to the most civilized, have legends pertaining to their own beginnings. While such traditions earnestly endeavor to offer a satisfactory explanation of animate creation, every one shares supernatural or metaphysical ingredients at varying levels of superstition and spiritual insight.

EARLY CONCEPTS

It is not to be supposed that only the savage and barbaric peoples of the world accepted a supernatural explanation of the origins of life, for such is far from being the case. Civilization does not at once remove superstition from its human possessors; even in the writings of noted scientists until the end of the nineteenth

89

century threads of it may be detected. And if the word "superstition" is defined as any blindly accepted belief or concept, a certain amount of it may be thought to exist in science today, for some of the existing ideas are largely of a traditional nature, founded on a modicum of fact, but accepted principally on faith.

Concepts in Ancient Civilizations. Much in the early—and later—beliefs regarding the origin of life centered around the concept that living things arise not only by hatching from eggs or by being born but also by springing into existence fully mature out of slime, mud, earth, air, or other lifeless matter. Such ideas of *spontaneous generation* are often called theories of *abiogenesis* in contrast to the present notion of *biogenesis,* which states that all life comes from pre-existing life. A few examples drawn from varied sources will serve to show the many variations on this theme that existed. In the earliest writings of ancient Babylonia and Egypt it is stated that the mud of the irrigation ditches and that of the Nile gave rise to worms, frogs, toads, mice, and alligators under the warming effects of the sun.

Later, among the many Greek writings on the topic, Empedocles (495–435 B.C.) wrote in an imaginative manner. This great thinker believed that life arose under the influence of two forces, love and hate, acting on the four basic elements, earth, water, air, and fire. In his concept the plants were spontaneously produced first, and later, the animals budded off them. However, they did not bud off as entire creatures, but only various bodily parts were formed, in quite an unordered manner. When hate happened to be the predominant force, these parts repelled one another and, unable to survive because of their incompleteness, soon perished. In contrast, when love ruled, the various parts joined with one another in random combinations. Many of the resulting unions, such as one leg on another or a head combined to a tail, were inviable, of course, but some more complete ones were capable of existence, and these gave rise to the animals of the earth. Aristotle (384–322 B.C.) also was an active proponent of the doctrine of spontaneous generation, and his writings on natural history are filled with descriptions of the origin of many organisms, including human beings.

Later Concepts. Under Aristotle's continuing influence the concept of abiogenesis acquired a mystical or theological rather than a philosophical flavor as many early Christian writers borrowed portions of his works, enlarging on them from a Biblical point of view. During medieval times and later all sorts of fantastic tales of a nontheological nature were related, and even the science of biology during its formative years became a curious mixture of keen observations and utter nonsense. One early plant physiologist, van Helmont (1577–1644), who performed many thoroughgoing experiments on the nutrition of plants, was completely convinced of the principle of abiogenesis. In fact, he published a formula for the artificial production of mice, the ingredients of which included a soiled chemise, a few grains of wheat, and a bushel measure. He found it particularly interesting to note that these spontaneously generated mice were exactly like those produced by ordinary sexual processes from other mice!

THE FALL OF ABIOGENESIS

The breakdown of the concept of spontaneous generation, a slow process, indeed, covered the greatest portion of three centuries and involved the efforts of many workers. Only the contributions

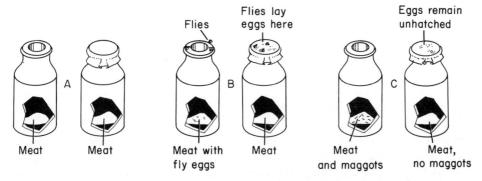

Figure 6–1. Redi's experiments. A. Meat is placed in two sets of jars, one open and the other covered with muslin. B. Flies are soon attracted to both jars, but in the case of the covered jars they can deposit eggs only on the muslin. C. Maggots develop solely in the open containers. Although to us today these results are obvious, in Redi's time it had not been known previously that maggots developed from eggs nor that flies arose from maggots.

of two of these scientists are discussed here: one an Italian entomologist named Francesco Redi (1626–1697), the other the French chemist and bacteriologist Louis Pasteur (1822–1895).

Redi's Experiment. Redi was the very first biologist to perform controlled experiments on the spontaneous generation of life. In his simple but effective study he set up a series of jars containing meat or fish, several of which were left open, while the rest were covered with the finest type of muslin. In the course of several days the contents of the open jars were swarming with maggots, whereas those of the protected ones were entirely free of these creatures (Figure 6–1). From his observations he demonstrated that flies and maggots did not arise spontaneously from decaying flesh, but came only from eggs deposited by other flies.

Pasteur's Studies. Although Redi's work and that of others gradually subdued the concept of spontaneous generation as far as macroscopic life was concerned, it persisted in full force regarding microorganisms until 1862 when Pasteur published the results of his conclusive experiments. He set out to demonstrate three principal items: (1) that microorganisms are present in the atmosphere; (2) that these microorganisms can initiate the growth of organisms in organic liquids; and (3) that sterilized organic liquids protected from contact with the air will not develop life within themselves.

The first point he demonstrated by drawing air through a cotton plug in a tube over a period of 24 hours and examining the organisms thus captured. The second and third points he demonstrated together. First he sterilized the meat and vegetable extracts used as organic liquids, employing the greatest precautions to prevent contamination. When the extracts had been thoroughly boiled, the flask was sealed and set aside. After periods of varying lengths, the contents were found to have been unchanged; no life of any sort was formed within it. On the other hand, when the seals of some flasks treated in this fashion were broken and exposed to the air, microorganisms of many sorts soon filled the contents. In this manner he established that microorganisms do not arise spontaneously and that the extracts he employed were capable of supporting the growth of living things. Only by his efforts did the principle of biogenesis become finally and firmly established.

THE BIOCHEMICAL
ORIGIN OF LIFE

Following Pasteur's studies, biologists for many years did not concern themselves with the problem of the origin of life, for until a sufficient knowledge of the chemical nature of life had been garnered no logical theory on the subject could be advanced. After this information had accumulated, many theories were proposed, so that now there exists a rapidly growing body of literature on the subject, the principal features of which are summarized below.

The Nature of the Primitive Earth. Many scientists today believe that the earth was once a flaming ball like a miniature sun. After it had slowly cooled, ultimately a temperature was reached that permitted the atmospheric water to descend as rain and gradually fill the hollows to form seas. These seas were, of course, entirely sterile, as were the lands, too, for no life could have survived the extreme heat of the earlier stages.

In addition to its sterility, the primitive earth was distinct from the modern one in several ways. In the first place, its atmosphere was quite unlike the present one in composition. Although nitrogen was probably abundant then as now, oxygen, on the other hand, was most likely tied up chemically in the rocks to a much greater extent. On the basis of studies of other heavenly bodies, it is postulated that the early atmosphere was rich in methane (CH_4), ammonia (NH_3), water, and possibly carbon dioxide. Moreover, in all likelihood volcanic activity was widespread and violent, for the interior had as yet had insufficient time to become stabilized, and it is more than possible that the continents were not great land masses but innumerable large and small islands among which the seas were interspersed. Still other differences

may have existed, but the foregoing seem to be the most important to the present topic.

The Origin of Energy Sources. Because all living things require energy from the catabolism of organic compounds to drive the anabolic processes, carbohydrates or other readily oxidizable substances had to be present in the seas before life could originate. It should be borne in mind that many unicellular organisms today can and do employ as energy sources such simple compounds as formic, acetic, and similar acids and methyl and ethyl alcohols. How even such relatively simple substances as these were produced spontaneously is still largely conjectural, but three chief methods have been proposed. The Russian biochemist Oparin and his followers have suggested that during the molten stage in the earth's formation much carbon had united with various metals to form metallic carbides. As the student probably already knows, carbides readily react with water to produce the gas acetylene. In the presence of certain minerals molecules of this chemical link together (i.e., they *polymerize*) to form long chains from which carbohydrates and fats might readily be synthesized. The second postulated set of reactions commences with methane and employs ordinary organic chemical reactions that can be carried out in the test tube. For example, methane combines with chlorine to form methyl chloride, which in turn reacts with water to produce methyl alcohol.

$$CH_4 + Cl_2 \rightarrow CH_3Cl + HCl$$
Methane   Methyl chloride

$$CH_3Cl + H_2O \rightarrow CH_3OH + HCl$$
Methyl chloride   Methyl alcohol

As already mentioned, this methyl alcohol can be used directly by some living things as an energy source; furthermore, it can be the starting point for other reactions, which can, given time and sunlight, end in the production of glucose. The third hypothetical method of producing organic energy sources makes use of irradiation, particularly that of cosmic rays and that produced by radioactive materials. The American biochemist M. Calvin and his colleagues have been especially active in investigating this approach. Using a cyclotron, they have irradiated solutions of carbon dioxide in water and have obtained formic acid, which after further irradiation can be built into fairly complex carbohydrates. Perhaps all three suggested procedures actually occurred, perhaps some of an entirely different nature. But the point is that by one method or another organic energy sources came into existence, and because of the sterile conditions that prevailed, they slowly accumulated in the seas as they formed.

The Origin of Nitrogenous Compounds. As is the case of the energy sources, many ideas have been advanced regarding the possible origin of the protoplasm-forming substances, the nitrogenous compounds, but two main schools of thought predominate. The oldest postulated procedure utilizes some of the energy compounds along with a nitrogen source, such as ammonia, nitric acid, or nitrates, and energy in the form of ultraviolet light from the sun. In this fashion it is possible to synthesize many of the amino acids, as in the following example:

$$CH_3COOH + NH_3 + E \rightarrow$$

Acetic   Ultra-
acid   violet
           light

$$CH_2NH_2COOH + H_2$$

Glycine
(an amino acid)

Recently it has been determined that if an electric spark is passed through a vial containing ordinary ammonium carbonate $[(NH_4)_2CO_3]$, which compound is the product of ammonia, water, and carbon dioxide, all the essential amino acids are formed. Hence it does not appear too difficult to explain the production of amino acids from inorganic substances. These upon coupling could produce proteins, so that over the millions of years the waters of the seas gradually seem literally to have become a rich broth. As the dissolved materials increased in content, they also increased in complexity, so that eventually the pyrimidines, purines, nucleotides and all other constituents of protoplasm came into existence. With the advent of all basic ingredients the first nucleoproteins appeared, capable of reproducing themselves. Thus the first of the unique properties of life, that of self-reproduction, came into existence. These large complicated molecules probably became centers of chemical activity and thus became particles, possibly similar to the objects we call viruses today (Figure 6–2).

Figure 6–2. An electronmicrograph of the vaccinia (cowpox) virus. Magnified 45,000×. (Courtesy of Dr. R. C. Williams, Virus Laboratory, University of California, Berkeley, and *The Cell*, Vol. 4, 1960, The Academic Press, Inc.)

The Kingdoms of Life

Now that progress has been made toward an explanation of how life arose, closer attention is being given to the problem of the true relationships of the various forms of living things. Particularly under scrutiny is the classical scheme of classification in which the whole living world is arranged in two kingdoms, one of plants, the second of animals. To overcome the weaknesses of this old but still popular concept, some workers propose three kingdoms and others four, while on the contrary still others suggest that only one kingdom actually exists. Thus it can be readily perceived that there are several concepts as to the proper disposition of the numerous plantlike and animaloid organisms. Since this is the case, in order that the current theories may be understood, it is necessary to include plant classification briefly in the following discussion, even though our sole concern is actually with the animals. The major approaches to the problem will be examined in sequence of their appearance in scientific history, beginning with the one that may even antedate civilization.

THE CLASSICAL APPROACH

Even before the Greek philosophers living things had been classified in two kingdoms, one of plants, the other of animals. In the *Plantae* are placed the organisms which are principally immobile, which obtain their food by photosynthetic or saprophytic means, and which have walls around their cells; the *Animalia* contains chiefly actively motile forms that ingest their food and whose cells lack a wall.

The Plant Kingdom. Customarily, this kingdom is first divided into two subkingdoms, the *Thallophyta* and *Embryophyta*. In the Thallophyta are placed all those plants that lack bodies differentiated into roots, stems, and leaves and whose embryos, when present, are not enclosed within an ovule. This subkingdom, in its turn, is subdivided into forms (the *Algae*) in which chlorophyll is present and those (formerly called the *Fungi*) in which chlorophyll is lacking (Table 6–1). Although much variation exists, the second subkingdom, the Embryophyta, is most frequently subdivided into the *Bryophyta* and *Tracheophyta*, containing the mosses and the seed plants and ferns, respectively.

The Animal Kingdom. Typically, the kingdom Animalia is looked upon as containing two subkingdoms, the *Protozoa*, including the essentially unicellular forms, and the *Metazoa*, in which the sponges and all multicellular animals are placed. Sometimes the sponges are viewed as intermediate between the protozoans and the true animals and are ranked accordingly as a third subkingdom, the *Parazoa*. The Metazoa are a well-marked unit, for all its members, barring the sponges and a small parasitic phylum called the Mesozoa, have contractile (muscular) and conductive (nerve) cells in their bodies, and almost all possess mouths and digestive tracts.

Unfortunately, in this system of classification, the same clear-cut distinctiveness is not present between all of its categories, and it is for this reason that other approaches to the problem have been advanced. Particular protest has been raised against this scheme on the grounds that the constituents of its two major taxa, the Plant and Animal Kingdoms, cannot always be clearly distinguished and that it fails to express the correct relationships of living things. The first weakness is especially pronounced at the unicellular level; for example, the case of a form known as *Euglena* may be

TABLE 6-1

COMPARISONS OF THE SEVERAL SCHEMES CLASSIFYING LIVING THINGS IN GENERAL

Classical System (modern version)	The Four-Kingdom System *	The Single-Kingdom System *
KINGDOM I. Plantae	**KINGDOM I. Monera (or Mychota)** (unicellular forms without true nuclei)	**KINGDOM Plantae (all living things)**
Subkingdom A. Thallophyta		Subkingdom A. Cyanophytaria (blue-green algae 2)
Chlorophyllous forms	Phylum 1. Archezoa (bacteria 8, blue-green algae 2)	Subkingdom B. Thiophytaria (sulfur bacteria 8)
Division 1. Chlorophyta (green algae)		Subkingdom C. Rhodobactophytaria (sulfur purple bacteria 8)
Division 2. Cyanophyta (blue-green algae)	**KINGDOM II. Protista (or Protoctista)**	Subkingdom D. Myxobactophytaria (slime bacteria 8)
Division 3. Euglenophyta (euglenoids)	Phylum 2. Rhodophyta (red algae 7)	Subkingdom E. Bactophytaria (true bacteria 8)
Division 4. Chrysophyta (diatoms, etc.)	Phylum 3. Phaeophyta (brown algae 6, diatoms 4)	Subkingdom F. Saccharophytaria (true yeasts 10)
Division 5. Pyrrhophyta (dinoflagellates)	Phylum 4. Pyrrhophyta (dinoflagellates 5; euglenoids 3)	Subkingdom G. Euglenophytaria (euglenoids 3, dinoflagellates 5, 13)
Division 6. Phaeophyta (brown algae)	Phylum 5. Opisthokonta (true fungi in part 10)	Subkingdom H. Arcellophytaria (simple amoeboids 13)
Division 7. Rhodophyta (red algae)	Phylum 6. Inophyta (true fungi in part 10)	Subkingdom I. Amoebophytaria (true amoeboids 13)
Colorless forms	Phylum 7. Protoplasta (protozoa in part 13; slime molds 9)	Subkingdom J. Enterophytaria (parasitic amoeboids 13)
Division 8. Schizophyta (bacteria, actinomycetes)	Phylum 8. Fungilli (sporozoan protozoa 13)	Subkingdom K. Protociliphytaria (protociliates 13)
Division 9. Myxomycophyta (slime molds)	Phylum 9. Ciliophora (ciliated protozoa 13)	Subkingdom L. Chlorophytaria (green algae 1; Embryophyta B)
Division 10. Eumycophyta (true fungi)	**KINGDOM III. Plantae**	Subkingdom M. Chrysophytaria (golden algae, diatoms 4; brown algae 6; red algae 7; Eumycophyta 10; ciliated protozoa 13; sponges 14; Eumetazoa E)
Subkingdom B. Embryophyta	Phylum 10. Chlorophyta (green algae 1)	
Division 11. Bryophyta (mosses, liverworts)	Phylum 11. Bryophyta (mosses, liverworts 11)	
Division 12. Tracheophyta (ferns, seed plants)	Phylum 12. Tracheophyta (ferns, seed plants 12)	
KINGDOM II. Animalia	**KINGDOM IV. Animalia**	
Subkingdom C. Protozoa (unicellular animals)	Subkingdom Parazoa (D)	
Phylum 13. Protozoa	Subkingdom Eumetazoa (E)	
Subkingdom D. Parazoa (funnel-celled animals)		
Phylum 14. Porifera (sponges)		
Subkingdom E. Eumetazoa (multicellular animals)		

* The figures and letters following the names of organisms correspond to those of the first column.

cited. In possessing chloroplasts and a cell wall of sorts, the representatives of this genus are quite plantlike; on the other hand, they actively swim and are therefore animal-like in behavior. Consequently, these unicellular forms are found twice in this scheme of classification, once as a plant in a division under the Thallophyta and again as an animal, placed in an order of the Protozoa. Furthermore, another organism, *Peranema,* has a cellular structure close to that of the above-mentioned form but naturally lacks chloroplasts, yet, although its relationships to *Euglena* are clear and universally recognized, this unicellular form is always classed as a protozoan, never as a thallophyte. Many other unicellular forms parallel the situation of *Euglena* and are dually classified.

These and other intergradations between the simpler members of the two kingdoms are explained by the proponents of the system to be a logical consequence of the manner in which life began. At the lower levels in the evolution of living things, they suggest, it is to be anticipated that the two kingdoms approach so closely that sharp distinctions may frequently be lacking (Figure 6–3).

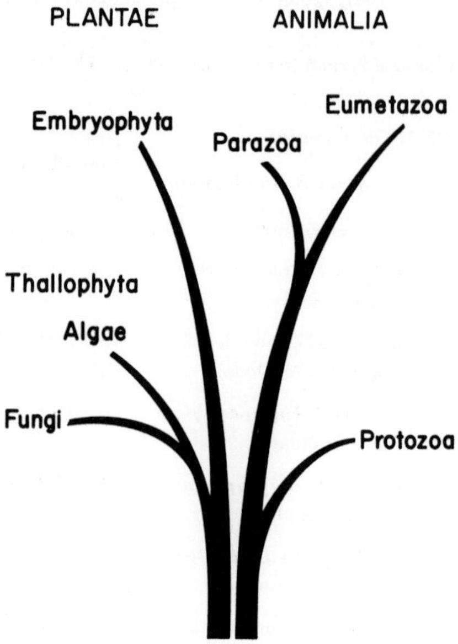

THE THREE- AND FOUR-KINGDOM APPROACHES

To eliminate what the antagonists of the foregoing system claim as weaknesses and to show more clearly the relationships of the unicellular forms, a third kingdom, known as the *Protista,* has often been proposed. In this kingdom are placed all the Thallophyta and Protozoa, the two groups being entirely eliminated as separate systematic entities. Many of the members of the former group of Protozoa, especially forms that

Figure 6–3. The classical arrangement of living things. In this diagram or "tree" of the evolutionary history (phylogeny) of organisms, the two kingdoms may be seen to be closely approximate at the lower, unicellular level but to diverge strongly at the upper ends. At the very base the two are conjoined by the earliest form of life.

move by means of flagella, are assigned to one or the other of the divisions of algae, regardless of the presence or absence of chlorophyll, and new divisions have been created for the remainder. In these schemes the kingdom Plantae is the equivalent of the Embryophyta, whose name has been dropped, whereas the kingdom Animalia is confined to the two subkingdoms Parazoa and Eumetazoa, which, as before, are often combined into one, the Metazoa.

As certain of the Protista—namely, the Cyanophyta (blue-green algae) and Schizophyta (bacteria)—do not possess chromosomes, cellular division in these groups is of necessity amitotic. Consequently, these organisms are sometimes removed from the Protista to a kingdom of their own, under the name of *Monera;* usually this new category is placed in the most primitive position in these systems of classification, which thus contains four of the largest taxon (Table 6–1).

Either the three- or four-kingdom approach has the distinct advantage over the classical in having the kingdoms more sharply defined, with the possible exception that intergradation between the Protista and Animalia is still present. Particularly distinguished are the Monera and the Plantae, for the Monera is based on a particular type of cell organelle and the Plantae on a whole set of cellular traits, including a peculiar combination

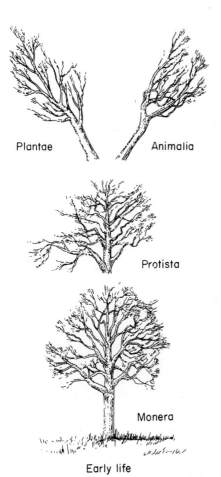

Plantae

Animalia

Protista

Monera

Early life

Figure 6–4. The four kingdom approach. The four kingdoms are depicted as unrelated trees representing successively more complex levels of organization. In the three-kingdom system, the lower two are joined into a single unit.

of photosynthetic pigments, a cellulose cell wall, and the formation of true starch. However, one objection to the classical scheme has not been removed by either the three- or the four-kingdom approach—the interrelationships of the organisms are not clearly shown, as may be seen in Figure 6–4. At a lower level, too, although a number of the phyla appear quite natural, others contain a number of evidently unrelated groups.

THE SINGLE-KINGDOM
APPROACH

A more recent attempt at classifying the members of the living world utilizes the structure of cell organelles exclusively in working out relationships and on this basis concludes that all organisms belong to a single kingdom. In this scheme the assumption is made that if life arose through biochemical means, as outlined earlier in this chapter, then it is possible that the cell did not come into existence in its final complex form but was at first quite simple and increased in complexity as time passed. It also supposes that the organisms presently existing possibly reflect some of the stages involved in the elaboration of the cell.

In attempting to trace the development of the cell the structure of the nucleus is principally relied upon, the simplest type being suggested to be that of the blue-green algae (Cyanophyta). In this group, as indicated in the discussion under the four-kingdom system, no true nucleus is present—there is only an irregular mass of chromatin strands; cell division is performed solely by the formation and growth of a new cell wall, the elongation of which divides both the cytoplasmic and nuclear matter (Figure 6–5). Above the lowest level represented by the blue-green algae are

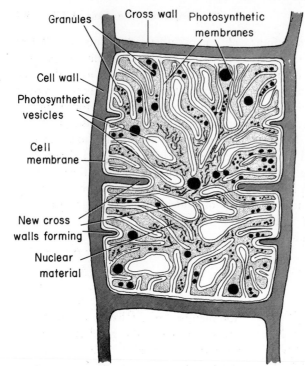

Figure 6–5. Ultrastructure of a blue-green alga. Although the structure of a blue-green alga appears quite complex, it nevertheless is evidently at a low level of organization. Note that the only trace of a nucleus is found in the fine filaments of chromatin scattered in clusters centrally in the cytoplasm. Division of both cytoplasm and the simple nucleus is by ingrowth of the new cell walls.

recognized four successively higher stages in the development of the nucleus, exemplified by the same number of diverse bacterialike organisms. In the simplest the nuclear matter is in granular form, scattered throughout the cytoplasm, but

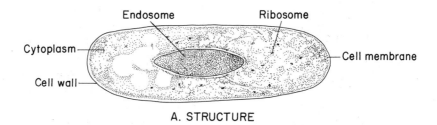

A. STRUCTURE

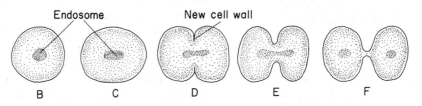

B-F. CELL DIVISION

Figure 6–6. Bacterial organization. A. Although a higher level of organization than in the blue-green algae can be perceived to exist in the bacteria, the nucleus is represented by a simple central mass of chromatin. B–F. While the cytoplasm is divided, as in the blue-green algae, by ingrowth of a new cell wall, the endosome divides through its own efforts, thus affording a control over the passing of genetic material to each of the daughter cells.

in the remaining groups it is organized into an *endosome*. By this term is denoted a mass of organized chromatin matter lacking an enclosing membrane and usually centrally located in the organism (Figure 6–6). At successively higher levels this endosome becomes covered by a nuclear membrane and a mass of nucleoplasm, then acquires chromosomes, and, finally, interzonal lines and spindle fibers. Following the acquisition of all these parts, higher levels are traced mainly on the reduction of the endosome to the state of the nucleolus in the higher green plants and metazoans, where it disappears during the course of mitosis (Figure 6–7). Finally, on the basis of cell-plate formation and development of astral rays, respectively, the establishment of these two groups is traced on branches

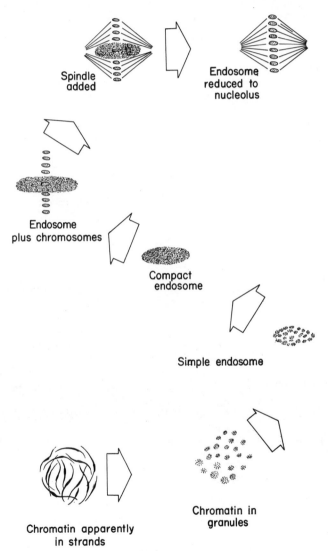

Spindle added

Endosome reduced to nucleolus

Endosome plus chromosomes

Compact endosome

Simple endosome

Chromatin in granules

Chromatin apparently in strands

Figure 6–7. Hypothetical steps in the evolution of the nucleus. In the diagram are shown some of the major stages conjectured to have existed in the formation of a complex nucleus out of the simple strands of chromatin that marked the beginnings of this organelle.

at the upper end of the nuclear history. Furthermore, the developmental histories of other cell organelles, such as the chloroplastids, flagella, and mitochondria, can be interpreted in a fashion that shows a corresponding sequence of representative organisms, and this fact is employed to corroborate the evidence presented by the nucleus.

As already stated, this system proposes

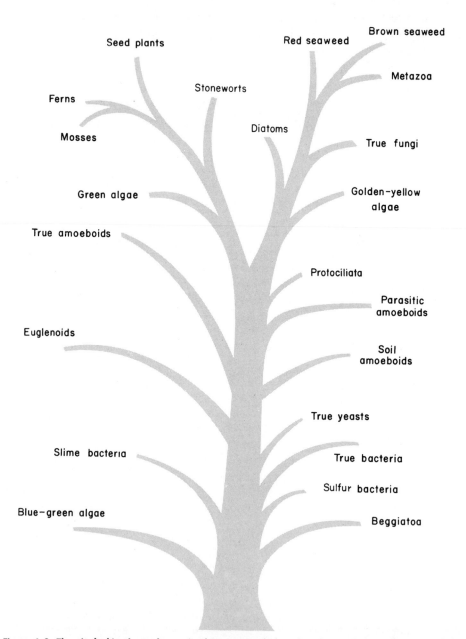

Figure 6–8. The single kingdom scheme. In this system, which is based on relative cellular complexity, all living things are suggested to form one tree of life bearing thirteen major branches or subkingdoms.

that only a single kingdom of living things exists, considered to be the Plant Kingdom on various bases, largely for technical reasons and because there is little choice. Conceivably, the term Biotic Kingdom could be used with equal justification. In this approach the term *animal* is confined solely to the Eumetazoa. Since it thus proposes considerable upset in the existing state of affairs, it offers some disadvantages. When diagrammed in tree form, the scheme (Figure 6–8) shows the single kingdom bearing 13 major branches, each called a subkingdom (Table 6–1).

PROVISION FOR FLEXIBILITY

Perhaps the resemblances and dissimilarities resulting from the various approaches to the problem of classifying the living world in a manner approximating the natural conditions are best studied from the chart (Table 6–1). From it and the preceding discussion each system is seen to hold its own advantages and objectionable features. Certainly, it is apparent that no universal agreement exists.

In consequence of all these considerations, no single scheme of over-all classification will be employed in the ensuing chapters, so that the student's instructor may decide which is to be followed. Instead the organisms are treated in what appear to be natural groups, mostly units of long recognition. Since no two writers are in agreement on the sequence of these groups, they will be arranged in order of increasing cell complexity, along with an indication of the position suggested for them in each of the three systems. In the long run, it appears that the organisms themselves, their activities, cellular structure, and modifications, are the facts pertinent to a biology student, not the hypothesized relationships.

Questions for Review and Thought

1. Without going into details, summarize the principal features of current theories on the origin of life. In what ways are they like the old ideas of abiogenesis and in which are they distinct?

2. Outline Redi's and Pasteur's experiments. For approximately how many years has it been known that flies always come from pre-existing flies by way of eggs? How long has man known about the "canning" of fruits and vegetables?

3. What chemical steps are involved in the spontaneous creation of carbohydrates and other organic energy sources out of inorganic matter? Outline the possible steps needed to form proteins spontaneously. The origins of what classes of organic compounds have not been explained on a biochemical basis?

4. Define the terms *animal* and *plant* as used in each of the major approaches to the classification of living things. In which system are additional terms needed for organisms?

5. Summarize the principal features of the three systems of classification and indicate the strengths and weaknesses of each.

Supplementary References

Adler, I. *How Life Began.* New York, Day, 1957.
Alexander, J. *Life, Its Nature and Origin.* New York, Reinhold, 1948.
Calvin, M. *Chemical Evolution.* Eugene, Oregon State System of Higher Education, 1961.

Copeland, H. F. *The Classification of Lower Organisms*. Palo Alto, Calif., Pacific Books, 1956.

Ehrensvärd, G. C. H. *Life: Origin and Development*. Chicago, Univ. Chicago Press, 1962.

Florkin, M. *Aspects of the Origin of Life*. New York, Pergamon, 1960.

Oparin, A. I. *The Origin of Life on the Earth*. New York, Academic Press, 1957.

Rusk, J. H. *The Dawn of Life*. Garden City, N. Y., Hanover House, 1957.

Wald, G. "The Origin of Life." *Sci. Amer.*, August 1954.

CHAPTER 7

Unicellular Animal-like Organisms

ALTHOUGH in two of the three major schemes of classification doubt is raised as to the validity of the common practice of distinguishing "plant-like" unicellular forms as Algae and "animal-like" ones as *Protozoa,* the latter term affords much by way of convenience, even when defined in nonsystematic terms. In instances where a nonclassical system of classification is followed, it can be confined to those unicellular (or essentially unicellular) forms, whether photosynthetic or not, which either actively move about during the major portion of their life cycles or parasitize the multicellular animals. Thus defined, the term in modern schemes embraces most of the same organisms generally included in the classical system.

Euglena and Related Forms

Many forms simpler than *Euglena* and its relatives exist, some of which, like the blue-green algae and the bacteria, completely lack a nucleus in the strict sense of the term, and others of which, including the true yeast, have a nucleus but no clear-cut chromosomes. But all of these simplest forms are more usually treated as plants; accordingly the most primitive group that can be considered protozoan is that to be discussed here. Many of its members, like the familiar *Euglena* itself, are active swimmers, propelling themselves through water by means of whiplike projections called *flagella* (sing., flagellum). Since this type of organization (i.e., "body type") is generally accepted as being the first to appear, flagellates are often believed to be the least complex protozoans. While these organisms are thus "flagellates," as are many other protozoans, not always is the presence of a flagellum taken to be indicative of close kinship, except among those who consider the protozoa to constitute a natural subkingdom. At times most euglenoids *encyst,* a process that includes, first, the retraction of the flagellum into the cell, followed in turn by a rounding-up of the body and the enclosure of the whole in a protective capsule. At the close a thick-coated immotile cyst is the result, often looked upon as representing a second body type of organization called the *coccoid*. In these forms related to *Euglena* are included both pigmented (photosynthetic) and unpigmented representatives. Several main groups can be placed here, the euglenoids proper and dinoflagellates.

The Euglenoids Proper. The constituents of this group are variously classed as composing the whole of the division Euglenophyta or as forming a subdivision in some larger taxon, among which can be mentioned Pyrrhophyta and Euglenophytaria under the Plantae or Protista and the Flagellata or Mastigophora in the Protozoa. Typically, whatever the name, the members have one free forward-projecting flagellum and a second frequently embedded in the thin body covering, or *pellicle;* both the free and attached flagella are seen under the electron microscope to have a single row of fringing hairs called *flimmer* along their entire length (Figure 7–1). As is the rule for flagellated organisms in general, but not without exception, the activity of the flagellum pulls the organism along. No starch is formed, but a related carbohydrate called *paramylum* is accumulated in granular form as the storage product. Only fresh waters are inhabited; however, one genus, *Euglenamorpha,* and a few species of *Euglena* live in the rectum of tadpoles, where they play an unknown symbiotic role.

In shape the euglenoids are quite

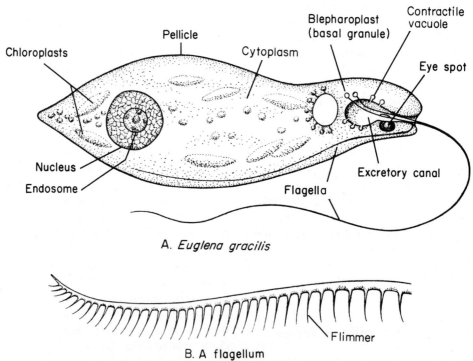

A. *Euglena gracilis*

B. A flagellum

Figure 7–1. Structure of the euglenoids. A. The gross structure of *Euglena*. B. The tip of a flagellum of a euglenoid, with fringing hairs (flimmer) confined to one side.

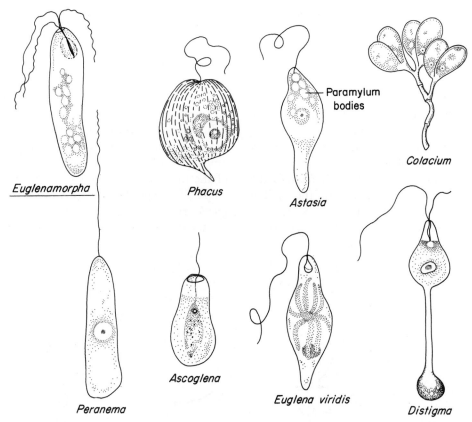

Euglenamorpha

Phacus

Paramylum bodies

Colacium

Astasia

Peranema

Ascoglena

Euglena viridis

Distigma

Figure 7–2. Types of the euglenoids proper. Very few colonial forms are known in this group, and these few, like *Colacium*, are simple in organization.

varied, ranging from extremely slender through spindlelike to oval or nearly spherical (Figure 7–2). Although for the greater part the cells are rounded in cross section, some like *Phacus* are strongly flattened. Frequently the posterior end terminates in a slender spine or, in flattened forms, in a broad keel. Usually the shapes are not fixed, for the pellicle is plastic and permits great freedom of movement; however, some have the pellicle replaced by a rigid *lorica,* particularly in the few sessile forms. In these, the lorica is loose, as in *Ascoglena,* and provides a sort of secreted "burrow" in which the organism can live. Except during cell division, *Ascoglena* is attached to the inside bottom of the lorica by means of protoplasmic strands.

The numerous species of *Euglena* are of particular interest as subjects for experimentation, especially along nutritional and genetical lines. By various treatments, such as prolonged cultivation in the dark or the addition of small amounts of streptomycin to the culture, forms provided with chloroplasts can be made to lose these organelles, either temporarily or permanently, depending on the nature of the treatment. During the absence of the pigment bodies even species which are normally phototropic can survive quite well in suitable culture media; thus they are capable of changing readily from a holophytic to a saprophytic type of nutrition. Once the chloroplasts have been entirely lost, they are never reacquired; consequently, these bodies are regarded as self-perpetuating structures, passed on from generation to generation, independent of the more usual type of inheritance.

The Dinoflagellates. Characteristically, the members of this group are phytoplankton, notably of the seas, for only a few fresh-water forms are known. Although the photosynthetic species have a mixture of pigments that results in a brownish color, so that sometimes they are known to botanists as the "yellow-brown algae," not all are provided with chloroplasts; a number of species are holozoic or parasitic. Most of the parasitic forms attack minute animals, such as water fleas and other crustaceans, either within the intestinal tract or as ectoparasites, but others live in marine worms and snails or even in other unicellular forms of life.

In body shape these organisms are still more diversified than the euglenoids; among them, in fact, are included some of the most striking forms of all microscopic life. Typically, a groove, called the *girdle,* runs transversely around the cell on the surface. Within this formation,

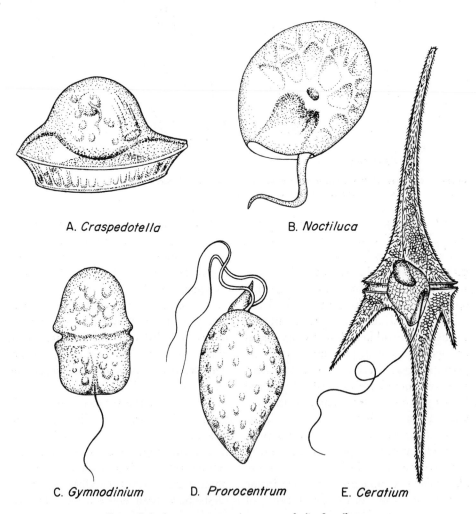

A. *Craspedotella*   B. *Noctiluca*

C. *Gymnodinium*   D. *Prorocentrum*   E. *Ceratium*

Figure 7–3. Some representative types of dinoflagellates.

embedded in the body covering except for a short tip, lies one flagellum; but a second, which is entirely free and extends posteriorly (Figure 7-3), provides most of the organism's forward movement, whereas the embedded flagellum rotates it on its longitudinal axis. Under the electron microscope it has been found that although the posterior flagellum lacks flimmer, the transverse has a single row exactly as in the same organelle of the euglenoids. Since these are the only two groups of unicellular life in which a single row of flimmer is found, this fact is employed by some as evidence of kinship between them. Although many species of dinoflagellates are "unarmored"— that is, not covered by a sheath of any sort—the "armored" ones have a thick rigid coat composed of plates (Figure 7-3). Often the armored types are equipped with long spines, as in *Ceratium,* and it is the presence of these sharp projections that provides the basis of the group's scientific name, the prefix "dino-" signifying "terrible."

Under favorable conditions of temperature and abundant nutrients, almost any microorganism is capable of building large populations in a short period of time. Such population explosions in aquatic environments are called *blooms* and are typically produced by photosynthetic species. Although at first glance blooms may appear favorable to the growth of those holozoic forms that feed on microscopic life, in reality they are quite detrimental. For one thing, certain species produce toxic substances as byproducts of their ordinary metabolic activities; these toxins in dilute amounts are harmless, but in the quantities manufactured during blooms they may often be fatal. More frequently, however, the blooming species is innocuous as long as it is growing; it is only upon death of the cells that other species are harmed, for

as the dead masses decompose, the oxygen store of the water is depleted and, especially in large ponds and lakes, thousands of fishes often perish. When on occasion the dinoflagellates produce a bloom in the sea, the red pigment of their cytoplasm imparts this color to the water. The "red waters" and "red tides" that sometimes mystify people are really just an abundance of these microorganisms, particularly those of the genera *Prorocentrum* and *Gymnodinium* (Figure 7-3).

Cellular Characteristics. The principal cellular characteristics of the foregoing groups lie in the type of nuclear structure, especially in features made evident during cell division. In the simpler forms, such as the euglenoids proper, within the nucleus is a large endosome that elongates and divides transversely during mitosis. Surrounding the endosome are chromosomes, typical in structure and behavior (Figure 7-4) except that their movements are unaccompanied by spindle threads and interzonal lines as in the more familiar mitotic divisions. In the dinoflagellates, too, the spindle and other fibers are similarly lacking, but this group differs in part from the euglenoids proper in that the endosome is reduced or even completely wanting.

The structure of only the euglenoids has reecived detailed study under the electron microscope. In these organisms true chloroplastids are present, but in simple form. Although this organelle is composed of a double membranous coat enclosing a series of plates, or lamellae, on which the photosynthetic pigments are embedded, as in the seed plants, the plates are noticeably thick and few in number, only 10 to 12 usually being present. The mitochondrion, too, is relatively uncomplicated in comparison with that of higher organisms (compare Figures 7-4 and 3-9), for only a few coarse folds

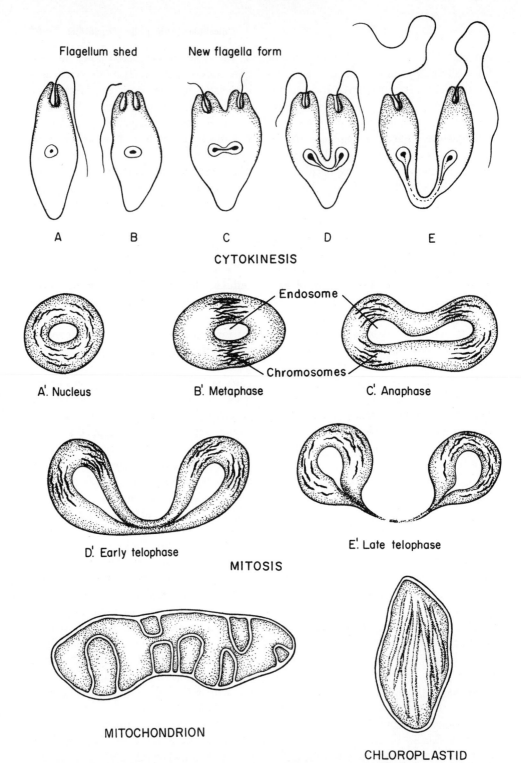

Flagellum shed   New flagella form

A   B   C   D   E

CYTOKINESIS

A'. Nucleus   B'. Metaphase   C'. Anaphase

Endosome

Chromosomes

D'. Early telophase   E'. Late telophase

MITOSIS

MITOCHONDRION

CHLOROPLASTID

Figure 7–4. Cellular features of the euglenoids. *A–E.* Mitosis in *Euglena*. Particularly characteristic of all euglenoids is the consistent absence of both spindle fibers and interzonal lines. The cristae of the mitochondrion are loose and few in number while the lamellae of the chloroplastid are similarly sparse in number as well as thick.

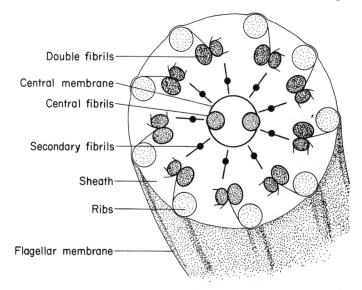

Double fibrils

Central membrane

Central fibrils

Secondary fibrils

Sheath

Ribs

Flagellar membrane

Figure 7–5. Structure of a typical flagellum. This diagram shows the remarkable complexity that exists in all typical flagella; not only are the types of structures present consistent, but their numbers and arrangement are strikingly uniform throughout motile organisms and ciliated cells.

are present; however, it is considerably more complex than in any lower group of organisms. Here, for the first time, occurs a flagellum of typical internal structure. In cross sections through the organelle electronmicrographs show it to consist of 11 fibrils running its entire length and embedded in a sheath. These fibrils are arranged in a pattern constant not only here but in all higher organisms as well—namely, nine fibrils composed of two microfibrils each placed around the periphery and two single fibrils in the center, along with ribs and other elements (Figures 7–5 and 7–6).

In the euglenoids and dinoflagellates

Figure 7–6. Electronmicrograph of cilia. In this section, taken through the cilia covering the gills of a mussel, the electronmicrograph shows that their structure, when compared with Figure 7–5, possesses a close correspondence. The same is true of all cilia and flagella from any organism higher than a bacterium. (Courtesy of Dr. Peter Satir, *Journ. Cell Biol.*, Vol. 18:365, Fig. 15, 1963.)

reproduction is solely by the mitotic processes briefly outlined above, during which cytokinesis occurs longitudinally. As a rule, when dividing, flagellated forms discard or absorb the existing flagella, and new ones are secreted by each daughter cell following cell division.

The Amoeba and Its Relatives

A large number of organisms move and feed by means of *pseudopods*. By this term are designated cytoplasmic extensions, usually temporary in nature, formed by the cell's constituents and often employed as a means of locomotion. Since this type of movement is characteristic of the amoeba and its relatives to be discussed here, it is called *amoeboid*. Many are naked cells, whereas others secrete a shell, called a *test* or *theca* (Figure 7–7), about themselves. Although most are free-living and aquatic, either floating in the water as plankton or crawling through the ooze of lake or sea bottoms, a number live

symbiotically, most frequently as commensals but occasionally as parasites. A few of the latter are pathogenic forms which cause serious diseases in man and his domesticated animals.

A type of body organization not previously noted is found among these organisms—the variety called the *plasmodium*. Characteristically, it consists of a large cytoplasmic mass in which are contained a number of nuclei, undivided into separate cells by cell membranes. Such masses may move about as amoebae by means (Figure 7–7) of pseudopods, but sometimes they cover themselves in a gelatinous capsule and form immotile cysts. Although this body type is particularly frequent among members of these groups, it is by no means confined to them, for it even occurs in higher animals, often under the term *syncytium*.

The Thecate Amoeboids and Related Forms. Although most of the shell-covered amoeboids are inhabitants of fresh waters, notably springs and small ponds, some species are marine; others are semiterrestrial, dwelling in mosses or moist

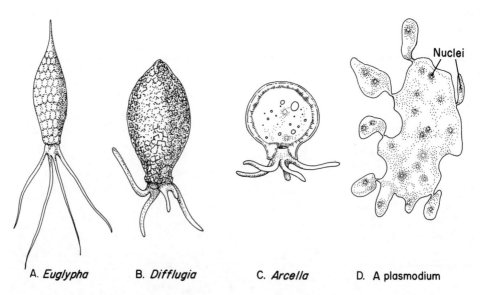

A. *Euglypha*   B. *Difflugia*   C. *Arcella*   D. A plasmodium

Nuclei

Figure 7–7. Various types of amoeboids.

soil, especially those of a peaty nature. In many the theca is basically membranous, sometimes covered in part by foreign objects. For example, in one of the best-known genera, *Arcella,* it is made of a chitinous membrane in the form of an inverted funnel (Figure 7–7), out of the open broad end of which the pseudopods are projected. In other genera, such as *Difflugia,* the shell is built by the organism of sand particles, bits of snail shells, and other objects cemented together. Only in *Euglypha* and its relatives is the covering really a shell in the strict sense of the term, for in these forms it consists of platelets of silica secreted by the cytoplasm.

The True Amoeboids. Ever since their discovery several centuries ago, *Amoeba* and related forms have excited the interest of scientists and laymen alike, for, with their uncovered cells and odd means of locomotion, they appear as so many animated chunks of formless protoplasm (Figure 7–8). Indeed, for many years, they were considered the lowest state of animal life, if not of all life in general. In more recent decades, however, this point of view has become altered, so that now flagellated organisms are believed to have developed earlier than the amoeboid ones. Despite this change in outlook, interest in these organisms continues undiminished. Especially is attention being given to the mechanisms involved in their means of locomotion, for it is often believed that, were they understood, light would be thrown on the contractile properties of protoplasm in general and on the nature of muscular contraction in particular. Although many theories on amoeboid movement have been presented, only one is discussed here; however, before this theory is outlined, the mechanics of progression in these organisms must be briefly described.

When viewed from above, as by the usual methods in light microscopy, new pseudopods seem to arise casually from an amoeba merely by a flowing movement of the cytoplasm. First a bulge forms; then, as it enlarges, a current of cytoplasm flows into it. If a closer examination is made, it is seen that the cytoplasmic movements are not random but occur in a definite pattern. Only the central, apparently fluid, portion engages in the flowing activity. When a particular set of the granular contents is followed, each granule in turn behaves in similar fashion. First each moves anteriorly until the tip of the pseudopod is attained, where it finds a place in a more solid-appearing layer and remains stationary. If a series of granules is lettered as in Figure 7–8, the action and the sequence of events may perhaps be better understood. When an amoeba is placed on one edge of a microscope slide and its movements are observed in profile, it can be noted that the cytoplasm does not flow over the surface but travels in such a manner that the main mass of the cell is carried well out of contact with the substrate (Figure 7–8).

A concept that attempts to explain this series of events is the *change of viscosity theory.* This idea essentially suggests that an amoeba consists of an outer firmer gelatinous layer surrounding an inner fluid mass. When in some manner the outer layer becomes liquefied locally, an outflow of protoplasm is induced in that area, producing a pseudopod. As the outflow continues, solidification occurs along the sides, while the center remains fluid. Hence a pseudopod can be thought of as a gelatinized tube provided with a liquid interior and tip. The local liquefaction of the gelatinous layer possibly results from a chemical reaction which induces the gel to become a sol, a mere change in phase of the colloid being involved.

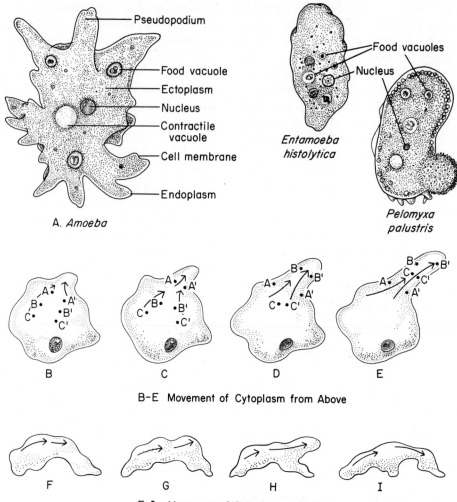

Figure 7–8. The structure of Amoeba and its method of locomotion. *B–E.* If during the movement of an *Amoeba* a few granules are watched, an orderly flow of the cytoplasm can be perceived; each granule in turn first moves forward and then laterally, becoming immotile once the side of the pseudopod has been attained. One pseudopod can be seen to decrease in size as the other elongates. *F–I.* In side view, movement is seen to be more complex than is apparent from above.

The Parasitic Amoeboids. Quite a number of amoeboid organisms inhabit the intestinal tracts of man and other animals. Particularly important as pathogens are species of the genus *Entamoeba,* one of which, *E. histolytica,* is the causative agent of amoebic dysentery. In this disease abscesses produced by the organisms invading the intestinal lining result in extreme diarrhea and bleeding. In severe cases the amoebae spread into the liver, spleen, and lungs and even the brain, inducing abscesses on all these organs. Transmission is largely by contaminated foods and water. Many other related forms do not cause disease but live as normal inhabitants of the digestive system, probably as harmless commensals. *E. coli* is an especially common species in the colon, whereas *E. gingi-*

valis occurs frequently in the mouth. Within these structures they apparently feed on bacteria, yeasts, and other microorganisms.

Cellular Characteristics. During the last decade many studies of the fine structure of the amoeboids have been made, particularly of the nuclear membrane and mitochondrion. Although the usual double membrane invests the latter, no folds or plates are present internally as elsewhere; instead, long fingerlike processes, called *microvilli,* project irregularly from the inner wall (Figure 7–9). The nucleus is highly varied in its chief characteristics. Although all forms have well-developed chromosomes and interzonal lines, in some simpler ones, including many of the thecate species, spindle threads are absent. In all an endosome is a prominent feature of mitosis. This organelle, however, does not remain

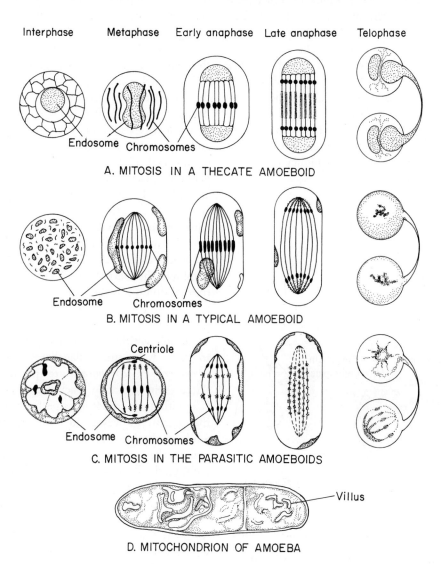

Interphase   Metaphase   Early anaphase   Late anaphase   Telophase

Endosome   Chromosomes

A. MITOSIS IN A THECATE AMOEBOID

Endosome   Chromosomes

B. MITOSIS IN A TYPICAL AMOEBOID

Centriole

Endosome   Chromosomes

C. MITOSIS IN THE PARASITIC AMOEBOIDS

Villus

D. MITOCHONDRION OF AMOEBA

Figure 7–9. Cellular properties of various amoeboid types.

intact after metaphase but breaks into several large fragments in the parasitic forms and into numerous granules in the others (Figure 7–9). Among the various forms included here only asexual methods of reproduction are known to occur.

Green Flagellates and Their Kin

If several major kinds of unicellular organisms were nonexistent, the problem of distinguishing protozoa from algae would be greatly eased. One such group is the present one, which includes besides the active animaloid types described here, threadlike colonies which are clearly ancestral to the flowering plants and their relatives. Among the whole constellation of traits which tie the present assemblage to the green algae and higher plants are

the sharing of the same varieties of pigments, a cellulose cell wall, the formation of true starch by photosynthesis, and the similarity of structure in such cell organelles as the chloroplast, flagellum, and nucleus. However, only a sample of the whole problem can be presented here, for we must focus attention solely on the animaloid types.

Flagellated Forms. Among the green flagellates are a fairly large number of species, including mostly chloroplast-bearing forms; however, some genera, like *Polytoma,* are unpigmented. The latter types show their relationships with the others through the presence of a cellulose cell wall, starch formation, and the characteristic arrangement of the flagella (Figure 7–10). Nevertheless, the pigmented types are far more numerous, and some, such as *Chlamydomonas,* are of unusual biological interest. In this genus are placed a large number of forms, all of which have a single cup-shaped chloroplast enclosing the nucleus and two equal flagella located anteriorly. Represented among them are numerous propagative processes. Of all the methods employed the asexual one of simple longitudinal division is the most frequent, but sometimes this method is modified by divisionary processes occurring twice in succession within the mother cell's wall, so that four small flagellates, called *swarmers* or *zoospores,* are produced. After their liberation, each increases in size with age and becomes perfectly normal again. However, in some species, while swimming, the swarmers encounter one another and attach at their anterior ends, gradually fusing to form a common mass. Later this cell becomes covered with a thick coat and develops into a cyst. These processes, in this form, are considered an example of *isogamy,* in which identical gametes are present (Figure 7–11). In some other species the

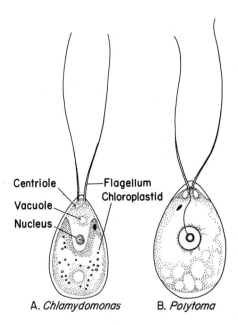

Centriole — Flagellum
Chloroplastid
Vacuole
Nucleus

A. *Chlamydomonas*   B. *Polytoma*

Figure 7–10. Some flagellated "green" protozoans. Although *Polytoma* and others like it are devoid of chlorophyll, they nevertheless are usually classified as close to chlorophyll-bearing types, such as *Chlamydomonas,* because so many other cellular traits are shared by all concerned.

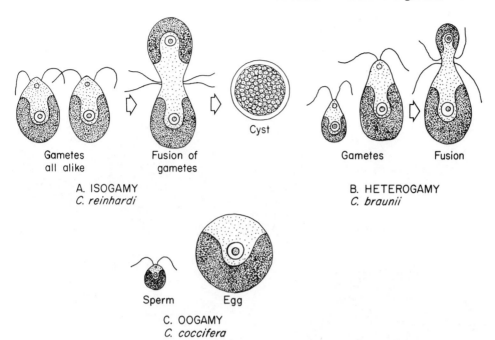

Cyst

Gametes
all alike

Fusion of
gametes

A. ISOGAMY
C. reinhardi

Gametes

Fusion

B. HETEROGAMY
C. braunii

Sperm

Egg

C. OOGAMY
C. coccifera

Figure 7–11. Reproductive types found in *Chlamydomonas*. Among the numerous species of *Chlamydomonas* are represented many types of sexual reproduction, divisible into three main categories. A. The simplest variety (classed as isogamous) is characterized by having the gametes alike in size, shape, and activity. Identical cells contact one another, arrange anterior ends together, fuse, and, following encystment, undergo division; *C. reinhardi* is one of numerous species with this type. B. In *C. braunii* and many other species, the gametes differ in size but are similar in activity. C. Among forms with the most advanced type of reproduction, the gametes are sharply differentiated as to size and function. Here, with *C. coccifera* as the example, one gamete is minute, biflagellated, and active, whereas the other is large, unflagellated, and quiescent; these are known respectively as sperm and egg. In all forms, encystment follows fusion.

gametelike swarmers are of two different sizes; as fusion takes place only between unlike cells, reproduction is of a *heterogamous* type. Since all degrees of heterogamy exist within the genus (Figure 7–11), from states with nearly identical gametes to those with completely different ones, its species are viewed as exhibiting steps involved in the formation of a sexual type of reproduction from an asexual one.

Spherical Colonies. Possibly the most outstanding of the green protozoans are the floating spherical colonies frequently found in ponds and lakes during early spring. In these species, projecting outward beyond the gelatinous coating that covers the whole, are the pairs of flagella borne by each cellular member. Some of the colonies, like *Pandorina*, consist of relatively few cells, perhaps only eight or ten, but at the other end of the scale are those of certain *Volvox* species which may be composed of 20,000 or more cells (Figure 7–12). Often the individual members, although widely spaced in the gelatinous coat, are interconnected by means of fine protoplasmic strands; apparently these living threads afford a mechanism whereby the activities of the individual components can be coordinated to some degree. In other similarly constructed forms, as exemplified by *Eudorina* and *Platydorina*, no such intercommunicative mechanisms are visible; however, it is suspected by many

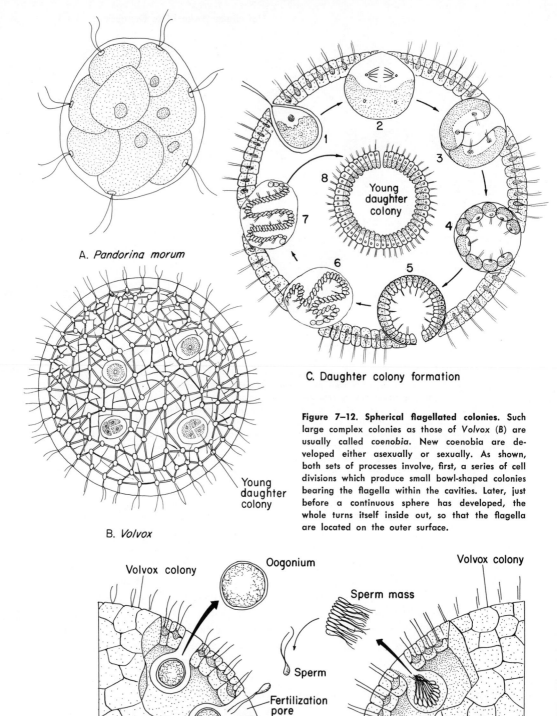

A. *Pandorina morum*

B. *Volvox*

Young daughter colony

C. Daughter colony formation

Young daughter colony

Figure 7–12. Spherical flagellated colonies. Such large complex colonies as those of *Volvox* (B) are usually called *coenobia*. New coenobia are developed either asexually or sexually. As shown, both sets of processes involve, first, a series of cell divisions which produce small bowl-shaped colonies bearing the flagella within the cavities. Later, just before a continuous sphere has developed, the whole turns itself inside out, so that the flagella are located on the outer surface.

Volvox colony

Oogonium

Volvox colony

Sperm mass

Sperm

Fertilization pore

D. Sexual reproduction

protozoologists that they are present but are merely too fine to be seen.

As a rule only a few members in any colony, or *coenobium,* of the more complex types are capable of reproducing a new colony asexually, even though all are able to divide mitotically to increase the size of their own assemblage. A daughter colony, formed in the interior cavity of the parent, is developed by a rather complicated set of processes that are briefly as follows: one of the original cells undergoes division longitudinally, but instead of separating as is usually the case, the two daughter cells remain closely attached on the anterior half. Each daughter then again divides longitudinally, but this time in a plane at right angles to the first division. For some time division of the resulting cells along with regrowth in size of the new individuals continues until a plate is established. Since the cells in this plate are closely attached side by side by their tapering anterior portions, this plate is really bowl-shaped, as can readily be perceived; all this time the flagella project into the cavity (Figure 7–12). Later, after the number of cells has increased further by numerous repetitions of the same processes, the "bowl" ultimately becomes a sphere but is not completely closed on one side. Through this opening, commencing with the side opposite to it, the sphere turns itself inside out, so that in the end the flagella project outward as normally. At certain seasons of the year, sexual means are also employed for reproducing these spherical colonies (Figure 7–12).

Cellular Characteristics. In the introductory paragraph of this chapter subdivision, several cytological traits of the green protozoa have already been pointed

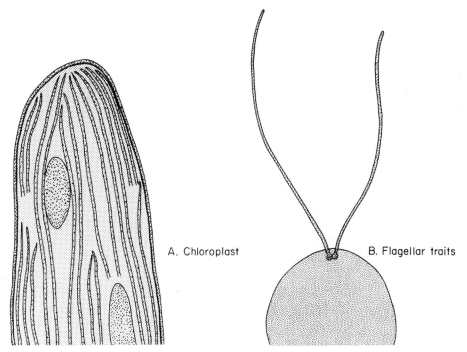

A. Chloroplast   B. Flagellar traits

Figure 7–13. Cellular characteristics of the green protozoa. A. Chloroplasts, when present, are composed of numerous fine lamellae, between which starch grains are frequently located. B. Flagella are typically present in pairs, both members being devoid of flimmer and directed forward. The very tips are usually simply rounded, not tapered as in the yellow flagellates (Figure 7–17).

out, such as their ability to form starch, the presence of a cellulose cell wall, and the peculiar set of pigments, including a predominance of the chlorophylls *a* and *b*, which provides the organisms with a green color. In addition to these properties, the nucleus is highly developed, with the endosome reduced to the state called a nucleolus, in which it disappears during mitosis. Centrioles are not conspicuous and in fact in some genera may be absent. As a whole, flagellar morphology is suggestive of kinship to the seed plants, for electronmicrographs show them to be similarly devoid of the flimmer mentioned under the euglenoids and to possess a simple rounded tip (Figure 7–13), quite as in the flagellated stages of mosses and ferns. Moreover the chloroplast's fine structure presents evidence of similar relationship, having an arrangement of plates comparable to that of the higher green plants.

Golden-yellow Protozoans

In much the same way as the above green protozoa show relationships with seed plants, the present ones bear many resemblances to such unmistakably algal forms as seaweeds. Among the representatives of this group are included both pigmented and unpigmented types. When pigments are present, the first similarity to the algae mentioned is shown, for in the two groups concerned, chlorophylls *a* and *c*, although present, are less abundant than certain yellow pigments, so that a golden-yellow color is often displayed. Moreover, the arrangement and structure of the flagella, to be described below, are features common to all, as the fine structure of the chloroplastids, the development of the centriole, and the presence of a nucleolus are also.

Flagellated Species. In this group, flagellated species are quite abundant as

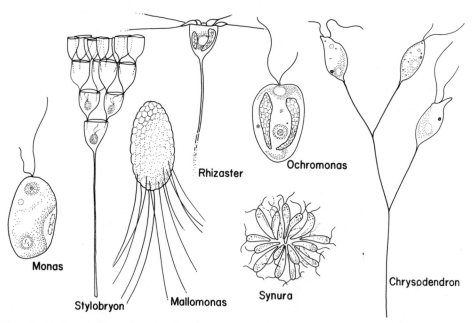

Figure 7–14. Some golden-yellow flagellated types. As in the green protozoa, both chlorophyll-bearing (*Ochromonas, Rhizaster, Mallomonas, Chrysodendron,* and *Synura*) and chlorophyll-lacking (*Monas,* and *Stylobryon*) types are found. Similarly, spherical floating colonies (*Synura*) are found, as well as sessile ones (*Stylobryon* and *Chrysodendron*).

well as diversified. Although a number of the pigmented varieties, including *Ochromonas* (Figure 7–14), are simply naked cells, many, like *Mallomonas,* have the body enclosed in an envelope composed of silicified scales; by means of recently developed techniques, examination of these scales shows them to be intricately sculptured (Figure 7–15). One of the unpigmented representatives, *Monas,* is quite like *Ochromonas* except for the lack of the chloroplast, while others, such as *Rhizaster,* form an open capsule about themselves and become attached to firm objects. Thus, although flagellated, these species are *sessile* (Figure 7–14).

Many *colonial types* are so similar to the foregoing examples that there is little point in attempting to discuss them in detail. *Chrysodendron,* for instance, is quite similar to *Ochromonas,* with the exception that several individuals are attached by slender stalks (Figure 7–14). On the other hand, *Synura* recalls the spherical colonies among the green flagellates, but its organization is distinct in lacking an enclosing capsule. Unpigmented forms also have colonies; representative among such aggregates are the neat inverted pyramids formed by species of *Stylobryon.*

Amoeboid Types. While *Chrysamoeba* usually travels about by means of slender pseudopods and thus appears typically amoeboid, at other times it acquires a flagellum and then assumes an appearance not unlike *Ochromonas* (Figure 7–16). When flagellated, its body becomes quite rounded in cross section,

Figure 7–15. Scales of Mallomonas. An electron microscopic study of a carbon replica of an intact *Mallomonas striata* var. *serrata.* The entire unicellular organism is covered with complex bristles and intricate scales. (Courtesy of Drs. Katharine Harris and D. E. Bradley, *Journ. Gen. Microbiol.,* Vol. 22, 1960.)

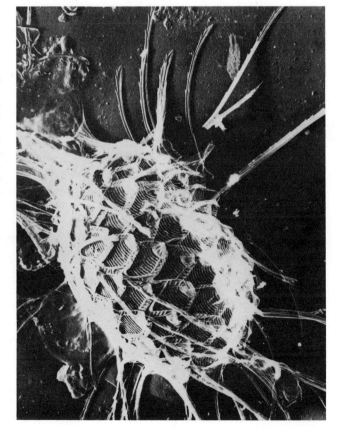

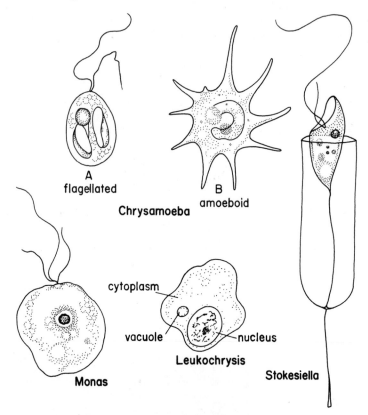

Figure 7–16. Representative golden-yellow amoeboid types.

although when amoeboid it is normally flattened. Under either condition a chloroplastid is a prominent feature that contains pigments identical in composition with those of the flagellated members of the taxon. But colorless amoebae too are known to belong to this group; among these are *Leukochrysis,* an active form, and *Stokesiella,* which makes cuplike envelopes attached to objects, closely similar to those of *Rhizaster.*

These organisms and their kin, as well as comparable but unrelated forms, point out a few of the difficulties that exist in classifying unicellular forms of life and the reasons behind present dissatisfaction with the classical scheme of dividing the protozoa into classes on the basis of flagellar, amoeboid, and other means of locomotion. Furthermore, distinctly algal

types are in existence that are provided with pigments, chloroplasts, and other structures similar to those of these protozoans; in addition others have flagellated or amoeboid stages during portions of their life cycles—thus the difficulties of separating plants and animals again may be perceived.

Cellular Traits. Although in two of the major approaches to the problem of classifying living things no close relationship is indicated between the golden-yellow organisms and any of those which follow, such is not the case in the single kingdom system. On the contrary, it considers the present and all subsequent species to comprise just one subkingdom, mainly on the basis of the cellular characteristics they share. Among these common features are included the pro-

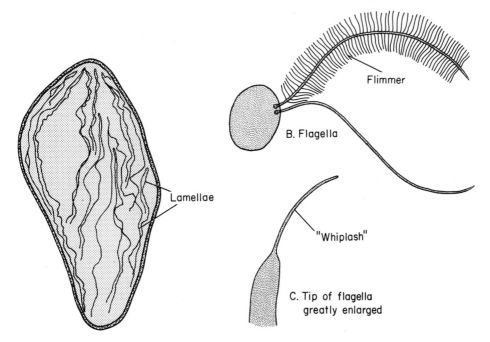

Figure 7–17. Characteristics of the golden-yellow organisms. A. In those members which bear chlorophyll, the chloroplastid is found to be of a peculiar form having thin interlocked lamellae. B. Generally, flagella, when present, are located toward one side. One of the pair projects forward and possesses flimmer, whereas the other trails and is naked. Both have tapered tips in the form of a "whiplash."

duction of fats and glycogen as the storage products of metabolism, the absence of a cellulose cell wall, a well-developed centriole, and a typical nucleolus. Moreover, in photosynthetic types the chloroplastid (Figure 7–17) has thin platelets that interconnect in a complex manner instead of lying parallel to one another; the flagella, too, often have a characteristic arrangement, for whereas in other groups usually all are situated at the cell's anterior end, here they are placed to one side. While both flagella, furthermore, are prolonged into a slender "whiplash" at their tips, only the posterior member of the pair possesses flimmer, the other one being bare.

Ciliated Forms

In lotic waters, whether fresh or marine, the members of this group are often very abundant; in these communities their role is either that of an herbivore or minute carnivore, for, always lacking chloroplastids, they cannot rank among the producers. Most commonly, these organisms are treated as a class *Ciliata* in the Protozoa, although sometimes they are ranked as a phylum under the name *Ciliophora*. Structurally, the ciliates possess unique features in the form of numerous short flagella known as *cilia* (Figure 7–18), excretory organelles called *contractile vacuoles,* and two unequal types of nuclei, based on relative size; a single large one and one-to-many small ones, called the *macronucleus* and *micronuclei,* respectively, are normally present. In fact, the presence of two different nuclear bodies is such an unusual trait that it alone is sufficient to identify the members of this group. By far the majority of species are solitary, and in the few colonial types, such as *Vorticella,* the

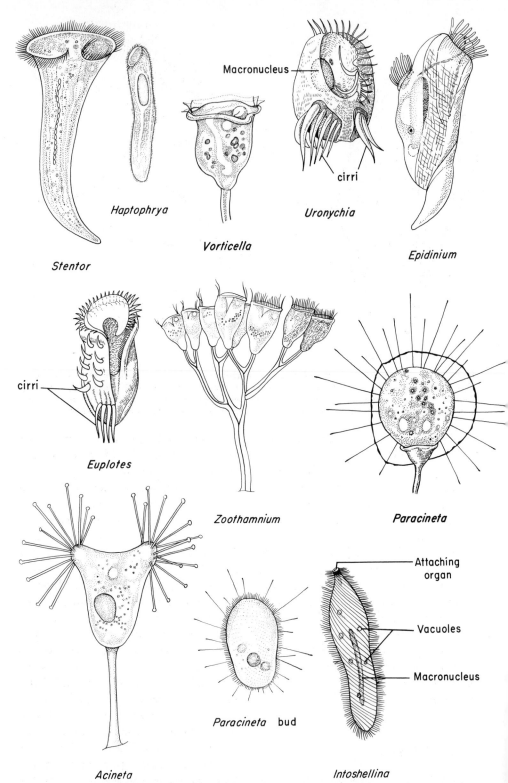

Figure 7–18. Some of the numerous types of ciliates. *Acineta* is one of the Suctoria, and the *Paracineta* in the figure is a ciliated bud of a related form.

organization is never complex. Among both solitary and colonial sorts three different methods of feeding are found, two of which are especially characteristic.

Habits. Most typically, the ciliates engulf their prey through an opening into the cell called the *cytostome* (meaning "cell mouth"), such as that possessed by *Paramecium* (Figure 7–19). The major portion of these forms is free-living, principally in fresh waters, although many others are confined to salt or brackish situations. Great diversity in shape is exhibited, ranging from slender and wormlike to spherical bodies, often with tail-like processes or with various devices, such as funnels, to assist in obtaining food. Frequently the cilia are highly modified for their locomotive functions. In *Euplotes,* for example, groups of these organelles on the posterior and lower surfaces are elongated and fused to form leglike apparati called *cirri* (sing., cirrus). By means of these and other structures the organisms move about with some rapidity, for all the ciliates are most active creatures, seldom still for a second. Only rarely are colonial types encountered. One is represented by *Zoothamnium* and relatives. In these examples the contractile fibers (myonemes) in the stalk are shared by all individuals, so that when one stalk contracts or expands the entire colony does so simultaneously. Not all species are free-living; many of the most complex are symbionts in the stomach of cattle and other ruminants.

A second means of obtaining nourishment, found in the class *Suctoria,* is possibly the most distinctive in the entire living world. Over the whole body or on particular regions are found elongated tubular projections, called *tentacles,* of two types. One is simply pointed at the free end and is used to pierce the body of the prey, whereas the other ends in a rounded knob and is used in sucking out the victim's protoplasmic contents. As adults, all are sessile and devoid of cilia (Figure 7–18); however, the young, produced by a process of budding, are entirely covered with such organelles and swim about freely. After a short period these motile immature individuals attach themselves to the substrate and ultimately assume the adult form.

Reproduction. Throughout the ciliated group the principal means of reproduction is by transverse fission. Accompanying such processes, the micronuclei divide by a highly developed type of mitosis, which includes a typically behaving nucleolus, whereas the macronucleus passes through mitotic stages not unlike those of the thecate amoeboids. Usually the micronucleus is considered in these organisms as chiefly involved in genetic activities, whereas the macronucleus appears solely concerned with the vegetative. In addition, a second propagative procedure, called *conjugation,* highly varied in details, frequently occurs. Under certain conditions two individuals of the same species approach each other and, on contact, form a *cytoplasmic bridge* following resorption of portions of the pellicle and cell membrane. In each member of the pair the micronuclei undergo meiotic division; on completion of these processes one of the resulting *pronuclei* is exchanged across the cytoplasmic bridge by each member of the pair. Once the exchange of nuclear material is consummated, the conjugating cells (*conjugants*) separate, soon dividing several times by fission (Figure 7–19). Under the electron microscope the cilia of a ciliate are shown to be interconnected in an intricate fashion (Figure 7–20); these interconnections are believed by many to serve in coordinating the beating of these organelles by the transmission of impulses. In electronmicrographs, too, it is observed that the cilia have the

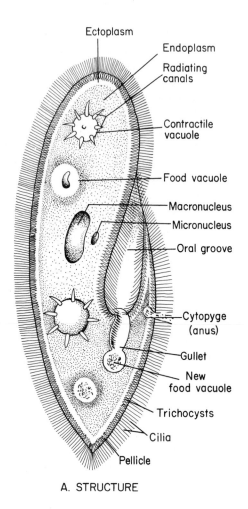

Ectoplasm

Endoplasm

Radiating canals

Contractile vacuole

Food vacuole

Macronucleus

Micronucleus

Oral groove

Cytopyge (anus)

Gullet

New food vacuole

Trichocysts

Cilia

Pellicle

A. STRUCTURE

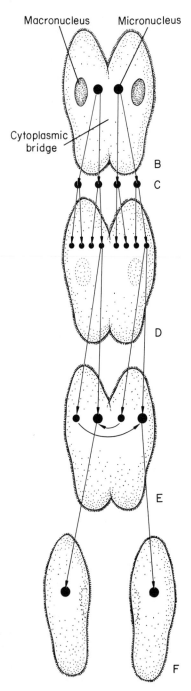

Macronucleus   Micronucleus

Cytoplasmic bridge

B

C

D

E

F

**Figure 7–19. *Paramecium*—structure and conjugation. *A.* **Structure of a typical *Paramecium*. *B–F.* Among the numerous species of this genus is found a type of reproduction called conjugation, each species possessing its own variation of the processes. Basically, the principal steps include union of the two individuals (conjugants), followed by a disappearance of the cell membrane along the area of contact so that the cytoplasm of the two is in contact (*B*). After this "cytoplasmic bridge" has been formed, the micronuclei divide twice (*C, D*), while the macronucleus disappears. Later, three of the micronuclei likewise disappear; the fourth one undergoes division in such a fashion that two unequal-sized daughters, called "pronuclei," are formed (*E*). The small, or wandering, pronucleus of each conjugant then travels across the cytoplasmic bridge, affording a mutual exchange of nuclear material; this act is followed by a separation of the pair (*F*). Each conjugant then undergoes fission, the number of divisions and other details depending on the species in question. In the end, one micronucleus develops into a macronucleus in each daughter cell.

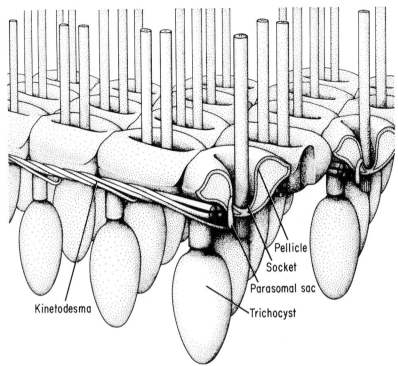

Figure 7–20. The structure of the ciliary system. In the composite diagram of the ciliary system in *Paramecium bursaria* are shown the kinetodesmata which interconnect the cilia and so appear to aid in coordinating their movements. Note the complexities of the pellicle folds and the fact that, in this species, the cilia are arranged in pairs. (Courtesy of Dr. John O. Corliss, *The Ciliated Protozoa,* Pergamon Press, 1961.)

same internal construction as the flagella of *Euglena* and of all other higher organisms, and the mitochondria are found to be identical in construction with those of the amoeboids.

The Sporozoa

In this taxon of unicellular forms some 3,000 known species are placed, all of which are parasites in metazoans and many of which have exceedingly complex life cycles. Here are included the smallest of the protozoans, for many rival the bacteria in body size. Although unicellular and devoid of means of locomotion during a large portion of their life history, multinucleated amoeboid stages (*plasmodia*) or multicellular types enclosed in

sheath (*palmella*) become important features prior to spore formation. However, certain phases of their cyclical changes possess pseudopods, and gamete-like forms with flagella are not uncommon.

The Gregarines. Without doubt the gregarines are the largest of the sporozoans, for some of these wormlike forms attain a length of more than half an inch. Most of the species live within organs of invertebrates outside the cells, i.e., *extracellularly*. Characteristically they are parasites of earthworms and insects but are found extensively also in starfish, snails, and clams. Frequently, the anterior end of the cell is provided with spines, hooks, and other means of adhering to the host (Figure 7–21). Asexual reproduction, of the type known as

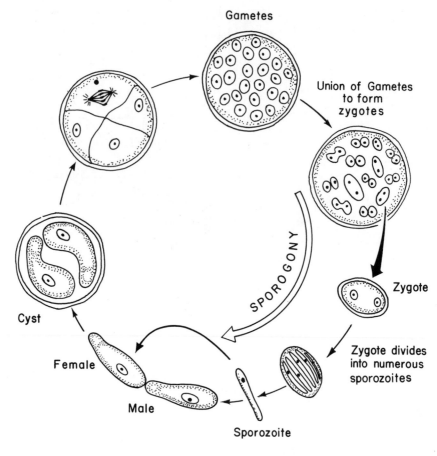

Gametes

Union of Gametes
to form
zygotes

SPOROGONY

Zygote

Zygote divides
into numerous
sporozoites

Cyst

Female

Male

Sporozoite

LIFE CYCLE OF A GREGARINE

Figure 7–21. The life cycle of a typical gregarine. The processes of spore production in the Sporozoa, called *sporogony,* is characterized by occurring within the confines of a cyst and by being preceded by union of gametes.

sporogony, is always preceded by a production and union of gametes. Before gametes are formed the male gregarine attaches himself to the posterior end of the female; then, still attached in chain fashion, the couple thickens and forms a spherical cyst (Figure 7–21). Inside the cyst, each undergoes multiple fission into numerous gametes according to their respective sexes. While sometimes the gametes are identical in form, both being simply small spheres, in other cases the sperm bears flagella and is otherwise dif-

ferentiated from the egg. After pairs have fused, the zygotes secrete a wall about themselves and divide into eight coccoid *sporozoites.* All these cellular divisions occur within the cyst formed by the original pairing male and female. As the large number of sporozoites growing within it causes an increase in diameter of severalfold, eventually its wall is ruptured and the contents freed to invade other hosts.

The Haemosporidians. The members of this order are far smaller and have much more complex life cycles than the sporozoans described above. Among them are included many pathogenic organisms, most of which are intracellular parasites in red blood corpuscles. To illustrate the processes, *Plasmodium,* with several species that are causative agents of malaria, may be used. In the section of the life history spent within vertebrate blood cells are included the reproductive processes known as *schizogony,* which primarily differ from sporogony in that no separate cyst is formed, the host's cells being employed for the purpose instead. In human malaria, the *sporozoites* are introduced through the skin with the bite of certain vector species of mosquitoes. After living in the liver for about 10 days, the sporozoans penetrate the red blood cells and grow into *amoeboids* intracellularly, gradually developing into a multinucleated plasmodium in the process. When the plasmodium has attained its full size and cell membranes have formed between nuclei, the resulting amoeboid types, called *merozoites,* are liberated

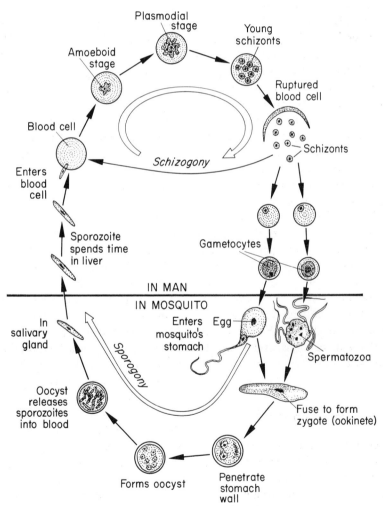

Figure 7–22. The life cycle of the malaria parasite. *Schizogony* differs from *sporogony* in being asexual and in occurring directly within the host's cells, not in a cyst.

through a rupture in the erythrocyte into the blood stream, ready to infect other blood cells. Inside other cells, these several processes which constitute schizogony are repeated over and over again indefinitely. Ultimately after many cycles have built up a heavy infection, some of the merozoites, instead of entering new cells, become converted into male and female *gametocytes*. These forms remain inactive until by chance they are taken up by the feeding activities of a mosquito and enter its digestive tract along with the ingested blood. Here in the stomach of this second host, the female gametocyte develops into an *egg,* while the male divides several times to produce four or eight *spermatozoa*. After one of these has united with the egg, the resulting zygote, called the *ookinete,* works its way by amoeboid movements between the cells of the stomach until it has nearly penetrated the entire thickness of the wall and lies beneath the outermost layer. In this position, growth and multiple mitosis occur, each resulting nucleus becoming developed into a *sporozoite,* until thousands fill the old ookinete, now referred to as the *oocyst*. The latter eventually bursts, and the released sporozoites migrate through the mosquito's body until they reach its salivary gland. After entering this organ, they are in position to be discharged into the next vertebrate host the mosquito feeds on (Figure 7–22), where the schizogonous cycles can be initiated once more.

Symbionts in Termites

In connection with symbiosis, earlier mention was made of the mutualistic flagellates that occupy the intestinal tract of termites and are so important to the latter's existence. Many kinds of these organisms occur in the multitude of termite species and in certain wood-eating cockroaches, all of which are typified by the presence of numerous flagella. The actual number of flagella begins with four. In one genus possessing relatively few organelles of this type, *Devescovina,* some of the complexity of cell structure characteristic of the group is shown unusually clearly (Figure 7–23). In a second genus, *Pyrsonympha,* the eight flagella embedded in spiral fashion on the pellicle keep the entire cell constantly undulating by their movements (Figure 7–23B). Other forms have literally thousands of these organelles arranged in rows or spirals around the organism. What the function of so many flagella can be has not even been guessed at, but all the protozoa with this abundance of such locomotive organelles are entirely confined to these wood-eating insects.

During growth, insects molt their body coverings, and in the process, part of the lining of the digestive tract is shed too; consequently the molting of the body covering in termites and roaches is accompanied by the loss of the symbionts. After each molt, the termites regain a population of the protozoans from other individuals, but the wood-consuming roaches become reinfected by swallowing the cysts that the flagellates form.

In addition to the extensive flagellation, these organisms show some other interesting cytological features during mitosis. As the student may have noted, in the cells of no preceding group has mention been made of those astral rays which are so characteristic of mitosis in the Metazoa. Here in these flagellates the rays do occur, but they are not quite in the same condition as in the typical animals. Instead of being the apparently stiff threads radiating outward from the centrioles found in the metazoans, in

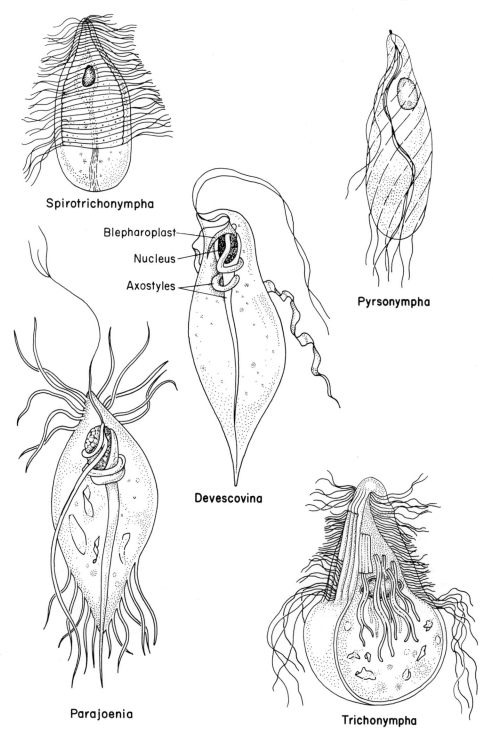

Spirotrichonympha

Pyrsonympha

Blepharoplast

Nucleus

Axostyles

Devescovina

Parajoenia

Trichonympha

Figure 7–23. Symbionts of termites.

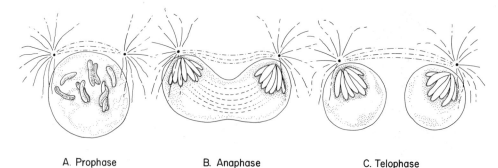

A. Prophase   B. Anaphase   C. Telophase

Figure 7–24. Mitosis in termite symbionts. Although present, astral rays are relatively poorly developed, being few in number and apparently soft as suggested by the frequent distortions that exist. (After Cleveland.)

these protozoans during the mitotic processes they seem soft and flexible, for they droop over the nucleus as it divides (Figure 7–24).

Questions for Review and Thought

1. Define the term *protozoa* in both a systematic and a nonsystematic sense.

2. In what way is *Euglena* and its relatives simpler than any other protozoan? In what ways do the dinoflagellates and other euglenoids resemble one another and in what do they differ?

3. In protozoology what is implied by the terms *pigmented* and *unpigmented*?

4. Define the following terms:

(a) cyst	(e) pseudopod	(i) swarmer
(b) flagellum	(f) plasmodium	(j) coenobium
(c) coccoid	(g) palmella	(k) cirrus
(d) bloom	(h) cilium	(l) amoeboid

5. Outline a possible evolutionary history of the development of sexual from an asexual mode of reproduction.

6. Compare the structure, both superficial and fine, of *Euglena, Chlamydomonas,* and *Ochromonas.*

7. Make a comparison of the types of colonies and of body form found among green and the golden-yellow protozoans.

8. State the chief characteristics of the ciliates, using *Paramecium* as the example. In what ways are suctorians distinct from other ciliates?

9. Outline the life cycle of *Plasmodium* and compare it with that of a gregarine.

10. Which of the protozoan groups do you think most complex, and why do you think so? Does an increase in cellular complexity necessarily result in an increase in complexity of performance? Cite examples to show the basis for your answer.

Supplementary References

Bonner, J. T. *Cellular Slime Molds.* Princeton, N. J., Princeton Univ. Press, 1959.

Corliss, J. O. *Ciliated Protozoa: Characterization, Classification, and Guide to Their Literature.* New York, Pergamon, 1961.

Fritsch, F. E. *The Structure and Reproduction of the Algae,* 2 vols. Cambridge, Cambridge Univ. Press, 1948.

Godjdics, M. *The Genus Euglena.* Madison, Wisc., Univ. Wisconsin Press, 1953.

Hall, R. P. *Protozoology.* Englewood Cliffs, N. J., Prentice-Hall, 1953.

Hegner, R. *Big Fleas Have Little Fleas.* Baltimore, Williams and Wilkins, 1938.

Hyman, Libbie H. *The Invertebrates,* Vol. I. New York, McGraw-Hill, 1940.

Kudo, R. R. *Protozoology,* 4th ed. Ithaca, N. Y., Comstock, 1960.

Pitelka, D. R. *Electron-microscopic Structure of Protozoa.* Oxford, Pergamon, 1963.

Satir, P. "Cilia." *Sci. Amer.,* February 1961.

Sleigh, M. A. *Biology of Cilia and Flagella.* New York, Pergamon, 1962.

Tartar, V. *Biology of Stentor.* New York, Pergamon, 1961.

The Sponges

For many years after the establishment of Linné's system of classification, the sponges' proper assignment was a subject of much debate, a situation that has now arisen again after an interruption of nearly a century. Some specialists today, as in years long past, claim that these organisms cannot be properly placed among the animals and, hence, must be classed as plants, whereas others still consider them to be metazoans. Many, following Thomas Huxley's example, take a middle position. This famous British biologist in 1875 pointed out that, if sponges really were animals, they display no close relationships to typical metazoans and accordingly he recommended that the phylum *Porifera,* to which these organisms belong, be removed to a subkingdom of their own, for which he suggested the name *Parazoa.* During recent years, this

treatment as a taxon removed from the true animals has gained wide acceptance, although often along different lines than that proposed by Huxley.

Here it is far from our intent to enter directly into the discussion, the facts outlined above being presented more to indicate the singularity of organization that exists in this taxon than to take a stand regarding its systematic relationships. The group is an interesting one and contains 5,000 known species, almost all of which are marine, with only a few simpler types occurring in fresh water. In the communities of the seas its members are of fundamental importance, especially in shallower areas where they grow in large numbers on the ocean floors, as all are strictly sessile except as larvae. Unfortunately their construction, in addition to including three highly diverse types, is so unique that to treat them in the comprehensive manner they deserve would require far more space than can be spared; consequently, only a superficial treatment can be accorded them here.

The Sponges Proper

General Morphology. So that the student may understand the nature of the poriferan structure and the problem it presents, a brief description of the principal features of the anatomy and histology are necessary. Essentially the body of a sponge is built like a vase, the walls of which are penetrated by many *canals* (Figure 8–1), opening externally and internally through *pores*. Frequently, the vase is distorted and infolded or highly modified by a colonial mode of living. In the simpler species, the body wall may be made of two layers of cells, between which is a layer of gelatinous material called *mesoglea*. Wandering about within the mesogleal matrix is a variable number of amoeboid cells, which serve in many capacities, such as storage and transport of foods, skeleton formation, and replacement of the other types of cells. The most distinctive constituent of the sponge wall is found in the lining of the canals. Here occur dense masses of minute *collar cells,* or *choanocytes,* each provided with a flaring collar of cytoplasm through the middle of which projects a single flagellum. By means of the beating movements of all these flagella, water is circulated through the canals. As the current passes over the choanocytes, fine organic particles occasionally adhere to the outer surface of the collars and are thence taken into the cytoplasm by a peculiar set of activities. These

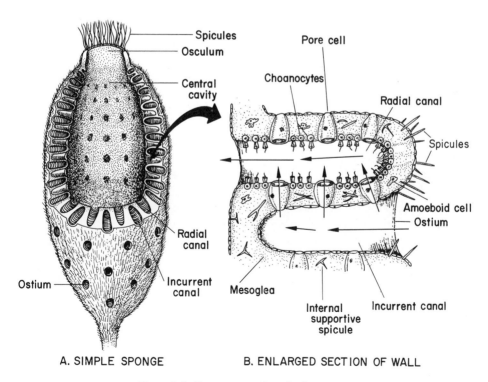

A. SIMPLE SPONGE   B. ENLARGED SECTION OF WALL

Figure 8–1. The structure of a simple sponge.

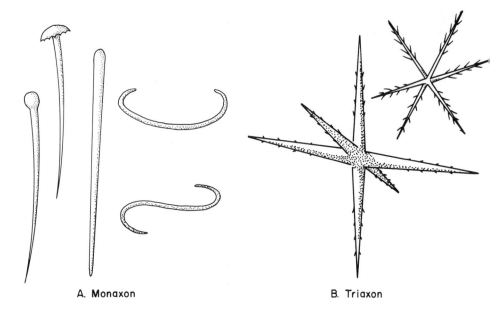

A. Monaxon   B. Triaxon

include both a retraction of the collar into the cell and a flowing of the collar's surface. Through the combined action of these two processes, any adhering particle is moved first upward into the open end of the collar and then downward toward the main body of the cell, movements that are accompanied by a shrinking of the collar. After the particle has entered the cell body, the collar re-expands and resumes its normal shape and size. Although the choanocytes digest a portion of the materials thus captured, a large percentage is conducted through the cells' length and passed to the amoeboid components in the mesoglea; these latter cells then digest the remainder and transport the products to areas in need of nourishment.

Skeletal Construction.   Among the most distinctive traits of the sponges is the peculiar structure of the skeleton, which consists either of elements called *spicules* or of fibers, both of which are produced by special amoeboid cells in the mesoglea. Fibers (Figure 8–2) are always made of *spongin,* a protein of the

fibrous class related to collagen (page 150), but spicules are of either calcium or silica compounds. In some sponges, such as the well-known bath sponges, only spongin is present, in others all skeletal elements are absent, but many types have either calcareous or siliceous spicules, often held together with spongin deposits. As spicules are highly varied in shape and are essential to the description and identification of the many species, a long list of names for the chief varieties has accumulated over the years. However, all these fall into five main categories, based principally on the number of axes present. For example, in the *monaxon* class, the spicules are built along a single axis and, as a result, are elongate and rodlike in shape, but can be curved as well as straight (Figures 8–2 and 8–3). In the *triaxon* type, three axes are present which cross one another at right angles, so that six-pointed figures result; such spicules are found only among those sponges whose skeletons are made of silica, known as the glass sponges. While the four-axis variety, or

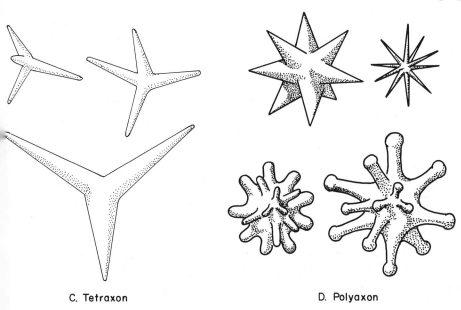

C. Tetraxon   D. Polyaxon

Figure 8–2. Types of spicules.

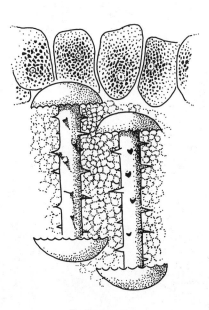

E. Desmas

tetraxons, exceed the triaxons in number of axes, they have fewer rays, for the axes, instead of crossing over one another, end upon contact (Figure 8–3). Among the many variations of this type that exist is one known as the triradiate, in which one ray is lost; it is of considerable importance as it is the most common spicule among calcareous sponges. In the fourth major category, the *polyaxons,* more than four axes are present, whereas *spheres,* which form the final grouping, are built of concentric layers around a central point.

In addition to the above, which are characteristic of all spicule-bearing sponges, another system of classification is found only among siliceous species, one based on comparative size. Two main categories are employed, *megascleres* and *microscleres* (Figure 8–3B). The first of these terms refers to the larger spicules that provide the major portion of the skeleton, and the second denotes the small elements that oc-

cur scattered throughout the mesoglea. In addition there is a special variant of megasclere which is also characteristic of these siliceous sponges, one referred to as a *desma.* This sort begins existence as an ordinary spicule but, with advancing maturity, it becomes heavily and irregularly coated with silica; the deposits form elaborate branches, tubercles, and other irregularities (Figure 8–3), so that all traces of the spicule's original form are concealed.

Cytological Characteristics. As almost no studies of the sponges have been made by electron microscopy, the fine structure of their organelles is virtually unknown. Scarcely more, in fact, has been done on the grosser aspects of the cytology, only a few investigations into the mitotic processes appearing to exist. However, what has been learned is very striking. In the collar cells, the flagellum is prolonged into the body of the cell to a prominent body called the *centroblepharoplast,* which organelle is a combination of the *centriole* with the *blepharoplast,* a body governing the movements of the flagellum. Below this a second organelle, the *parabasal body,* is attached by means of a threadlike projection to both the centroblepharoplast and the nucleus (Figure 8–4). During cell division, the parabasal

Figure 8–3. Skeletal elements of sponges. A. Spongin fibers from a commercial sponge. B. While all these spicules from *Spongilla* are of the monaxon type in construction, they are further classed on a size basis. The larger ones are referred to as *megascleres* and the smaller ones as *microscleres*. (Both photomicrographs courtesy of the General Biological Supply House, Inc., Chicago, Ill.)

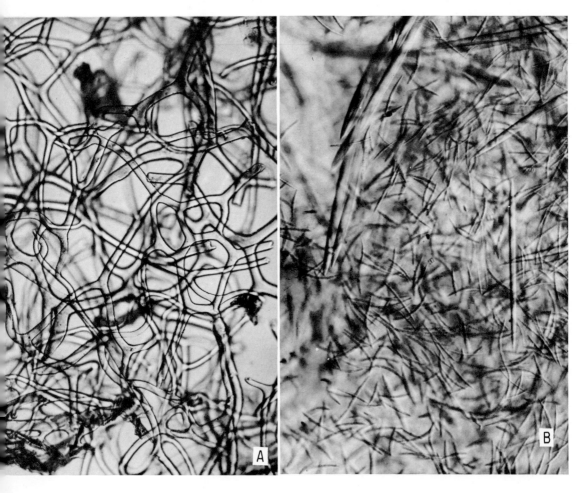

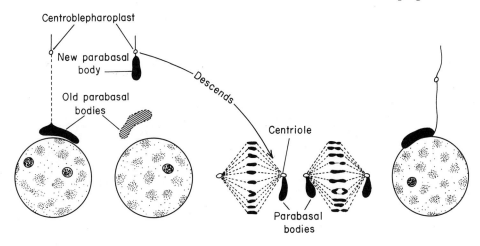

Centroblepharoplast

New parabasal body

Old parabasal bodies

Descends

Centriole

Parabasal bodies

A. Early prophase   B. Middle prophase   C. Metaphase   D. Anaphase   E. Late telophase

Figure 8–4. Cellular characteristics of sponges. Although all true animal cells during mitosis develop those astral rays described in Chapter 4, such is not the case with sponges. Moreover, an organelle called the *parabasal body* is prominently associated with the centrioles. Early in the processes the old parabasal body is absorbed; then, later, a new one is secreted by each centriole.

body descends to the nucleus and then is absorbed into the cytoplasm. As mitosis (Figure 8–4) continues, the centriole, after leaving the blepharoplast, descends to the nucleus and divides. While attached here to the spindle, both daughter centrioles secrete a new parabasal body, so that each cell has a full complement of cytological equipment on completion of mitosis and cytokinesis. When comparison is made of these processes with those characteristic of all the Metazoa (Chapter 4) one can readily understand why the sponges are frequently considered to be unrelated to the animals proper and are removed to a separate taxon.

Reproduction in Sponges

Asexual Reproduction. Particularly characteristic of fresh-water sponges, although the processes occur also in some marine species, is a type of asexual reproduction in which bodies called *gemmules*

are developed. While the gemmules may be looked upon as buds, they are formed in a peculiar manner, commencing with the amoeboid cells. Certain of the latter become filled with food materials consisting of either glycogen or lipids combined with proteins; toward these ends they are assisted by other amoeboid cells, referred to as "nurse cells" or *trophocytes,* which supply them with foodstuffs. During the course of time a whole group of the amoeboids thus attain an overfed condition, with stores of nutrients in their cytoplasm (Figure 8–5). Once the mass of these storage cells has reached suitable proportions, other amoeboid cells surround it and invest it with a coat of epidermis, which serves both as a temporary covering and as a gland. In its glandular functions the coat deposits an inner and outer layer over its own surface. While these two layers are being formed, skeleton-forming cells throughout the sponge secrete special two-headed spicules that are carried into the epidermal coat and deposited there between

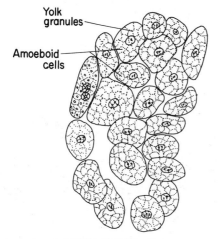

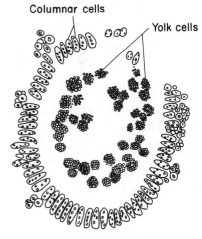

A. VERY YOUNG GEMMULE
(greatly enlarged)

B. SLIGHTLY OLDER

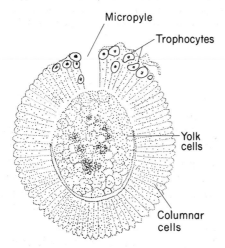

C. LATER STAGE

Figure 8–5. Steps in the formation of a gemmule. The characteristic asexually produced immature stage of sponges begins with a cluster of amoeboid cells which become overfed, assisted by nurse cells or *trophocytes*. When the cluster has attained a suitable size, other amoeboid cells surround it and form an epidermal layer. This epidermal layer secretes an inner and outer coat about itself and later receives special two-headed spicules from other parts of the sponge. In fall the gemmules are set free after the mature specimen in which they formed has perished.

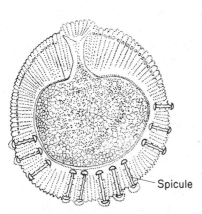

D. SPICULES FORMING

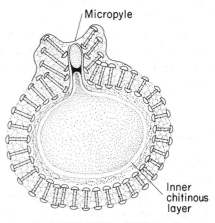

E. COMPLETED GEMMULE

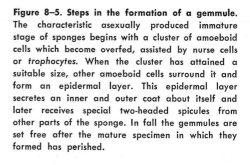

the inner and outer layers as the latter are secreted. When the whole is completed, the trophocytes and epidermal cells depart to other portions of the organism, leaving the gemmule as a small, hard ball containing a central store of foods and bearing a small pore or *micropyle* at one end. In the fall of the year, the old sponges die and disintegrate, releasing their contents of gemmules to survive the winter. The next spring after the temperature of the lake rises to around 20°C, the amoeboid cells in the gemmule's interior pass out into the water through the micropyle and, by undergoing multiple cell division and differentiation, form a small sponge, which soon grows to maturity.

Regeneration. Perhaps no set of facts is so enlightening as to the level of organization represented by the sponges than is that of the regenerative powers they possess. In the first place, a piece of almost any size at all from a live sponge is capable of growing into a mature organism if maintained under natural conditions, although months or even years may be required for completion of the processes. But still more illustrative of their remarkable abilities are the series of experiments performed first by H. V. Wilson in 1907 and since repeated many times. In the original study this American zoologist placed sponges on finely woven silk and, after closing the cloth to form a sort of sac, squeezed it to eject the sponges' cells forcibly through the meshes, separating the organism into individual or into small clumps of cells. These isolated parts were then kept under natural conditions for observation. First the amoeboid types moved about, and whenever individuals collided, they adhered to one another, slowly forming small masses in this fashion. Any choanocytes in the clumps, although still retaining their flagella, were devoid of collars.

Later after the masses had gained considerably in size, some of the amoeboid cells arranged themselves over the whole as an epidermis, while others developed into other cellular types characteristic of the sponges. The choanocytes grouped themselves into cavities and soon reformed their collars and otherwise assumed their normal activities; however, they consistently appeared unable to form any other kind of cell. Indeed, masses that contained no other cells save this collared variety were found incapable of reconstructing a complete organism, but those which included amoeboid varieties could do so.

Because of their relatively simple level of organization, much debate occasionally arises as to whether a single sponge represents an individual or a colony of cells. Those who consider them colonies in the ordinary sense of the word also cite the lack of a nervous system or of any integrating mechanism as evidence supporting their point of view. Other specialists in this field, however, consider each sponge (or portion of a complex group) that contains an osculum along with a canal system to constitute an individual, for such units alone are capable of functioning; only larger masses with several oscula and canal systems are treated as colonies.

Sexual Reproduction. Although all sponges possess sexual means of reproduction, the details are not so well known as are those of the asexual methods. Spermatozoa not unlike those of the typical animals are produced, but whether these arise from collar or amoeboid cells has not been established. On the other hand, the egg mother cells are known to be derived from the amoeboid type in the mesoglea. Each undergoes meiotic division during maturation but develops only into a single egg. When a sperm enters a sponge, it is picked up by either

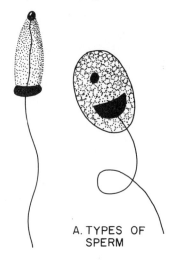

A. TYPES OF
SPERM

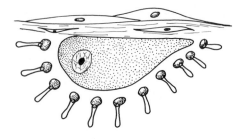

B. EGG IN SITU

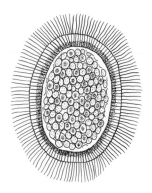

C. PARENCHYMULA
LARVA

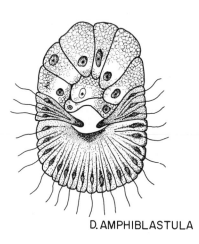

D. AMPHIBLASTULA

Figure 8–6. Sexual reproduction in sponges. Although the gametes do not differ markedly from those of the Metazoa, the processes of fertilization are quite distinct in that a third cell is involved. This third cell, either a choanocyte or an amoeboid cell depending on the species, carries the sperm to the egg and assists in the union of the two gametes. Several distinct types of larvae are found in the group.

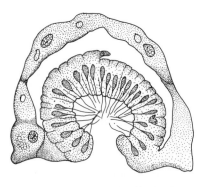

E. AMPHIBLASTULA
METAMORPHOSING

a choanocyte or an amoeboid cell and carried through the mesoglea to the egg for fertilization. The fertilized egg then undergoes development into a small ciliated larva, called an *amphiblastula* in the calcareous types, which works itself into the canal system to leave the parent by way of the osculum. After swimming about for a matter of hours, the larva attaches itself to some firm object or to the sea floor and soon develops into a small sponge (Figure 8–6).

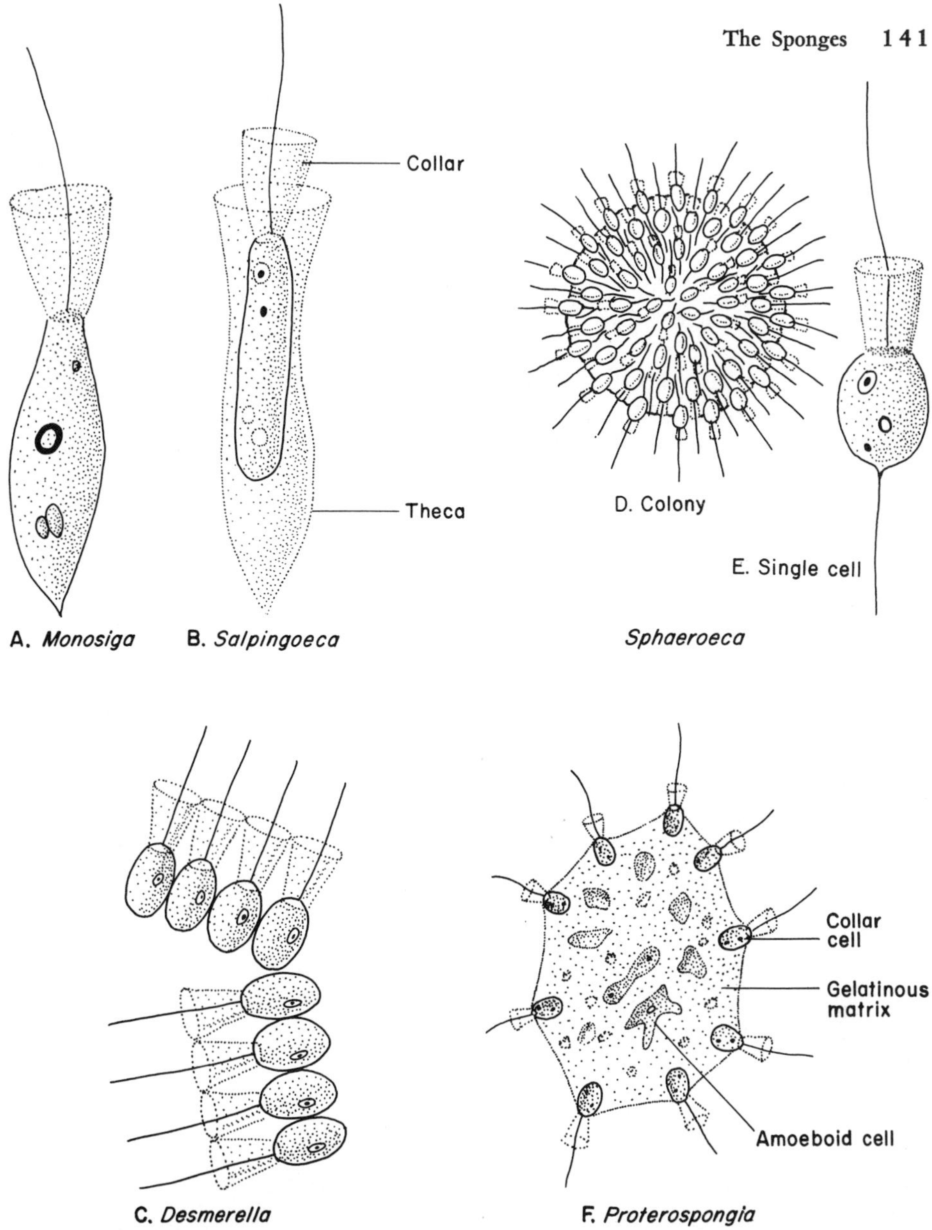

A. *Monosiga*   B. *Salpingoeca*   *Sphaeroeca*

C. *Desmerella*   F. *Proterospongia*

Figure 8–7. Some possible relatives of sponges. The collared flagellates (or *craspedomonads*) include naked and thecate forms, as well as simple colonies like *Proterospongia*. Because of the presence of the peculiar collars as well as other cellular traits found in the sponges, these organisms are often considered ancestral to the latter.

Possible Relatives of the Sponges

Among the numerous unicellular organisms claimed by both zoologists and botanists is a group of flagellates known as the *collared flagellates* or *craspedomonads*. As a whole these are devoid of chloroplastids and, except in a few cases, are provided with a cytoplasmic collar surrounding a single flagellum. Within the bodies of the cells, the same peculiar centroblepharoplasts and para-basal bodies are present, attached to the nucleus in the same fashion as in the cho-anocytes of the sponges. In recent years, too, an American protozoologist, J. B. Lackey, has described the method of feeding in one of these flagellates as being quite comparable to that found in the sponges proper. Hence it is becom-ing increasingly clear that the Porifera are probably derived from unicellular organisms of this sort.

Although many of the organisms are solitary, living in loose loricas attached to the floors of lakes and ponds by means of short stalks (Figure 8–7), a number of species form simple colonies of the pal-mella type. In this variety many cells are embedded in a gelatinous matrix, in the present instance with the collars and flagella projecting into the water. The matrix itself is not too different from the sponges' mesoglea, not only in its physical and chemical nature, but also in enclos-ing several amoeboid cells within its interior.

Questions for Review and Thought

1. Describe the major features of sponge anatomy. What cells are especially character-istic of the Porifera?

2. Define the term *spicule,* and describe the major types. Where and of what materials are spicules formed? For what purposes are they employed?

3. Describe the processes of mitosis in sponges, and state the chief resemblances to and differences from the same activities in metazoans.

4. In what ways are sponges animal-like and in what are they distinct from the true animals with which you are familiar?

5. Describe gemmule formation in the sponges. What type of larva is found in the calcareous sponges? List some other peculiarities of sexual reproduction in this group.

6. To what simpler group are the sponges possibly related? On what are these supposed relationships based?

7. Do you consider a sponge unit of an osculum with its associated canal system a colony of cells or a single sponge individual? On what bases are each of these points of view valid? Could the same lines of thought be equally applied to the human being for example? Why or why not?

Supplementary References

Borradaile, L. A., *et al. The Invertebrata,* 3rd ed. Cambridge, Cambridge Univ. Press, 1958.

Carter, G. S. *General Zoology of the Invertebrates,* 3rd ed. London, Sedgwick & Jackson, 1951.

Hyman, Libbie H. *The Invertebrates,* Vol. I. New York, McGraw-Hill, 1940.

Pennak, R. W. *Fresh-water Invertebrates of the United States.* New York, Ronald, 1953.

The
Diversity
of
Animal Life

I
N ADDITION TO PRESENTING an outline of basic biological concepts, the two preceding sections describe certain fundamental resemblances of animals to other
forms of life. Although still other likenesses in structure and processes are
shared by all living things, these can be pointed out to best advantage after the
student has acquired a deeper knowledge of the subject. For the present, in contrast,
our attention shall be occupied by the distinctions and innumerable variations that
exist among the numerous taxa of animals, a diversification that extends far beyond
the obvious differences of body form and structure. It will be seen to reach into the
organisms' respective abilities of carrying out the common bodily functions and of
reacting to changes within their environments. The various animals, in short, not
only appear different from one another on the surface but are in actuality distinct
both in organization and in the adaptations they have acquired for a particular mode
of life.

The universe is not to be narrowed down to the limits of the understanding, which has been man's practice up to now, but the understanding must be stretched and enlarged to take in the image of the universe as it is discovered.

FRANCIS BACON

The Organization of the Metazoa

T HE TRUE animals form a natural group, variously called the Metazoa, Eumetazoa, and Histozoa, which as a whole is characterized by the presence of muscular and nervous elements and, most frequently, by the possession of a digestive tract. However, among the simplest forms, all these traits are absent. Nevertheless, the group is sharply definable on a cellular basis, for every member shows the well-developed astral rays during mitosis described in detail earlier, a feature that distinguishes them from all other forms of life save the brown seaweeds. From the latter they at once differ in body organization, in lacking chloroplastids, and in having a posteriorly flagellated sperm. While the cytological evidence thus establishes the group soundly, usually the active movements and quick responses of its members suffice to identify them at once.

The Cellular Organization of True Animals

Although the unicellular forms of life described in the preceding pages often possess amazing powers of survival and self-reproduction, they are of necessity restricted both in size and complexity. For example, they can never develop specialized parts for effectively engaging in such activities as flying, excavating holes in the earth, or lifting objects. Just as long as an organism remains unicellular or practically so, it must stay simple functionally as well as structurally. Only after organisms have acquired a body of many cells are they able to develop, by evolutionary means, groups of cells highly adapted for one particular purpose. As an increasing number of uniquely modified cellular masses are attained by comparable methods, their possessor becomes correspondingly diversified in function and is enabled to engage in many activities which previously had been impossible. One natural assemblage of specialized organisms that has come into existence by such processes is the Metazoa or true animals, the representatives of which form the topic of the present and subsequent portions of this book. Among the members, as the student probably already knows from his earlier training, there exists a high degree of cellular organization, expressed biologically in a whole hierarchy of terms. First the cells are arranged into tissues, the latter into organs, and these in turn are grouped into the systems which together constitute the whole organism.

Tissues

The term *tissue* may be defined as a group of cells, usually of similar form but sometimes of several types, working together along with their products to serve one or more specific functions. Since the number of metazoan groups is a large one and each possesses tissues or

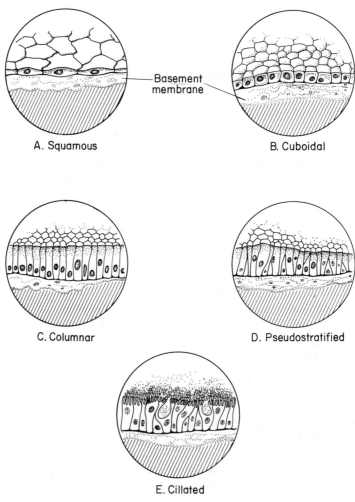

A. Squamous

B. Cuboidal

C. Columnar

D. Pseudostratified

E. Cillated

Figure 9–1. Types of simple epithelial tissue.

a tissue structure peculiar to itself, the discussion here must be confined to those found in vertebrates. Later, as the various types of animals are described, comparison, when pertinent, may be made against the examples presented here. Although there are extant several logical schemes of classification of the vertebrate tissues, the one apparently in most widespread use arranges them in six categories: epithelial, connective, vascular, contractile, nervous, and reproductive.

Epithelial Tissues. An *epithelial* tissue, often called simply an *epithelium,* covers surfaces, both external and internal. As would be expected from their position, tissues of this type serve a protective function. Furthermore, they are concerned with absorption and secretion; hence the secretory parts of complex glands and the whole of simple ones are composed of epithelium. A distinctive feature of tissues of this sort is that the cells lie close to one another; intracellular fluids and cellular products in the form of a matrix are almost completely absent. In addition, they almost always lie upon a very thin sheet of gelatinous material, called the *basement membrane,* whereas the other surface is, of course, free. Blood vessels are rarely present; metabolic needs and wastes enter or leave by diffusion between the cells. In spite of this lack, epithelia have a large capacity for regenerating themselves and for repair following an injury. Since they cover inner surfaces of such diverse structures as the digestive organs, the urinary bladder, the lungs, and the eyes, among many others, the conditions under which they function are highly varied, and, accordingly, their morphology differs from place to place. Hence many varieties are recognized (Figures 9–1 and 9–2).

Connective Tissues. As the name implies, tissues of this sort serve in the capacity of joining one part to another;

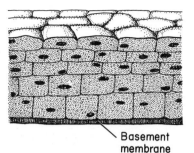

A. STRATIFIED SQUAMOUS

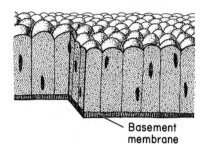

B. STRATIFIED COLUMNAR

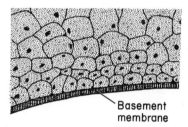

C. TRANSITIONAL (Relaxed)

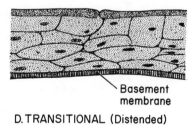

D. TRANSITIONAL (Distended)

Figure 9–2. Stratified and transitional epithelia.

moreover, they often function in support of various structures and in the formation of an unyielding framework to

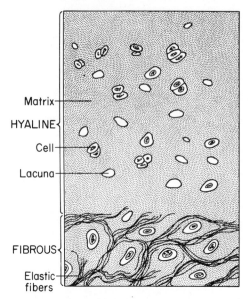

Matrix

HYALINE

Cell

Lacuna

FIBROUS

Elastic
fibers

Figure 9–3. Cartilage. Two main varieties of cartilage are recognized, hyaline and fibrous, which differ largely in the absence or presence of fibers in the matrix. The latter is the term applied to the substance in which the cells are embedded.

is tough or sometimes hard, as in bone; it is secreted by the cells and does the actual connective or supportive work. As in epithelia, this tissue is almost universally present throughout the body and is exposed therefore to many diverse conditions. Consequently, it, too, has developed many variants to meet the local requirements. Three major types are recognized. *Cartilage* (Figure 9–3) is the heavy tough material such as that which constitutes the nose and ear, the disks between the vertebrae, and the tubes leading into the lungs—namely the larynx, trachea, and bronchi. It also occurs where two bones join—for example, at the connection of the arm to the shoulder. The second variety, *bone* (Figure 9–4), is familiar to everyone and needs no description, whereas the third, *connective tissue proper* (Figure 9–5), is known in the form of tendons and ligaments. In addition, connective tissue forms coatings around every muscle, blood vessel, and nerve; it serves as filling in otherwise unoccupied spaces and composes the marrow of bones.

which the other body parts are attached. In their morphology they are diametrically opposite to epithelial tissues, for in the present type more intracellular material than cellular is present. This material, called the *matrix* (Figure 9–3),

In connective tissue proper three types

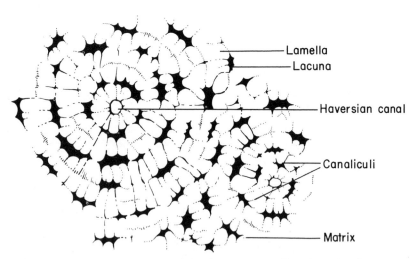

Lamella
Lacuna

Haversian canal

Canaliculi

Matrix

Figure 9–4. Diagram of bone structure. Bone is laid down in the form of circular sheets, or lamellae, surrounding a central canal. The lacunae are pockets in which the bone cells are located.

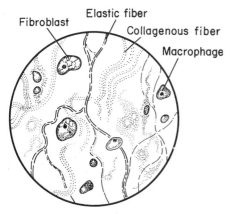

Fibroblast   Elastic fiber
              Collagenous fiber
                  Macrophage

A. LOOSE CONNECTIVE TISSUE

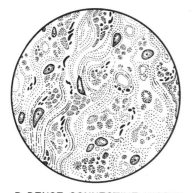

B. DENSE CONNECTIVE TISSUE

Figure 9–5. Some types of connective tissue.

what resemble macrophages in their granular cytoplasm but differ by lacking lobes. They serve in the secretion of heparin, a substance that prevents blood from coagulating.

Several of the less abundant tissues of the body are also classed as connective tissues on the basis of their structure. Fatty deposits are usually considered properly grouped here under the term *adipose tissue,* and *pigment cells* are highly specialized examples.

Vascular Tissue. This tissue is confined entirely to the blood stream, so that a full discussion of its constituents and physiology is more appropriate in a later chapter; however, a knowledge of some of its fundamentals is essential to the student at this time.

Vascular tissue consists of a fluid matrix, the *plasma,* and a largely cellular portion referred to as the *formed elements.* Plasma is composed of water in which globulins and other proteins, gases, inorganic salts, and innumerable other chemical components are dissolved. It constitutes about 55 per cent of the whole.

of cells are found (Figure 9–6), the *fibroblast* being the chief sort, since it performs the work of secreting the fibers of the tissue. The two remaining types, macrophages and mast cells, have no direct function regarding the connective tissues in which they occur and which they partially characterize. *Macrophages* (called *histocytes* by some writers) are large, bluntly lobed cells whose cytoplasm is densely packed with dark-staining granules. Under ordinary conditions they seem to carry out no special function; however, when infection or inflammation develops, they move about actively, engulfing foreign bodies. Only recently has the function of the third kind of cell been established. These *mast cells* some-

Elastic fiber   Mast cell   Matrix

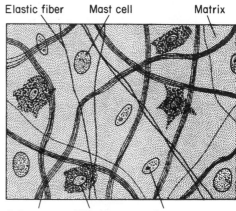

Collagenous Fibroblast   Histocyte
fibers

Figure 9–6. Cells and fibers of connective tissue. Most of the various kinds of cells and two of the three varieties of fibers that comprise the several types of connective tissue are shown in this diagram.

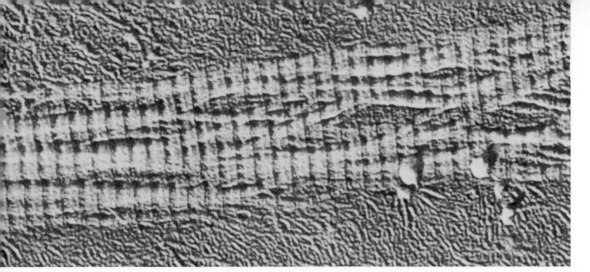

Figure 9–7. An electronmicrograph of a collagen fiber. This fibril from a fish was swollen in dilute acetic acid before being examined under the electron microscope. Magnified 30,000×. Collagen is the chief constituent of the collagenous fibers shown in Figure 9–6. (Courtesy of Dr. Jerome Gross.)

Among the components of the formed elements which compose the remainder are the red blood cells (*erythrocytes*), white blood cells (*leucocytes*), and the *blood platelets* (Figure 9–8). The *platelets* are in reality mere cellular fragments,

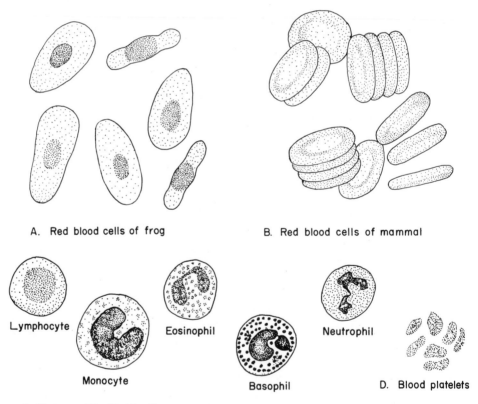

A. Red blood cells of frog

B. Red blood cells of mammal

Lymphocyte

Eosinophil

Neutrophil

Monocyte

Basophil

D. Blood platelets

C. Various white blood cells

Figure 9–8. The major varieties of formed elements found in the blood. Blood platelets are fragments of cytoplasm and, hence, all formed elements are not cells in the strict sense of the term.

representing the remnants of certain cells placed into the blood stream to serve a special function in clot formation.

Nervous Tissue. Paralleling the case of blood, *nervous tissue,* although spread throughout the body, is everywhere a continuous unit of a single system; hence it too is discussed in greater detail in a more appropriate chapter. Its functions are those of conducting impulses.

The conductive cell, the *neuron,* is admirably adapted in form for this function, consisting as it does of a cell body from which radiate long telephone-wire-like projections (Figure 9–9). Sometimes these processes may be extremely elon-

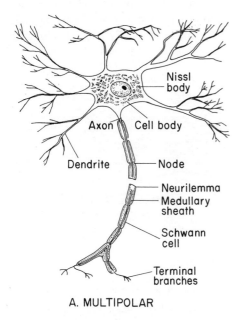

A. MULTIPOLAR

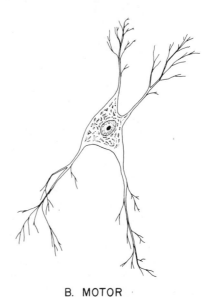

B. MOTOR

Figure 9–9. The principal types of cells found in vertebrate nervous tissue. Neurons are distinguished from neuroglia structurally by the presence of Nissl bodies in the former.

C. PYRAMIDAL

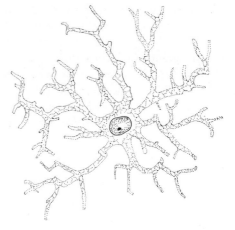

D. NEUROGLIA CELL

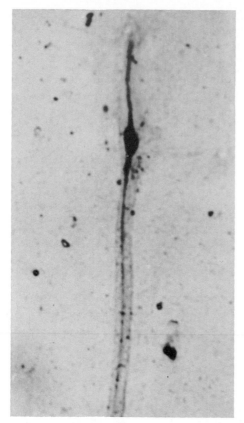

Figure 9–10. A neuron from a sense organ of a fly larva. This bipolar neuron from an arthropod differs little in organization from those of vertebrates. (Courtesy of Dr. M. P. Osborne, *Quart. J. Micr. Sci.,* 104:227–241, 1963.)

it is nearly entirely absent, the tissue appears gray. The neuroglia cells are found chiefly in the brain and spinal cord. Although they resemble the true nerve cells in form, especially in possessing long radiating processes, they differ in lacking the Nissl bodies.

Muscle Tissue. In some respects this tissue resembles the epithelial type, for it too occurs in many places in the body and is made of closely packed cells with

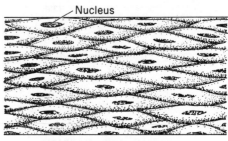

A. SMOOTH MUSCLE

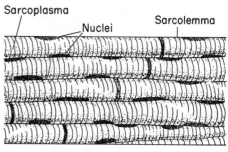

B. SKELETAL MUSCLE

gated; those in the hind leg of a giraffe or elephant attain a length of more than 6 feet. Especially in the cell body and certain of the processes, the cytoplasm contains granules of RNA known as the *Nissl bodies,* the function of which is unknown. Two other types of cells are found in this tissue, both of which the *Schwann* and the *neuroglia,* are supportive in function. Moreover, the Schwann cells provide a protective coat, the *neurilemma,* over the long projections of the neuron and a semifluid layer called the *myelin.* When present in sufficient quantity, myelin imparts a white appearance to the nervous tissue; when

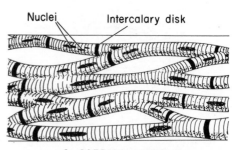

C. CARDIAC MUSCLE

Figure 9–11. Vertebrate muscle tissue.

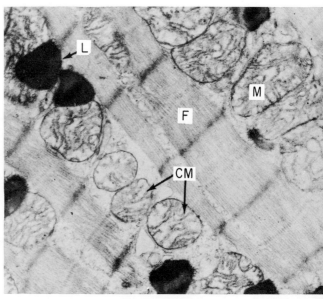

Figure 9–12. Electronmicrograph of cardiac muscle. The striations on the muscle fibers (F) from a ground squirrel heart are quite different from those shown in Figure 13–9 of skeletal muscle. Between fibers mitochondria, crowded closely together, are shown both in longitudinal (M) and in transverse (CM) section, while large granules (L) are irregularly scattered through the whole. Magnified 20,000×. (Courtesy of Dr. James R. Moreland, *Anat. Record*, 142:155, Fig. 3, 1962.)

little tissue fluid. Unlike the epithelial, however, muscle tissue has but a single function—namely, that of contracting. Three types can be distinguished histologically: smooth, skeletal, and cardiac (Figure 9–11). Not only are they distinct in appearance, but they differ in action as well. Both *skeletal,* found in the familiar muscles of the body, and *cardiac,* which composes much of the heart (Figure 9–12), are capable of contracting quickly, whereas the visceral, or *smooth* (e.g., that of the digestive tract), is relatively slow. On the other hand, the smooth muscles are capable of remaining completely contracted indefinitely, but the other two soon become fatigued and require relaxation.

Reproductive Tissue. In *reproductive* tissue are grouped the sperm and eggs and the cells which produce these gametes, along with other closely associated types. As a few details differ between the two sexes, it is advantageous to study the male and female tissues separately.

The sperm-producing, or *spermatogenic,* tissue forms a thick lining within the tubules of the testes and consists of

two principal types of cells. The first, called the *Sertoli cells,* are relatively few in number (Figure 9–13), are quite large

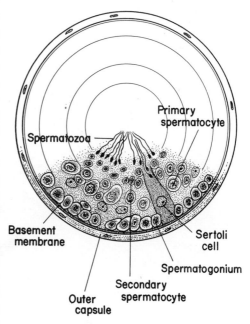

Figure 9–13. Male reproductive tissue. Frequently in vertebrates the earliest stages in sperm formation (spermatogonia) are found toward the periphery of the tubules, while the successively later stages (primary and secondary spermatocytes and spermatozoa) develop more and more centrally.

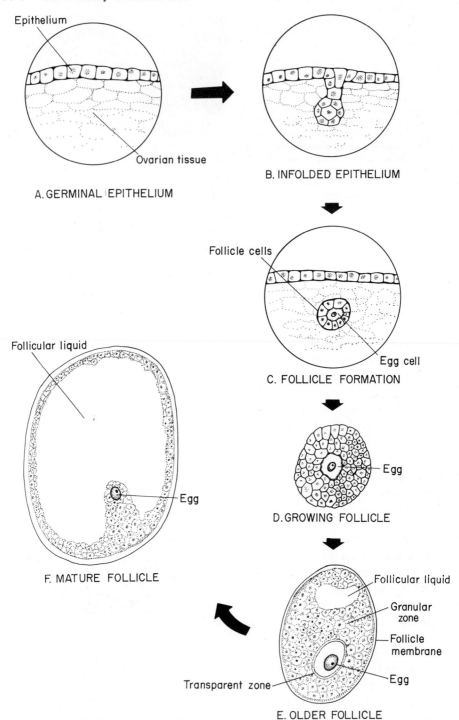

Epithelium

Ovarian tissue

A. GERMINAL EPITHELIUM

B. INFOLDED EPITHELIUM

Follicle cells

Egg cell

C. FOLLICLE FORMATION

Follicular liquid

Egg

F. MATURE FOLLICLE

Egg

D. GROWING FOLLICLE

Follicular liquid

Granular zone

Follicle membrane

Transparent zone

Egg

E. OLDER FOLLICLE

Figure 9–14. Development of the egg in mammals. In the follicles, budded off the epithelium during prenatal life (A, B), one cell develops into an egg (C) while the rest increase in number (D). While the cavity of the follicle becomes quite swollen with follicular fluid (E, F), the egg undergoes meiotic division preparatory for fertilization.

and irregular in shape, and appear to support and nourish the second type, the actual *sperm primordia,* which in mature vertebrates consist of cells in various stages of sperm production. Around the periphery of the tubules are the undifferentiated cells, the spermatogonia, which reproduce themselves throughout the life of the individual by ordinary mitosis. As meiosis and sperm production commence, the cells move inward so that the actual sperm are produced at the very center of the tubules. The sperm is derived from a spermatogonial cell which first undergoes a growth process, followed by two divisions, one of which is reductional, and finally by the formation of a tail and loss of cytoplasm.

In the female the egg-producing layer, known as the *germinal layer,* coats the outer surface of the ovary, but this tissue does not produce eggs directly. Instead, it first forms buds that develop into minute sacs, called *follicles,* in each of which a single egg matures (Figure 9–14). The follicular cells are thought by many to correspond to the Sertoli cells of the testes, for they seem similarly to provide support and nourishment to the maturing gamete. Within the follicle each original egg cell undergoes two divisions, in which the chromosome number is reduced, as described earlier. But here cytokinesis is grossly unequal; as a result three minute cells, called *polar bodies,* and only one mature egg, or *ovum,* are formed. The polar bodies serve no known function and soon disappear, whereas the egg cell increases greatly in size, until its maturity has been attained, by additions to its cytoplasm.

ORGANS AND SYSTEMS

OF ANIMALS

In animals the various types of tissue described above are combined structurally into *organs,* which, through the functional cooperation of the tissues, are able to perform particular tasks. Usually organs are joined into series to form a *system* that carries out one of the major activities of the body. In turn, the several systems together comprise the individual living creature, the *organism.* Among animals, the most frequently encountered systems are the following: (1) the *digestive,* concerned with the ingestion, digestion, and absorption of foods; (2) the *skeletal,* which provides a firm supportive structure; (3) the *muscular,* involved in movement and locomotion; (4) the *integumentary,* whose function is protection; (5) the *nervous,* concerned with detection of environmental changes and the coordination of the body parts; (6) the *reproductive,* which functions to perpetuate the species; (7) the *excretory,* whose duty is to eliminate excess water and other waste products of metabolism from the organism; (8) the *endocrine,* which assists in regulating the bodily processes by chemical means; (9) the *respiratory,* which provides the organisms with oxygen and eliminates carbon dioxide; and (10) the *vascular,* involved in mechanically carrying the diverse requirements of the body from one part to another. Various combinations of the foregoing and a few additional ones will be found as the several groups of animals are described and discussed.

The Basis of Metazoan Classification

Among existing true animals, more than one million species have been described. While these are placed in as few as 15 or as many as 30 phyla in accordance with the views of the particular zoologist, the vast majority of forms regardless of the scheme employed are concentrated in less than a dozen major groups. Consequently these few of greatest biological importance shall alone receive attention here.

The grouping of animals into the various phyla is never based on a single characteristic but always on combinations of traits. Ordinarily, the relationships of these organisms at the level of the phylum is such that only by considering all their traits can the real kinships be determined; even then there is much difference of opinion. In the main, four general aspects of structure are considered—namely, type of symmetry, number of germ layers, type of body cavity, and the presence or absence of segmentation. Other characters, such as the structure of the various body organs, along with unique features, also are extensively used, but these require no preliminary discussion.

Type of Symmetry. The over-all plan of organization, or *symmetry,* of an animal is one of the first morphological aspects taken into consideration. When no particular type of plan is apparent, the body is said to be *asymmetrical;* when one is present, the test of its type is determined by making sections, usually imaginary ones, through the organism. If limitless sections can be made through the center, as long as they are vertical to a transverse plane, as in a circle, the animal shows *radial* symmetry (Figure 9–15); since a jellyfish is built essentially as a circle, it illustrates this type. In almost all the Metazoa, however, only a single plane drawn through the center results in mirror-image halves. Since this sole section is longitudinal and vertical, it divides the animal into its two sides; accordingly, it is said to possess *bilateral* symmetry (Figure 9–15).

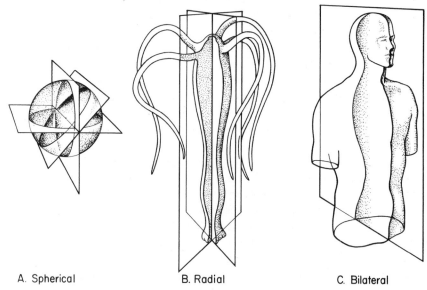

A. Spherical   B. Radial   C. Bilateral

Figure 9–15. Types of symmetry. The test of symmetry in an object lies in its ability to form identical halves when a plane is passed through its central point or line. A. If an indefinite number of planes can cut it into identical halves, the organism possesses spherical symmetry. B. Radial symmetry is similar to spherical except that identical portions can be formed only by planes passing through a central line, not just through a central point. C. Only a single plane can form identical (mirror image) halves in bilaterally symmetrical animals.

In radially symmetrical animals the portion bearing the mouth is the *oral* surface, whereas the opposite surface or end is the *aboral;* no sharply defined sides are present (Figure 9–15). Only in bilateral symmetry are definite *anterior* (front) and *posterior* (hind) ends, right and left *sides,* and *dorsal* (back) and *ventral* (belly) regions present. Three types of *sections* important in zoology can be made through bilaterally symmetrical animals. First, the longitudinal plane that divides the body into its right and left halves is the *sagittal.* The second, or *frontal,* similarly runs the length of the body; it, however, is vertical to the sagittal and separates the dorsal and ventral halves. Finally, any section across the body is *transverse* if it is at right angles to the sagittal and frontal; any number of transverse sections can be made, but only one sagittal and one frontal.

Germ Layers. When an animal is developing from the zygote, the embryo usually passes in succession through a single-layered, a two-layered, and a three-layered stage. The outermost of these layers, the ectoderm, is followed in sequence by the mesoderm and endoderm. From these three *germ layers* all tissues and organs of the adult develop, as we shall see when the science of embryology is discussed. However, in the jellyfishes and their allies only two layers, considered as the ectoderm and endoderm, are formed.

Body Cavity. When the body of a complex animal such as a chicken, frog, or deer is opened, it is found that the body wall surrounds a cavity in which the digestive tract and other vital organs lie. Such a *body cavity* may be of different types in the several phyla or may even be absent entirely in some simpler groups. When present, the cavity may be lined with a layer of tissue, as in the frog and chicken and in mammals; all lined body cavities are designated as *coeloms.* Unlined ones occur in a few groups and are called *pseudocoels,* or false body cavities. Occasionally, the *haemocoel,* a special sort of body cavity which is really an intimate part of the circulatory system, serves in the conduction of blood, as in the insects and their relatives.

Segmentation. A characteristic morphological feature of several groups of higher animals is the fact that the body is comprised of numerous repetitions of a single basic unit, with little or no modification from area to area. Although the earthworm is a good example of such segmentation, so are our own bodies in great part; we need only think of the backbone and the set of ribs which makes up the chest to understand the principle of repetitiousness that is involved in a segmented body. As the members of only a few phyla possess this trait, it has much value in classification and sometimes in indicating possible relationships.

Questions for Review and Thought

1. Define the terms *cell, tissue, organ, system,* and *organism.*

2. What are the functions of epithelial tissues, and how are they adapted for carrying them out? List the various types and state where each is found.

3. Examine each of the following statements and select from them those that are incorrect in any way, giving the reason for your selection in each case.

(a) A tissue consists of an aggregate of cells of similar structure performing like functions.

(b) Epithelial cells always cover surfaces.
(c) The cells of connective tissues have a single function—namely, that of secreting a matrix which provides support.
(d) On a morphological basis, the blood might be considered a type of connective tissue.
(e) The cells that compose the whole of nervous tissue, that is the neurons, are involved solely in the conduction of impulses.
(f) Of all the animal tissues the various types of muscular tissue come the closest to consisting of only one kind of cell.

4. In answering the following questions, any given system may be listed any number of times.

(a) Which systems are directly concerned with chemical functions?
(b) Which engage chiefly in mechanical activities?
(c) Which ones are involved directly in secreting?
(d) Which are concerned with a regulatory or coordinative function?
(e) Which ones supply the chemical requirements of the body?

Supplementary References

Arey, L. B. *Human Histology,* 2nd ed. Philadelphia, Saunders, 1963.

Bloom, W., and D. Fawcett, *Textbook of Histology,* 8th ed. Philadelphia, Saunders, 1962.

Copenhaver, W. M., and D. D. Johnson. *Bailey's Textbook of Histology,* 14th ed. Baltimore, Williams & Wilkins, 1958.

Finerty, J. C., and E. B. Cowdry. *Textbook of Histology.* Philadelphia, Lea & Febiger, 1960.

Gillison, M. *A Histology of the Body Tissues,* 2nd ed. Baltimore, Williams & Wilkins, 1962.

Gross, J. "Collagen." *Sci. Amer.,* May 1961.

Ham, A. W., and T. S. Leeson. *Histology,* 4th ed. Philadelphia, Lippincott, 1961.

Hoskins, M. M. *Bevelander's Outline of Histology,* 5th ed. St. Louis, Mosby, 1963.

Hydén, H. "Satellite Cells in the Nervous System." *Sci. Amer.,* December 1961.

The Simpler Metazoans

NOT ALL the representative types among the true Metazoa display every major feature described as characteristic of the group in the preceding chapter; some indeed possess no true tissues of any sort, let alone organs or systems. This fact is often the source of confusion to beginning students and, quite as frequently, the wellhead of much debate among zoologists. So prone are we to think in terms of our own bodily organization and of that shown by the familiar and larger animals around us that at times we experience difficulty in relating simpler forms of life to the obviously complex ones. Yet even the most complicated species have had simpler beginnings. Through the whole account of the true animals, briefly though it is presented here, a threadwork of increasing complexity can be traced as organs and systems are gradually developed and then perfected in each successively more advanced phylum.

The Simplest Metazoa

Nor should it be supposed that the simpler animals are of less intricacy solely in regards to their structure; their physiology too is equally primitive. Processes for which we and other higher forms possess special systems or at least organs are, at primitive levels, performed by tissues or, at more advanced states, by organs or systems which more typically are occupied solely in quite unrelated activities. For example, the lining of the digestive cavity in the jellyfish aids in contraction of the body and conduction of nervous impulses, to mention only a few of its functions. The specialization of parts in matters of both morphology and functioning, then, is the target toward which the whole of metazoan history appears to be aimed.

The Mesozoa

Inhabiting the seas is a small group of minute animals, endoparasites of various marine invertebrates, which would be of no biological significance whatever were it not for their extreme simplicity. Indeed, they are so simple that they would be difficult to establish as true metazoans were it not for the fact that their cells show astral rays during mitosis. Two sharply differentiated adult stages, one reproducing sexually, the other asexually, alternate during their life cycle, a feature more typical of plants than of animals. Although the details vary from one order to another, one of the best-known cycles is essentially as follows: the parasite occurs in the reproductive organs of certain starfishes and clams in the form of multinucleated *plasmodia,* moving in an amoeboid fashion and feeding on the tissues of the host. Occasionally these plasmodia break into a number of smaller masses—that is, they undergo *fragmentation*—and in this manner reproduce additional plasmodial bodies. Later the plasmodia engender spores known as *agametes,* which germinate, still within the body mass, into male and female individuals. These are composed of a small number of ciliated cells arranged over a series of central (or axial) ones (Figure 10–1); in adult specimens

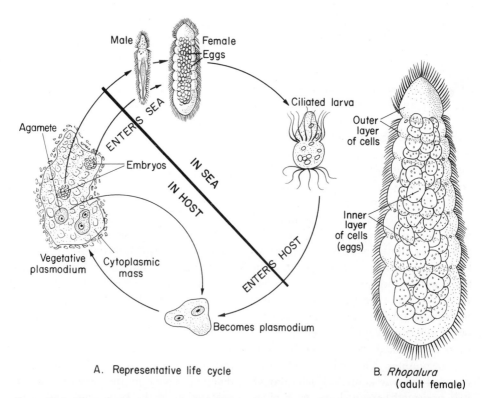

A. Representative life cycle

B. *Rhopalura*
(adult female)

Figure 10–1. Life cycle of a mesozoan. The Mesozoa are a poorly known phylum of metazoans which are parasitic for a portion of their life cycle within the bodies of various marine invertebrates.

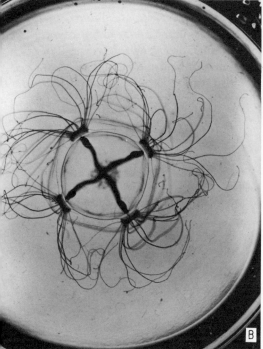

Figure 10–2. Some relatives of Hydra. A. *Aiptasiomorpha luciae*, a marine form, is considerably larger and more complex than the familiar freshwater *Hydra*. B, C. This Atlantic species, a medusa (jellyfish) named *Nemopsis backei*, is shown here in top and lateral views respectively. In C can be seen the membrane that partially closes the lower surface, the thick mesoglea between upper and lower surfaces, and the four sets of gonads. (Courtesy of the Virginia Institute of Marine Science.)

the central cells ultimately divide many times to form the eggs or sperm. When fully matured, males are 0.1 millimeter in body length, whereas the females are two or three times as long; these forms leave the body of the host and swim about in the sea, where mating occurs. After fertilization, the eggs develop within the body of the female into minute ciliated *larvae* (Figure 10–1). Upon leaving the parent, the larvae enter a host and mature into plasmodia within the gonads to commence a new life cycle.

THE COELENTERATA

Another group of Metazoa, known as both the *Coelenterata* and the *Cnidaria*, although far more complex in morphology than the Mesozoa, are still relatively simple in their fundamental organization. In this phylum approximately 12,000 species have been described, all of which are *radially symmetrical*. Constituting this phylum is a variety of organisms, including *Hydra* and other hydroids, jellyfishes of many sorts, the Portuguese man-o'-war and other floating colonies, corals, and sea anemones (Figure 10–2). Essentially, the body consists of two layers of cells, between which lies a gelatinous secretion, the *mesoglea;* this secretion varies from the very thin deposit of *Hydra* to the thick jellylike mass that characterizes the jellyfishes. The outer and inner cellular layers, which form, respectively, the *epidermis* and *gastrodermis,* surround a digestive cavity known variously as the *gastrovascular*

cavity or *coelenteron*. From this word, meaning "cavity-gut," has been derived the more frequently employed name of the phylum. Each layer contains an assortment of contractile, epidermal, nervous, secretive, and undifferentiated cells, and hence cannot really be thought of as a tissue in a strict sense (Figure 10–3). Among the cells of the epidermis are found numerous *stinging cells* or *nematocysts;* in some classes these cells are particularly abundant on the elongated bodily processes known as the *tentacles*. In the sessile form of coelenterate, called the *polyp,* the tentacles are directed upward, whereas in the free-swimming type, the *medusoid,* they dangle downward; in both they surround the *mouth,* which is the only opening into the gastrovascular

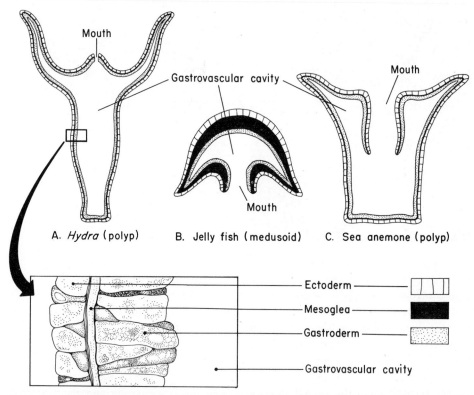

A. *Hydra* (polyp)   B. Jelly fish (medusoid)   C. Sea anemone (polyp)

Ectoderm
Mesoglea
Gastroderm
Gastrovascular cavity

Figure 10–3. Types and structure of coelenterates. Polyps are attached (sessile) types, whereas medusoids are actively swimming jellyfish-like forms. Basically, however, the morphology is the same regardless of habit.

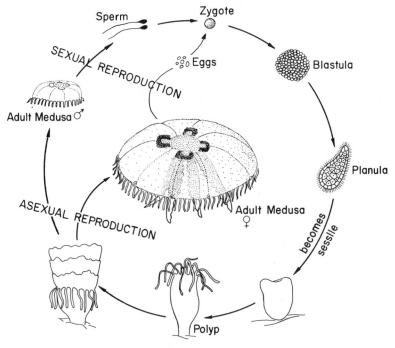

A. A GENERALIZED LIFE HISTORY

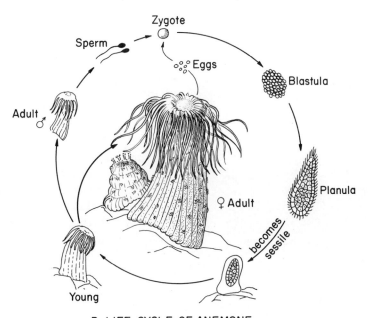

B. LIFE CYCLE OF ANEMONE

Figure 10–4. Life cycles of the Coelenterata. *A.* Among many coelenterates an "alternation of generations" exists—a sessile polyp stage reproduces asexually, whereas its progeny are free-swimming medusae that propagate sexually. *B.* A number of others, however—such as *Hydra,* the sea anemones, and the corals—lack a medusoid stage. Frequently the fertilized egg develops into a flattened ciliated larva known as the planula.

cavity. Reproduction is frequently by the simple asexual process of budding off new individuals; it may also be by sexual means, in which a *planula* larva develops from the zygote. In some classes the two methods interplay to form an alternation of generations in which the polyp and medusoid body types may be involved in turns too (Figure 10–4).

Nematocysts. Since the stinging cells are unique, both structurally and physiologically, they have aroused the curiosity of many zoologists, so that numerous studies have been conducted on them. Because the *cnidoblasts,* or cells that form them, are self-contained bodies in no way connected with the nerve cells, investigations are frequently concerned with the mechanism of release. In nature these

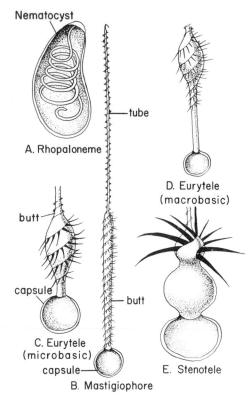

Figure 10–6. Structure and varieties of nematocysts.

Figure 10–5. A Portuguese man-o'-war (*Physalia*). Although this colonial form related to *Hydra* is particularly noted for the potency of its nematocysts, some organisms like this commensal fish (*Nomeus gronovii*) live symbiotically among its tentacles. (Courtesy of Dr. Charles E. Lane.)

cells are employed in defense and in capturing prey, for all species are carnivorous (Figure 10–5). To understand the mechanism by which they are released, the structures involved must first be examined.

In their normal position in the epidermis cnidoblasts appear as small capsules, each enclosing the tightly coiled nematocyst; over this is a trap-doorlike *operculum* on which is borne a bristle or *cnidocil*. When the cnidocil becomes properly stimulated, it triggers the opening of the operculum and releases the contents of the cell. When thus released, the enclosed nematocyst uncoils into a long threadlike projection, at the base of which is found a bulbous enlargement and often several spines (Figure 10–6). In the simple polyp form, *Hydra,* two

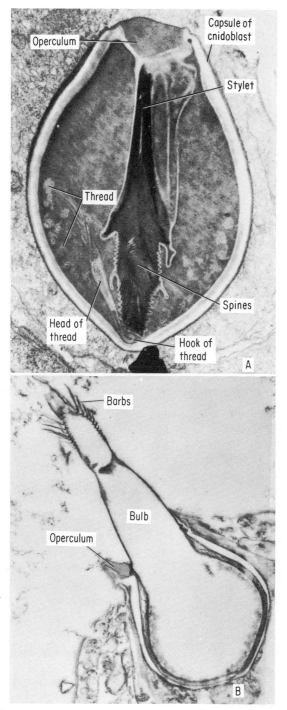

Figure 10–7. Cnidoblasts and nematocysts of Hydra. A. Electronmicrograph of a cnidoblast containing its coiled nematocyst. Magnified 8500×. (Courtesy of Dr. George B. Chapman and *The Biology of Hydra,* Howard M. Lenhoff, the University of Miami Press, and the Loomis Institute for Scientific Research.)   B. The base of same type of nematocyst after release. Magnified 7000×. (Courtesy of Dr. George B. Chapman, *Journ. Biophys. Biochem. Cytol.,* 5:79–84, 1959, Pl. 33, Fig. 16.)

principal sorts of nematocysts are present. The *penetrants,* as the name suggests, are capable of penetrating the body of the prey and injecting a poison, whereas the *volvents* serve much as lassos by wrapping around any hairs or other projections the victim may possess. The stimuli involved in activating the cnidocils and opening the opercula are still in great part a matter of speculation, but it appears that a combination of tactile and chemical factors is necessary. By themselves, physical factors are ineffective, as may be demonstrated by allowing a chemically inert substance such as sand grains to strike against a living hydra. No matter what size the grains nor the force with which they contact the specimen, no triggering of the cnidocils occurs. Nor does any re-

Figure 10–8. Nerve net of a sea anemone (*Metridium senile*). The nerve net is seen to consist of bipolar nerve cells loosely interwoven with one another. Magnified 160×. (Courtesy of Drs. E. J. Batham, C. F. A. Pantin, and E. A. Robson, *Quart. Journ. Micro. Sci.,* 101, 1960.)

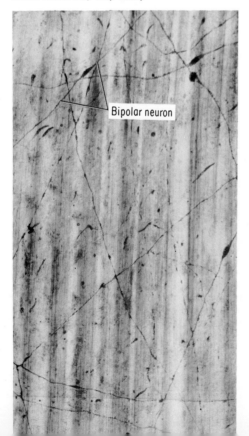

Bipolar neuron

action take place when a solution of lipids, such as given off by most organisms, is added to the culture medium. When a ciliate, however, emitting minute quantities of lipids as it travels, encounters a hydra, a discharge of nematocysts occurs immediately on contact (Figure 10–7).

Nervous Organization.   Many activities of the coelenterate's body are not under the control of the nervous system; apparently the nerve cells of these organisms are concerned chiefly with coordinating the muscular movements. When properly stained, the neural apparatus can be seen as a loose network made of cells whose long filamentous axons lie in contact with one another (Figure 10–8). The level of organization of the nervous net can be demonstrated as follows by use of a sea anemone and suitable electrical apparatus. When electrodes are placed against the body wall surrounding the mouth and mild electric shocks are delivered at a rapid rate, the entire body contracts. If the frequency but not the strength of the impulses is diminished, then the tentacles alone react, showing movement or twitching. When the rate is further retarded, the mouth opens as if to feed, and the animal tries to swallow the electrodes. Seemingly, then, the sea anemone (Figure 10–9) distinguishes between pain, tactile, and chemical, or food, stimuli on the basis of the frequency at which the nervous impulses are conducted.

The Wormlike Phyla

Since only the foregoing phyla are derived from less than the normal number of germ layers, the fact that derivation is from three such layers need not be mentioned in subsequent discussions. Similarly, the groups described below

Figure 10–9. Other types of coelenterates.   A. The sea anemone is a beautiful example of the fixed type of coelenterate, the polyp. When alive these animals, like this Mediterranean sea anemone (*Cerianthus dohrni*) are often brilliantly colored. (New York Zoological Society photo.)   B. The true jelly-fish, like this western Atlantic species *Cyanea capillata,* are far more complex than the hydroid medusae shown in Figure 10–2. (Courtesy of the Virginia Institute of Marine Science.)

and all that follow, with one exception, are *bilaterally symmetrical;* hence only in the exceptional case is symmetry noted. Because the name "worm" is applied to any animal of an elongated form which moves without assistance of legs or other prominent appendages, it has been employed liberally in common terminology to designate many unrelated and quite dissimilar organisms. Although types of "worms" are legion, only four major groups are outlined here.

THE FLATWORMS

Usually the phylum of flatworms, the *Platyhelminthes,* is divided into three classes, most of which have in common the dorsoventrally flattened body responsible for their popular name. One class, the *Turbellaria,* includes the free-living *planarians;* a second, the *Trematoda,* contains the *flukes;* and the *Cestoda* is made up of the *tapeworms.* The last two classes are entirely parasitic, whereas only a few members of the first are. Throughout the phylum the body cavity is absent, and the digestive tract when present is *incomplete,* communicating with the outside through a single opening, the *mouth.* Both asexual and sexual means of reproduction are employed, almost all species being *hermaphroditic,* with complex dual systems. Well developed, too, are the muscular and nervous systems, but skeletal and circulatory organs are completely absent. In addition, an excretory system, of a simple type in which peculiar ciliated cells are utilized, is present; since these structures occur in several phyla, at least in the larval stages, a fuller discussion appears to be appropriate.

In these worms the essential excretory structure is the *flame cell,* whose name is derived from the seemingly flickering movements of the tuft of cilia each bears (Figure 10–10). Apparently excess water from the body along with soluble wastes enters the cell and passes through its cytoplasm into the tubular neck; there the beating of the cilia impels the waste ma-

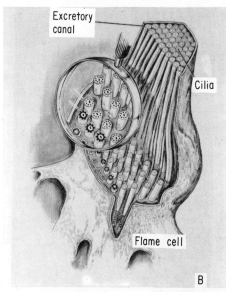

Figure 10–10. Flame cells. A. Diagram of a flame cell. Wastes and excess water are conducted first into the cell, then into the cavity, and thence pumped along the excretory canal by movement of the long cilia. (After Wiley and Kirschner.) **B.** In this diagrammatic drawing of a flame cell, the relationships of the cilia to the cell are shown along with the ultrastructure of the cilia. (Courtesy of Dr. R. R. Cardell, Jr., *Trans. Amer. Micro. Soc.,* **81,** 1962.)

terials into the excretory tubules and, finally, through the excretory pore to the outside.

The Planarians and Relatives. For the greater part the *Turbellaria* are unsegmented, flattish worms, less than half an inch in length, found beneath rocks or on decaying vegetation in fresh and salt waters. Not all are so small, however; some forms, such as the land planarians and other advanced species, attain a length of more than 2 inches. In many cases a head is quite apparent, marked off by a necklike constriction or by earlike projections; on the other hand, in several forms the head is indistinguishable, as it is actually the narrowest part of the body (Figure 10–11). Although the organisms are provided with three layers

of muscles, locomotion is principally by other means. Over the entire surface located on the epidermal cells is a uniform coat of cilia that serves for this purpose. Through the beating of the cilia, the animals move over the substrate as though gliding. As may be seen in Figure 10–12, the nervous system is well developed; although many variations are to be found, by and large the ladder type illustrated is characteristic of the group. Particularly outstanding is the construction of the digestive tract. This system varies considerably from one order to another, but its principal features may best be noted in the figure of the fresh-water planarians (Figure 10–12). Essentially it consists of a *mouth* and a muscular *pharynx* which can be projected through

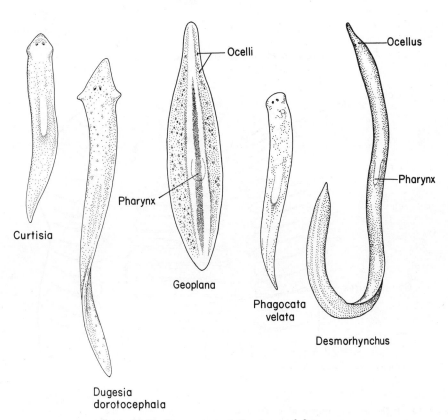

Figure 10–11. Some representative types of flatworms.

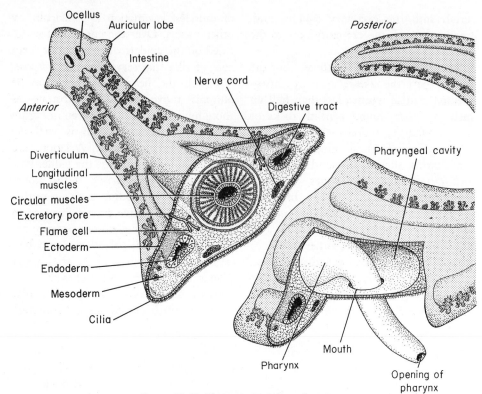

Figure 10–12. The structure of a planarian.

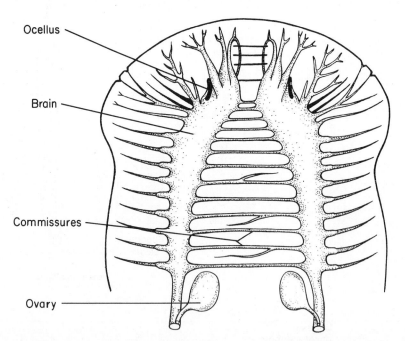

Figure 10–13. The nervous system of a planarian. The nervous system of the flatworms as a whole is of the ladder type illustrated, with several major "uprights" and numerous "rungs." (After Micoletzky.)

the mouth, a short *esophagus,* and *intestines*. In the planarians the intestines are subdivided into three parts, one portion reaching forward, the other two projecting posteriorly, one on each side; all subdivisions often have numerous sac-like extensions called *diverticula* (Figure 10–12).

The Flukes. As members of the class *Trematoda,* the *flukes* are a highly specialized group of parasites, possessing the most complex life cycle of any metazoan (Figure 10–14). Morphologically, they differ from the planarians in lacking an epidermis as adults, for this entire layer is shed, cilia and all, when the first larval stage penetrates its first host, which in most species is a snail. Moreover, the mouth is located at the anterior end of the body, and suction disks for attachment are found in various positions on the surface. As may be noted in Figure 10–14, the principal features of the anatomy, aside from the bipartite digestive tract, pertain to the reproductive system. Though most of the flukes are minute, those parasitic in larger vertebrates average close to half an inch in length, and several species attain nearly 2 inches.

The Tapeworms. As in the flukes, members of the *Cestoda* shed their epidermis during the larval period and therefore lack such a coat as adults. In body length a great variability can be noted, however; the range is from a fraction of

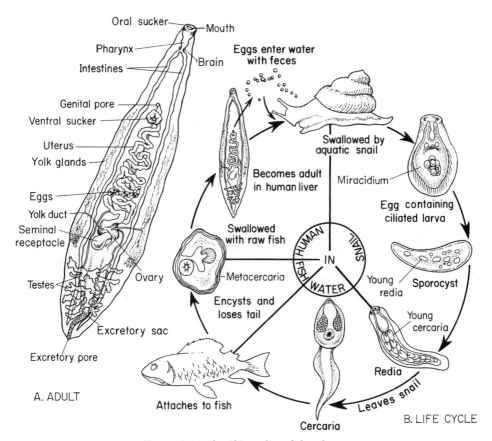

Figure 10–14. The Chinese liver fluke of man.

an inch in some species which attack fish to more than 25 feet in the beef tapeworm of man and even longer in certain parasites of horses. In addition, no digestive tract, not even a mouth, is present in these worms at any stage in their complex life cycles (Figure 10–15), their food being taken in saprozoically

A. STRUCTURE

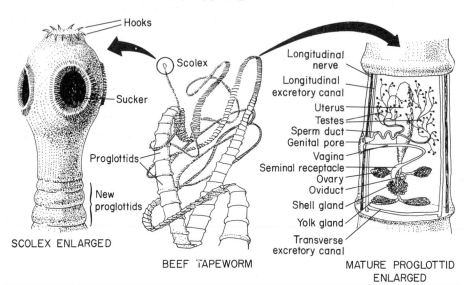

SCOLEX ENLARGED

BEEF TAPEWORM

MATURE PROGLOTTID ENLARGED

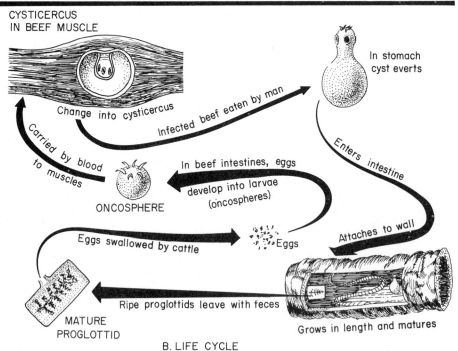

B. LIFE CYCLE

Figure 10–15. The beef tapeworm of man.

through the body wall. All species are parasitic, especially in fishes, but their hosts are well represented among all the vertebrates. One particular feature sets these tapeworms apart from other flatworms—namely, the presence of segmentation in their bodily arrangement. On the posterior end of the parent organism, called the *scolex,* segments known as *proglottids* are budded off. Each segment is hermaphroditic and develops into a self-contained reproductive body in which full complements of organs of both sexes are present. Although, as a rule, mating is between adjacent animals, self-insemination is known to occur. Following fertilization of the eggs, the proglottid is transformed into an egg case, which ultimately breaks free of the worm and carries the eggs to the outside of the host.

THE ROUNDWORMS

In contrast to the flatworms, all *Nemathelminthes* (a word meaning "threadworm") are quite elongated and slender in form. Although most of the members are free-living, many are highly developed parasites, occurring especially endoparasitically in the higher green plants as well as in both vertebrate and invertebrate animals.

The Nematodes. The typical roundworms are the *nematodes (Nematoda)*, whose elongated unsegmented bodies are covered as a rule by a tough flexible cuticle (Figure 10–16). Whereas almost all the plant parasites and free-living species are minute, some that attack vertebrates, especially the females, are quite large. Members of this sex in the kidney worm and guinea worm of man, for example, attain a length of more than 3 feet. Although the digestive tract of these metazoans is complete it is not complex, for it consists only of a *mouth,* a muscular

pharynx, a flat ribbonlike *intestine,* and an *anal opening.* This system, along with that of reproduction, is located in the peculiar unlined type of body cavity called a *pseudocoel;* on the other hand, the excretory tubules, which are devoid of flame cells, and the six longitudinal nerve cords are embedded in the body wall, at least for their greatest extent.

In all nematodes the sexes are separate, the males being smaller than the females, sometimes noticeably so, as indicated above. In both sexes the reproductive organs are tubular and, although extensive, are relatively simple in structure. Nor is the life cycle intricate, for, though larval stages are occasionally present, the larvae are closely similar to the adult except in size and internal development. No asexual means of propagation is known to occur within this group.

As it is at least partly associated with development, one unique feature of nematode histology may be appropriately mentioned here, a distinctive trait that involves constancy of cell number. Despite the extensive increment in body length, after hatching, the total number of cells in a given individual does not increase as the worm grows into adulthood, except in the reproductive organs. By way of illustration, in one species of *Rhabditis,* a coprophagous nematode, the count shows the presence of 68 muscle, 120 epidermal, and 200 nerve cells, plus 172 in the digestive tract, regardless of the age or body length of the individual. In other genera comparable counts are obtained.

Metabolic Activities of Parasitic Worms. Since endoparasitic worms of all types, whether fluke, tapeworm, or nematode, frequently occupy quarters in which oxygen is not abundantly present, such as the intestines, liver, and bladder, some attention is being given in recent years to their metabolic activities in an

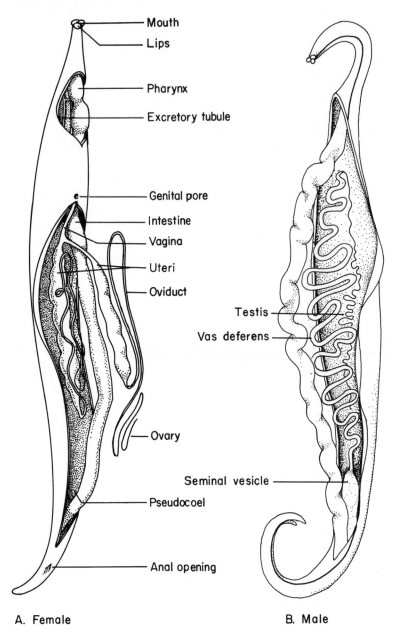

Figure 10–16. The structure of a nematode (*Ascaris*).

attempt to learn how they survive under these relatively anaerobic conditions. In most animals, when cellular respiration is proceeding at a very high rate or when the oxygen supply is otherwise proportionately low, pyruvic acid is converted into lactic acid, as has already been seen

(page 43). This acid, however, is quite soluble in water and is rather reactive, being credited in our bodies for the production of the condition of fatigue to a large extent. In all of the parasitic worms we have studied it has been found that although the actual products vary widely fatty acids are formed instead of lactic, and because the fatty acids are relatively insoluble and less reactive than lactic acid, much of the unfavorable effects of accumulation are thus avoided.

THE ROTIFERA

During an examination of cultures of protozoa strange actively swimming "ciliates" whose insides appear to be constantly in motion often come into the field. Frequently, when we learn for the first time that these organisms are not really ciliated protozoans but metazoans called *rotifers,* it is difficult to believe that a multicellular animal can actually be so minute (Figure 10–17). Essentially the organism consists of little more than an open funnel situated at the anterior end of a short wormlike body. Around the large opening of the funnel are rows of cilia, the activities of which provide locomotion and propel food particles down the funnel into the mouth. From the mouth the food, consisting principally of

bacteria and small protozoans, enters the pharynx, or *mastax.* Here are found the *trophi,* a variable number of hardened grinding organs, the movements of which seem to keep the animal's insides in a constant whirling motion. Although the body cavity of this organism is a *pseudocoel,* the rotifers differ from the nematodes, to which they are allied, in having *flame cells* for excretory purposes.

Almost all rotifers are fresh-water inhabitants, living either planktonically or

Figure 10–17. A few examples of rotifers. More examples are shown on page 176.

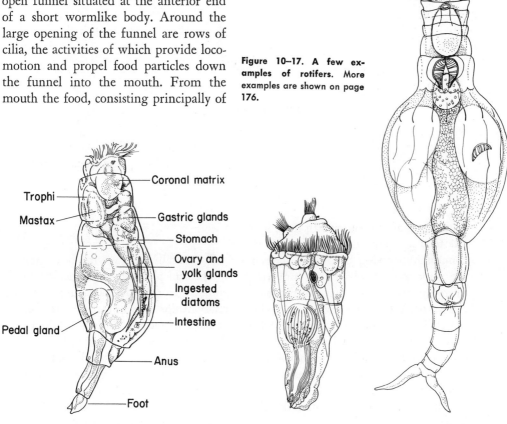

Trophi

Mastax

Coronal matrix

Gastric glands

Stomach

Ovary and yolk glands

Ingested diatoms

Intestine

Pedal gland

Anus

Foot

A. *Proales reinhardti*

B. *Synchaeta vorax*

C. *Rotifer socialis*

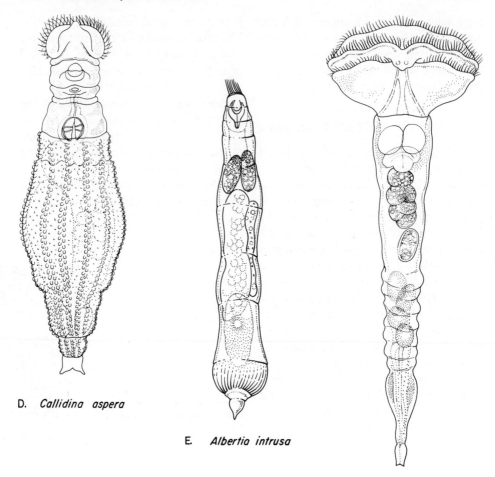

D.   *Callidina aspera*

E.   *Albertia intrusa*

F.   *Pseudoecistes rotifer*

Figure 10–17 (Continued).

in the mud of the bottoms. In these habitats they are important members of the community, serving as intermediates in the processes involved in converting microorganisms into macroscopic particles available to larger organisms. While especially abundant in ponds and lakes, these animals occur wherever there is even a limited supply of fresh water, as in moist soil, in sandy margins of lakes and rivers, and in the drops adhering to the leaves of mosses and the disks of lichens.

The Annelida

Structurally, the worms belonging to the present phylum are so sharply differentiated from those preceding that the relationships between them are remote at best. In fact, it is often believed that the pseudocoelomate groups just discussed represent a "blind" sideline, in which no animals of greater complexity have ever developed, whereas the annelids are considered to represent the base of a separate stem derived from the flat-

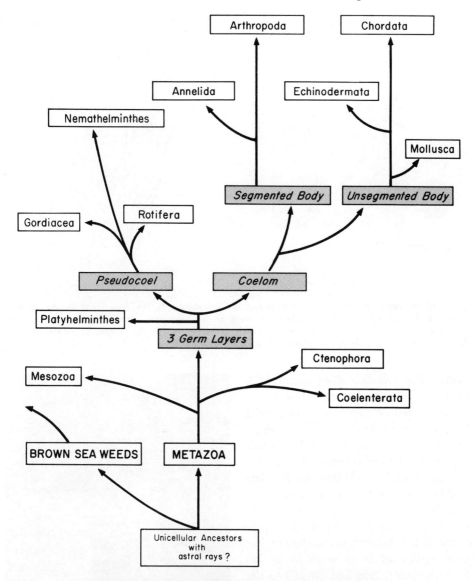

Figure 10–18. Possible relationships of the metazoan phyla.

worms leading to the insects and other highly complicated forms (Figure 10–18). Among morphological features that distinguish the worms now under discussion can be mentioned the *segmented* body and the presence of a true *coelom* as the body cavity; this structure is shared by all higher animals as well. Another organ characteristic of all subsequent animals, although often highly modified, is the excretory organ called the *nephridium*. Essentially, a nephridium is a funnel-like apparatus, sometimes closed at the inner end and provided with specialized flame cells called *solenocytes*, at other times opened and ciliated (Figure 10–19).

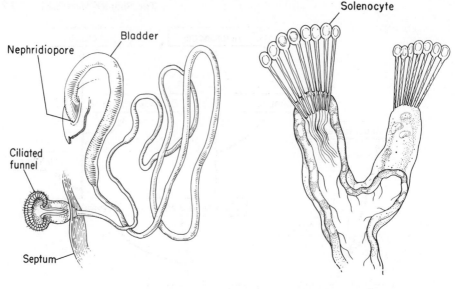

A. Funnel type   B. Solenocyte type

Figure 10–19. Types of nephridia found among the Annelida. A. The type found in the common earthworm has an open ciliated funnel-like structure at its inner end. (After Benham.) B. In other types the inner end is closed, the excretory products being filtered into the tubules by means of modified flame cells called solenocytes. (After Schearer.)

Within the Annelida three distinct major groups may be recognized.

The Fresh-Water and Terrestrial Worms. Of all the Annelida, the *Oligochaeta,* as they are technically designated, are undoubtedly the most familiar, for among them, in addition to the less readily observed fresh-water forms, are included the earthworms. As a whole, the *segmentation* of the body is quite pronounced, the segments ordinarily ranging from as few as 16 to as many as 250 (Figure 10–20). Attached directly to the outside of the body and normally arranged in four rows are small groups of *setae* or bristles, which assist in locomotion. Externally also can be found a thickening near the anterior quarter of

Figure 10–20. The giant earthworm of Australia. This worm (*Megascolides australis*) is confined to wet river banks of southern Victoria and reaches lengths of 6 to 12 feet. (Courtesy of the Australian News and Information Bureau.)

the length, appearing not too unlike a scar. This enlargement of the epidermis is the *clitellum,* a gland which secretes a mucuslike substance employed in various ways during reproductive processes as described below. In aquatic forms these glands are usually thin and inconspicuous. The circulatory system is a *closed* one—that is, both veins and arteries are present; the blood is pumped by contractile vessels and also by paired hearts in many species. In addition, a well-developed nervous system is found in these worms, consisting of a brain, a subesophageal ganglion located below the esophagus, and a double nerve cord running the length of the body. Other details of the morphology of the groups,

such as the septate coelom and the subdivisions of the digestive tract, can be better gleaned from a study of specimens or from the illustration of the earthworm's anatomy (Figure 10–21).

Reproduction among the earthworms is exclusively by sexual means, but asexual methods are also employed in the simpler fresh-water representatives. Since all species are hermaphroditic, copulation involves mutual insemination. In mating, the worms lie in opposite directions with the ventral surface of the anterior region in contact, held securely by the slime tube secreted by the clitellum. Some time after the worms have finished this action and have separated, the clitellum secretes a tubular container for the ova. When

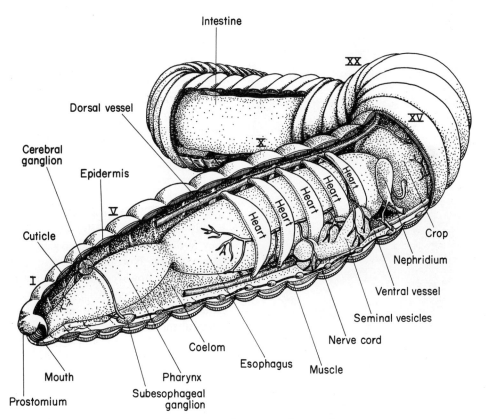

Figure 10–21. The internal anatomy of an earthworm.

completed, the tube moves forward and receives the eggs from the openings of the oviducts; later, as it passes still farther anteriorly, sperm leave the seminal receptacles and fertilize its contents. The tube then slips off the anterior portion of the worm, and its ends seal shut to form a *cocoon,* in which the eggs develop

Figure 10–22. A fresh-water leech. Not all aquatic leeches are provided with external gills as is this specimen of *Ozobranchus branchiatus.* (Courtesy of Dr. L. R. Penner, *Trans. Amer. Micro. Soc.,* **81,** 1962.)

into minute worms without passing through any larval stages.

The Leeches. In so many ways the class *Hirudinea,* or leeches, resembles the Oligochaeta that often the two are placed together in a taxon under the name *Clitellata,* with the clitellum a unique feature shared by both. Morphologically, however, many marked distinctions between them are found. In the first place, the segments in the leeches are constant in number, 34 being uniformly present; these parts are not set off by septa internally as in the earthworms but are indicated principally by the ganglia of the nervous system. Although externally the body appears to have numerous segments, this appearance results from the series of muscular rings into which each actual segment is divided (Figure 10–22). At the posterior end of the body is a large *suction disk,* and frequently another located around the mouth. Particularly distinct in structure are the stomach and intestines; each is provided on both sides with a series of sacs or *caeca* capable of undergoing great distention, a feature useful in the storage of the blood on which many of these organisms feed. To assist in obtaining its fluid meals, the leech secretes an *anticoagulant,* which prevents the formation of blood clots.

As a whole, this group of animals is largely confined to fresh water, where they feed on turtles and other vertebrates or on worms. Not all leeches are fresh-water forms, however; a few are marine and several are terrestrial. Possibly the land-dwelling types rate as the most harmful members of the group, for they occur in such large numbers in rain forests from India to Australia that they make some areas uninhabitable by man. Apparently, the worms detect their prey by means of vibrations to which they seem sensitive. An explorer on a jungle trail need pause only an instant before

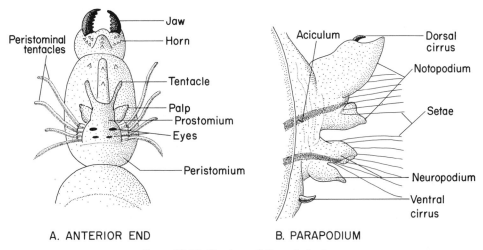

A. ANTERIOR END   B. PARAPODIUM

Figure 10–23. Structure of the polychaetes.

seeing himself converged upon by dozens of these leeches; so many of the pests are often present that their movements over the vegetation produce a distinct rustling sound.

The Marine Worms. As implied by their technical name, *Polychaeta* (meaning "many bristles"), these worms have numerous setae on their bodies, usually in the form of tufts. The tufts are not attached directly to the body wall but are borne on special projections (or appendages) called *parapodia,* a word meaning "nearly a foot" (Figure 10–23). These organs serve many purposes, including locomotion and respiration, and are frequently highly modified to render specialized functions. In addition to the parapodia, distinctive structural features of the group are found in the well-marked

Figure 10–24. Tentacles of a burrowing polychaete. On well-developed coral reefs, these brilliantly colored polychaetes frequently drill burrows in which they wait, tentacles projecting and waving about in the water. The tentacles of the worm shown (*Spirobranchus giganteus*) are bright red and around one-half inch in length.

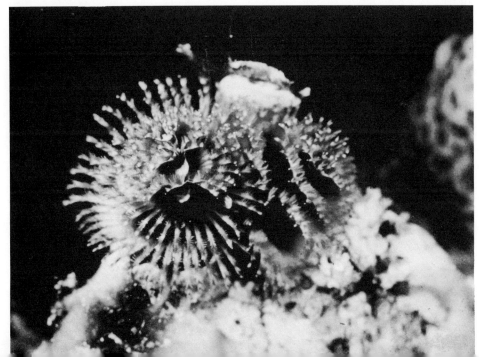

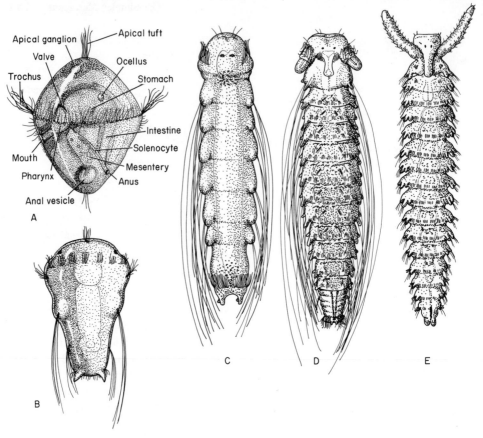

Figure 10–25. The larva and stages in the development of a polychaete (composite). *A.* A trochophore larva. *B–E.* Development of the trochophore into a mature specimen involves the addition of segments and a metamorphosis which includes, among many other things, a change from a floating to a bottom-dwelling existence.

Labels in figure A: Apical ganglion, Apical tuft, Valve, Ocellus, Trochus, Stomach, Intestine, Solenocyte, Mouth, Mesentery, Pharynx, Anus, Anal vesicle

head, provided with numerous sensory organs including *ocelli* (simple eyes) and *palpi,* and in the presence of a protrusible *pharynx,* which is usually armed with jaws. Although additional characteristics are included in the internal morphology, they are of no moment here.

Some of the polychaetes crawl actively about on the sea bottoms, feeding on clams and other animals, whereas many others construct more or less U-shaped tubes within the substrate or among coral and spend their entire lives therein. Among the tube-dwelling species feeding is accomplished by filtering the organic matter from the water (Figure 10–24).

In addition to the numerous morpho-logical distinctions, the polychaetes exhibit an important development in their life cycle in the form of a planktonic larva called a *trochophore.* The name, translated as "wheel bearer," refers to the band of cilia encircling the more or less pear-shaped body (Figure 10–25). At the upper end of the larva is a tuft of sensitive hairs attached to an apical plate, and a similar tuft often surrounds the anus at the lower end. Internally, there are a few muscles, a simple digestive tract, flame-cell nephridia, and little else. Chiefly this larva is important because several other phyla of animals manifest a nearly identical immature stage, a fact that is often taken to be indicative of close relationships between the groups concerned.

The Nervous System and Behavior of Annelids. The level of development at which the members of this phylum lie can perhaps be most clearly illustrated by the functioning of their nervous system and their ability to learn. Most routine movements of these worms appear to be under the control of *reflexes*—that is, responses contained, as it were, within the muscles and the nerves directly associated thereto, without intervention of the brain or similar higher centers. For example, locomotion in the earthworm essentially involves the lengthening of the body by means of transverse circular muscles and shortening it by means of a longitudinal set. If a single segment is removed for study and kept alive, it is found that a stretching of either of these muscular layers causes a reflexive contraction to set in. Hence, when the circular muscles contract, the resulting elongation of the segment stretches the longitudinal muscles, instigating a reflexive shortening within them. In turn, when the longitudinals shorten, the circular muscles are stretched, thereby setting a contractile reflex into motion. These muscular activities can continue to alternate in this manner indefinitely, until fatigue sets in or an outside stimulus intervenes. In intact worms contractions in one segment apparently initiate neural impulses which reach adjacent segments, and coordinated movement is achieved.

By training methods the behavior of many of the annelids may be altered, at least temporarily. Often unpleasant stimuli, such as electric shocks, are administered as a part of the training regime. Although such stimuli are usually applied to the posterior end of the body, if this part is removed after training is completed, the worm still "remembers." If the anterior segment including the brain is removed beforehand, training can still be accomplished, but it proceeds at a slower rate. Hence the cephalic ganglion apparently is not the sole seat of central control but only the chief one.

Questions for Review and Thought

1. List the major features of the Mesozoa. Do tissues in the strict sense of the term appear to be present? Do organs? What cells appear to have a specialized function in the sexual stage? In this same stage what functions are performed by the outer layer of ciliated cells?

2. What are the basic characteristics of the Coelenterata? Which features are truly distinctive? For what reasons might this group be considered to represent a side-shoot from the main stem of the Metazoa? Give the name of the body cavity if one is present.

3. Define the following terms and indicate in which phylum each occurs:

(a) polyps	(g) nematocysts
(b) pharynx	(h) nephridium
(c) worm	(i) plasmodium
(d) coelom	(j) coelenteron
(e) tentacles	(k) flame cell
(f) pseudocoel	(l) clitellum

4. In which ways do the flatworms appear more complex than the coelenterates and in which are they simpler than the Annelida? Which bodily systems seem to be absent in the Platyhelminthes? What are the traits they possess that most sharply distinguish them from the other phyla described here?

5. List the groups studied so far that are parasitic; indicate in each case whether parasitism is characteristic of all, the larger part, or a few members of the group concerned. Which are parasitic principally in invertebrates? In vertebrates? In green plants?

6. Outline the life cycles of a fluke and a tapeworm.

7. Show in what ways the Annelida are more complex than the Nematoda and how the Nematoda compare with the Platyhelminthes. What traits of the Nemathelminthes are most distinctive? List the traits that are indicative of a close relationship between the Rotifera and Nemathelminthes and those that show lack of affinity. What in the rotifers appears to imply a relationship to the Platyhelminthes?

8. Outline the principal characteristics of the phylum Annelida.

9. Test the statement made in the introduction to this chapter concerning the gradual increase in complexity shown by the Metazoa by examining the history of the digestive system. First list the phyla in the sequence given here; then indicate after each one (treating the phyla as entire units by omitting the occasional exceptions) whether this function is carried out by the whole organism, an unspecialized layer, a tissue, an organ, or an organ system, being certain to apply *strictly* the definitions provided in Chapter 9 and to examine the figures closely.

10. Repeat question 9 but trace the histories of the following functions: reproduction, excretion, nervous response, movement, and support.

11. If first appearance as a definitive system might be taken as an indication of relative importance, which function according to your findings in questions 9 and 10 is of greater significance to the species, reproduction or feeding? Movement or excretion? Neural response or support?

Supplementary References

Baer, J. G. *Ecology of Animal Parasites*. Urbana, Univ. Illinois Press, 1952.

Berrill, N. J. "The Indestructible *Hydra*." *Sci. Amer.*, December 1957.

Buchsbaum, R., and L. J. Milne. *The Lower Animals*. Garden City, N. Y., Doubleday, 1960.

Carthy, J. D. *An Introduction to the Behaviour of Invertebrates*. London, Macmillan, 1958.

Caullery, M. *Parasitism and Symbiosis*. London, Macmillan, 1952.

Hadži, J. *The Evolution of the Metazoa*. New York, Macmillan, 1963.

Hardy, A. C. *The Open Sea*. Boston, Houghton Mifflin, 1956.

Hyman, Libbie H. *The Invertebrates*, Vol. 1. *Protozoa through Ctenophora*. New York, McGraw-Hill, 1940.

Lane, C. E. "The Portuguese Man-of-War." *Sci. Amer.*, March 1960.

Lenhoff, H. M., and W. F. Loomis. *The Biology of Hydra and of Some Other Coelenterates*. Coral Gables, Florida, Univ. Miami Press, 1961.

Monkman, N. *From Queensland to the Great Barrier Reef*. Garden City, N. Y., Doubleday, 1958.

Zappler, G. "Darwin's Worms." *Natural History*, 67:488–495, 1958.

Some Complex Metazoa

FORMING the upper portion of the phylogenetic tree of the metazoans (Figure 10–18) are a number of phyla, not all of which are necessarily related but which, nonetheless, possess a skeleton of one sort or another. Were it not for the absence of this feature, the Annelida too could be included here, for its members display a level of organization that scarcely can be considered simple. Nor is it the intent here to suggest other than a high degree of complexity for that phylum. The treatment accorded them by their inclusion with the simpler animals is one solely of convenience, for it permits the presentation of all wormlike phyla within the confines of one chapter, since none of the remainder are typically vermiform in construction, with one minor exception.

The Arthropoda

If numbers of species currently existing are of any significance, this is the group of animals that dominates the world today, for to it belong 80 per cent of all extant metazoans. Perhaps much of its success can be ascribed in great part to the presence of well-developed appendages, which give to its members a motility equaled only by the vertebrates and which have permitted the conquering of many ecological situations through their great adaptability. As shall be seen shortly, these appendages are highly modified to perform a great diversity of tasks, including locomotion, food getting, respiration, transfer of sperm, and water pumping, to mention only a few. Perhaps, too, the presence of a skeleton, despite its being of the exoskeletal type

185

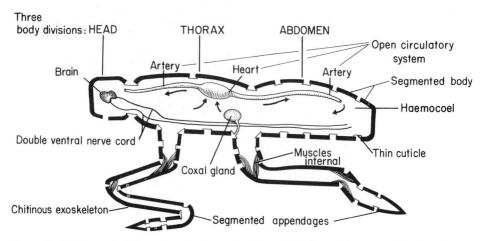

Figure 11–1. Characteristic features of arthropods. Often the head and thorax are fused to form a single body division called the cephalothorax.

that restricts growth by completely enclosing the body, has contributed much in providing a protective coat of resistant *chitin* and the rigid support that powerful muscles require. Because of the presence of the exoskeleton, the appendages are *segmented*—that is, constructed of a series of short rigid pieces held together at the joints by soft tissues. The body, too, is segmented and is divided into three major divisions, *head, thorax,* and *abdomen* (Figure 11–1). Although these body divisions are almost always present, in some crustaceans and arachnids the head and thorax are combined as a *cephalothorax.* In these animals the coelom is largely replaced by a *haemocoel,* derived from and forming a part of the *open circulatory system,* in which the blood flows through vessels to a limited extent and through the haemocoel for the remainder of its course. No hemoglobin is present in the blood. In addition to the segmentation of the body, a clue to the relationships of the arthropods is found in the nervous system, which is essentially the same as that of the Annelida. In both groups the system consists of two sets of ganglia strung together beadlike down

the length of the body. Excretion, too, is by modified nephridia called *coxal glands* (also antennary and green glands) in the crustacea and relatives. On the other hand, in insects and their allies the excretory organs are slender tubes, called *Malpighian tubules,* which discharge the wastes into the terminal portion of the digestive tract.

THE CRUSTACEA

In this class are found a number of well-known edible forms, such as crabs (Figure 11–2), crayfish, lobsters, prawns, and shrimp, which, although familiar and easy to study in the laboratory because of their size, really do not represent the class as a whole. In contrast, the vast majority of Crustacea are minute plankton that play an important role in fresh-water and marine communities, in which they serve as intermediaries between the microscopic producers and small carnivores in the capacity of filter-feeding herbivores. Such animals as the water fleas (*Daphnia* and *Simocephalus*), copepods (including *Cyclops*), barnacles, and fairy shrimp are far more representative of the class (Fig-

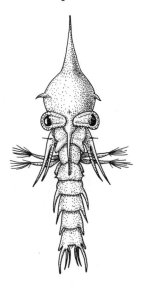

B. ZOEA

Figure 11–2. Contrasts among hermit crabs. A. The large hermit crab (*Petrochirus diogenes*) is occupying an empty shell of *Strombus gigas,* while the small species (*Clibanarius tricolor*) is making use of a turret shell more appropriate to its own size. (Photograph by William M. Stephens.) B, C. Typical larvae of crabs.

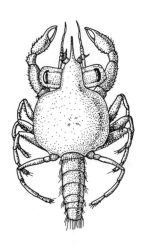

C. MEGALOPS

ure 11–3). Many parasitic members occur as well, including some of the most highly modified types in the animal world. In fact, some would not be recognizable as crustaceans were it not for the presence of a characteristic larva (the *nauplius*) in their life cycle (Figure 11–4).

Molting. Because the skeleton encloses the entire body in these animals, crustaceans, like all arthropods, are able to increase in body size only through a series of molts or *ecdyses,* in which the old skeleton is cast off and a new one secreted in its place.

Although many factors are involved in the control of molting, including temperature, regulation is exercised mostly by certain *hormones,* which are chemicals secreted in one body part to produce reactions in another. Currently under active investigation, the molting hormones

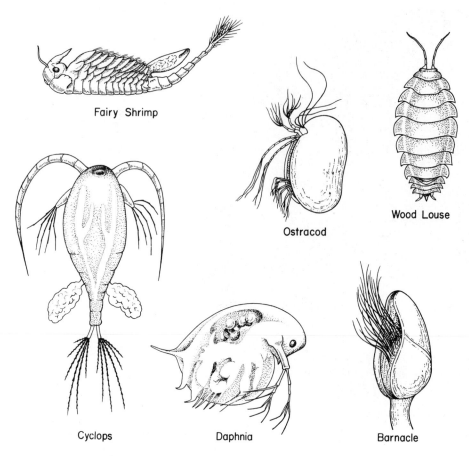

Fairy Shrimp

Ostracod

Wood Louse

Cyclops

Daphnia

Barnacle

Figure 11–3. Typical representatives of the Crustacea.

appear to be secreted by the *sinus glands* located in the stalks that bear the eyes (Figure 11–5). Apparently the secretions have an inhibitory effect on shedding the body covering, for when the eyestalks or glands are removed all the processes of ecdysis are initiated. Furthermore, growth is found to be greatly accelerated in specimens in which the eyestalks have been removed and the period between molts lessened; however, the total lifespan is also considerably shortened.

Hormonal Control of Bodily Activity. The sinus gland hormones have been found to have many activities in addition to inhibiting molting. Although results are still of a preliminary nature, the

secretions of the sinus gland seem to increase the rate of heart beat and to be involved in the control of the movements of pigments in the eye in response to light and darkness. But the effects that have received greatest attention to date are the reactions of the pigment bodies, called *chromatophores,* contained in the body covering. In lobsters and crayfish and others having long abdomens, removal of the sinus gland results in darkening of the coat by relaxation (dispersal) of the chromatophores, whereas an injection of a glandular extract produces lightening by concentration of the pigment. On the other hand, the crabs and other "short-tailed" species react in precisely the opposite manner. On the basis of experimentation, at least two hormones appear to be present, for separate control of white chromatophores and of red or yellow ones has been demonstrated by placing animals on differently colored backgrounds.

Reproduction. Although sexual means alone are employed for reproductive pur-

poses, the processes vary infinitely in detail. Among the smaller forms fertilization is frequently *external*—that is, the gametes are deposited in the water—but in all the larger species, and in some minute ones as well, the sperm are deposited in the female's body, and hence it is *internal*. To assist in the introduction of the male gametes, some appendages

Figure 11–4. The life cycle of a parasitic copepod. Many parasitic species are so highly modified that they would be difficult to recognize as crustaceans were it not for the presence in their life cycle of a characteristic nauplius, a larva that possesses only three pairs of appendages.

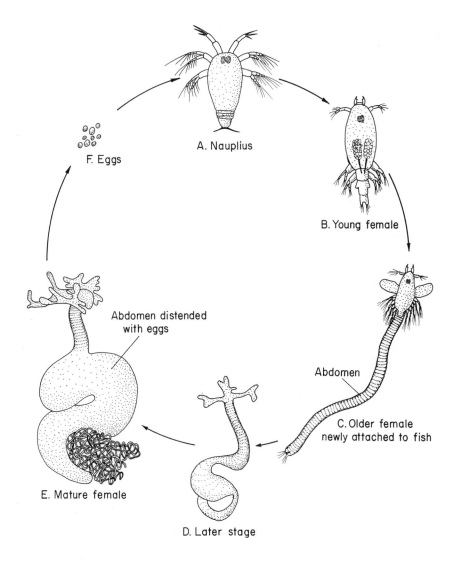

F. Eggs

A. Nauplius

B. Young female

Abdomen distended with eggs

Abdomen

C. Older female newly attached to fish

E. Mature female

D. Later stage

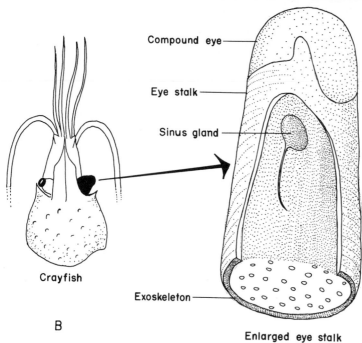

Compound eye

Eye stalk

Sinus gland

Crayfish

Exoskeleton

B

Enlarged eye stalk

Figure 11–5. Molting in a crab and the glands that control the processes. *A.* A blue crab (*Callinectes sapidus*) emerging from the old hard shell as a "soft-shelled crab." After emergence is completed, the body enlarges before the new shell hardens. (Courtesy of the Virginia Institute of Marine Science.) *B.* Location of the sinus glands in the stalks of the eyes.

are often modified to serve as a penis. Subsequent to fertilization, development may be direct in a few forms, but characteristically one or more larval types are present. In simpler varieties the three-appendaged larva called the *nauplius* is frequently found, whereas in crabs and allies the *zoea* is the first free-swimming stage (Figure 11–2).

THE ARACHNIDA

Almost as varied in representative types as the Crustacea, this class includes spiders, scorpions, ticks, and mites and many less well-known forms. As a whole terrestrial, its members are distinguished from other anthropods by the lack of jaws and the presence of two peculiar

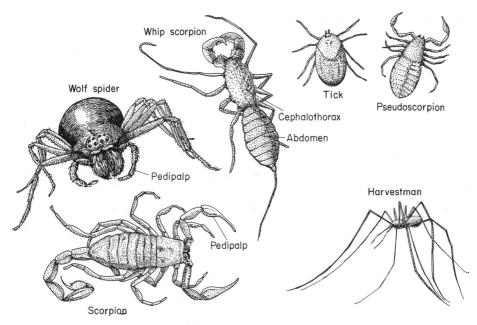

Figure 11–6. Structure and types of Arachnida. Many peculiarities of structure and of body form characterize the members of this class.

pairs of appendages called chelicerae and pedipalps, in addition to four pairs of walking legs. The *chelicerae* (meaning claw-horn) are short and pincherlike structures located just before the mouth, whereas *pedipalps* are leglike sensory organs attached to the body behind the mouth and in scorpions bear the pinchers (Figure 11–6). Almost always the head and thorax are fused into a *cephalothorax*.

In spite of a bad reputation, most arachnids are quite harmless. Certainly, there are a few deadly poisonous mem-

bers, including the black widow spiders and several scorpions, but by and large their unsavory reputation is entirely undeserved. In fact, by far the most harmful orders are the rickettsia-carrying mites and ticks, forms of which most persons have no dread, whereas those that frighten many people, the spiders and tarantulas, are for the most part quite innocuous.

In feeding, the legs and pedipalps are often used to capture live prey; after the victim has been subdued, it may be torn

Figure 11–7. The whip-scorpion's defense mechanism. The mouse, seen disappearing beyond the horizon, has just received spray from the tail of the whip-scorpion it had been molesting. (Photograph by Dr. Thomas Eisner.)

to bits by the chelicerae and passed into the mouth. Sometimes, as in the spiders, the chelicerae are provided with sharp toothlike fangs into which poison glands open; usually these fangs are also hollow and serve as hypodermic needles through which the body contents of the victim are sucked into the spider's digestive tract. Spiders are often discriminating in their food habits. For example, in the genus *Amaurobius,* which constructs a web on the ground, the terrestrial crustaceans called woodlice are not relished as food and are left unharmed if by chance they become caught in the meshes of the web. However, the spiders quickly respond to vibrations, such as those produced by the buzzing of insects ensnared in their nets, and will readily attack even a tuning fork of similar pitch held against the webbing. It is interesting to note that if a vibrating tuning fork is placed on the web close to a woodlouse the spider readily attacks and consumes

the crustacean as it would normal prey. Hence it appears that tactile rather than visual stimuli are often utilized in recognition of food.

Reproduction is always by sexual means and development is usually direct, the young being identical with the adult in form. However, in the mites and ticks a larval form with only three pairs of legs is present. Usually this stage is followed by one or two nymphal stages, in which the normal number of legs is developed but sexual organs are lacking.

The Insecta

Most of the immensity of the phylum Arthropoda is due to the members of this class, the known species of which number close to a million. Since one order alone, the beetles, includes more than 500,000 described species, one out of every five known organisms living today is a beetle, and every second species

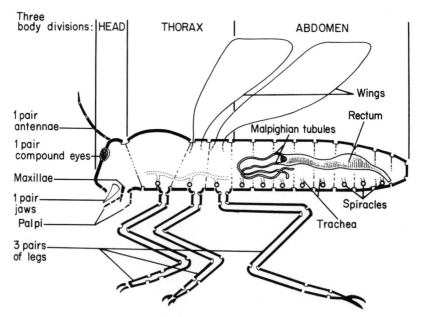

Figure 11—8. The characteristic features of insects.

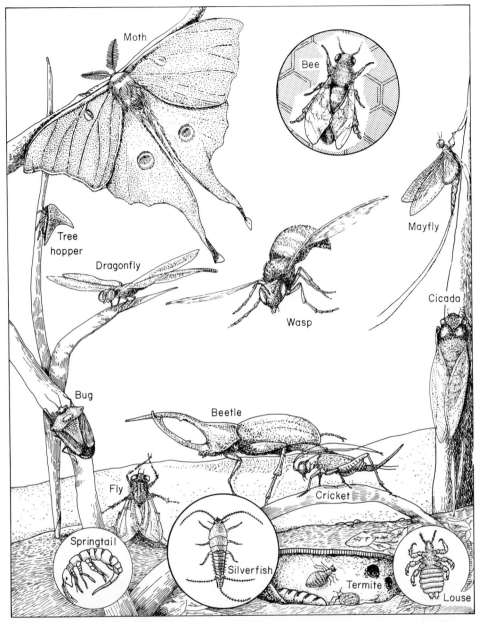

Figure 11-9. A few representatives of the class Insecta. Many pages would be required to illustrate just the major types of this great and highly varied class.

of living thing is an insect of one sort or another. Hence there can be little doubt of the predominant form of macroscopic life on earth today; these insects have mastered the lands and fresh waters to an extent far beyond any other group.

Because of their abundance, they are a fundamental constituent of all terrestrial communities, and many carnivorous birds, such as flycatchers, and mammals, such as anteaters, are adapted to feeding solely on them. Furthermore, many producers among the flowering plants depend on members of this group for pollination; orchids and numerous other types would soon vanish were all insects to become extinct.

Chief among the features that distinguish this highly diversified class (Figure 11–8) from other arthropods are the jaws, the presence of only three pairs of walking legs and frequently of wings, a separate head, thorax, and abdomen, and respiration by means of *tracheae*. The last-named structures are respiratory ducts, opening to the outside through pores called *spiracles* and branching internally into finer and finer tubules to supply individual cells directly with atmospheric oxygen. Wings, although absent from primitive members, such as silverfish, and from specialized orders, including fleas, have undoubtedly contributed greatly to the success of the class as a whole. Unlike the comparable structures of birds and bats, the organs themselves have no muscles of any sort attached to or within them; all the contractile structures are connected to the wall of the thorax. When the thorax is set into vibration by muscular contrac-

tion, the movements of the wings are produced secondarily. In the numerous orders the wings are modified in characteristic fashions. Sometimes one instead of the usual two pairs is present, and often the fore pair may be thickened as in grasshoppers, bugs, and beetles, or all may be covered with scales as in moths, butterflies, and caddis flies (Figure 11–9). In all orders except in the most primitive forms *compound eyes* are characteristic features; these are made of numerous complex eyes fused into a single organ.

Reproduction.   Although without exception reproduction is by sexual means and internal fertilization, sometimes the processes are modified by elimination of the male of the species. In such cases the egg develops without fertilization and typically produces a haploid individual. Among some species of plant lice or aphids reproduction is by unfertilized eggs, or *parthenogenesis,* for most of the season, from which only females develop. However, toward fall, special eggs are formed which develop into males. The males then serve to fertilize females, which lay eggs capable of overwintering. As the student probably knows, bees,

Figure 11–10. Stages in the life history of a European chafer. From the egg on the extreme left hatches the larva placed adjacent to it. After feeding for a while, it molts and emerges as a larger larva, and so on, the fourth larva forming a pupa when it molts. This pupal stage is one of the most distinctive features of insects with the complete type of metamorphosis. (Courtesy of Drs. H. Tashiro and F. L. Gambrell, *Ann. Ent. Soc. Amer., 56,* 1963.)

wasps, and relatives produce queens and workers from fertilized eggs, but males or drones arise parthenogenetically. In the several orders development may be direct or indirect. During the life cycle in the orders lacking larvae a juvenile stage called the *nymph* is present, in which the wings develop gradually with each successive molt. A similar *incomplete metamorphosis* characterizes all the groups, which include the grasshoppers and roaches, true bugs, aphids and cicadas, and others of lesser importance. Many additional insects, however, have several larval stages that differ strongly from the adults. Usually the young are *grubs* or *caterpillars* and are followed by a resting stage (the *pupa*); in the larvae the wings develop internally and appear suddenly in the pupal period. *Complete metamorphoses* of this sort are typical of the more complex insects, among which can be mentioned the moths and butterflies, the bees, wasps, and ants, the beetles, the fleas, and the flies and mosquitoes (Figure 11-10).

Control of Molting. Except in the primitive orders, growth is confined entirely to the immature stages and proceeds as in the crustaceans by a series of *molts*. As in the crabs and their allies, too, control of molting is by means of hormones, but in the insects the endocrine glands concerned are located in the brain and associated structures, not in an eyestalk. Within the brain, between the two major ganglia that comprise it, are secretory cells known as the *intercerebral glands,* from which nerve cells extend to a small gland called the *cardiac body.* In addition, two other secretory organs are involved, the *corpus allatum* and the *prothoracic gland* (Figure 11-11).

Much of the original work indicating the presence of a hormonal mechanism was done on the blood-sucking bug

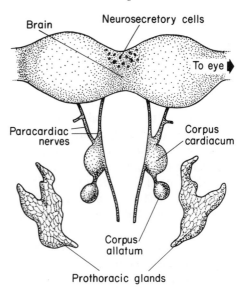

Figure 11-11. The glands that appear to control molting and development in insects.

Rhodnius, in which each immature stage feeds only once, following which it molts at the end of a definite period. If the head of the insect is removed soon after it has fed, it survives for some time, perhaps as long as a year, but never sheds its body covering. On the other hand, if a period of seven days elapses after feeding before decapitation, it undergoes ecdysis normally. In these and comparable studies *parabiotic pairs* are frequently used. Parabiosis involves the surgical union of two (or more) individuals, whether of mice, insects, or any animal, in such a way that the blood of one mingles with that of the other. When a *Rhodnius* decapitated after the seven-day interval is united parabiotically with one decapitated immediately after a meal, both insects molt. Even unfed headless specimens which have just completed a molting can be induced to undergo a second molt by use of this procedure. So the presence of a hormone that controls shedding is strongly indicated. In many similar studies on a variety of insects it has been found that the control of molting apparently centers in the secretory cells of the brain but involves an indirect route. In intact forms the hormone seems to travel by way of the nerve cells first to the cardiac body; from this organ it is conducted to the prothoracic glands where the actual growth and molt hormone, called *ecdyson,* is produced. In addition, growth and transformation into the adult condition is governed by a second hormone secreted in the corpora allata, one named the *juvenile hormone.* This substance has a restraining influence, for, as long as it is present, immature forms are prevented from acquiring the adult body form and reproductive organs. Normally, the corpora allata are functional only in juveniles; by their becoming inactive in the last larval stage, pupal and adult features are permitted to develop. If the corpora allata are removed from even very young juveniles, the adult form is acquired at the next molt.

Neural Control and Behavior. As in all arthropods, the heads of insects contain two sets of ganglia: one, the *subesophageal ganglia,* lying below the esophagus, and the *brain,* which forms a large mass between the eyes. The first set appears to be the principal *motor* center, governing the movements of the jaws, legs, wings, and all the other innumerable muscular processes of the body. On the other hand, the brain appears to be chiefly concerned with *sensory* functions; it receives stimuli from the various sense organs and regulates the movements of the entire insect according to them. To some extent an insect's reactions are strictly mechanical. For instance, if the antennae of an intact grasshopper are contaminated with a bit of tar or paint and the insect is offered a bristle at the same time, it will busily clean the bristle and neglect its own appendages. Nevertheless, reactions are not completely instinctive, for adjustments to abnormal situations are frequently made. Water beetles, which normally use the hind legs in swimming, will employ the middle pair if the usual set is removed, and, when deprived of the forelegs usually employed in cleaning its antennae, grasshoppers will make use of the middle legs instead.

That all behavior is not mechanical nor inborn as instinct in these animals is also shown by the fact that many have displayed a capacity for learning. Numbers of them have been trained to make the proper turns in simple mazes or to associate colors with the presence of food; in nature, too, advanced forms such as wasps and bees have exhibited a limited degree of intelligence. Although it is certain that numerous inborn behavior patterns do exist, they are frequently so integrated and adjusted by the brain that they are constantly made to serve the needs and purposes of the insect as a whole.

OTHER ARTHROPODA

Although a number of classes still remain undescribed here, only two are of sufficient importance to merit our attention. Superficially, these two are similar both in appearance and in structure. On the basis of the fact that all members have wormlike bodies and walking legs on the abdominal segments as well as on the thorax, the two groups were formerly united as a class, the Myriapoda, but today rank as full classes is usually accorded to each.

The Diplopoda. For the greater part the *millepedes* (Figure 11–12) are found beneath or within decaying logs, among fallen leaves, or in other moist situations

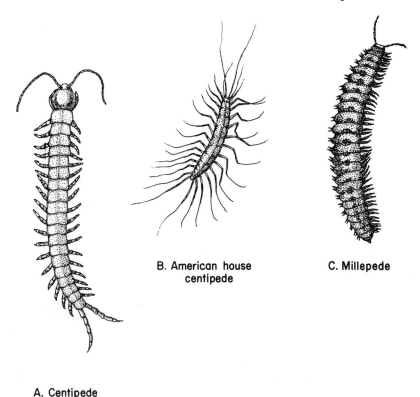

B. American house
centipede

C. Millepede

A. Centipede

Figure 11–12. Millepedes and centipedes. Diplopoda (A) have numerous short, week legs, whereas centipedes (B, C) have less abundant but longer and sturdier ones.

amply supplied with rotting vegetation. On the head are found a pair of antennae, a cluster of simple eyes (ocelli) on each side, and a pair of jaws. Behind the head, the first segment of the thorax lacks legs, but the remaining three are provided with a pair apiece. Typically, the abdomen is made of numerous segments, each of which is really double and consequently bears two pairs of legs. However, the legs are short and weak, so in spite of their numbers they are not great assets in locomotion and move their possessors only at a slow pace indeed. When handled, millepedes curl their bodies into loose spirals and exude a purplish secretion, which, aside from its staining effects, is quite harmless.

Their food seems to consist largely of fungal spores, yeasts, and bits of dried vegetable matter. As in all terrestrial arthropods, reproduction involves internal fertilization. From the egg hatches a larva more like an insect than a millepede, with but three pairs of legs, which increase in number at each molt.

The Chilopoda. While no dearth of legs occurs among these *centipedes,* the number present is much smaller than in the preceding group (Figures 11–12 and 11–13). Although fewer, these appendages are long and strong and carry the animals with sufficient speed to catch their prey of live mosquitoes, flies, and other insects. Except for the fact that the antennae are better developed, the head and its appendages are not strikingly distinct from those of the Diplopoda; however, the highly modified appendages of the first body segment reach forward below the mouthparts and are hollowed to form *poison claws* by means of which the prey is killed. No differentiation of the body is made into thorax and abdomen, the 18 or so segments present being virtually identical in all respects, including the number of legs each bears. Although often feared, possibly because of their unusual appearance, these animals are quite beneficial in the control of insects. No larval stages are found in this class; the newly hatched young resemble the adult except in number of legs.

The Mollusca

What the insects are to terrestrial communities, the members of this phylum are to the aquatic, for they too are highly diversified and abundant. Currently, more than 90,000 species are known. In contrast to the arthropods, it is not the means of locomotion that has been behind the success of the present phylum,

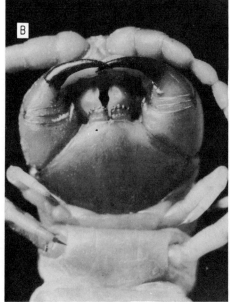

Figure 11–13. A typical centipede (*Scolopendra*). A. A European centipede (*Scolopendra cingulata*). B. This greatly enlarged view of the anterior end of the same species shows the poison claws of the first body segment with unusual clarity. (Courtesy of Dr. Friedrich Schremmer, Vienna, Austria.)

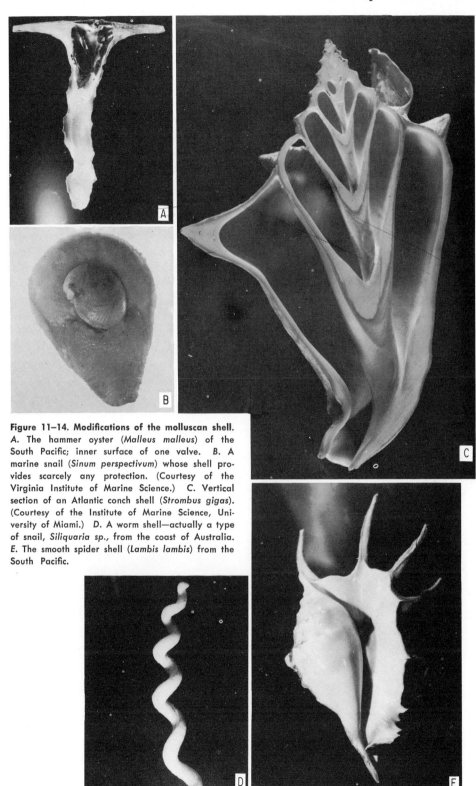

Figure 11–14. Modifications of the molluscan shell.
A. The hammer oyster (Malleus malleus) of the
South Pacific; inner surface of one valve.   B. A
marine snail (Sinum perspectivum) whose shell pro-
vides scarcely any protection. (Courtesy of the
Virginia Institute of Marine Science.)   C. Vertical
section of an Atlantic conch shell (Strombus gigas).
(Courtesy of the Institute of Marine Science, Uni-
versity of Miami.)   D. A worm shell—actually a type
of snail, Siliquaria sp., from the coast of Australia.
E. The smooth spider shell (Lambis lambis) from the
South Pacific.

for the singular muscular foot with which these animals are provided is not especially efficient—one need only think of the snail for an illustration of this point. Perhaps here the hard shell which usually protects the body is more probably the underlying factor, a shell which in spite of its rigidity shows a high degree of plasticity in its adaptation to a wide variety of situations (Figure 11–14).

In addition to the two traits named above, the phylum is characterized by the soft body, such as that of an oyster, to which trait the name Mollusca (meaning "soft") refers. Around this is found the *mantle,* a skinlike covering which secretes the shell when the latter is present; often the mantle is prolonged into flaps, and the space between is referred to as the *mantle cavity.* Although present, the *coelom* is proportionately small (Figure 11–15). The circulatory system is variable but always has one or more well-developed hearts. An unusual trait is found in the digestive system in the form of a rasping organ called the *radula,* which consists of a series of

movable plates amply provided with toothlike projections (Figure 11–16). Although the phylum includes six classes represented by modern species, only four are of sufficient importance to warrant separate discussion.

The Chitons. Along rocky shores of oceans, firmly attached to boulders below the level of high tide, live the chitons, which are flattened grublike creatures that often attain a length of 8 inches or more. These members of the class *Amphineura,* protected by a leathery mantle and a shell consisting of eight plates ("valves"), cling so tightly to the substrate that they are difficult to pry loose, even with a sharp instrument. No head is apparent, nor are tentacles present; although eyes are absent anteriorly, sets of simple ones are found on each plate. The food, which consists of algae of various types, is taken in through the mouth found on the underside of the body. On the undersurface, too, is the broad flat foot, which serves to attach the organism firmly. Around the foot in the nearly circular mantle cavity are numerous gills

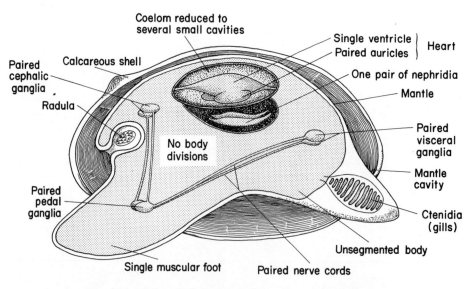

Figure 11–15. The principal distinguishing traits of the Mollusca.

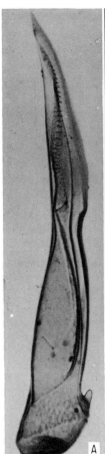

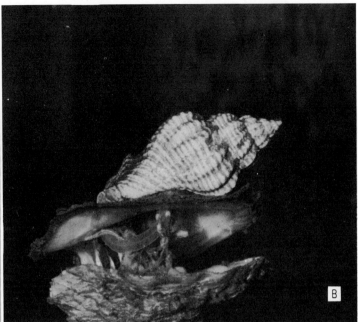

Figure 11–16. Feeding mechanisms in molluscans. A. The radula, a series of flat plates bearing teeth on one edge, is among the most distinctive features of molluscans. (Courtesy of Dr. A. J. Kohn, *Ecol. Mono.*, 29, 1959.) B. After drilling a hole through the shell of its prey, the common oyster drill (*Urosalpinx cinerea*) inserts the feeding tube through the hole and is here seen in the act of consuming the oyster's soft parts. (Courtesy of the Virginia Institute of Marine Science.)

called *ctenidia.* As a rule these animals are considered to be the most primitive living molluscan, for they occur as fossils over a span of nearly a half billion years.

The Snails and Relatives. In the class *Gastropoda* (meaning "belly-foot") are placed a highly diversified assortment of species, including forms with spirally twisted shells, such as the snails, whelks, and conchs, shell-less "snails," the slugs, and still others with flattened shells covering twisted bodies, such as the limpets and abalones. The gastropods start life as bilaterally symmetrical larvae, but early in development, after the posterior end has undergone a twisting movement, the anus becomes located above and behind the head. All members of the class have their heads marked by the location of one or two pairs of tentacles, one set bearing a distinct eye. In many species below the head is found a *mucous gland,* which secretes a substance useful in lubricating the surface over which the single foot must glide; the foot provides locomotion by a series of movements which pass wavelike along its length. In a number of marine forms active swimming is accomplished by undulations of the mantle spread out as "wings" on each side of the body; some sea slugs are called "magic-carpets," for they seem literally to sail through the sea water (Figure

A

Figure 11–17. Sea slug or nudi-branch. *A.* A nudibranch, with its curious gills on its back, is seen resting on the substrate after de-positing the string of eggs sus-pended in the eelgrass. (Courtesy of the Virginia Institute of Marine Science.) *B.* Tropical sea slugs, like this rose and white one from the Great Barrier Reef, are often brilliantly colored. This fact, to-gether with the graceful move-ments of their mantle while swimming, has led them to receive the name "flying carpets" in some parts of the globe.

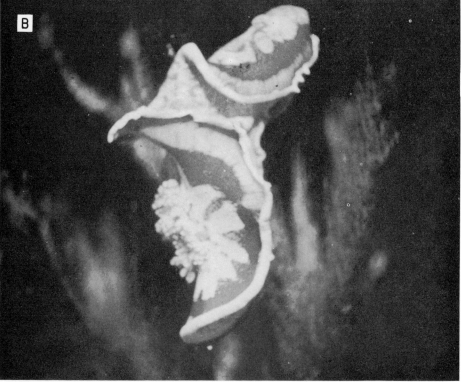

B

11–17). Much of the variety that exists in this class is provided by modifications of the shell; diversity arises not only by alteration in shape and color but by outgrowths in the form of spines and horns. As a result, shells are often highly attractive to the human eye, and collecting them is a popular and fascinating hobby.

The Clams, Oysters, and Allies. The members of this class, the *Pelecypoda* (meaning "hatchet-foot"), are distinguished from all others in having a shell consisting of two valves, one on each side of the body. Since among them are included such popular items of food as oysters and clams, little needs to be said about their general appearance. When the clam moves about on the floor of sea or river, its valves are partially opened, so that the ventral foot may be projected to push the animal along, the edges of the shell being used much as the runners of a sled. Other methods of locomotion are frequently employed, however. That delicacy, the scallop, for example, propels itself quite rapidly through the seas by snapping its valves together to eject water forcibly from the mantle cavity lying between them. In all members of the phylum folds of the mantle, the *siphons,* act as pores through which water enters to flow over the gills and to bring in the organic particles that serve as food. On the ctenidia and mantle are numerous microscopic cilia. When algae or other minute food particles become deposited on the surface, the beating action of the cilia moves them forward toward the mouth. As they progress, they become entangled in a mucous secretion and ultimately form a sort of rope which moves into the mouth by way of the *food groove.* Before entering the mouth, however, the particles are examined by means of the palpi, and any distasteful substances are rejected and

directed into the outgoing current of water. Thus these bivalves employ a filter form of feeding, a method of ingestion more typical of sedentary than of motile organisms. Hence it is not surprising to find that many members of this class have assumed a sessile mode of living; such forms, like the oysters, for example, attach themselves to the floor of the sea or other firm object by secreting a stalk.

The Squids, Octopi, and Nautili. All the living members of the class *Cephalopoda* (meaning "head-foot"), except the nautili mentioned later, either have their shells embedded within their mantles or lack them altogether, dependence being placed on their remarkable powers of locomotion for protection rather than on a body covering. In these animals the single foot is subdivided into two parts, one portion being tubular, the other produced into tentacles. The tubular section forms a *funnel* through which water can be forcibly expelled from the mantle cavity (Figure 11–18); by changing the position of the tip of this funnel, the animals can alter, or even reverse, the direction of their courses quite abruptly. Suction pads on the tentacles help to hold food securely; often the pads are enclosed by low ridges and armed with teeth which assist in holding such slippery objects as fish and crabs. Despite adventure stories, organisms of these sorts, not human beings, are the chief items of the cephalopod diet. Only rarely are divers attacked; even the fearsome-appearing octopus is in reality a shy creature that avoids contact with man as far as possible.

The two most interesting species of nautili, the *chambered* and *paper nautilus,* need mention here as the remnants of a formerly dominant group whose fossils record with great clarity the establishment and historical development of this class. The details of their life

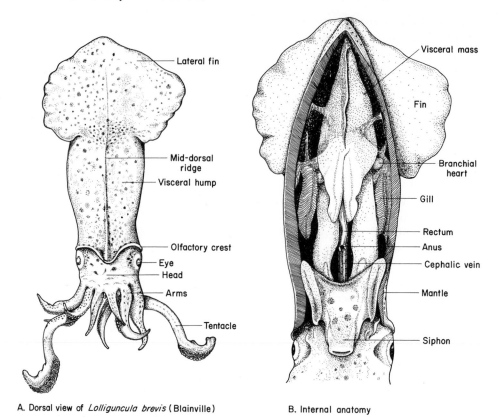

A. Dorsal view of *Lolliguncula brevis* (Blainville)

B. Internal anatomy

Figure 11–18. The internal anatomy of a squid.

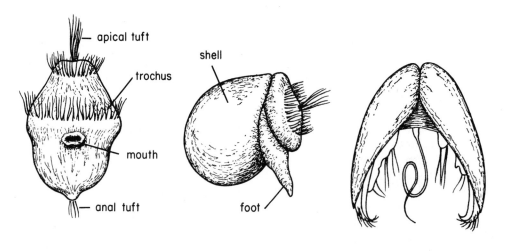

A. TROCHOPHORE

B. VELIGER

C. GLOCHIDIUM

Figure 11–19. Some larval types found in the Mollusca. *A.* Although some molluscans develop directly (i.e., without any larval stages), many marine forms have a trochophore larva not unlike that of certain annelids. In marine clams the trochophore develops into a veliger (B), but in freshwater clams a glochidium (C) larva is present that temporarily parasitizes fish.

story can be told much more effectively in a later chapter, however, and are reserved until then. For the present it must be pointed out that these forms have a free shell; in the chambered nautilus it is divided into chambers by means of septa. Except for a slender extension of the body through perforations in the cross walls, only the outermost chamber is occupied by this animal, the remainder being filled with gas not unlike that of the atmosphere. Beneath its outermost layer are found wavy lines, the *sutures,* where the septa fuse with the outer wall. These impressed markings are an important item in the cephalopod history and should be borne in mind. In the second species, the paper nautilus, only the female has a shell. Each year a new one is secreted after the old has been used as a floating container for the eggs.

Reproduction. All the mollusks reproduce solely by sexual means, the sexes being separate, as a rule, except in gastropods. Usually a *trochophore* larva, similar to that of the polychaete annelids, hatches from the egg. Later, as development proceeds, the band of cilia becomes thickened into a prominent rim about the body and is known as the *velum* (Figure 11–19), marking the second larval stage of the group, called the *veliger.* Not all mollusks have larval stages in their life histories; the cephalopods for one develop directly. In the fresh-water clams the trochophore stage is passed while still enclosed in the egg, where development proceeds to the formation of a minute bivalve called the *glochidium.* After hatching, the larvae float in the river until by chance they are taken into the mouth of a fish as it takes in water. On the way out of the fish they pass over the gills and ultimately become attached to these organs by means of long teeth on the edges of their valves. Following development as a parasite in this location, they eventually drop off and live a normal clamlike existence.

Biological Value. As a whole, the members of this phylum have remained relatively unexplored as experimental subjects in biology; only in recent years have they been found to possess features useful in the study of biological activities in general. The cephalopods are proving especially valuable in the study of neural action, for some of the nerve fibers, called giant fibers, attain a diameter of nearly 1 millimeter and are really gigantic in comparison to many nerves, which may be only 1 micron thick. Because of the relative ease of placing electrodes within these fibers, much knowledge of nervous conduction is being garnered through their use. Also present in these organisms is a well-developed brain and eyes that rival those of vertebrates in complexity.

The Echinodermata

Representing the second principal case within the Metazoa proper, a radial type of symmetry is found in the present phylum, the *Echinodermata,* a strictly marine assemblage. In contrast to the first example displayed by the Coelenterata, however, this type of body plan characterizes only the adults, the larvae being bilateral in organization; hence it is of a secondary nature. Another peculiarity of the starfishes, sea cucumbers, brittle stars, sea lilies, sea urchins, and others which constitute this group is found in the presence of an *endoskeleton* made of lime and composed of interlocking plates or of particles scattered through the epidermis. The name of the phylum, which can be interpreted as "spiny-skinned," refers to a third distinctive feature in the form of spines or tubercles which often cover the surface. The fourth

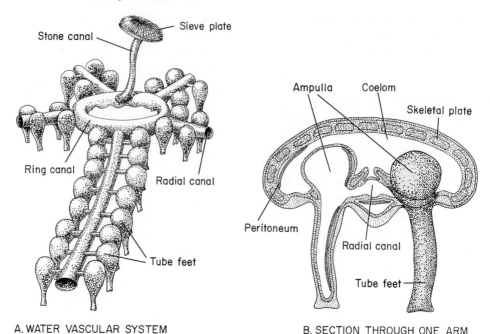

A. WATER VASCULAR SYSTEM   B. SECTION THROUGH ONE ARM

Figure 11–20. Prominent features of the Echinodermata.

outstanding trait is a *water-vascular system,* which occurs in no other phylum and is used in locomotion and other activities. This system opens to the waters of the sea by means of a pore often covered with a *sieve-plate.* From this run a number of tubes within the body or arms. Attached to these tubes are whole series of tubular blind sacs, called *tubefeet* (Figure 11–20), which serve to hold objects and to provide locomotion. This means of progression, however, is not conducive to speed, and the larger starfishes are probably the only animals that surpass snails in slowness; small species, on the other hand, can travel as many as 6 feet in one minute by the same means. In the entire phylum only approximately 10,000 species are known to exist at present (Figure 11–21).

Figure 11–21. Representative types of echinoderms. *A, B.* In addition to the familiar five-armed varieties of starfishes, there exist related forms with numerous arms, such as this crown of thorns from the South Pacific (*Acanthaster plauca*) which has a diameter of 15 inches. Other forms have no arms, as witness the pincushion type (*Calcita sp.*) of the Great Barrier Reef. *C.* Brittle stars have slender arms which can move quite rapidly; the species illustrated is *Ophiolepis elegans* of the Caribbean area. (Courtesy of the Marine Studios, Marineland, Fla.) *D.* Sea cucumbers are sluggish, cumbersome creatures that creep slowly about the ocean floor. *E, F.* Sea urchins are usually prickly as the *Arbacia punctulata* (E) shown here; sometimes the spines are flattened into plates (*F, Podophora sp.*). (E, courtesy of Carolina Biological Supply Co.; F, courtesy of the General Biological Supply House, Inc., Chicago, Ill.)

Yet it must not be supposed that this group is of no particular concern biologically, for such is not the case, as the members are abundant and widespread in the seas. In fact, it is an unusual assemblage of animals, organized in a fashion unlike all others—Libbie Hyman in a volume devoted to this phylum closes her preface with a salute to the echinoderms "as a noble group especially designed to puzzle the zoologist"! Their uniqueness is possibly most readily illustrated by the ingestive processes of the starfishes. Among these animals the food consists of clams, oysters, and similar shellfish. To obtain the contents protected by the shell, the starfish wraps its body about the intended victim, secures a firm hold by means of its tubefeet, and exerts a steady pull on the valves over a considerable period of time. Eventually the mollusk becomes fatigued and relaxes the muscles which close its protective coat. The starfish then everts its stomach, projecting it through its mouth in the process (Figure 11–22), and, after enclosing the victim within the folds of the digestive organ, partially digests its meal. After a few minutes, the stomach and its more or less digested contents are withdrawn into the body.

Moreover, the means of locomotion is highly distinctive. Since much of starfish behavior is manifested in this matter, considerable attention has been given to the water-vascular system, tubefoot action, and the coordination of their parts. Contrary to popular notion, the tubefeet do not pull the starfish along, except on vertical surfaces, but they have a stepping action that moves the creature forward by exerting a push (Figure 11–23). The tubefoot is extended forward, and when contact is made with the substrate, the center of the sucker is pulled in to produce a vacuum; secretion of mucus also helps to secure the sucker firmly. Still fully extended, the tubefoot

Figure 11–22. The everted stomach of a starfish. In this unusual photograph the stomach has been everted through the mouth and is distended as if in the act of ingesting food. (Courtesy of the Virginia Institute of Marine Science.)

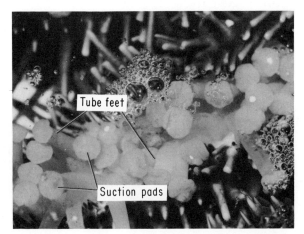

Figure 11–23. Tubefeet of a star-fish.

is then swung backward, thereby carrying the animal forward, as though each tubefoot were a leg. Finally, it releases its hold, contracts, and extends anteriorly again. In these activities all the tubefeet participate; even those that are out of contact with the substrate engage in coordinated movements, at least in intact animals. If, however, the nerve ring is severed on each side of a radial nerve (Figure 11–20), the tubefeet on the neurally isolated arm move entirely independently of the remainder, working in the opposite direction or becoming active when the rest are quiescent. Even arms completely detached from the body are able to move about in this manner, although at a slower rate than ordinarily.

Reproduction. Although echinoderms are noted for their ability to regenerate lost parts, no form of asexual reproduction occurs within this phylum. From the fertilized egg is hatched a bilaterally symmetrical larva, similar to a trochophore in general construction but highly modified in form. At first the *dipleurula,* as the newly hatched larva is called, is ciliated over its entire body; as it matures, these cilia are reduced to bands running vertically around the organism rather than transversely. Later the bands become prolonged outward into the form of flaps, recalling those of the veliger of the mollusks. These flaps become greatly elongated and subdivided to form efficient swimming organs. Still later five tentacles develop around the mouth. As additional tentacles become established arranged outwardly from the first ones, a five-parted radial symmetry is acquired and adult features develop, while the larval body and its complex flaps are lost.

The Hemichordata

Until recently the members of this group were uniformly treated as a subphylum of the phylum Chordata; modern practice, however, places them as a taxon separate from the latter in an effort to express better their positions relative to one another. No matter what the treatment, whether as an independent or a subordinate taxon, they are universally recognized as a side branch located on the stem that eventually leads to the chordates proper; in other words, they are a primitive branch of the chordate line (Figure 11–24). One characteristic of the adult that is suggestive of such kinship is the presence of gill slits opening into the pharynx. As shall be seen shortly, such *pharyngeal gill slits*

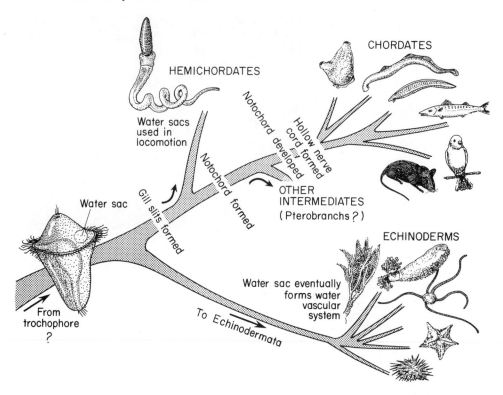

Figure 11–24. Diagram of the phylogeny of the chordates and related groups.

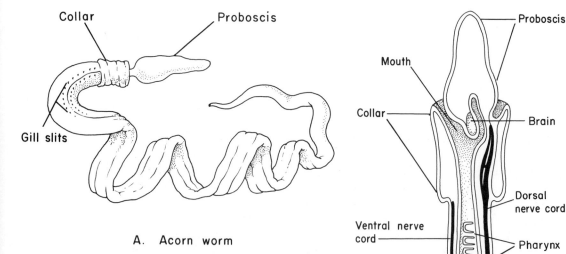

A. Acorn worm

Figure 11–25. An acorn worm and its structure. In the processes of creeping about on the ocean floor, the proboscis and collar are alternately expanded with water and then emptied.

B. Section through anterior end

constitute one of the few distinctive traits of the phylum Chordata, to which we ourselves belong. However, were it not for the peculiar larva that forms a part of the life cycle, the wormlike adults, called *acorn worms,* would be of little interest biologically, no matter what their supposed relationships, for their lives are spent in burrows in the ocean floor, merely feeding on algae by filter processes.

The thick *proboscis* and the *collar,* which form prominent features of their anatomy, are used in locomotion (Figure 11–25). In turn, each of these structures is inflated with water and contracted, the movements alternating in such a manner that the body is dragged

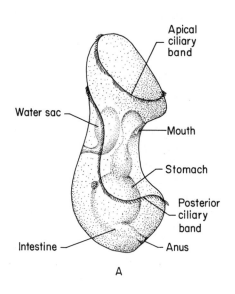

A

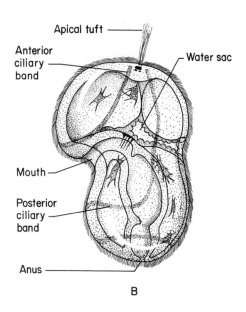

B

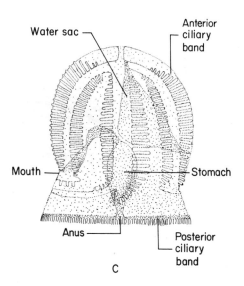

C

Figure 11–26. Larvae of the acorn worm and of a starfish. Similarities exist in the presence of the transparency of the body, in the expansion of the ciliated bands into lobes, in the curved body, and in the presence of a water sac.

slowly forward. Inflation is accomplished by means of the cilia that surround the pores pumping water into the respective structures, whereas contraction is by muscular activity. Unlike typical chordates, no notochord is present, and the poorly developed nervous system consists mostly of a series of nerve tracts not entirely differentiated from the body wall; dorsally in the collar, however, a short hollow cord is to be found.

As stated above, it is the larva that gives the group its importance, for, were this peculiar *tornaria* lacking, no evidence of any sort would exist to link this phylum to others. The tornarian shares several traits with larval echinoderms which are so unusual that little doubt of the common ancestry of the two groups can exist. In the first place, both have transparent bodies of the same general shape and construction (Figure 11–26), each provided with bands of cilia running lengthwise of the body. Not only do these bands correspond in general arrangement, but in each group they become prolonged into folds employed in swimming. Moreover, in recent years, it has been pointed out that both types of larvae have a *water sac* located above

the digestive tract and opening to the outside by a single dorsally situated pore. In the echinoderms the sac ultimately becomes prolonged into the tentacles and forms the water-vascular system, whereas in the acorn worms it eventually develops into the water sac of the proboscis.

The Chordata

In contrast to the Echinodermata, the present phylum shows only three traits that distinguish its members, and not all of these are universally present among the several classes. These features, shown in Figure 11–27, include first of all a set of slitlike openings into the pharynx, known as *pharyngeal gill slits,* at some time in the life history. The second distinctive structure is a supportive rod of turgid cells, the *notochord,* which extends the length of the body; in most vertebrates this rod is present only in the embryo, being replaced by the vertebral column in the adult. Finally, the nervous system includes a dorsally situated central portion that is hollow, a character that is usually referred to as a *dorsal hollow nerve cord*.

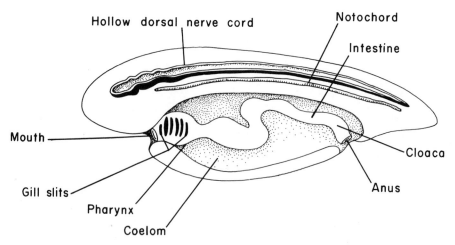

Figure 11–27. The characteristics of the phylum Chordata.

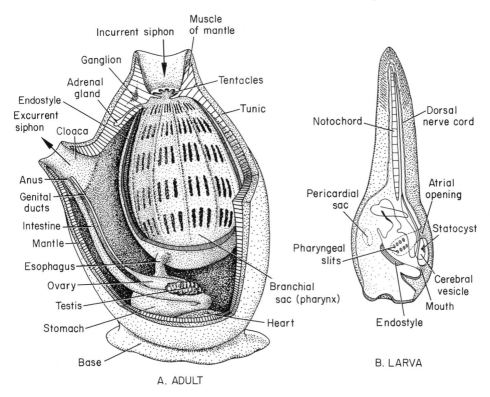

Figure 11–28. Structure and larva of a tunicate.

THE PROTOCHORDATA

Although there is room for some doubt regarding the proper affinities of the acorn worms, there is none concerning the tunicates and the lancelets correctly being considered as chordates, unlike the vertebrates though they may be in bodily form. All the distinctive features—notochord, pharyngeal gill slits, and dorsal hollow nerve cord—are quite apparent, at least in immature examples. In this subphylum the members are characterized by the presence of a *branchial chamber,* the walls of which are penetrated by the gill slits in such a fashion that a basketlike enclosure is formed. Moreover, the external openings of the gill slits are enclosed in a special cavity, the *atrium,* into which water flows from the pharynx before leaving the animal

(Figure 11–28). The above-mentioned organisms constitute the two principal classes that share these characteristics.

The Tunicata. Although three main types of body organization are found within this class, attention is devoted only to the typical *tunicates,* or *sea squirts,* as they are sometimes called. These animals begin life as free-swimming larvae not unlike tadpoles in appearance but quite distinct in internal structure (Figure 11–28). In this immature form is a pronounced notochord and dorsal hollow nerve cord, along with the small atrium and other structures found in the adult. After a short active period, often only hours in duration, the larva attaches itself head down onto the substrate by means of the fixing disks. In this position the body undergoes a series of extreme changes. First of all the entire tail, including the noto-chord and dorsal nerve cord, is absorbed into the body, and the internal organs undergo a rotating movement. As many of the typical chordate features found in the larva are reduced or lost in the adult, these animals are frequently looked on as degenerate forms. However, they could also be considered specialized for a fixed existence.

The Cephalochordata. In this class are contained small animals which at first glance appear to be fish but which on closer inspection are seen to be head-less, eyeless, and without external openings for gills. Nor are any jaws or pairs of fins present; nor, for that matter, is there any indication of a brain except in the larva. These *lancelets* are confined to shallow portions of the oceans and feed by filter mechanisms similar to those of the tunicates. In these organisms the muscles and certain other organs are arranged in a segmented fashion. As this characteristic is also prominent in the vertebrates, the lancelets are often believed to represent a transitional stage between the higher tunicates and the simpler vertebrated animals (Figure 11–29).

THE VERTEBRATA

In spite of the fact that the 50,000 species known to belong to this subphylum do not constitute an especially impressive array in terms of numbers when compared to some other taxa described in this chapter, nevertheless they are of such importance from other considerations that they shall be given special treatment in the chapter that follows. Here the Vertebrata receives brief mention so that its members as a unit may be seen in their proper position relative to the other animals. Chiefly the group is distinguished from the preceding chordates by the absence of a character rather than by the presence of any peculiarity, for actually there exists no structural trait that is a constant feature among all its constituents. This statement is true even regarding the vertebral column for which the subphylum is named, as the lowest fishlike forms lack this characteristic. The absent organ that really distin-

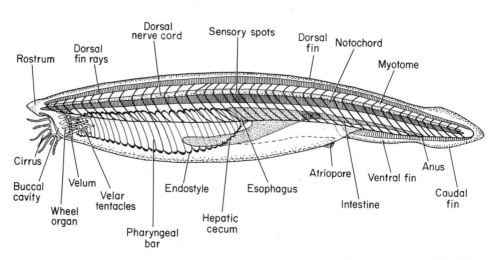

Figure 11–29. Lancelet structure. Adults are often referred to as *Amphioxus*, but this generic name really applies only to certain Eastern Atlantic species. The excretory system is distinctive in that it includes solenocytes like those of some annelids.

TABLE 11–1
OUTLINE OF METAZOAN CLASSIFICATION FOLLOWED IN THIS TEXT

Phylum	Classes	Common Names
1. Mesozoa		mesozoans
2. Coelenterata		coelenterates
(Cnidaria)	Hydrozoa	hydroids, hydromedusae
	Scyphozoa	jellyfish
	Anthozoa	sea anemones, corals
3. Platyhelminthes		flatworms
	Turbellaria	planarians
	Trematoda	flukes
	Cestoda	tapeworms
4. Nemathelminthes		roundworms, nematodes
5. Rotifera		rotifers
6. Annelida		segmented worms
	Polychaeta	sandworms, clamworms
	Oligochaeta	earthworms, fresh-water worms
	Hirudinea	leeches
7. Arthropoda		arthropods
	Crustacea	crabs, water fleas, lobsters, etc.
	Arachnida	spiders, harvestmen, etc.
	Diplopoda	millepedes
	Chilopoda	centipedes
	Insecta	beetles, ants, wasps, etc.
8. Mollusca		mollusks, shellfish
	Amphineura	chitons
	Aplacophora	solenogastres
	Gastropoda	snails, slugs, etc.
	Pelecypoda	oysters, clams, mussels, etc.
	Scaphopoda	tooth-shells
	Cephalopoda	nautili, squids, octopi
9. Echinodermata		echinoderms
	Crinoidea	sea lilies
	Asteroidea	starfish
	Ophiuroidea	brittle stars, basket stars
	Echinoidea	sea urchins, sand dollars
	Holothuroidea	sea cucumbers
10. Hemichordata		acorn worms
11. Chordata		chordates
Protochordata (subphylum)		tunicates, lancelets
Vertebrata (subphylum)		vertebrates
	Agnatha	lampreys, hagfish
	Elasmobranchii	sharks, rays
	Osteichthyes	ray-finned fish
	Coelacanthia	lobe-finned fish
	Choanichthyes	lungfish
	Amphibia	salamanders, frogs, toads
	Reptilia	turtles, lizards, snakes, etc.
	Aves	birds
	Mammalia	mammals

guishes them from the Protochordata is the atrium, for in the present group, the gill slits open directly to the outside, not into an atrial cavity. In addition all vertebrates possess a well-developed coelom and a segmented body.

Questions for Review and Thought

1. What are the advantages and disadvantages of an exoskeleton in contrast to an endoskeleton? Name all the phyla studied that have skeletons of each type. How have some of the disadvantages of an exoskeleton been overcome by their possessors?

2. List the characteristic features of the five phyla discussed in this chapter. In addition list the classes into which each is subdivided, with representative types and distinctive characteristics as far as this information is available.

3. In what ways do the Arthropoda show relationships with the Annelida? What, if any, relationships are indicated between the Annelida and Mollusca? The Mollusca and Echinodermata? The Echinodermata and Hemichordata? And the latter and Chordata? Give the bases for your answers in each case.

4. What is meant by the term metamorphosis? What other animals have you studied that appear to metamorphose?

5. Compare the known hormonal activities of the crustaceans with those of an insect.

6. What methods of obtaining food are used by various types of mollusks? What means of locomotion are found within this phylum? What do you consider the Mollusca to be, more complex or simpler than the Arthropoda? Explain your answer.

7. Describe the means of locomotion found among the starfishes. In what other ways would you consider the echinoderms a unique assemblage?

8. List the lower chordates and the features that resemble those of the vertebrates.

Supplementary References

Barnes, R. D. *Invertebrate Zoology.* Philadelphia, Saunders, 1963.

Borradaile, L. A., and F. A. Potts. *The Invertebrata,* 4th ed. Cambridge, Cambridge Univ. Press, 1962.

Cloudsley-Thompson, J. L. *Spiders, Scorpions, Centipedes and Mites.* New York, Pergamon, 1958.

Fritsch, K. von. *Bees, Their Vision, Chemical Sense, and Language.* Ithaca, Cornell Univ. Press, 1950.

Gilmour, D. *The Biochemistry of Insects.* New York, Academic Press, 1961.

Hyman, Libbie H. *The Invertebrates,* Vol. 4. *Echinodermata.* New York, McGraw-Hill, 1955.

———. *The Invertebrates,* Vol. 5. *Smaller Coelomate Groups.* New York, McGraw-Hill, 1959.

Imms, A. D. *Social Behaviour in Insects.* London, Methuen, 1947.

Parker, T. J., and W. A. Haswell. *A Textbook of Zoology,* 7th ed., 2 vols. London, Macmillan, 1962.

Stirton, R. A. *Time, Life, and Man.* New York, Wiley, 1959.

Tinbergen, N. *The Study of Instinct.* Oxford, Oxford Univ. Press, 1952.

Wigglesworth, V. B. *Insect Physiology,* 5th ed. London, Methuen, 1956.

The Vertebrata

W HILE occasionally this category of animals is elevated to the level of a phylum by some animal systematists, most usually it is treated as a subphylum of the Chordata. That its members are closely related to the simpler chordates is clearly established by their sharing such unique traits as the notochord, pharyngeal gill slits, and dorsally situated hollow nerve cord; but as the phylogenetic history has not yet been completely unraveled, the degree of relationship between these two taxa still remains uncertain. In contrast, within the limits of the present taxon the evolutionary history, while still far from being complete, is doubtlessly more thoroughly known than that of any other group of animals. This situation in great measure stems from a combination of factors, including the relative abundance of many of its species, their attainment of proportionately large body size, and their possession of such hard objects as teeth and bone which fossilize readily and provide clear records of past phylogenetic steps. Even the extant types alone, those to be discussed in the following pages, present a remarkably clear account of the changes involved in the transition of the primitive strictly aquatic forms into advanced varieties perfected for an existence on land.

The Aquatic Groups

The Agnatha. The agnathans, including the cyclostomes represented today by such eel-like forms as the *lampreys* and the *hagfishes,* are the most primitive of living vertebrates. In the first place their primitiveness is shown by their lack of jaws, to which condition the term

Agnatha (meaning "jawless") refers, the mouth being developed to form a rasping and sucking organ. Through its use, adult lampreys, which occur in both fresh and salt water, attach themselves to the bodies of fish and suck their blood, whereas the entirely marine order of hagfishes attack sick or dead fish, penetrating the body wall and consuming the flesh. Furthermore, the simplicity of the cyclostomes is often considered to be reflected in the absence of a bony skeleton, for only cartilaginous supportive elements exist in this group. Nor is a vertebral column present; the notochord remains intact throughout life and provides the principal longitudinal support. Along the sides of the body are a variable number of gill slits, ranging from 7 to 14 in the lampreys and most hagfishes. No paired fins are found on the body; only single ones, called *median* fins, are placed along the middle of the back or belly (Figure 12–1).

As indicated above, the lampreys in the course of their life history pass through a larval stage. After hatching, the *ammocoetes* larva lives for several years in burrows in muddy ocean or lake bottoms, feeding on algae and other uni-

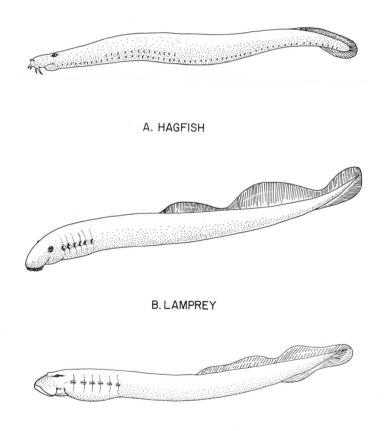

A. HAGFISH

B. LAMPREY

C. AMMOCOETES

Figure 12–1. Examples of modern agnathans. Modern agnathans are represented today by a number of species each of hagfish and lamprey eels. Most species of lampreys pass through a larval stage called an *ammocoetes.*

Figure 12–2. A lemon shark (*Negaprion brevirostris*) swimming in shallow water. (Photograph by William M. Stephens.)

cellular life by filter methods, slowly increasing in size, and eventually assuming the adult form and structure (Figure 12–1).

The Elasmobranchii. In the members of this class, the *sharks, rays,* and *skates,* the jaws are well provided with teeth. When the jaws were originally formed, use was made of the cartilaginous elements that supported the first pair of gills, so in these animals the number of gill slits is reduced, as a rule, to six. No

Figure 12–3. A stinging ray. This specimen, about 16 inches in length, was captured off the coast of Queensland, Australia.

bone is found in the endoskeleton, only cartilage, but the notochord is largely replaced by a series of *vertebrae*. In addition, two sets of *paired fins* and a variable number of the median variety are found on the body (Figure 12–2). Embedded in the skin are numerous fine toothlike scales on which an enamel layer covers an inner portion of dentine.

It is well known that sharks are carnivorous, feeding on fish, crabs, and other animals of the sea. In size they range from the dogfish, a foot or so in total length, to the whale shark which attains a length of 50 feet—the largest cold-blooded vertebrate extant today. Skates and rays are strongly dorsoventrally flattened derivatives of sharks; among them are represented the devilfish or manta, stingrays or stingarees, electric rays, and sawfish (Figure 12–3).

The Osteichthyes. Translated, the name of this class means "bony fishes" and refers to one of the distinctive

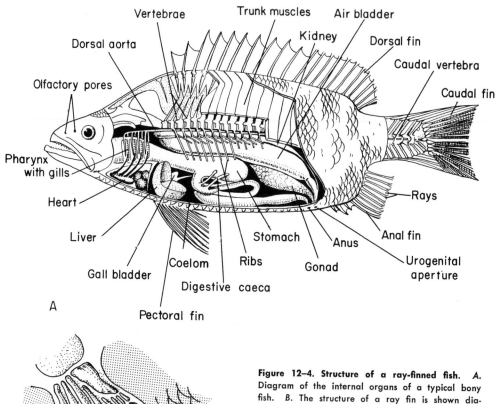

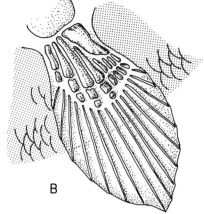

Figure 12–4. Structure of a ray-finned fish. A. Diagram of the internal organs of a typical bony fish. B. The structure of a ray fin is shown diagrammatically. C, D. The roentogram (C) of *Chaetodon falcifer* (D) shows the major features of the skeletal system with unusual clarity. (Courtesy of Dr. Carl L. Hubbs.)

features of its members. The presence of bone in the endoskeleton is a trait that is sometimes secondarily absent in some representatives. To it belong all the typical fish of both fresh and salt waters —bass, trout, snappers, gar, catfish, perch, and all the rest. Sometimes these animals are called *ray-finned fishes,* for their paired fins consist of a large number of small bones from which numerous fine *rays* extend to support the main portion of the appendages (Figure 12–4). In the body the skeleton has become highly perfected, with the development of a bony vertebral column and the resulting reduction of the notochord, while externally an *operculum* has been developed (Figure 12–4) covering the gill slits, now reduced to five pairs. This is a highly successful group and contains upward of 25,000 known species, many of which, especially in tropical waters, are brightly colored and beautifully patterned (Figure 12–5).

Transitional Types

With the development of efficient swimming appendages in the form of ray fins and broad tail, the acquisition of buoyancy through the formation of a swim bladder, and the protection of the delicate gills by the growth of an opercular plate, the mastering of an aquatic environment appears to have reached a climax with the Osteichthyes, as attested by the wide diversity of bony fishes living today. But the conquering of the land, whether by vertebrates or any other aquatic organism, involves many drastic changes in body structure, and some of the organs demanded by an air-breathing existence need to be acquired before life on land is a possibility. For example, gills must remain moist to function at all and for efficient operation require a flow of water over them. Hence the first stages in the transition from water dwellers to land inhabitants are necessarily repre-

Figure 12–5. A young queen angelfish. Strikingly shaped and brightly colored fish abound in tropical waters, especially around coral reefs. (Photograph by William M Stephens.)

Figure 12–6. A modern coelacanth. *Latimeria chalumnae,* found at considerable depths in the Indian Ocean off the coast of East Africa, is the only known survivor of this group.

sented by certain strictly aquatic organisms—that is to say, forms that are in a measure preadapted for a terrestrial existence.

The Coelacanthia. Until recently all coelacanths, or *lobe-fin fishes,* were believed to have been extinct for more than 70 million years, for no fossils of a later age had ever been encountered. During the last decade, however, a living representative was found off the east coast of Africa, a discovery that aroused much excitement among zoologists and paleontologists alike. Since then several additional specimens have been obtained, and

detailed studies of the anatomy are in progress. Perhaps the most valuable aspect of this find is the fact that its morphology has been ascertained to correspond closely to the restorations of fossil species made by paleontologists, in spite of the existence in their morphology of many unique features, including such things as a three-parted tail (Figure 12–6). Although the modern form, called *Latimeria chalumnae,* is entirely aquatic —in fact, it lives at exceedingly great depths in the Indian Ocean—its fins, or at least those of its ancestors, show a construction usually believed to eventually

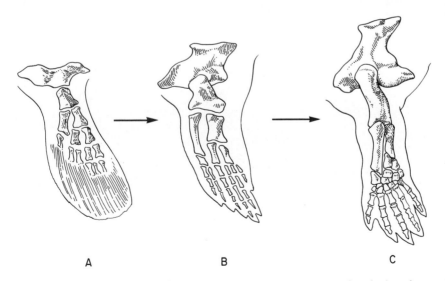

A   B   C

Figure 12–7. The lobe-fin and the origin of legs. One current theory suggests that the leg of terrestrial vertebrates arose by modification of the lobe type of fin.

lead to the formation of a structure necessary for an active terrestrial life. In the fossil forms the bones in the paired fins are arranged so that a series of long ones form a main axis capable of bearing a much greater weight than the small units of the bony fishes' fins. One existing concept holds that these lobe fins gave rise to the ancestral legs of the first land-dwelling vertebrates (Figure 12–7). Otherwise the coelacanths show no advances over the Osteichthyes, for they are essentially identical in structure and possess the same number of gill slits.

The Choanichthyes. "Nostril fishes" is the meaning of the name for this class and refers to one of two advances that its members show, for the nostrils here open internally into the mouth cavity, whereas such is not the case in earlier vertebrates. The second organ that suggests progress is indicated by the common name "lungfishes" for this taxon; among its living representatives for the first time is found a respiratory structure capable of employing air, although these early lungs are indeed far simpler than our own. Possibly at first this structure was of value chiefly when the lakes in which these fish lived became deficient in oxygen, as is the case today with the Australian species. In the more advanced forms of present-day Africa (Figure 12–8) and South America, use is made of the lung for a semiterrestrial existence in mud burrows, which the fish build during the annual periods of drought. The eggs too show an additional step in a forward direction—namely, the acquisition of a thick gelatinous coating, not

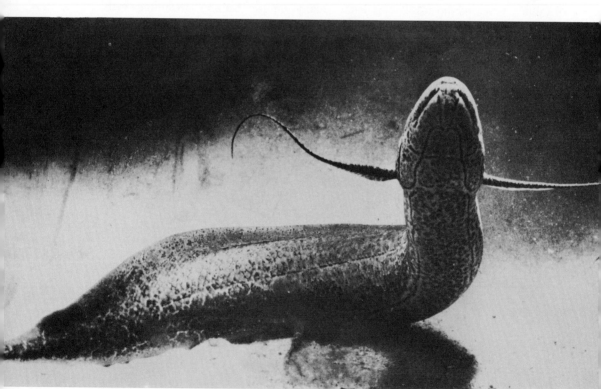

Figure 12–8. An African lungfish. This example of an African species of lungfish (*Protopterus aethiopicus*) was photographed in the aquarium of the Université Libre de Bruxelles by Prof. J. Bouillons, Brussels, Belgium.

unlike that of the following class, whereas the more primitive groups for the most part lack a protective covering.

The Amphibia. While the foregoing fishes display some of the adaptations essential to any sort of existence surrounded by air, the amphibians are the very first vertebrates that can be considered terrestrial to any extent. Nevertheless, the frogs, toads, salamanders, and caecilians (Figure 12–9) that constitute this group are limited in their capacity to live in this new environment. Although lungs are present, they are so inefficient that the skin carries out much of the respiratory function; as a result these animals are restricted to the moister areas of the earth. Moreover, though the legs are well developed, their state of imperfection is indicated by the absence of claws or other form of armature on the digits' ends. An even stronger tie to water is found in the reproductive processes. Generally the eggs, invested only by a soft gelatinous coat, are deposited and fertilized in water, and from these eggs are hatched larval forms, which, provided with gills but without lungs and legs, require an aquatic medium for further development. Thus the amphibians are

Figure 12–9. Three types of amphibians. *A.* A canyon tree frog (*Hyla arenicolor*) clings to a tree trunk in Big Bend National Park, Texas, by means of its suction pads. *B.* Spadefoot toads (*Scaphiopus hammondi*) are rarely seen as they are strictly nocturnal; the hind foot bears a backward-projecting flat tubercle used as a spade by the toads in digging burrows in which they spend the day. *C.* Caecilians are wormlike amphibians which have lost their legs in becoming adapted to their burrowing existence. Most of these creatures, like this Brazilian species (*Siphonops annulatus*), are found in the tropical regions. (*A, B,* courtesy of Dr. W. G. Degenhardt; *C,* courtesy of Dr. Carl Gans.)

Figure 12–10. Restoration of a fossil amphibian. Such labyrinthodonts, as shown in the drawing, were among the first vertebrates to have become terrestrial. They are usually considered to be ancestral to both the modern amphibians and reptiles.

chained to a watery environment for much of their life cycle, as well as for a portion of their bodily functions. Only several thousand species of Amphibia survive today, but in former years they once dominated all the continents, having made their first appearance about 300 million years ago (Figure 12–10).

Predominantly Terrestrial Forms

The Reptilia. Most of the steps toward a complete terrestrial life beyond the level represented by the Amphibia are not known, for the next higher group, the *reptiles*, possess all the features essential for a life on land (Figure 12–11).

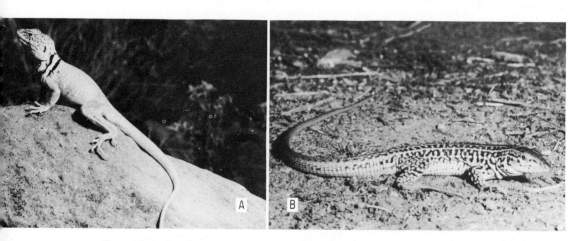

Figure 12–11. Two lizards of western North America. *A.* The male collared lizard (*Crotophytus collaris baileyi*) is often brilliantly colored, being yellow or orange and having blue spots along the black bands of the collar. *B.* The tessellated racerunner (*Cnemidophorus tessellatus*) from New Mexico is known to occur only as females; hence, it is becoming to be accepted that this species is probably parthenogenetic—that is, arises from unfertilized eggs. (Both photos courtesy of Dr. W. G. Degenhardt.)

Figure 12–12. A marine turtle. This female Pacific ridley turtle (*Lepidochelys olivacea*) was captured off the coast of Mexico. (Courtesy of Dr. Archie Carr.)

The digits are provided with claws, the skin, having lost most of its respiratory functions, no longer needs to remain moist and is provided with scales, and the lungs are completely developed, along with movable ribs to serve as a pump. Moreover, the egg is protected by a resistant covering, and within it the growing embryo possesses a series of membranes through means of which it respires, entirely independent of an aquatic medium. But in spite of the fact that all these requisite attributes had been acquired, the earliest reptiles did not at once free themselves from their freshwater habitations. Rather, as shown by modern descendants of one primitive group, the *turtles* (Figure 12–12), the ancestors probably lived both in and out of the water, exploring the banks along streams and lakes for food and laying their eggs in the soil at the proper seasons, but equally capable of catching fish or of seeking shelter within the rivers when necessary, for it must be remembered that only a relatively few, highly evolved turtles have become entirely

dwellers of the dry land; most species even today are inhabitants of ponds, streams, and the oceans. The members of a second group, though considerably advanced structurally over the foregoing reptiles, the *crocodiles* and *alligators,* similarly show the same duality of adaptation, as is equally true of numerous fossil reptilians. In contrast, most *snakes* (Figure 12–13) and *lizards* (Figure 12–11), as well as an ancestral form, the *tuatara* (Figure 12–14), found only in a few localities of New Zealand, show the complete loss of this character and for the most part have become strictly terrestrial—in fact, many of them are the characteristic vertebrates of the desert regions of the earth. Nevertheless, some snakes are seagoing animals, even mating and giving birth to living young far removed from land.

In addition to the establishment of an egg protected against its external environment, the reptiles show a second feature refining the reproductive processes. As the eggs no longer are deposited openly in water, fertilization has to occur before

Figure 12–13. Snakes of various types. *A.* The taipan, a slender and handsome species found in Queensland and New Guinea, grows to a length of about 8 feet and is rated as the world's most poisonous snake. (New York Zoological Society photo.)   *B.* The coral snake (*Microroides euryxanthus*) of southern United States is a small relative of the taipan and is quite poisonous too; it is most attractive in color, being bright yellow with red and black bands.   *C.* In the same region as the latter, a similar appearing species occurs which is quite harmless—the banded king snake (*Lampropeltis doliata annulata*). It is readily distinguished by the fact that the red bands are bordered with black. (*B, C,* courtesy of Dr. W. G. Degenhardt.)

Figure 12–14. An ancestral lizard. Along rocky beaches in a few areas of New Zealand is found the tuatara (*Sphenodon sp.*), noted especially for its retention of an eye in the middle of its head that the primitive lizard stock possessed. (San Diego Zoo photo.)

the shell has been added; in other words, the process has to take place within the female's body. To assist in internal fertilization, the male reptilian possesses a *penis* by means of which the spermatozoa are transferred from the body of the male to that of the female. Through all these advances along with a highly plastic body, the reptiles, although reduced to only about 5,000 species today, were the ruling vertebrates in the world for more than 100 million years. The familiar dinosaurs, flying pterodactyls, and fishlike mosasaurs are only a few examples of the extreme diversification that this group developed from its origin 325 million years ago.

The Aves. Successful as the foregoing reptiles may have been in conquering many varied ecological situations, they were never capable of living in cold regions, for as the air temperature drops, their metabolic rate decreases accordingly and at points lower than 50°F nearly ceases. To conquer frigid areas or seasons, two things are required over and above the anatomical equipment already possessed by these forms—namely, a coat resistant to thermal radiation and an efficient circulatory system. The scaly covering of the cold-blooded reptiles provides only a slight degree of insulation against the loss of heat; however, when these scales are modified in the form of the *feathers* characteristic of all *birds,* they become highly resistant to the passage of heat (Figure 12–15). In the reptiles, too, the blood is pumped by a strong organ, but the heart is not entirely perfected, as it is incompletely subdivided into four chambers. The two receiving chambers, the atria, are completely separated and maintain the freshly oxygenated blood after its return from the lungs isolated from the deoxygenated portion returned from the body. However, the septum between the two pumping chambers, the ventricles, is not entirely closed; consequently, the blood becomes intermingled here, so that which goes to the body is only partly oxygenated while that to the lungs is already partly saturated with oxygen—an inefficiency in both the receipt and supply of the gas. While some reptilians, including the crocodiles, have overcome this handicap to some extent and through evolutionary processes have acquired a nearly complete partition that largely divides the ventricle into two, in the birds the septum has become entire. In the latter, blood from the body and lungs thus never becomes intermixed, with greatly increased over-all performance as a result.

Although not widely diversified except in color, birds are doubtlessly the most highly specialized of the vertebrates. As a whole they are strictly adapted to aerial life (Figure 12–16), except for a few running forms, such as the ostrich and emu and the semiaquatic penguins and auks (Figure 12–17). As adaptations for flight, birds have acquired many modifications, among which can be mentioned light, hollow bones, a series of air sacs connected to the lungs for added buoyancy, and particularly a set of wings. These wings are unique among flying animals of all types in consisting of a web of feathers rather than of membrane, as in bats, insects, and the former ptero-dactyls. Other adaptations are found in the exceptionally well-developed eyes, the reduction of the number of ovaries and oviducts through the loss of the right set, and the partial fusion of the ribs and the modification of the breastbone (sternum) into a keel for the support of the powerful muscles required for flight. A high rate of metabolism is maintained, too, toward the same end, the body temperature of most flying species being maintained at 110 to 112°F.

While modern birds are sharply differentiated from existing reptiles, their reptilian ancestry is reflected in many of their internal parts and in the possession of similarly constructed scales on the legs

Figure 12–15. The adaptability of birds to climate. The ability of birds to become adapted to extremes of climatic conditions is well indicated by the two species shown here. The snowy owl of North America (A) lives on the barren tundra islands in the Arctic Ocean, while the red bird of paradise (B), as others of its ilk, thrives in the hot humid forests of New Guinea. (Both photos courtesy of the San Diego Zoo.)

Figure 12–16. Some African birds. Although these two species look familiar to residents of Europe and North America alike, both the spoonbill (A) and the eagle owl (B) shown here are indigenous to South Africa. (By kind permission of the Natal Parks Game and Fish Preservation Board.)

Figure 12–17. A pair of emperor penguins. Penguins have become so adapted to an aquatic existence that they have lost the ability to fly; their wings are used solely in "flying" under water. (San Diego Zoo photo.)

and feet. Moreover, early fossil forms, extremely rare because of the fragility of the skeleton, show many resemblances to certain extinct running reptiles, the saurischians. The notorious fossil form, *Archaeopteryx,* has a skull, legs, hip girdle, and long tail, quite like those of the Saurischia. In addition, in this and other early fossil birds, teeth identical in morphology to those of the cold-blooded reptiles and correspondingly set in sockets are found in the jaws (Figure 12–18). As a matter of fact, birds are so slightly distinguished morphologically from the ancestral line that frequently they are referred to as "glorified reptiles."

The Mammalia. While in contrast to the avians the *mammals* are largely adapted to a terrestrial life, the present class shows many structural features paralleling those of the foregoing one. A heat-retaining coat composed of scales, modified as hair in the present group, is similarly found, as well as a four-chambered heart. However, the enumerated traits are similarities, not identities; in the mammals, for instance, the aorta that leads from the left ventricle turns to the left to form the dorsal artery, whereas in birds it turns to the right. Also it might be pointed out here that while the hairy coat and efficiency of the heart mecha-

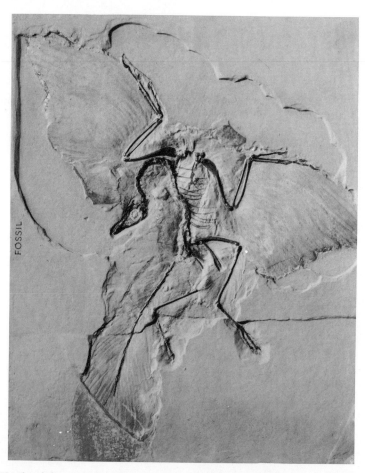

FOSSIL

Figure 12–18. The skeleton of *Archaeopteryx*. The presence of teeth in the jaws, claws on the wings, and the long bony tail are indications of the relationships of birds to reptiles. (Courtesy of the American Museum of Natural History.)

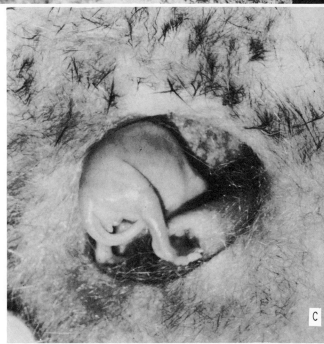

Figure 12–19. Several of the more primitive mammals. Two of this trio of figures show mammals that lay eggs not too unlike those of reptiles. A. The duckbill platypus is a semiaquatic form that feeds on earthworms and other animals on the bottoms of rivers. Burrows are built along the banks and contain a nest in which the female deposits eggs covered with a leathery shell. B. The spiny anteater, or echidna, is a relative of the platypus but is entirely terrestrial; each year the female produces a single egg, covered by only a thin membrane, which she places in a pouch on the abdomen to hatch. C. The marsupials, including the American opossum illustrated here, usually have pouches like this one on the abdomen; only parts of two of the many 3-week-old young that make up this litter are exposed. (A, B. Australian News and Information Bureau photographs. C. Photograph by Oscar B. Greenleaf.)

nism are in part directed toward the control of body temperature, more than these characteristics are required to attain the end. The egg-laying mammal, the duck-billed *platypus,* though possessing both dense body fur and a four-chambered heart, is able to regulate its temperature only within broad limits. Without correlation to external conditions, fluctuations ranging between 86° and 98°F occur throughout each day.

All mammals (Figure 12–19) have a number of unique structures, among which may be mentioned *milk,* or *mam-* *mary, glands* and a muscular *diaphragm* used in breathing. Moreover, the teeth are subdivided into several types, each specialized for particular functions, and the lower jaw is comprised of only a single bone, while the middle ear contains three bones instead of one as in other vertebrates. From a paleontologist's point of view, in fact, these last two items are the only sound criteria that distinguish mammals from certain fossil reptiles of a type called the *therapsids*. Whereas modern reptiles and birds have four bones in the lower jaw, in those of the line that eventually produced the mammals, the number of elements was gradually reduced. Accompanying this series of changes, the bone that bears the teeth slowly increased in size and, finally, in the highest therapsids constituted the entire jaw save for a small remnant of one other. Eventually this remnant, along with a reduced bone from the cranium, becomes detached and enters into the auditory mechanism to form two elements of the middle ear (Figure 14–18). After loss of this fragment, the jaw thereafter consists of one bone forming the whole mandible. It is at this level that paleontologists arbitrarily draw a line between mammals and reptiles. Also indicative of a link between the two groups, it may be mentioned that the platypus shows many reptilelike features. For instance, its egg is quite identical with that of turtles or lizards in having a leathery, membranous coat, a well-developed yolk, and a precisely similar set of membranes within it during the course of its development into a young platypus. Furthermore, within its heart and brain are shown other reptilian features. Since the boundaries are thus strictly man-made, if the birds are "glorified" reptiles, are mammals any the less "disguised" ones?

As stated earlier, mammals are principally adapted to a terrestrial mode of life, and many species have acquired modifications in the structure of the appendages, resulting in a better performance in running. Among the jumping mice, rabbits, and kangaroos particularly, the hind leg shows specializations toward this end, while both pairs are modified for the function in the carnivores and hoofed mammals. On the other hand, a large number of mammalian types are specialized in different directions (Figure 12–20). The squirrels and the monkeys, for instance, are highly adapted for an arboreal existence, while seals, walruses, dugongs, and whales are aquatic. Even the aerial habitat has been successfully invaded by the bats; and moles and marsupial moles are highly perfected for a subterranean mode of life. All in all, a much greater diversity in bodily form has been achieved by the mammals than by the birds, but the latter greatly excel in the matter of coloration.

In the discussions above and in the preceding chapters perhaps the fact becomes clear that any particular group of organisms can only be thoroughly understood through a knowledge of others. Even the most advanced vertebrates share structural and physiological features with simpler ones, which have organs identical with those of the higher invertebrates. The latter in turn have traits in common with lower ones, so that the whole group of Metazoa form a well-integrated unit, tied together in addition on a cellular basis by the astral rays. Closely related forms share many *homologous* (i.e., corresponding in type of structure and in origin, but not necessarily in function, as, for example, the wing of a bird and foreleg of a dog) organs, less closely related ones still fewer, so that while the beginnings and ends of any given line may show no apparent likenesses, in between them occur many of the transitional steps. Perhaps, as has been suggested, the Metazoa may be related to the brown algae, as indicated by the homologous cellular features shared by these groups; perhaps some other unicellular form may prove to be ancestral, after further investigations have been made. Regardless of what may prove to be the actual case, gradually diminishing ties

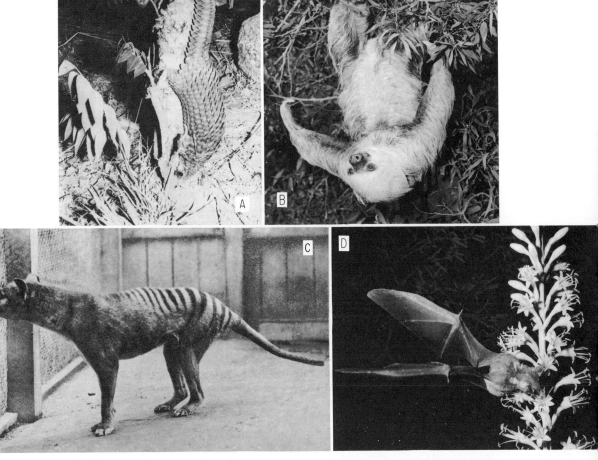

Figure 12–20. Some of the many specializations of mammals. A. The pangolin of Africa, which lives on a diet of ants and frequently climbs trees, wears a coat of armor made of leaflike plates. (Courtesy of Sylvia K. Sikes.) B. The two-toed sloth of South American tropics is adapted to an arboreal life in a most unusual way. (San Diego Zoo photo.) C. Carnivores which capture their prey by running them down are abundant among mammals, but this is not one of the usual type. This is the last known living Tasmanian tiger, photographed in the Hobart zoo in 1933, a marsupial but how much it resembles a dog! (Courtesy of the Australian News and Information Bureau.) D. While bats, the only aerial mammal, typically feed on insects, some varieties like this long nose (or hummingbird) bat of Arizona and central America seen feeding on agave blossoms, live on nectar. (Courtesy of Dr. Bruce J. Hayward.) E. In East African savannah country, two baby elephants play while the old cow keeps her eyes on the photographer. (Photo by Uganda Ministry of Information, Broadcasting, and Tourism.) F. A number of mammals have become secondarily adapted for an aquatic existence including whales, dugongs, and seals like this male elephant seal of the California coast. (Photo by Dr. R. A. Boolootian.)

will be established through them with still simpler forms, down to the very beginnings of life. But even though the blue-green algae and the bacteria are thus far remote from both the metazoans and flowering plants, within their cells occur corresponding series of chemical reactions performed by largely homologous compounds, which fact serves in linking the whole of life together.

Questions for Review and Thought

1. List the characteristics of each of the lower aquatic groups in such a manner that the series of changes involved in their development from a simpler to a specialized condition is shown. If the more highly evolved groups possess fewer gills than the more primitive, what might be deduced to be true concerning the former's efficiency in gill functioning?

2. Before a fishlike form can even begin to live on dry land, what organs must be acquired? Of what value are nostrils and why are they essential to a terrestrial organism but not to an aquatic one of similar food habits?

3. By what measures are the amphibians adapted to a terrestrial life and by what are they still dependent on water? Some highly specialized salamanders have secondarily lost their lungs; how do you suppose they survive for long periods on land?

4. State the features by which reptiles are more highly perfected for living on land than the Amphibia. What evidence suggests that the early reptilians did not at once completely abandon aquatic situations?

5. How are birds and mammals still more fitted for occupying the land than the cold-blooded reptiles? On what bases are birds considered specialized for an aerial existence?

6. For what environment are mammals as a whole particularly specialized? Which features of mammalian anatomy are especially distinctive of the group? Name some mammals that have secondarily assumed an aquatic type of life.

7. As a whole would you say mammals are more, less, or equally highly adapted compared with birds to the terrestrial environment? Give the reasons for your answer.

8. State whether you consider mammals or birds more highly diversified as a group and cite the basis for your reasoning.

Supplementary References

Barbour, T. *Reptiles and Amphibians*. New York, Houghton Mifflin, 1926.

Berrill, N. J. *The Origin of Vertebrates*. Oxford, Oxford Univ. Press, 1955.

Broun, M. *Hawks Aloft*. New York, Dodd, Mead, 1949.

Colbert, E. H. *Evolution of the Vertebrates*. New York, Wiley, 1955.

Curtis, B. *The Life Story of the Fish*. New York, Harcourt, Brace, 1949.

deBeer, G. R. *Vertebrate Zoology*, rev. ed. London, Sedgwick and Jackson, 1951.

Hartman, C. G. *Possums*. Austin, Univ. Texas Press, 1952.

Newman, H. H. *The Phylum Chordata*. New York, Macmillan, 1939.

Pettingill, O. S. *Silent Wings*. Madison, Wisconsin Society for Ornithology, 1947.

Parker, T. J., and W. A. Haswell. *A Textbook of Zoology*, 7th ed. London, Macmillan, 1962.

Romer, A. S. *The Vertebrate Story*. Chicago, Univ. Chicago Press, 1959.

Schultz, L. P., and E. M. Stern. *The Ways of Fishes*. New York, Van Nostrand, 1948.

Smith, H. M. *Evolution of Chordate Structure*. New York, Holt, Rinehart and Winston, 1960.

Weichert, C. K. *Anatomy of the Chordates*, 2nd ed. New York, McGraw-Hill, 1958.

PART IV

The Structure and Functioning of Vertebrates

I N THE PRECEDING section the attempt is made to portray in brief the changes that have occurred in the Metazoa as they developed from simple, nearly uni-cellular organisms to those of such complexity as the chordates. Notwithstand-ing the occasional reference made there to the level of organization as reflected in their physiology, discussion of necessity is chiefly concerned with structure. Here it is our purpose to show how complexly integrated the more advanced organisms are in physiology, behavior, and development as well as in morphology. To achieve these ends the vertebrates will serve as the example, not because they necessarily are the most advanced of animals but rather because their functional processes have been more thoroughly investigated than any other taxon's. Although the vertebrates, as do many specialized metazoans, consist of series of such compartmentalizations as systems, organs, tissues, and cells, each individual functions, not part by part, but as an integrated whole—a fact that will become particularly clear toward the close of this section.

You must always be students, learning and unlearning till your life's end, and if, gentlemen, you are not prepared to follow your profession in this spirit, I implore you to leave its ranks and betake yourself to some third-class trade.

JOSEPH LISTER

Support and Movement

AFTER organisms have become multicellular and then have increased in size and complexity, they tend to reach a point where the enlarging body, before still further increment in size can be attained, requires a means of locomotion to provide a basis for greater efficiency in obtaining food. For effective movement of larger organisms two essential requirements are evident—namely, musculature to change the position of the body or of the appendages, and skeletal elements to serve in support of either the muscles or, at times, the entire organism. Throughout the higher Metazoa locomotion is accomplished by the joint functioning of these two features, although the nature of the support may vary from the rigid calcareous shell of the mollusks or resistant chitinous exoskeleton of the arthropods to the calcareous endoskeleton of the echinoderms.

Similarly in the vertebrates these two major constituents work together as a *skeleto-muscular system*. While often each is treated as a separate system, a treatment not without considerable merit, it appears more logical to conceive of them together as a single unit, for one cannot function without the other. Skeletons deprived of muscles are unable to support even their own weight, and muscles loosened from their bony supports are able to contract endlessly but can produce no movement.

Although functioning as an integrated unit, the skeleton and muscles are so distinct in structure and in metabolism that to some extent they require separate discussions. But before entering into their descriptions, it must first be pointed out that the word "system" is employed rather loosely by anatomists and physiologists. Although it always signifies a group of organs working together to perform a major bodily function, it may refer to subdivisions as well as to the entire system. For example, the skeleto-muscular system is divisible into the muscular and skeletal "systems," and these in turn into finer subdivisions like-wise called "systems." This old custom may at first be the cause of some confusion, but in time it will be found not without value.

The Skeletal System

Although endoskeletons, as possessed by the vertebrates, are accepted as being advantageous over the exoskeletons, like those of the arthropods, because they are able to grow continuously, whereas exo-skeletons need to be shed periodically, they still do not appear to be the remedy for all supportive problems. Perhaps their limitations act to restrict body size in terrestrial vertebrates; at least none of these animals has ever attained a stature approaching that of the greatest seed plants. In contrast to some eucalypts of Australasia and the giant redwoods of North America, which grow to heights exceeding 300 feet, the largest land verte-brate, certain dinosaurs like *Diplodocus,* have never surpassed 90 feet in length. Be that as it may, many problems are involved in providing support for the body, whether on land or water, some of which are mechanical or metabolic and still others of a biological nature. Two of these aspects, mechanical and bio-logical, provide the chief subdivisions of the present discussion, whereas meta-bolic facets form a portion of a later one.

Mechanical Aspects

Although the assistance of the muscles is required, much of the weight of the vertebrate body is supported directly by the bones; hence the strength of these parts must be sufficient to meet the forces that act on them, plus an adequate mar-gin of safety to meet emergencies. Aside from the unique load-carrying habits of man, the stress on the skeletal constitu-ents results chiefly from the gravitational effects on the other bodily parts in the form of weight and from internal forces involved in movement and in counteract-ing gravity.

First of all it should be kept in mind that in mechanics the term *stress* refers to action on an object by a set of bal-anced forces, whereas *strain* is the change in shape of a body under stress. Stress classification is based on two considera-tions: the direction in which the forces act and whether the actions are in line with one another and, hence, *colinear,* or whether they are *parallel* (Figure 13–1). Colinear forces produce *compres-sion* when they are directed toward one another and *tension* when the direction of one is away from the second. Parallel forces produce *shear* when one part acted upon tends to slide upon the other and *torsion* when a twisting motion in the body is induced. In bending an object, either tension or compression operates together with shear but at different points on the surface.

As the student may recall from his study of elementary physics, when a weight is placed on an object, such as a block of stone or a bone, compression is effected in a vertical direction but ten-sion is produced at right angles (Figure 13–2), a fact best visualized by imagin-ing the vertical axis to consist of a series of spheres. After the load is applied, a section taken through the vertical axis shows that each sphere is now com-pressed into an ellipsoid still containing the original volume. In accomplishing this change, it elongates horizontally at right angles to the vertical axis; in other

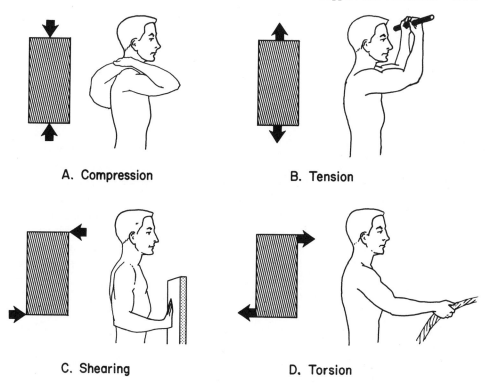

Figure 13–1. The principal types of stress.

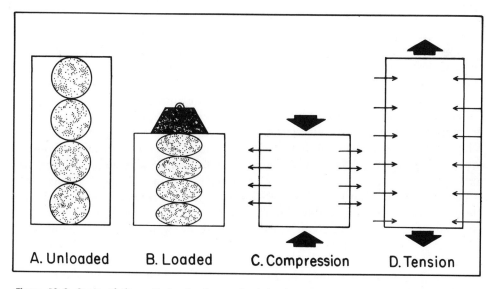

Figure 13–2. Strain. If the vertical axis of an unloaded column is imagined to consist of a series of spheres (A), upon a load being applied (B), these spheres may be visualized as becoming ellipsoids of an equal volume. Hence, distortion (that is, *strain*) is effected both in vertical and horizontal directions under the compression of load (C). Under tension (D) the same phenomena occur but the directions of the strains are reversed.

words, strain is produced horizontally at the same time it occurs vertically. As the horizontal elongation appears to result from colinear forces directed away from one another, an object bearing a load is seen to be under compression vertically and under tension horizontally. Similarly, when an object is subjected to tension along its vertical axis, strains due to compression also occur on the horizontal axes. Both along the strain axes of compression and of tension, lines called *trajectories* may be drawn; although the lines may be curved or straight, the two sets, at right angles to each other, are drawn so that the proximity of corresponding members is correlated to the degree of stress. As the load or pull on a column is increased, it may ultimately reach a point at which the column will break, the point depending upon the material's strength, expressed as breaking stress. *Breaking stress* is the amount, stated in pounds or kilograms per unit of surface in square inches or square centimeters, required to break a given substance by compression or other form of stress. In construction engineering it is customary to allow a *safety factor* in the building materials and plans—that is to say, if the breaking stress of steel is 60 tons per square inch under compression, the structure could be designed so that its parts would never be subjected to compression greater than 30 tons per square inch, thus allowing a safety factor of 2.

The manner in which the stress is applied to a column considerably affects the amount of strain produced. When the stress is applied with equal force to the entire column it is said to be *symmetrical;* if it is applied more to one side than to the other, it is *asymmetrical.* As an example, take a case in which a load of 500 pounds is placed symmetrically on 25 square inches of surface;

when 500 is divided by 25, a compression stress of 20 pounds per square inch is obtained. In the illustration (Figure 13–3) this amount of compression is indicated by a series of vertical arrows of arbitrary but equal length in the first figure (*A*), evenly distributed across the column. If the weight is then moved to one side as in *B*, the length of the arrows indicating compression no longer remains equal but ranges in expression of value from a compression of 40 to 0 pounds per square inch on one side and to tensions of some magnitude on the other. As asymmetry of loading increases, the stresses may at some point come to exceed the breaking stress and result in the fracture of the column (*C* and *D*).

To avoid breaking under such loads, the diameter of the column would have to be increased or some other device employed, such as *counterweighting*—that is, the addition of weights to the other side of the column to reduce the stresses below the breaking point. Thus in Figure 13–3*E*, although the total load actually is increased over *C*, the amount of stress is nevertheless decreased. Comparable results can also be obtained by appropriate *bracing* without the objectionable increase in weight involved in counterweighting (*F*). Undoubtedly it has been noted that the greatest stresses in asymmetrical loadings are borne by the outer surfaces of the column, those in the interior becoming reduced to nil or to negligible amounts. Since this is true, the weight of a column can be greatly reduced without materially affecting its strength by using a tubular type of construction.

BIOLOGICAL ASPECTS

The mechanical principles briefly presented above are of the utmost importance in the construction and functioning of the skeletal parts, and biophysicists

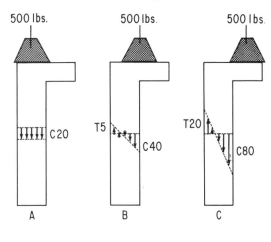

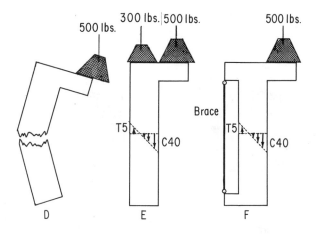

Figure 13–3. Asymmetrical loading. As long as it is loaded symmetrically (i.e., with the weight centered over the vertical axis), only compression results in a column (A). However, if the weight is moved slightly to one side (B), the amount of compression increases in that same side of the column, while tensions develop on the opposite. As the weight is moved still farther sideward, these trends increase (C) and, finally, if carried too far, may reach the breaking stress (D). Although an additional weight adds to the total load borne by the column, if it is placed over the side under tension, the stresses are reduced; this principle is known as counterweighting (E). The addition of a brace as in F can achieve the same end without adding significantly to the total weight.

have devoted much effort to the application of these fundamental considerations to bone structure. In their investigations the bones and skeleton have been found to conform remarkably well to engineering standards, bearing in mind the limitations of materials available to the organism. Although from a strictly engineering point of view, bones ideally should be constructed of stainless steel or other substances that combine maximum strength with minimum weight, the organism is restricted to the carbon compounds for its basic ingredients. Nevertheless, the vertebrate body has done remarkably well with the material available to it, for if a ratio of tensile strength

per unit of weight is employed, bone is found to be half as strong as steel and to possess nearly 20 times the strength of granite on the same basis.

Formation and Growth of Bone. Before the functioning and adaptations of bones can be discussed, a background of knowledge of its formation and growth must be obtained. Toward this end, the student may find it helpful first to review the structure of bone and other supportive tissues (page 147). Bones are of two principal types, *dermal* and *cartilage,* depending upon whether they originate in a connective tissue membrane, such as the dermis of the skin, or in a cartilaginous mass. Since in the two types the processes of formation are comparable except in small details, attention here is confined to cartilage bones. In these bones the earliest activity is found in the cartilaginous mass, the cells of which become arranged in rows and then die. Later the mass is invaded by blood vessels and by an ingrowth of loose connective tissue; some of the fibroblasts of the tissue then become differentiated into *osteoblasts,* cells that are capable of secreting the enzymes necessary for the deposition of bone. As the bony tissue is deposited, it becomes arranged in concentric layers around each osteoblast; ultimately the osteoblasts develop into mature bone cells. Before the organ assumes its final shape, however, it undergoes reconstructive processes, in which some of the tissue is removed by means of plasmodia called *osteoclasts* formed by fusion of several osteoblasts and functioning by dissolving away any unwanted bone.

In mammals the deposition of bone tissue (*ossification*) in a cartilaginous bone, such as any of the long skeletal elements in the legs, proceeds in a characteristic manner. First it is laid down as cartilage in the early unborn young (fetus), generally shaped as the actual bone, and covered by the *periosteum,* a

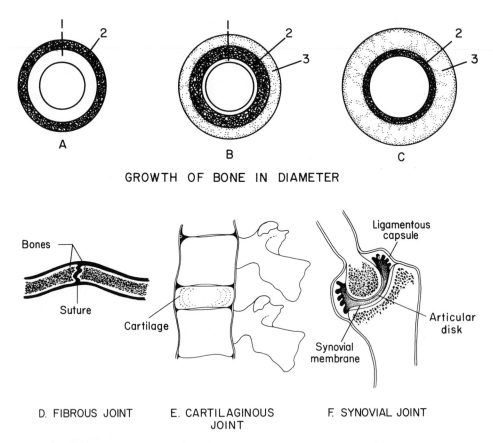

GROWTH OF BONE IN DIAMETER

D. FIBROUS JOINT   E. CARTILAGINOUS JOINT   F. SYNOVIAL JOINT

Figure 13–4. Bone growth and types of joints. A–C. As a bone increases in thickness by adding new layers (2, 3), the innermost and earliest layers (1) are resorbed; thus the internal cavity increases in diameter as the width of the shaft does likewise. D–F. Some principal types of joints.

membranous coat. After the periosteum has secreted osteoblasts and after blood vessels have invaded the cartilage, bone deposition initially forms a fine-bore tube along the main axis of the shaft. As ossification continues, the tube is increased in over-all diameter by deposition around the osteoblasts. While the outside diameter is being enlarged, removal of bony tissue by osteoclasts in the cavity concurrently produces enlargement of the bore (Figure 13-4). Then while the shaft, or *diaphysis,* continues to enlarge, the ends, or *epiphyses,* of the bone ossify independently; their growth, though commencing somewhat later in the fetal period, is accomplished by the same series of events, except that their interiors, instead of becoming hollow, are filled with a spongy type of bone. After birth, increment in length is provided by the formation of new cartilage between the two epiphyses and the shaft, followed by the conversion of this tissue into bone. Only after the young mammal has attained its adult proportions do the ends become fused to the remainder of the bone by ossification of the cartilaginous remnants. Once this has occurred, no further growth in length is possible, only in diameter.

Skeletal Organization. In all vertebrates the skeleton is divided into three systems—the axial, visceral, and appendicular. In the *axial* system are included those bones (or cartilages in some fish) that occur along the main axis of the body—namely the cranium, vertebral column, ribs, and breastbone. The *visceral* skeleton consists of the cartilages or bones that support the gill arches and their derivatives; among its members are the upper jaw (maxilla) and lower jaw (mandible), the bones of the middle ear, and the hyoid apparatus that supports the tongue muscles and parts of the throat. In the *appendicular* system are

placed the skeletal parts of the appendages and their supportive mechanisms, that is, the pectoral girdle and bones of the foreleg or arm and the pelvic girdle and bones of the hind leg (Figure 13-5). As the individual bones are studied to better advantage in the laboratory, no further space need be devoted to them here.

Design of the Skeleton and Its Parts. The vertebrate skeleton is the product of many factors, some of which are biological and inheritable, others, at least in part, the result of mechanical stresses during growth, and the remainder largely unknown. Certain of the biological and mechanical effects can be noted during the course of development of a single bone, as for example, the femur. Because its head is placed on a neck prolonged to one side, this organ is especially useful in demonstrating the effects of asymmetrical loading. In the developing human fetus the bone from the very onset has a shape approximating that of the adult, so in general it is evident that much of its over-all form is an inheritable trait, and hence of a biological nature. As the epiphysis, of course, is not yet ossified, changes in internal arrangement of the linear deposits of spongy bone, called *trabeculae,* can be followed as this tissue subsequently undergoes growth. In the fetus, as may be seen in the illustrations (Figures 13-6*A–D*), before the bone is placed into use, the trabeculae run in accordance with the long axis of the femur, a state of affairs that continues until the child begins to walk. Once placed in use, even when walking has just been commenced, the bony lines are seen to shift and to become aligned with the stress trajectories; these realignment processes continue into adulthood. Actually, the trabeculae do not move; the shift occurs through the ordinary activities of bone growth, deposition by osteo-

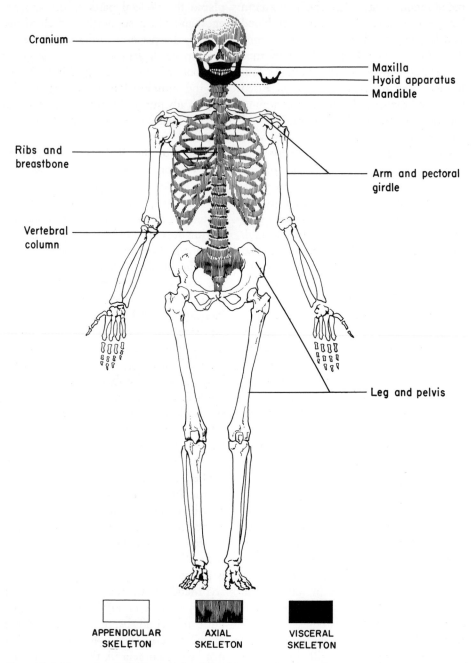

Cranium

Maxilla
Hyoid apparatus
Mandible

Ribs and
breastbone

Arm and pectoral
girdle

Vertebral
column

Leg and pelvis

APPENDICULAR
SKELETON

AXIAL
SKELETON

VISCERAL
SKELETON

Figure 13–5. The major subdivisions of the skeletal system. In addition to the jaws and hyoid apparatus illustrated, the visceral skeleton includes the bones of the middle ear (Figure 14–18).

blasts and dissolution by the osteoclasts. When a comparison of the stress lines in the adult femur is made with a photograph of a section through the head and upper epiphysis, the lines are seen to correspond closely (Figures 13–6E, F).

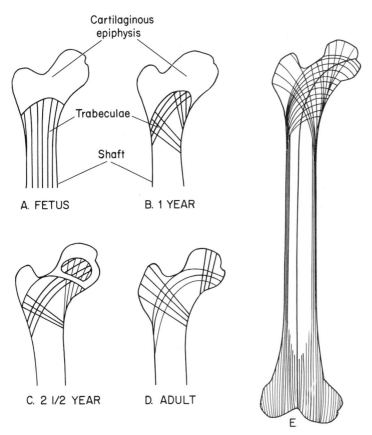

A. FETUS   B. 1 YEAR

C. 2 1/2 YEAR   D. ADULT

E.

Figure 13–6. Changes in bony structure.
A. In the fetus and new born child, before the legs are used to support the body's weight, the trabeculae run directly along the shaft's length. *B.* After the legs have been used in walking, the trabeculae become rearranged to align with the lines of stress and continue thus throughout life (*C, D*). *E.* The principal lines of stress in the adult femur. *F.* The trabeculae of an adult femur to be compared with *E.*

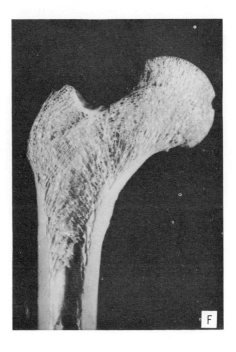

The Muscular System

Although the prime function of muscles is to move one another or the various bones, they also actively serve to support the latter and other structures. To perform these activities, the muscles have become developed in many ways, all made unique largely through the fact that the organs of this system perform their work in one direction only, for a muscle can exert pull by contraction but is unable to effect a pushing movement by expansion.

THE ORGANIZATION
OF MUSCLES

The Anatomy of Muscles. Anatomically, muscles are quite simple organs, consisting of a wide portion, the *belly,* covered by a layer of *fascia,* and two (or more) tapering ends usually connected to bones; one end, the *origin,* remains relatively stationary when contraction occurs, whereas the *insertion* obviously is moved (Figure 13–7). Moreover, in-

sertions are often provided with a connective tissue *tendon,* though origins may be similarly equipped. Essentially, it should be realized, origins and insertions are identical, the stated differences being often relative rather than absolute, for not infrequently their identities depend upon the activity being engaged in. For example, when the biceps of the upper arm is employed for lifting objects, its insertion is on the bones of the lower arm, whereas when it is utilized in pulling the body upward, as in chinning the bar, the former origin on the shoulder bones becomes the insertion and the other way around.

Internally, the muscle proper is found under the microscope to be comprised of numerous fibers of striated muscular tissue (page 152); each fiber consists of a striated substance embedded in the cytoplasm (in muscles called *sarcoplasm*) and enclosed in a membrane known as the *sarcolemma.* Large groups of such fibers, arranged end-to-end and side-by-side in irregular series, held together by connective tissue, make up each muscle.

The Arrangement of Muscles. Since muscles can function only in contraction, they are arranged in the body as opposing pairs, or, more usually, as opposing groups. For every action produced by one muscle or group there is an antagonistic action that produces the opposite effect. Thus, if one or more muscular organs raise a skeletal part, an antagonistic set lowers it. For instance, attached to the mandible is an entire group of *levators* which raise it, as in closing the mouth, whereas another, the *depressors,* lower it when the mouth is opened. Antagonistic groups, found in all situations, bring about the movements of the body and its parts; the various types, and their actions, are grouped together by opposing sets in Table 13–1.

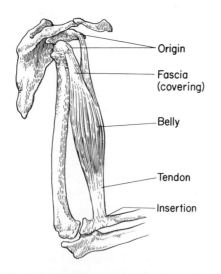

Origin

Fascia
(covering)

Belly

Tendon

Insertion

Figure 13–7. The gross anatomy of a muscle.

TABLE 13-1

OPPOSING SETS OF MUSCLES

Protagonist	Antagonist	Action	Example
Levator		Raises or lifts a part	As in closing the mouth
	Depressor	Lowers a part	As in opening the mouth
Abductor		Draws an appendage away from the median line	As in raising arm to the side
	Adductor	Pulls an appendage toward the median line	As in pressing the arm against the side
Flexor		Bends an appendage or one of its parts	As in bending elbow or raising arm forwards
	Extensor	Straightens an appendage or one of its parts	As in straightening elbow or lowering arm
Rotator	Rotator	Turns one bone on another	As in moving the raised arm from side to side
Suppinator		Special types of rotators	Turns the palm upwards
	Pronator		Turns the palm downwards

MUSCULAR ACTION

In dealing with muscular action, one must be careful to keep in mind the nature of its fine structure and to discriminate between the contraction of a muscle and that of a fiber. Although muscles are capable of partial contraction, the fine units are not. These units follow what is known as the "all or none law"; they either contract to their maximum extent or not at all. On the other hand, muscular organs can contract to nearly any degree, a flexibility made possible by employing varying numbers of fibers lying in sequence; the larger the number of contractile constituents employed, the greater the contraction of the entire organ.

The Nature of a Contraction. Even after removal from the body, muscles retain their ability to react for long periods if properly supplied with water and physiological salts. By attaching fibers to a special apparatus, it is possible to make recordings of activities produced by artificial stimulation, timed by intervals provided by a vibrating tuning fork or by electronic means. When a fiber is stimulated, two types of reaction are found, depending on the frequency at which the stimulus is applied. The first type, the *twitch,* results from the application of a single short stimulus. In the recording of a twitch of frog muscle fiber, it is seen that the entire contraction wave (Figure 13–8) can be broken into three parts. Immediately following the stimulus, there is a *latent period,* lasting for 0.01 second, in which nothing seems to happen. Then in the *contraction period* the fiber shortens, rapidly at first, then more slowly, requiring around 0.03 second for the complete process. Upon completion of contraction, a *relaxation period* follows, during which the muscle fiber resumes its original length, a period that consumes 0.06 second.

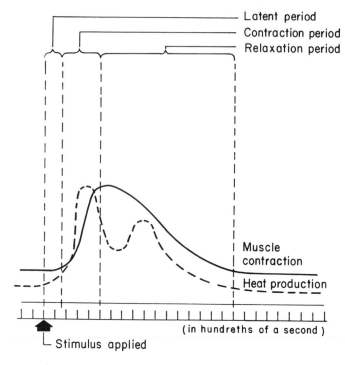

Latent period
Contraction period
Relaxation period

Figure 13–8. Graph of muscle contraction.

Muscle contraction

Heat production

(in hundreths of a second)

Stimulus applied

In the second type of reaction, the *tetanic,* a succession of stimuli is supplied at high frequency, as by normal nerve action or by a series of close-spaced electric shocks. When a muscle is thus stimulated, the first two periods of its wave are found to be normal, except that contraction is sustained as long as the stimulus endures, while relaxation occurs only after stimulation ceases. Normally, in the intact body, this type of contraction is typical; the fibrous units of which each muscle consists are stimulated by nerve action so that various sets alternate with one another in relays. Moreover, under normal conditions muscles are never completely relaxed; some of their fibers always remain under tetanic contraction, probably alternating with one another, to keep the muscles under *tone.*

If a muscle or a fiber is kept in a state of tetany for a prolonged period or if it is made to contract frequently, eventually it will reach a point at which contrac-

tions are slow and painful or at which no further movement occurs. These observations are the result of *fatigue.* When fully fatigued, muscles are unable to relax and in their contracted state produce cramps. Similarly, rigor mortis results from the simultaneous contraction of all the body muscles after death. As fatigue and rigor mortis actually arise from the accumulation of certain chemicals produced anaerobically in muscular metabolism, their real nature will become more apparent after those processes are described.

The Metabolic Activities of Muscles

While basically muscle metabolism is in no way distinct from that of other organs, several aspects are somewhat modified to apply to the particular requirements of contraction, and others are unique.

The Chemical Basis of Contraction. The many fine threadlike structures running lengthwise in a muscle fiber are called *myofibrils* and are believed to be responsible for the fiber's ability to contract. These myofibrils have been found to be composed of two proteins, *myosin* and *actin,* capable of uniting to form *actomyosin;* although a globulin, actomyosin possesses characteristics of the fibrous type of protein, including the property of contractility. Even in a pure chemical state, it retains this latter ability. If ATP is added to a beaker containing a solution of this protein, the whole mass contracts; the ATP here, as elsewhere, is believed to be the source from which the necessary energy is obtained.

Though thus the basic ingredients involved in contraction are well enough known, the mechanism by which it is performed is still a matter of much controversy. But to understand the two chief concepts, a closer look at the muscle fiber must first be taken.

When a muscle fiber is examined under the low power of an electron microscope, the striations that characterize skeletal muscle tissue are found to result from the alignment of corresponding myofibril parts (Figure 13–9) across the fiber. The dark striations (A-bands) are assumed to be the product of a series of plates either on or between sets of myofibrils. Between the A-bands are light-colored areas (I-bands), possibly representing interspaces between the plates. These I-bands are subdivided by a fine vertical dark line, which is currently accepted as representing a septum (called the Z-membrane) supporting all the myofibrils; the similar appearing M-lines, which divide the A-bands, so far have eluded explanation. When the muscle fiber undergoes contraction, the I-bands

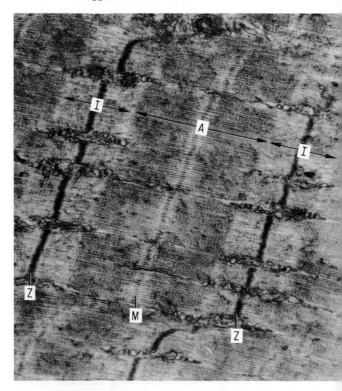

Figure 13–9. Ultrastructure of skeletal muscle. This electronmicrograph of rat muscle shows the various types of bands that comprise the striation of this type of tissue. Magnified 25,000×. (Courtesy of Drs. K. A. Siegesmund and C. A. Fox.)

become strongly narrowed, whereas the A-bands remain unchanged in width. Therefore it is believed that during this activity the parts of the myofibrils lying in the I-bands are drawn into the A-bands; the difference in the two schools of thought lies in the details by which these changes are supposedly brought about. By many workers the A-band plates are believed to be myosin, and the myofibrils actin links located in the I-band, which are held together in series by a contractile portion. During contraction this contractile portion is thought to pull the actin links into position between the myosin plates (Figure 13–10). In contrast, the second school suggests that no such contractile links exist and

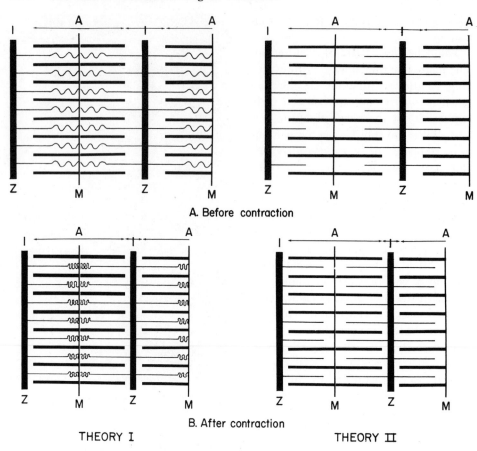

A. Before contraction

B. After contraction

THEORY I   THEORY II

Figure 13–10. Two theories of muscle contraction. The major differences between the two current concepts is that one supposes contraction on the part of the fibrilar molecular arrangement (left-hand set of figures) while the other suggests a sliding action of molecules between one another (right-hand set).

that the actin links merely slide over the myosin plates, perhaps in response to electrical charge changes or possibly because of short-term linkages forming between the actin and myosin elements. Obviously, much still remains to be discovered regarding this mechanism.

Also in the sarcoplasm are two additional ingredients important in muscular activity. One, known as the *relaxing factor,* appears to be associated largely with the mitochondria and microsomes of the sarcoplasm and is necessary for relaxation, whereas the second com-

pound, *myoglobin,* is somewhat similar to hemoglobin in molecular composition and activity. Principally, myoglobin seems to accept oxygen from the blood stream and to hold it in readiness for muscular contraction.

Energy Sources for Contraction. In contrast to the disagreement that exists concerning the physiochemical processes involved in producing the shortening of the myofibrils, there is general assent regarding the necessity for energy in this activity. Most of the processes concerned with the supply of energy have been thoroughly investigated, at least in their essentials, and appear to be the three that follow.

The first and only direct energy source is apparently *ATP*. In fact, it may prove to be not only a source of energy but an active participant in the processes of contraction, although insufficient evidence as yet exists to clarify this point. Nonetheless, it is one of the prime requisites of contraction, breaking down, as in other reactions, into ADP and inorganic phosphate and releasing energy as it does so.

Since ATP exists in muscles only in small amounts, the supply of this compound would be quickly exhausted but for the presence of another substance somewhat similar in chemical behavior. This compound, *creatine phosphate*, occurs in muscular tissue in slightly greater quantity than ATP and is the second energy source for contraction. When the

supply of the first source diminishes or as the amount of ADP increases, creatine phosphate breaks down in the presence of an enzyme to form creatine and a phosphate ion; this reaction releases sufficient energy to recombine a phosphate radical to ADP, thus restoring some of the ATP. It should be noted that neither of the foregoing reactions requires oxygen (Figure 13–11).

But the supply of creatine phosphate cannot be limitless; it, too, is soon exhausted. To bring about its restoration, a third source of energy is drawn upon; in these processes ordinary respiratory means, which employ glycogen as the initial component, are used. This substance is converted into glucose and then passes through the whole series of intermediate products outlined in Chapter 4 until the level of pyruvic acid formation in the respiratory cycle is attained. At this point either of two reactions may

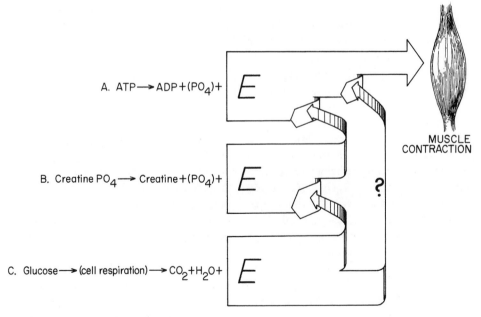

A. ATP $\longrightarrow$ ADP + (PO$_4$) +

B. Creatine PO$_4$ $\longrightarrow$ Creatine + (PO$_4$) +

C. Glucose $\longrightarrow$ (cell respiration) $\longrightarrow$ CO$_2$ + H$_2$O +

MUSCLE CONTRACTION

Figure 13–11. The energy sources for contraction. Only ATP can directly supply energy for muscle contraction; the rest appear merely to restore the ATP.

occur, depending on the amount of oxygen present. When an ample supply is at hand, the pyruvic acid breaks down into an acetyl radical, followed by the ordinary steps in the citric acid cycle; the resulting energy may be applied to bring about the reformation of creatine phosphate through reversal of the chemical reaction outlined above and possibly to reconstitute ATP from ADP as well. When muscular activity is proceeding at a high rate, however, the supply of oxygen held by the myoglobin is exhausted more rapidly than the blood stream can replenish it, so a second set of reactions may be followed by pyruvic acid instead. These reactions differ only slightly from the processes of the fermentation by yeasts of sugar into alcohol, at least as far as making possible further respiration under anaerobic conditions. In this alternative chemical route the pyruvic acid is converted into *lactic acid* by the addition of hydrogen; since this element is taken from reduced DPN, the latter substance is freed to participate further in the glycolytic steps. During periods of active contraction lactic acid accumulates in muscles at a rate corresponding to the amount of work being done, and as it accumulates, the condition of fatigue results. Later, when the muscles are resting, the available oxygen soon exceeds the immediate demands of the body, permitting the lactic acid to be reconverted into pyruvic acid, largely after being transported to the liver. In this organ about 30 per cent of the pyruvic acid passes through the citric acid cycle, using oxygen and supplying sufficient energy to restore the remaining 70 per cent to glycogen by way of the glycolytic reactions in reverse. During periods of active muscular functioning there is thus built up an *oxygen debt* as the lactic acid is formed, a debt that is paid off, as it were, during periods of inactivity.

Other Activities in Contraction. By means of a sensitive galvanometer and thermometric devices the energy released by muscular contraction can be recorded simultaneously with a single twitch wave described earlier. When thus plotted, electrical activity (Figure 13–8) is found to occur in the latent period and earliest portion of the contraction period, usually in the form of a single wave. As yet the significance of this feature has not been deciphered, but it appears to result from a shift in the electric charges lying on the sarcolemma. By similar recordings heat production has been studied and found to be distributed unequally between the contraction and relaxation periods in a wavelike pattern. As shown in the diagram (Figure 13–8), there is a sudden burst of released heat as contraction is initiated, which rapidly decreases in intensity before this phase closes. Then, some time after relaxation has begun, the initial burst is followed by a second of approximately equal duration but of lower intensity. So far the correlation of heat production with the chemical and physical activities postulated to be involved in contraction has not been explained.

Relations of Muscles and Bones

Now that the structure and fundamental activities of the two major components of the skeleto-muscular system have been outlined, certain features of the two working as a unit remain to be discussed.

Arrangement of Muscles in Relation to Bones. In the illustration of a typical muscle (Figure 13–7), the muscle is shown as having its origin on one bone and activating a second articulated with the first. As this muscle extends across only one skeletal joint, it represents a type

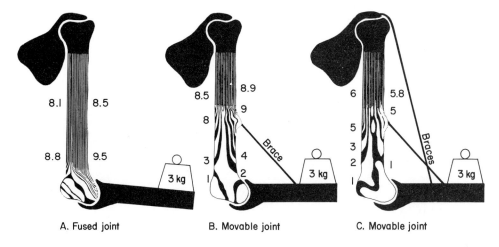

8.1   8.5

8.8   9.5

3 kg

A. Fused joint

8.5   8.9

8   9

Brace

3   4

2

3 kg

B. Movable joint

6   5.8

5

5

3

2   1

Braces

3 kg

C. Movable joint

Figure 13–12. The role of muscles in bracing. A plastic model of an arm, the elbow immovably fused at A but loosely jointed in B and C; stress is expressed in kilograms per square centimeter. The high stresses of A are only slightly diminished by a brace representing a one-joint muscle; however, they are dispersed over a greater area. C. A brace representing a two-joint muscle decreases the stresses considerably. (Based on Pauwels.)

known as a *single-joint muscle;* others, such as the familiar biceps of the upper arm, reach across two joints, in this example the shoulder and elbow, and are accordingly named *two-joint muscles.* Although, in some parts of the body, broad bands of connective tissue serve as *braces* to alleviate stress on bones, in others muscles may play a similar role. When a model is prepared of the upper and lower arm bones arranged as though flexed at right angles (Figure 13–12*A*) but immovably fused at the elbow, great stress is found on the humerus portion when a weight is added to the wrist end. If then the model is altered as in *B,* so that a movable joint corresponding to an actual elbow is formed and a single-joint muscle comparable to the brachialis is attached between the two components, the stress on the lower portion of the humerus model is seen to be considerably diminished. On the other hand, when a model of a two-joint muscle such as the biceps is added, it is found to act as a brace in decreasing stress over the entire humerus.

General Architecture of the Vertebrate Body. The skeleto-muscular system of the vertebrates is unique in its construction, for in no other group of animals is a central beam present that carries the main burden of body support. Often the general plan of the body organization in this group is compared to that of a bridge of either suspension or cantilever type, depending on the author; comparisons to a plank footbridge would be equally valid. In actuality the essential features of all three types are included in the plan, depending on the species, the varying positions of the body (e.g., fully extended or crouched), and the skeletal section under consideration. In fishlike forms, whose chief bodily movements are in a horizontal plane, the vertebral column resembles the straight beam of an ordinary footbridge. Contrastingly, in many terrestrial groups the backbone is principally arched in a fashion not unlike the main supports of a cantilever (Figure 13–13). In this case the bony processes on the dorsal surface may be considered as representing the struts, the muscles

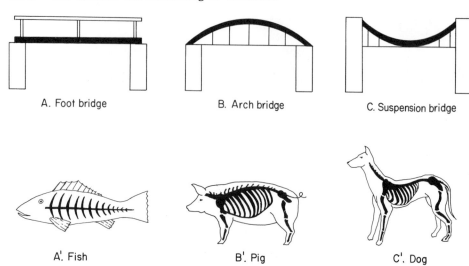

Figure 13–13. Bridges and skeletons. Since the mechanics of supporting weight are universally the same, comparisons of bridges and skeletons can be made with some degree of validity.

Figure 13–14. Kangaroos in flight. The possible usefulness of the tail as a counterweight is especially clearly shown by the large specimen just right of center. But other species of kangaroos have slender tails and yet are equally skillful in running. (Australian News and Information Bureau photograph.)

between them forming the ties and the principal tension members. However, with a change in posture, such as that assumed when running or as a permanent arrangement in some species, the vertebrae more closely compare to the downward arched cable that carries the weight in a suspension bridge, with the muscles serving as secondary suspensors (Figure 13–13). In all types the two pairs of legs in terrestrial species fulfill the capacity of the pillars. As long as these analogies are not taken too seriously, they may be of value in illustrating the mechanical principles incorporated into the body design and in contributing to an understanding of the nature of the plan. But in the long run, the skeleto-muscular system is especially contrived to render a function never demanded of bridges— namely, that of providing movement— and it is built accordingly.

Counterweighting. The principle of *counterweighting* occurs occasionally in the design of the terrestrial vertebrate skeleto-muscular system, most commonly in the development of the tail. Perhaps the best example is found in a familiar animal, the kangaroo (Figure 13–14), in which the tail is thick and heavy. Undoubtedly, when this mammal is running, the outstretched caudal member counterbalances some of the body's weight and thereby diminishes stress on the femora. Nevertheless, it should be borne in mind that any such mechanical function is strictly a secondary one and that some members of the kangaroo family, which run in identical fashion, have only thin, ratlike tails. In those species in which this appendage is robust, its principal use is as a fifth leg, as it were, on which the rest of the body can be balanced to free the powerful hind legs when occasion demands in protection against an attacker.

Questions for Review and Thought

1. Differentiate between the terms *stress* and *strain, tension* and *compression, shear* and *torsion, colinear* and *parallel forces*.

2. What is meant by asymmetrical loading? By what mechanical means can stress resulting from such loading be alleviated? What biological equivalents serve in these capacities in the skeleto-muscular system? While retaining their present level of strength, how much lighter could bones be if made of steel? If made of granite?

3. Name the two types of bone. Describe the processes involved in bone formation. Sketch a live bone and indicate its four chief parts. Would you classify a bone as an organ or a tissue and on what basis?

4. What are the chief subdivisions of the skeletal system? List by name as many bones as you can of the human body under their respective systems.

5. Name the parts of a muscle. How are muscles arranged in the body? List the various types and describe their activities.

6. Outline the nature of a muscular contraction and the chemical processes involved in producing it. Which parts of the fiber are chiefly myosin and which are actin? Where is ATP located? Describe the chemical means by which a supply of ATP is maintained. Why are muscles able to contract for a while even when suspended in some inert gas such as nitrogen?

7. Define fully the terms *tetany, tone,* and *fatigue*.

8. Describe as fully as you can the structure of a muscle fiber. What changes occur during contraction?

9. Show in what ways the muscles and skeleton function as a single unit and as separate systems. Describe the over-all design and functioning of the vertebrate body, using mechanical comparisons as far as feasible.

Supplementary References

Gray, J. *How Animals Move.* Cambridge, Cambridge Univ. Press, 1960.

Harrow, B., and A. Mazur. *Textbook of Biochemistry,* 8th ed. Philadelphia, Saunders, 1962.

Hill, A. V. *Muscular Movement in Man.* New York, McGraw-Hill, 1927.

Hollinshead, W. H. *Functional Anatomy of the Limbs and Back,* 2nd ed. Philadelphia, Saunders, 1960.

Huxley, H. E. "The Contraction of Muscle." *Sci. Amer.,* November 1958.

Karpovich, P. V. *Physiology of Muscular Activity,* 5th ed. Philadelphia, Saunders, 1959.

McLean, F. C. "Bone." *Sci. Amer.,* February 1955.

Stumpf, P. K. "ATP." *Sci. Amer.,* April 1953.

Szent-Györgi, A. *Chemical Physiology of Contraction in Body and Heart Muscle.* New York, Academic Press, 1953.

Williams, M., and H. R. Lissner. *Biomechanics of Human Motion.* Philadelphia, Saunders, 1962.

CHAPTER 14

The Nervous System

ALL AROUND and within us countless changes occur constantly. The air becomes warm as we approach a hot oven or cool as we near an open window. There are ever-changing sounds of automobiles moving, of people walking, children playing, rain falling, winds rustling the leaves. There are odors of foods cooking, or of a factory, or of diesel trucks. The scenes before our eyes constantly move; the intensity of the light decreases as we leave the sunshine for shade or as day turns to night. Within us we feel when our stomachs are empty or our bodies need water or sleep, and when our muscles have too much lactic acid in their fibers. Keeping the organism aware of the changes that occur in the environment, both internal and external, and aiding it to react to these changes are the functions of the nervous system.

Basic Structure and Function

The changes in the environment that cause an organism to react, or *respond,* are known as *stimuli.* But not all stimuli cause the same type of reaction; in some cases the human being or other organism is attracted toward the stimulus, a *positive* reaction, such as to a lighted fireplace on a very cold day. Other stimuli repel, producing a *negative* reaction, as, for example, the odor from burning sulfur. But the same stimulus will not provoke the same reaction at all times nor under all conditions. This variability in reaction to the same stimulus is one of the fundamental differences between living and nonliving things. When an inorganic substance such as water is heated it expands until it boils; when cooled it contracts to a certain point, then becomes solid;

when treated with a polarized electric current, it breaks into its components. The changes are always the same, in both kind and amount, to any given degree of any stated stimulus. In biological material such is not the case. Would the lighted fireplace, for example, produce the same reaction in the midst of summer as on a wintry day? A plain unbuttered slice of bread might look most appealing after a day of hunting or hiking on a brisk autumn day, but how does it look after a big holiday dinner? An organism's reaction to a stimulus is dependent not only upon the variety and intensity of the latter but also upon its capabilities of receiving or detecting the stimulus, as well as upon its own state of being.

THE BASIC UNIT OF THE NERVOUS SYSTEM

Nerve Structure. The ability of metazoans to detect and respond to stimuli depends entirely on the capabilities of special cells, called nerve cells or *neurons,* to transform stimuli into nervous impulses and to transmit these impulses to other parts of the organism. A neuron is a highly specialized cell that varies immensely in mass, shape, and length—from fractions of a millimeter to several meters. Although differing greatly in details, all neurons share certain peculiarities of structure. Each possesses a *cell body* in which the nucleus is located (Figure 14–1), one or more *dendrites,* fiberlike projections, which carry impulses toward the cell body, and a single *axon,* which carries impulses away from the cell body. The dendrites lie in contact either with stimulus-receiving organs (*receptors*) or with the axons of another nerve, from either of which stimuli are received and transmitted. On the other hand, axons carry impulses either to the dendrites of another neuron or to a muscle or gland (*effector*), which produces a reaction.

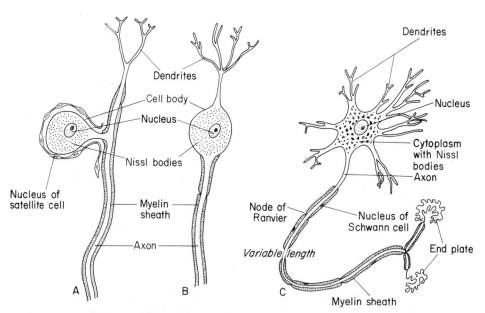

Figure 14–1. Types and structure of neurons. A, B. Neurons may be relatively simple or even bipolar (A) but frequently may have many dendrites radiating from the cell body (multipolar, C). The Nissl bodies are granules consisting mainly of RNA.

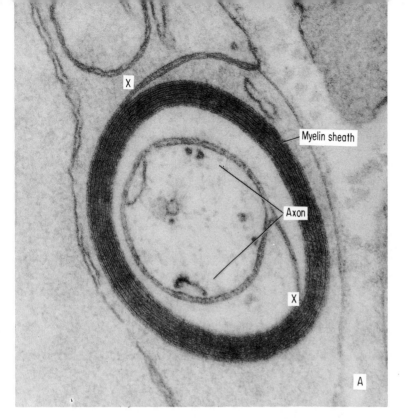

X

Myelin sheath

Axon

X

A

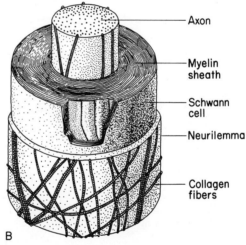

Axon

Myelin sheath

Schwann cell

Neurilemma

Collagen fibers

B

Figure 14–2. The myelin sheath. *A.* That the myelin sheath is formed by extremely flattened cells enveloping the axon is suggested in this cross section of a young mouse sciatic nerve; note especially the regions marked with an X. This is a so-called unmyelinated fiber, magnified 90,000×. (Courtesy of Dr. J. David Robertson, Harvard Medical School, and the *Annals,* New York Acad. Sci., Vol. 94, 1961.) *B.* The diagram shows more clearly the relationships of the myelin sheath to the axon and neurilemma.

All nerves that form part of a nerve fiber, regardless of their thickness, are enclosed in a sheath (*medullated*) (Figure 14–2). Even in the very finest, in which no sheath is visible under a light microscope and therefore formerly believed to be "unmedullated," the electron microscope discloses the presence of a sheath that is different from those of larger nerves only in relative thickness.

The sheath, composed of a fatty material called *myelin,* is formed by the bodies of *Schwann cells,* each wrapped many times around the axon (Figure 14–2). The Schwann cells are separated from one another by the *nodes of Ranvier,* a single cell occupying each internode, which ranges up to one tenth of an inch in length. Around these cells is arranged the *neurilemma,* a tough membrane made of a protein. Nerve fibers are composed of numerous such axons and dendrites bound together.

Neural Action. Even today, after many years of investigation, the precise manner in which a neuron conducts an impulse along its length is not clearly understood. Two principal theories are in vogue, the more generally accepted of which is the *electrochemical*. This concept is based on several observable facts, among which is the existence of a positive charge, to the extent of 90 millivolts, on the surface of the neural membrane, in contrast to that existing within the cell (Figure 14–3). These electric charges of the cell have been found to be due largely to potassium, chloride, and

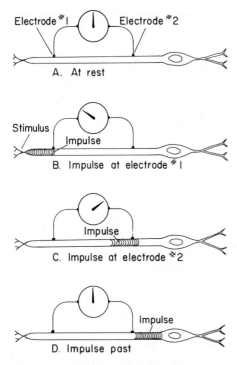

Figure 14–3. **Changes in potential on a neuron's surface.** When two fine electrodes are attached to a neuron, the indicator remains at zero (A) as long as the latter is inactive. If an impulse is initiated, however, the potential is changed first under electrode 1 (B), then under electrode 2 (C) as the impulse is conducted along the length of the fiber.

sodium ions, the cell being rich in potassium but poor in sodium and chloride, whereas the opposite condition prevails in the fluids around the nerve. The surface membrane of the cell is therefore assumed to be moderately permeable to potassium and chloride ions but not to the sodium nor to the negative ions (anions) in the cell. Thus it is the diffusion of potassium ions to the outside and chloride ions to the inside that brings about the surface charges observed while the cell is resting. When an impulse passes along the fiber, the membrane becomes permeable to the sodium ions, which pass with the potassium ions into the interior of the cell. Later, after the impulse has passed on its way, the sodium ions are pumped out in some fashion, while those of the potassium diffuse out as before, restoring the charge to the neural membrane. A weakness in this theory is that the same electrical changes can be observed even when sodium is entirely absent.

In contrast, the adherents of the *chemical theory* of nerve-impulse propagation hold that the electrical charges are merely by-products and that the actual impulse is transmitted by means of a chemical, possibly acetylcholine, which spreads along the surface of the cell. Neither of these theories is totally satisfactory, for other cell activities can be noted than those detailed above while an impulse is being conducted. For one thing, heat, as well as an electrical charge change, is produced along the nerve fiber as the impulse travels. Furthermore, oxygen is consumed and carbon dioxide produced; hence some sort of metabolic activity is certainly indicated. But this is only one of many fascinating problems in biology the solution of which awaits some alert young student who is ready to devise a new approach and who has the perseverance to employ it successfully.

The speed of nerve action is by no means uniform nor very rapid. In cells of large diameter in the human it approaches a speed of 120 meters per second, but as the diameter of the nerve fiber decreases it slows to as little as 1 meter per second. After an impulse has traveled along a nerve, there follows a brief period during which no further impulse can be propagated. This period, which endures for 2 to 5 milliseconds, is referred to as the *refractory period*. Nerves resemble muscles in having a similar *all-or-nothing* type of reaction; either a nerve transmits an impulse at full capacity or it conducts none at all. Finally, it should be pointed out that the impulse that reaches the end of the axons is exactly of the same magnitude as that initiated along the dendrites—a magnitude that is constant for any given nerve. No matter what the nature of the stimulus, whether light, sound, heat, pain, or an inward desire to move, the impulse that reaches the brain or muscle is the same in all cases.

The Synapse. In conducting an impulse from one point of the body to another, nerve cells as a rule lie in series, the axon of one in contact with the dendrites of the next and so on. Thus a sensation in the skin is transmitted as an impulse along one neuron as far as the spinal cord, a second neuron transmits it the length of the spinal cord into the brain, where it is carried by a third, then a fourth, and on until its terminus is reached. The junctions formed in this fashion are referred to as *synapses* (Figure 14-4), and special problems arise regarding the manner in which impulses are transmitted across them from one neuron to another. But first it is necessary to have an understanding of the structure of the synapse.

As the fiber of a nerve is examined, it can be noted that the axon divides into numerous small branches, each of which ends in a tiny knob called the *terminal button* (Figure 14-4). These buttons, which are packed full with mitochondria and are therefore probably centers of high metabolic activity, rest on the dendrites or even on the cell body of adjacent neurons. Only axons bear these terminal buttons; hence transmission across the synapse is in one direction only—namely from axon to dendrite.

Although much remains to be learned about the nature of the transmission of impulses across the synapse, it is becoming increasingly clearer that a secretion formed in the terminal buttons may be involved. In many nerves this secretion is acetylcholine, a substance mentioned above in connection with neural conduction of impulses; within the terminal buttons it appears to be stored in minute sacs or *vesicles* (Figure 14-4). Current hypotheses conjecture that when a neural impulse reaches a terminal button, the chemical contents are released from one or more vesicles lying adjacent to the dendrite of the next nerve in the series. When the released acetylcholine contacts the dendrite, it arouses an impulse in the second neuron that travels thence to the next synapse, and so on. Immediately after the acetylcholine has initiated one wave of activity, it is destroyed by the enzyme *cholinesterase* constantly present in the blood. Were this enzyme absent, the synaptic connections of just a few motor nerves could release a sufficient quantity of acetylcholine to activate all the motor neurons of the body when distributed by the blood stream, including the nerves which retard the heart beat. In fact, the action of "nerve gas" of military forces is that of inactivating the cholinesterase of the blood, with convulsions and cessation of heart beat as a consequence, all within a few seconds of time.

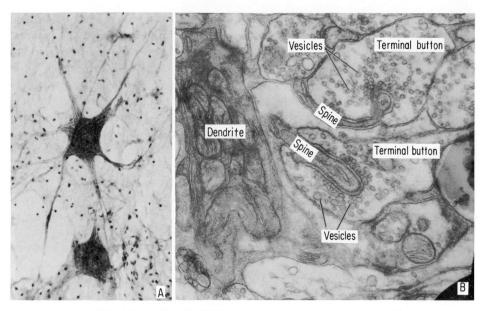

Figure 14–4. Structure of the synapse. A. Surrounding the spinal motor cell in this photomicrograph are seen numerous terminal buttons of neighboring axons. (Courtesy of Ward's Natural History Establishment, Inc., Rochester, N. Y.) B. Electron microscopy reveals intimate contact between the terminal buttons and fine branches ("spines") of a dendrite. Within each button are numerous vesicles containing acetylcholine; it is believed that, upon an impulse reaching a button, one or more vesicles release their contents into the contacting spine and thereby initiate the impulse in the next neuron. Cat cerebellar cortex, magnified 24,000×. (Courtesy of Drs. K. A. Siegesmund, C. A. Fox, and S. K. Dutta.) C. A diagram of a terminal button. (Based on Boycott, Gray, and Guillery.)

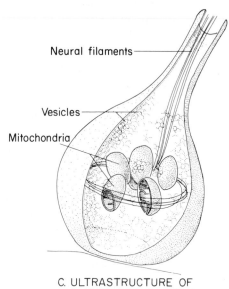

C. ULTRASTRUCTURE OF
A TERMINAL BUTTON

The Organization of the Nervous System

Although the nervous system is a continuous, closely knit unit, for convenience in discussing its structure and functioning it is customary to subdivide it into three parts. Two of these parts are referred to as "systems," but only in a loose sense of the word; they are the *central* and *peripheral* nervous systems. The third part consists of the organs that receive stimuli, the *sense receptors*. In studying the anatomy of the whole, the parts will be treated separately, as is customary; the functions will then be approached through discussions of the nervous system as a single unit.

Because of space considerations, discussion here and in most of the remainder of this chapter centers around the mammalian brain, with man's, of necessity, frequently providing the example.

The Central Nervous System

The central nervous system consists of the *brain* and the *spinal cord,* each of which is covered by a series of three membranes called the *meninges.* These membranes contain the blood vessels which carry food and oxygen into the nervous tissue beneath it, and between the inner two flows the *cerebrospinal fluid.*

By far the largest bulk of the entire nervous system is contained in the brain. For the sake of convenience this organ may be considered to consist of three main parts: the *cerebrum, brainstem,* and *cerebellum.* If a section is cut through any one of these portions, two layers, the *white* and *gray matter,* are revealed,

variously and irregularly arranged. For the greater part, gray matter forms an outer layer called the *cortex* and is made up of billions of short neurons. In contrast to the cortex, the white matter is composed of long neurons which form the conducting tracts from one area to another. These cells are heavily sheathed, hence their white appearance.

The Cerebrum. The cerebrum taken as a whole is roughly spherical in shape and envelops much of the rest of the brain. Viewed from above (Figure 14–5), it is seen to be divided by a deep *longitudinal fissure* into *right* and *left hemispheres,* which are connected to one another by a large transverse nerve tract known as the *corpus callosum* and a small *anterior commissure.* Each hemisphere is subdivided superficially by several shallower fissures into four lobes,

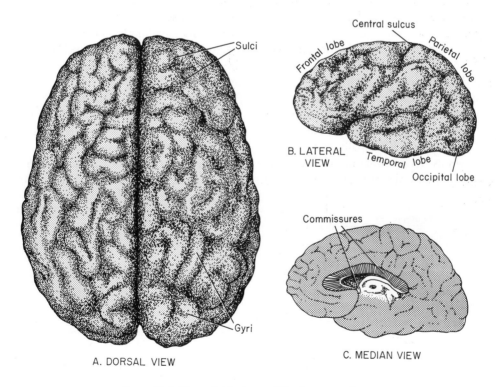

Figure 14–5. The major features of the human cerebrum.

which will serve as convenient landmarks later in discussing the functions of the brain. The other folds and grooves of the cerebrum provide greater surface for the cortex; it has been estimated that 67 per cent of the surface of the human cortex lies within these folds. Although the cerebrum does become more folded as a child grows to maturity, once body growth ceases so does the formation of new grooves, the pattern of the fissures being constant for any given species.

It should be noted here that in right-handed persons the left hemisphere is more active than the right and bears a greater number of responsibilities, as will be seen later. Hence the left hemisphere is said to be *dominant*. Formerly it was believed that left-handed persons had the right hemisphere dominant, but this has been found to be true in only a minority of cases; more frequently it is the left one, as in right-handed individuals. In young children, if injury occurs to the dominant hemisphere, the other can acquire its abilities, but such is not the case in older people.

The Brainstem. If the cerebral hemispheres are carefully removed the brainstem is exposed to view and is seen to be composed of a number of subdivisions (Figure 14–6). Principally, the brainstem serves as the coordinating center for the whole brain; all impulses arriving from the various sense organs and from the body, as well as most impulses arising in the cortex or cerebellum, pass through this brain part on their way to or from the spinal cord. Therefore it forms an ideal location for the coordination and distribution of nervous activities. Most of the integrational activities center in the *thalamus,* located at the anterior end of the brainstem. In this structure is localized the sensation of pain, and, most important of all, in it consciousness appears to be centered, too. Below the thalamus lies the *hypothalamus,* which appears to be the chief control center of metabolic and involuntary activities. Detailed discussions of these two parts are presented later.

On the dorsal wall of the brainstem lie four low, rounded mounds, arranged in two pairs. The forward pair, the *anterior colliculi,* are concerned with sight, whereas the two *posterior colliculi* receive impulses from the auditory organs. Both pairs have motor outlets by way of the spinal cord and are principally involved in reflex movements of the eyes and head.

The most posterior portion of the brainstem, as well as of the entire brain, is the *medulla oblongata,* which consists of a complex of centers for sense reception, face and upper body muscle control, and involuntary action regulation. Not

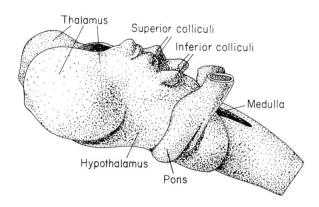

Thalamus
Superior colliculi
Inferior colliculi
Medulla
Hypothalamus
Pons

Figure 14–6. The brainstem. Once considered to be merely a set of nerve tracts, the brainstem is more and more being found to be the principal center of brain function.

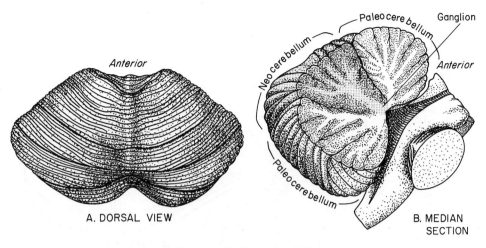

Figure 14–7. The human cerebellum.

only does it assist in the control of separate automatic functions such as breathing, heart rate, digestive-tract action, and the like, but it also appears to integrate the many internal functions of the body. It is a brain region that is absolutely indispensable to the life of a human or other vertebrate; hence it should never be viewed as a simple reflex center, as is frequently done.

The Cerebellum. Just behind the cerebrum on the upper surface of the brainstem lies the cerebellum, the last principal subdivision of the brain, which consists of a number of transversely arranged lobes (Figure 14–7). In section, the cerebellum is seen to resemble the cerebrum in having a layer of gray matter lying over white nerve tracts, the slender processes of which are referred to as *arbor vitae*. In humans and apes the cerebellum is extensive, being larger in proportion to body size than in any other vertebrate.

The Spinal Cord. Structurally, the spinal cord differs from the remainder of the central nervous system in having the white matter on its exterior, whereas the gray matter forms the central mass. On both the dorsal and ventral surfaces the white matter is deeply incised by fissures (Figure 14–8); as a result of these incisions, the gray matter is strongly narrowed medially and forms a butterfly outline in cross section. The whole cord is enclosed in a bony canal within the vertebral column. Nerve fibers leave or enter between the vertebrae, each being connected with the spinal cord by means of two roots. From the ventral root (Figure 14–8); the dorsal one differs in having a *ganglion* in which cell bodies are congregated; the neurons in the ventral root have their cell bodies located in the gray matter of the spinal cord. In addition to these cell bodies, the gray matter contains a number of small neurons, parts of others entering the cord, and supportive cells, the *neuroglia,* as in the gray matter of the brain. The white matter, which also resembles that of the brain, consists of long nerve fibers covered with thick sheaths; the fibers are arranged in tracts and carry impulses to and from the brain.

Tracts leading to the brain (*afferent* or sensory neurons) as well as those leading out of that structure (*efferent* or motor neurons) may be connected eventually to a brain part on the same side

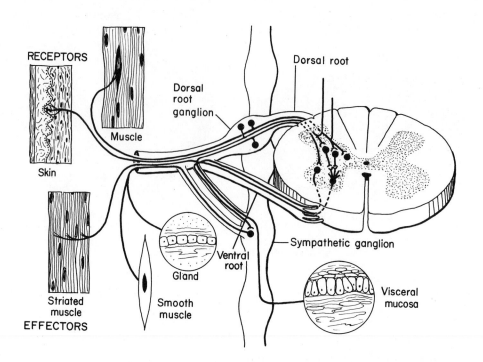

Figure 14-8. Internal anatomy of the spinal cord.

as the part of the body involved. That is to say, sensations from the right side of the body may be connected to a structure on the right side of the brain; such an arrangement is referred to as *ipsilateral*. However, in a more frequent arrangement the neurons cross over so that a right-sided organ has a left-sided connection in the brain, referred to as a *contralateral* condition. Other parts of the body may be controlled by two sides of the brain, or one side of the brain may control two sides of the body; in either case the arrangement is a *bilateral* one.

The Peripheral Nervous System

This part of the nervous system consists of all the nerves that connect with the spinal cord or brain. Some terminate or arise in skin structures or in skeletal muscles, and together they form the *somatic nervous system*. The remainder terminate in the internal organs, such as the blood vessels, heart, and digestive tract, and compose the *visceral nervous system,* the major portion of which is often called the *autonomic system*. In both cases the systems include sensory and motor fibers, but the visceral includes a much smaller percentage of sensory strands than the somatic system. In both cases, too, the afferent fibers enter the spinal cord through the dorsal root, their cell bodies lying in a ganglion on the same root. Efferent impulses enter both subsystems through the ventral root from the spinal cord, their cell bodies lying in its gray matter. But the two differ in structure beyond the spinal cord in that the visceral system has a varying number of ganglia between the central system and the organ it innervates whereas the somatic has not.

The visceral system (Figure 14–9) includes two major subdivisions whose locations and actions are quite distinct, namely the *sympathetic* and the *parasympathetic* systems. In actions one system is opposed to the other. Where the sympathetic system causes contraction of a given set of muscles, the parasympathetic induces relaxation and vice versa; where the sympathetic retards the tempo of an action, the parasympathetic stimulates it, and so on (see Table 14–1). Furthermore, the nerve endings of the parasympathetic system secrete *acetylcholine,* whereas those of the sympathetic system liberate *sympathin.*

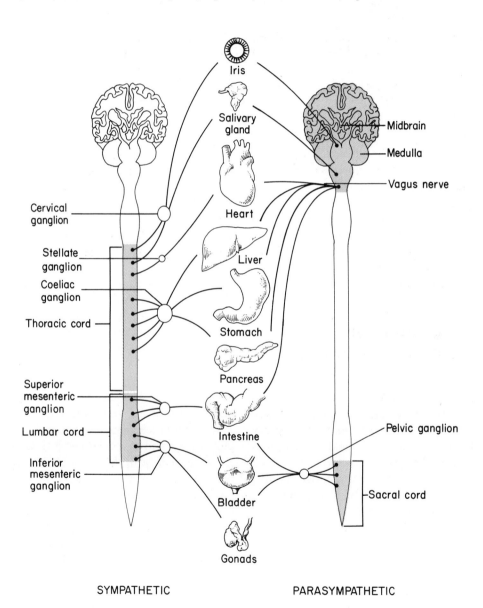

Figure 14–9. The visceral nervous system. In vertebrates, the visceral nervous system includes two major subdivisions—the sympathetic and parasympathetic systems.

TABLE 14-1

COMPARISONS OF ACTIONS OF AUTONOMIC NERVES

Organ	Sympathetic Action	Parasympathetic Action
Eye; iris	Relaxation	Contraction
Skin; sweat glands	Stimulates secretion	No action
Heart rate	Increases	Reduces
Coronary artery	Dilates	Constricts
Other blood vessels	Constricts	Dilates or no effect
Digestive tract	Relaxation	Stimulates
Digestive glands	No action	Stimulates secretion
Bladder wall	Relaxation	Contraction
Bladder sphincter	Contraction	Relaxation

Thus far in the discussion of the peripheral system attention has been confined to the *spinal nerves,* those that connect to the spinal cord. In addition, the system includes 12 pairs of *cranial nerves* which arise directly from the brainstem. These are varied in function; some are strictly sensory, others are entirely motor, and many are both.

The Awareness of Environmental Changes

Above has been outlined a scheme of subdivision of the nervous system based mainly on anatomical considerations; quite a different and simpler scheme can be derived on a functional basis. For example, the sense receptors and nerves and nerve tracts which conduct impulses to the brain are involved in keeping the organism aware of the changes that occur in the environment, both external and internal. These change-detecting parts then may be looked upon as forming a separate division of the nervous system, the *afferent system.* All responses of the organism, internal and external, in turn, are brought about by brain parts,

nerve tracts, and nerve fibers, which carry impulses from the brain to muscles or glands. These parts may be grouped as the *efferent system.* It seems most appropriate in this study of functions to begin with those dealing with the receipt and conduction of stimuli from the environment.

Since the environment itself consists of external and internal aspects, it is not too surprising to find special receptors for each of these major types. Accordingly, those organs which are concerned with changes in the external environment are classed as *exteroceptors,* whereas those that deal with changes within the organism itself are *interoceptors.*

With few exceptions, the senses detect only changes in the environment; after a new ingredient in the environment has been detected for a while and the nerves no longer react to it, they are said to have become *adapted.* For example, after a hand has been held in moderately warm water for a while, the water loses its feeling of warmth. Similarly, we become accustomed to the usual noises and odors about us or the "feel" of a ring on the finger and are not conscious of them.

Exteroceptors are of three sorts: those that detect changes in or on the skin are *cutaneous* receptors, those that detect odors or tastes are *chemical* receptors, and those that perceive changes remote from the organism through light or sound are grouped as *distance* receptors.

Cutaneous Receptors

The skin with its sense receptors (Figure 17–1) forms a highly sensitive organ through which alone many objects can be distinguished. Solely by the feel of it, one can tell whether an object is made of wood, metal, plastic, or glass, whether it is smooth or rough, warm or cold, wet or dry, hard or soft, oily, slimy, or sticky or any of a host of other qualities. How some of these discriminatory sensations are received by the skin is not at all understood today. Even in the more generally recognized cutaneous senses, classed as *pressure, thermal,* and *pain,* there is no broad agreement on the mechanisms involved. But it appears that, contrary to earlier beliefs, these nerves do not usually end in special receptors but react to different chemical changes brought about through the skin or by a change of shape in the skin itself. Only three types of endings are now recognized: free, encapsulated, and basket, the last of which is confined to hair follicles.

Pressure Sense. Under this term are grouped a large number of contact senses, most of which are referred to popularly as touch or feeling. In order to arouse this sensation, it is necessary to indent the skin, at least ever so slightly, to produce a bent area. However, it is not

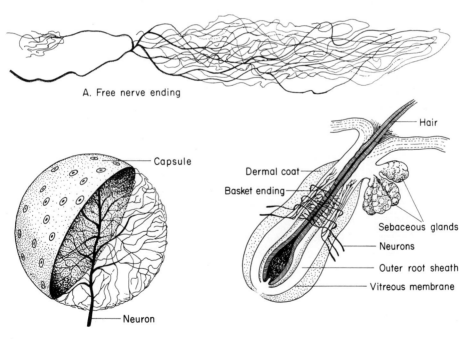

A. Free nerve ending

Capsule

Neuron

B. Diagram of Pacinian corpuscle

Hair

Dermal coat

Basket ending

Sebaceous glands

Neurons

Outer root sheath

Vitreous membrane

C. Basket ending

Figure 14–10. The three types of nerve endings found in the skin. Although at one time perhaps a dozen distinct types were suggested to exist, today it is known that only three occur. Free nerve endings (A) have no special modifications, while encapsulated ones (Pacinian corpuscles) are encased in a bulbous enclosure (B), and basket endings are woven around hair follicles (C).

necessary for an object to come in direct contact with the skin; touching a hair and causing it to bend also produces a tactile sensation. In hairless regions of the skin, such as on the hands and lips, pressures of all sorts seem to be received by *encapsulated endings* (Figure 14–10B). No such endings are present in hair-covered areas, so that pressure sensations must be detected by the hairs or by *free endings* (Figure 14–10A). From hairs these sensations appear to be received by the *basket endings* located about the bases of the follicles (Figure 14–10C). From both the epidermis and the hairs the sensations are carried by nerve tracts to the thalamus and possibly to the cortex of the cerebrum.

Thermal Sense. Recent experiments with cold and warmth reception on the tongue and sensitive paw of the cat seem to indicate that the vertebrates react to thermal conditions in a manner precisely opposite to that of nonliving substances. In physics, cold is defined as the absence of heat; in the vertebrates heat may prove to be the absence of cold! One team of researchers found that cold elicited responses in the nerves associated with the skin and that warmth merely caused the cessation of these impulses. No specialized nerve endings appear to be involved in the reception of cold and heat, as the nerves react directly, nor has a specific area of the brain yet been found that receives stimuli of this sort.

Pain. Sensations of pain seem to be received in the skin by neurons of rather fine diameter and to be conducted largely through long ascending nerve tracts in the white matter of the spinal cord to the thalamus. Here, again, no specialized ending is involved. Recent experiments point to the release of chemicals in the skin by an abrasion as the activating agent. Extracts made from

the serum in blisters or from painful wounds caused pain when injected beneath the skin; these substances proved to be polypeptides and other proteinaceous compounds. Similarly, itch, which is related to pain, can be induced by an injection of histamines or of enzymes which break down proteins.

Chemoreceptors

Although some doubt has been raised that smell is actually a chemical sense, it does detect changes in the composition of the atmosphere by its response to the presence of foreign molecules, and hence does detect "chemical changes," although not in a chemist's usage of the phrase. And in this light it is treated here.

Smell. The olfactory sense receptors are located in the upper portion of the nasal chamber (Figure 14–11), embedded in the mucous lining in a cleft on each side. The bipolar nerve cells, which receive the stimuli, extend to the *olfactory bulbs* lying on the ventral surface of the cerebrum in which they synapse with cells of several types. The nature of the olfactory sense is not too well understood. For a substance to possess an odor detectable to man it must first be somewhat volatile, so that its molecules will readily diffuse into the atmosphere and enter the nose. Second, it must be able to be freely adsorbed by the mucous coating of the nasal passages. And, finally, it must be soluble in the fatlike materials (lipoids) that cover the terminal rods of the olfactory receptors. Since man is able to distinguish by smell an almost endless number of substances, no widely accepted theory explaining the sense of smell has yet been introduced.

Taste. In contrast to the wide range of the sense of smell, taste is limited indeed, for with it alone we can distinguish

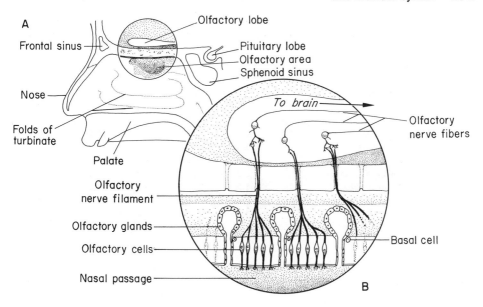

Figure 14–11. The olfactory detectors. A. The olfactory sense receptors are confined to one region of the nasal passages. (After Allison.)   B. Structure of the olfactory sense receptors.

only four qualities—sweet, sour, salt, and bitter. Most of the other flavors we "taste" are actually through the sense of

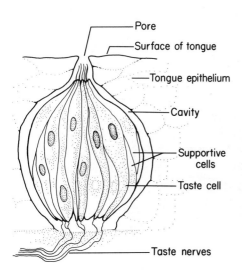

Figure 14–12. The structure of a taste bud. Taste receptors or "buds" essentially are mixtures of supportive and taste cells embedded in the tongue, palate, and pharynx just below the surface of the epithelium.

smell, supplemented by the sense of touch. For example, with the nostrils held shut, it is impossible to distinguish thin slices of apple from similar slices of potato or onion. To possess taste, a substance must be soluble in water, so that it will dissolve in the saliva and be brought into contact with the taste buds (Figure 14–12).

Although the number of actual types of tastes that man can detect are limited, the four possibilities can be united into limitless combinations. In Table 14–2 relative taste intensities are shown for some common foods and beverages.

From the taste buds the nervous impulses are carried along branches of three cranial nerves to the thalamus; from that center they are distributed contralaterally to areas in the cerebral cortex (Figure 14–13), one far to the side on each parietal lobe and another on the ventral surface of each hemisphere.

TABLE 14–2

CHARACTERISTICS OF CERTAIN FOODSTUFFS, IN GUSTS *

	Sweet	Bitter	Sour	Salt
Cola drink	11.2	2.2	5.0	1.3
Ale	2.5	28.2	10.0	1.3
Unsweetened grapefruit juice	3.2	2.0	35.5	2.0
Consommé	1.4	1.3	4.5	7.9
Riesling wine	1.0	7.5	6.7	1.3
Coffee, unsweetened	1.0	42.3	3.2	1.0
Coffee, 5% sucrose	3.2	23.8	3.2	1.3
Anchovy fillet	1.3	23.8	5.6	10.0
Sweet pickles	3.2	3.2	13.4	3.2
Sour pickles	1.0	1.8	18.0	3.2
Raspberry jam	23.8	1.8	10.0	1.3
Honey	56.4	2.4	1.8	1.3

* After Beebe-Center; a "gust" is an arbitrary unit of taste.

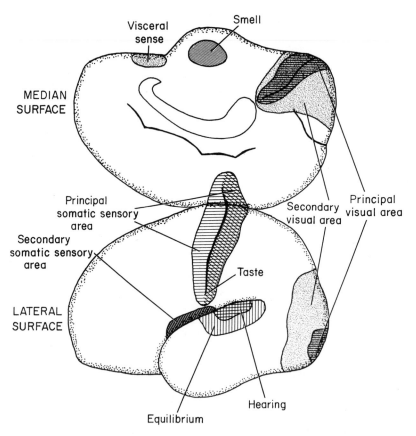

Figure 14–13. The sensory areas of the cerebral cortex. Specialized areas of the cerebrum serve as receptor centers for many of the senses.

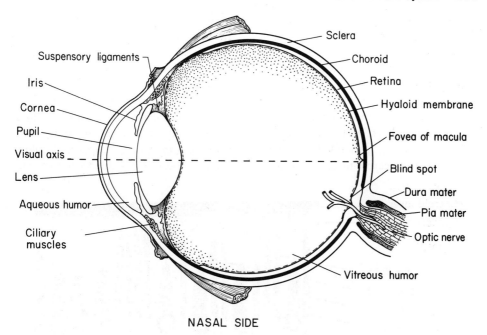

NASAL SIDE

Figure 14–14. The structure of the human eye.

Distance Receptors

Under the term *distance receptors* are grouped two sets of sense organs which detect two entirely unrelated types of physical phenomena and which are really not at all related one to the other. The only property shared is that of reaction to stimuli which arise usually at some distance from the receptor organs.

The Eye and Vision. As can be seen in Figure 14–14, the eye is a fairly complex optical instrument which serves efficiently to gather light and focus the image. The outer connective tissue wall of the eye, the *sclera,* becomes transparent and bulges anteriorly to form the *cornea,* which lacks blood vessels; the cornea together with the *lens* serves to focus the image upon the *retina.* The second layer in the wall of the eye, the *choroid,* is continued anteriorly by the *iris,* a pigmented curtainlike structure which regulates the brightness of the

image by contracting and expanding. To perform this function, it is provided with two groups of muscle fibers; one set, arranged in a circle around the pupil, narrows the latter upon contraction, whereas the second set, arranged radially, causes dilation. Like the iris, the choroid is highly pigmented and probably serves to help absorb stray and excess light rays. A change in the focus of the lens (called *accommodation*) is accomplished by contraction of the muscles in the *ciliary body.* By their contraction, tension on the *suspensory ligaments* which support the lens is diminished; this, in turn, allows the lens to become more rounded, thus shortening its focal length and bringing closer objects into sharp focus. When the ciliary muscles relax, the elasticity of the sclera pulls on the ligaments and flattens the lens. Usually, when close objects are viewed, the pupils are also narrowed.

The *retina,* the part of the eye that actually detects light stimuli, is a complex structure composed of many types of specialized nerve cells. In line with the principal path of light entering the eye, directly opposite the lens, lies a specialized portion, the *macula lutea,* named for its yellowish color. In the middle of this yellow spot is a rounded impression, the *fovea,* and nearby, toward the nose, is a whitish area, the *papilla,* which marks the point at which the *optic nerve* joins the retina. Since this area is devoid of light-sensitive cells and is covered with small arteries and veins, it forms the so-called *blind spot* of the eye. Under the microscope the retina is seen to be made up of a large variety of neurons, interconnecting in a most complicated fashion (Figure 14–15). Only the deepest (or out-

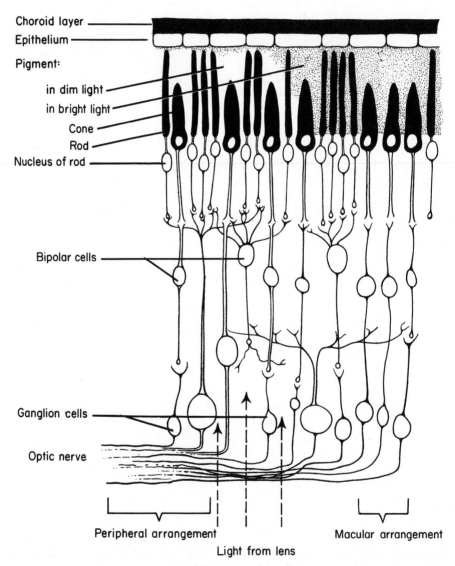

Choroid layer
Epithelium
Pigment:
  in dim light
  in bright light
  Cone
  Rod
Nucleus of rod

Bipolar cells

Ganglion cells

Optic nerve

Peripheral arrangement   Macular arrangement

Light from lens

Figure 14–15. The structure of the mammalian retina. The retina consists of a whole series of intricately interconnected nerve cells, beneath which are the actual receptor cells, the rods and cones.

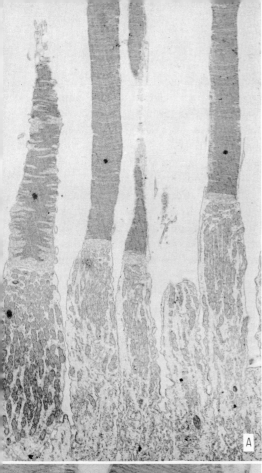

Figure 14–16. Fine structure of rods and cones. A. In this electronmicrograph of a longitudinal section of several rods and a single cone from a human retina, the basic similarities and slight differences between the two types of receptors can be seen. The thick portions are placed toward the light coming from the lens, while the slender parts extend toward the choroid and thus the outside of the eye. Magnified 3,000×. B. The slender outer portion ("segment") of two rods are shown to be densely filled with double membranous disks. Magnified 17,000×. (Both electronmicrographs courtesy of Drs. A. Bairati, Jr., and N. Orzalesi.)

ermost) layer of these nerve cells, consisting of the *rods* and *cones,* is actually sensitive to light; the others serve to coordinate, integrate, or transmit the impulses.

The rods and cones differ in both distribution and function (Figure 14–16). In the human the former are found in greater relative abundance in the periphery of the retina, becoming gradually less frequent toward the center, whereas the number of cones increases until at the fovea only they are to be found. Functionally, cones appear to be sensitive to bright light and to color, whereas rods are color-blind and respond to low intensities of light. Acute vision, that is, the ability to see objects sharply outlined, is confined entirely to the fovea of the retina, where the cones are individually connected to neurons in the optic nerve. Reading would be impossible were this area absent from the eye.

To date, the most widely acceptable explanation of the mechanism by which the retina actually detects light seems to be provided by the *photochemical theory.* According to this hypothesis, a chemical substance S, present in the cells of the retina, breaks down by the action of light into various products that can be designated for convenience as P_1, P_2, P_3, and so on. In the absence of light, that is, in darkness, these products are able to regenerate the original substance S.

Further, it is supposed that one of the products, such as P_1, undergoes a secondary reaction within the cells and unites chemically with a compound present there; it is this chemical reaction that is conjectured as producing the stimulus which the nerve detects as light. Many of the requirements of this concept are fulfilled by the actual conditions found within retinal cells. From the rods, a pigment, *rhodopsin* or visual purple, has been isolated which breaks down first into an orange compound and then into a yellow one under the influence of light. Furthermore, this substance has been found to be regenerated in darkness if a sufficient quantity of vitamin A is present. Recently, two other pigments, both related to vitamin A as rhodopsin is, have been detected in the living human eye by means of an ingenious reflection technique. These pigments have been named *erythrolabe* and *chlorolabe* and react to red and green light, respectively; the presence of a third pigment, *cyanolabe,* which is sensitive to blue light, is suspected. These pigments are assumed to be located in the cones, but to date they have defied attempts to isolate them because of their unstable character and minute concentration. Whatever may be the origin of the stimulus that elicits a response in the rods and cones, the impulses travel across the retina and into the optic nerve, by which means they are distributed to several portions of the brain. Chiefly, they are conducted to the occipital lobes of the cerebral cortex (Figure 14–13), where actual vision is located. Note that one half of each eye is connected to the ipsilateral half of the cerebrum, the other to the contralateral side (Figure 14–17). Also note around each principal visual area a secondary visual area, which, while blind to color, is concerned with sight and perhaps serves to help elaborate or associate the visual impulses. The impulses that are carried to the anterior colliculi of the midbrain are involved in reflexes (see page 285) which regulate the diameter of the pupil, keep the eye centered on an object, and possibly help in accommodation.

Theories attempting to explain *color vision* have by no means been lacking, but so far none has been found to be universally acceptable; therefore the two chief concepts are only briefly outlined. In one (the Young-Helmholtz theory) it is supposed that there are four cone types, each provided with a distinct pigment. One responds to bright white light, whereas the remaining three respond, respectively, to the three primary colors, red, green, and violet, the actual hue resulting from a combination of these three colors and white (or its absence, black). Although this hypothesis is satisfactory in many ways, all the conjectured pigments have not yet been isolated, although they have been detected. The second hypothesis (the Hering theory) has a similar weakness. It differs from the first principally in proposing only three types of cones, one as before involved in black and white vision. It is suggested that the other two contain distinct pigments which react differently in different wavelengths of light. One is thought to break down in the presence of red and to be synthesized by green, whereas the second breaks down under yellow light and is restored by blue. Although this second proposal satisfactorily explains two common sorts of color-blindness found in humans, it has no other basis on which to stand.

The Ear and the Acoustical Sense. The ear of the higher vertebrates is peculiar in its dual nature, for it is the receptor for two unrelated senses—sound and gravitational effects. Since only the acoustical sense makes the ear a distance re-

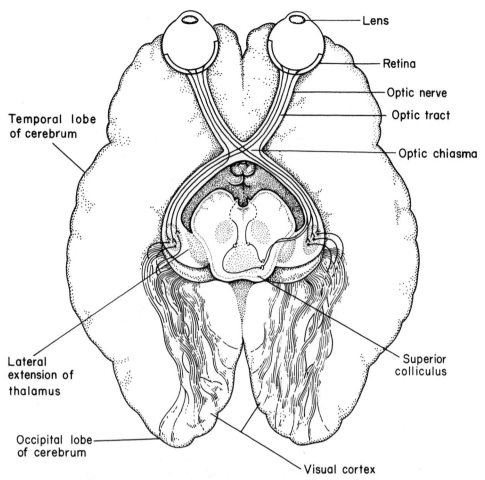

Lens

Retina

Optic nerve

Optic tract

Optic chiasma

Temporal lobe
of cerebrum

Lateral
extension of
thalamus

Occipital lobe
of cerebrum

Superior
colliculus

Visual cortex

Figure 14–17. The path of the visual impulses. While the exact distribution of fibers varies from one species of vertebrate to another, in the human being the impulses from the inner half of each eye cross over to the opposite side of the cerebrum, whereas the rest are conducted ipsilaterally.

ceptor, it alone is discussed at this time.

The acoustical sense involves the interpretation of sound waves in the air which impinge on the eardrum. As a rule, sound waves consist of a number of atmospheric vibrations superimposed upon one another and differing only in frequency (pitch) and amplitude (loudness). By the interpretation of these sound waves, we are able, when a good acquaintance, for example, speaks even a monosyllabic word, such as "No," to recognize the word and the emotion with which it was spoken, to distinguish the

note of the scale to which it would correspond, and even to recognize the person who spoke it solely by the quality (timbre) of the voice. Understanding how a human organism is able to translate vibrations in the air in so many ways involves a knowledge of the structure of the ear and how its parts function.

Structurally, the auditory organ is relatively simple and consists of three major parts (Figure 14–18), the *external* ear, the *middle* ear, and the *inner* ear. The first part consists of the *pinna* and *auditory canal,* the second, of the *tympanic*

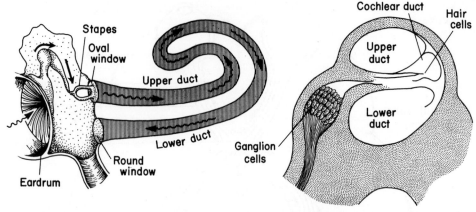

A. Cochlea, l.s.   B. Cross section through a portion of cochlea

Figure 14–18. Structure of the middle ear and cochlea. The actual sound receptor, the cochlea, receives sound vibrations by way of the middle ear.

membrane and a set of three bones, called the *ossicles,* and the third, of a coiled tube, the *cochlea,* in which the *auditory nerve* terminates. Of these, the first two function primarily in collecting and conducting sound waves, by means of either air or bone, to the inner ear in which the actual detection of the sound takes place. The external ear does most of the collecting of the sound waves and directs them against the tympanic membrane, which marks the beginning of the middle ear. The sound waves, which consist of rhythmically alternating layers of high and low air pressures, cause the eardrum to move in and out in unison with them. In the middle ear conduction is the primary function; for the most part, this is carried out by the ossicles' transmitting vibrations from the tympanic membrane to the *oval window* of the cochlea.

Each ossicle bears an individual name, descriptive in Latin of the bone's shape in humans. The *malleus* (hammer) is firmly attached to the tympanic membrane, and the *stapes* (stirrup) ends the series at the oval window of the cochlea, whereas the *incus* (anvil) lies in between

and connects the two. In transmitting vibrations, the stapes is made to move with a rocking motion which exerts considerable pressure on the oval window. The chamber of the middle ear in which the ossicles lie opens by way of the *Eustachian tube* into the pharynx. Normally, the pharyngeal end of this tube is closed by a small muscle. During the act of swallowing, the muscle relaxes, permitting the tube to open, and thus allows the pressure in the middle ear to become equal to that on the outer surface of the eardrum.

In the inner ear is located the organ of actual hearing, the cochlea, which contains the sensitive endings of the *auditory nerve.* Essentially, the cochlea is a long tapering tube, coiled in a snaillike spiral of three turns and divided internally into two ducts throughout its length by the *basilar membrane* and a bony platelet (Figure 14–18). One of these ducts is divided unequally in turn by an oblique membrane; the smaller of the two, the *cochlear duct,* is the site of the auditory nerve endings which lie in the spiral organ that rests on the basilar membrane. In great part this organ is made up of sensory *hair cells* surrounded by supportive cells. Overhanging the hair cells is a gelatinous *tectorial membrane* which lightly contacts their cilia. The entire cochlear duct is filled with a rather viscous fluid called the *endolymph* and is continued into the other nonauditory parts of the inner ear by a membranous tube at its wide end. On the other hand, the other ducts, which are filled with a different sort of fluid known as *perilymph,* communicate with one another at the narrow end; the wide end of one bears the *round window,* which is covered over by a thin membrane. The broad end of the remaining duct connects with the vestibule in which is located the *oval window,* closed by the footplate of the stapes.

Although the explanation of the processes of hearing is still primarily a theoretical one, the evidence points largely to the following mechanisms as being chiefly involved: the vibrations of the tympanic membrane are transmitted to the oval window of the cochlea by a rocking motion of the stapes, as pointed

out above. In turn, the vibrations of the oval window are passed on to the perilymph. Some of these waves of compression are passed through the whole of the perilymph in the two ducts by way of the apical interconnection, the membrane over the round window at the far end yielding in response. Other waves, however, are set up in the column of perilymph which traverse the cochlear duct at points relative to the wavelength of the sound. Long waves (low notes) penetrate almost to the very apex of the cochlea, whereas higher notes are transmitted across the cochlear duct near the base, the highest perceptible sounds (16,000 cps) being received at the extreme base in the human ear (see Figure 14–19). As these waves traverse the cochlear duct, they set the basilar membrane in that area into vibration. These vibratory movements press the hair cells upward toward the tectorial membrane, distorting the hairs and initiating an impulse along the fibers of the auditory nerve. Soft sounds cause vibrations in only a narrow region of the basilar mem-

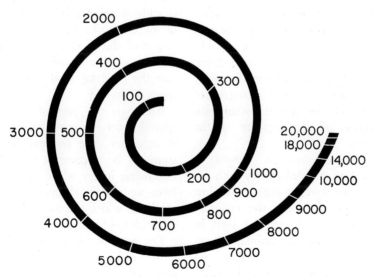

Figure 14–19. The areas for detecting specific pitches within the cochlea. The numerals indicate the wave length of the sound received in cycles per second by the particular areas of the cochlea, here shown diagrammatically.

brane; as sounds increase in volume, broader and broader areas of the basilar membrane vibrate. Too broad areas of vibration are interpreted by the cerebrum as "noise." Even beautiful music played too loudly will ultimately reach the point of noisiness.

After leaving the inner ear, the impulses are carried by the auditory nerve to the brainstem and thence through the thalamus to the temporal lobe of the cerebral cortex (Figure 14–13), each cochlea being represented on both lobes. Apparently the fibers from the different portions of the cochlear basilar membrane are arranged in the cortex in the same sequence as in that membrane, so that sounds of differing pitch are received by separate areas. En route from the cochlea connections are made with the inferior colliculus, but its role in hearing is uncertain.

Interoceptors

The receptors of this category detect all the many sorts of changes that occur within the body. In some cases these alternations, as in the sense of equilibrium, arise in response to outside factors; others, however, come as a result of variations within the body itself, as in thirst and hunger. Still others, presently poorly understood, do not report changes but seem to provide the central system with an awareness of the presence of the bodily parts.

Thirst. The sensations known as thirst, of course, are tied closely with the body's need for water to replace that lost through evaporation and the ordinary bodily functions. Although the level of water in the blood is maintained remarkably constant largely by withdrawal of the substance from glands and organs, a point arrives at which no more moisture is readily available and the blood

water level drops. The slightest drop is detected by receptors in the hypothalamus, which cause the individual to begin seeking water—in other words, to feel thirsty.

But there is another route through which the sensation of thirst can be aroused. As stated above, water is withdrawn from many bodily organs as its level in the blood demands. One of the chief sources of this water is the salivary glands, the secretions of which are largely aqueous, ranging from 98 to 99 per cent water. Hence, as the blood requirements for water are met, these glands produce less saliva and in the absence of saliva the surface of the pharynx becomes dry. In the wall of the pharynx nerve receptors appear to be present which respond to the dry condition and thereby elicit the feeling of thirst.

Hunger. As in the above sense, hunger too appears to have more than one channel through which it may be aroused but the actual mechanisms are poorly known indeed. The level of sugars in the blood, upon falling below a certain point, may cause a sense of hunger, which is quickly alleviated by the consumption of sweet drinks or foods. The second source of this "feeling" is usually rhythmic in patterns established by habit, so that the need for food is felt at regular times of the day.

Although the part of the brain responsible for the reception of this sense is unknown, the cerebral frontal lobe seems to be responsible for its control. Following injury to or removal of this lobe, an abnormal appetite frequently results in which the patient desires large quantities of food.

The Somatic Sense. Under this term is included a vague sensation discovered and explored largely through brain surgery. When the region of the cerebrum adjacent to the central fissure (Figure

14–13) is stimulated electrically, a tingling sensation is felt in various parts of the body surface, depending on the area stimulated. Thus application of the electrode to the uppermost portion of the cerebrum will elicit a response in the leg. Each bodily part has a region in which it is principally represented, the arrangement and extent of the area for each part being indicated in the figure. Surgical removal or injury to portions of this region results in the lack of awareness of the part represented, similar to the loss of feeling when an arm or foot "goes to sleep."

Just below this *primary somatic sensory area,* there is a less extensive *secondary somatic sensory area.* Little is known of its activities except that the arms and legs appear to be principally represented.

Equilibrium and Proprioception. These final two major senses are discussed together, for it is difficult to distinguish between them in all their rami-fications; in fact, they are really just two aspects of one and the same sense. Several of the important components of this sense center in receptors in the inner ear. Here are to be found two small membranous sacs and the three *semicircular canals* (Figure 14–20), all of which are continuous with the cochlear duct, discussed above in connection with hearing. The two membranous sacs, called the *utricle* and *saccule* and located in the vestibule, contain a sensory layer, the *macula,* in which fibers of the vestibular nerve terminate. Similarly, each of the semicircular canals has at one end a sensory layer, the *crista,* in which fibers of the same nerve terminate. The two maculae and three cristae resemble the basilar membrane of the cochlea in structure, consisting of hair cells in which hairs project into an overlying gelatinous mass. In this mass in the saccule and utricle are grains of calcium carbonate called *otoliths.* Movements of the fluid

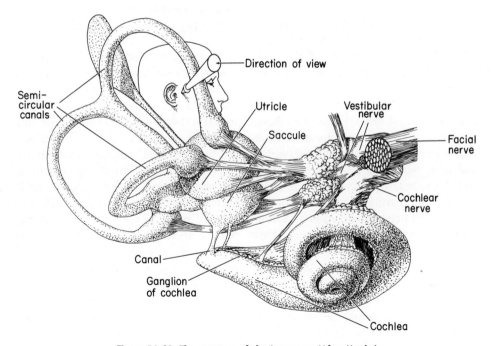

Figure 14–20. The structure of the inner ear. (After Hardy.)

(*endolymph*) which fills the tubes agitate the gelatinous mass; this, in turn, distorts the hairs, instigating impulses in the vestibular fibers, which are conducted to the temporal lobe of the cerebrum.

Although the function of the saccules in man is uncertain, that of the utricles seems to be the sensing of changes in position of the head, whether it is in motion or not. The utricles are particularly sensitive to an upside down position, as when one is standing on his head. On the other hand, the semicircular canals respond to movements of the head. As can be noted in Figure 14–20, each of the three semicircular canals occupies different planes set at right angles of 90°. Turning of the head to one side, for example, stimulates the cristae of the pair of horizontal canals, for although the canals move with the head the endolymph inside tends to remain still because of its inertia. Similarly, when the head is tilted forward, movement of the endolymph within the vertical pair of canals results.

But detection of the movements of the head is only a part of the whole equilibrial occupation; the sensing of the position of the trunk and limbs is equally important. Toward this end are provided many types of receptors on the muscles, tendons, and skeletal joints. Of these, the articular receptors are most sensitive to changes in position, the hip, shoulder, and large toe joints ranking highest in sensitivity. Sensory endings on tendons respond to tension changes whether caused by muscular contraction or stretch stimuli from the outside, such as weights and movement. Almost all impulses from muscles, tendons, and joints ascend the spinal cord to the cerebellum.

Deep Pain. As can be testified by anyone who has experienced the intense pain of muscular cramps or who has suffered a sprain, muscles and tendons are well supplied with pain receptors. The internal organs, too, are so equipped, but they are not sensitive, as a rule, to lesions; surgeons do not need to narcotize viscera when performing internal surgery. Chiefly, these receptors react to strong distention of the part (as in gas pains) or to cramping of their muscles. In appendicitis, for example, in which an internal part becomes inflamed, pain is not felt in the part but only in surface muscles or the skin. Such "referred pains" are the result of the large number of impulses coming from the diseased organ over visceral nerves to the spinal cord and setting off impulses in the central nervous system; that is to say, the amount of acetylcholine or other chemical secreted by the visceral nerves accidentally spreads to afferent nerves running to the thalamus, where they are translated as pain "located" in the overlying muscle or skin.

The Response to Environmental Changes

Above we have seen how an organism is kept aware of all the changes that occur without and within by means of numerous, diverse, and complex types of receptors and their afferent neurons. The control and initiation of the organisms' reactions to these stimuli make up the remainder of this account. In contrast to the afferent system, the response mechanisms are extremely simple. Only two types of reactions are possible in any animal—a muscle may be contracted or relaxed or the secreting of a gland may be begun, halted, or altered. Muscles and glands are the only *effectors* in the entire body. In this connection it should be noted that nerve impulses may have either a *stimulating* or *inhibiting* action.

Paralleling the afferent system's classification of the receptors, effectors too may be effectively grouped as *somatic* where muscles and glands of the body wall are concerned and as *visceral* where the resulting activity occurs in the internal organs.

SOMATIC RESPONSES

Reactions to stimuli can be instigated over two major types of routes, one direct, the other indirect. Both are found in visceral as well as somatic reactions, but because of the basic similarity in the two areas only the somatic need be discussed. However, it should be noted that a given stimulus may in some cases cause reactions in somatic and visceral regions simultaneously.

The Principal Routes

The Direct Route. The simplest type of reaction that can be effected is the *simple reflex arc* system involving a re-ceptor, an afferent neuron running to the central nervous system, an efferent neuron, and an effector. As an example of this sort may be cited the stretch reflex. If the muscle in Figure 14–21 is stretched by a slight (or great) increase of stress on it, the resulting stimulus will cause impulses to be transmitted by the receptors of the muscle along the sensory neuron to the spinal cord. In the gray matter of the spinal cord there are a number of synaptic endings, including some in contact with motor neurons. Impulses from the afferent neuron cross these synapses and travel to a muscle, stimulating it to contract to a greater or lesser degree, depending on the number of incoming impulses. As a rule, it is the muscle which has been stretched that is stimulated to contract, thus compensating for the additional load placed on the part of the body it supports.

More frequently, in simple reflex arcs,

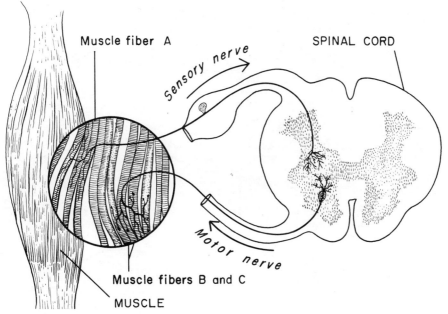

Figure 14–21. A simple reflex. When the muscle fiber A is stretched, impulses are initiated by the spindle receptor and transmitted along the sensory nerve. Upon arriving in the spinal cord, these impulses are conducted across the synapse to a motor nerve without first going to the brain. After traversing the motor nerve's length, they induce contraction in muscle fibers B and C and thus counteract the stretch on A.

instead of the direct formation of a synapse by the afferent and efferent neurons, a third nerve cell, known as the *internuncial* neuron (Figure 14–22) lies between the two. This type of arc is involved when one accidentally touches a hot object. The stimulus causes thermal receptors to send impulses over appropriate neurons to the spinal cord, thence via the internuncial neurons to motor neurons. When these motor impulses reach the muscles, the latter react by contracting, and the fingers are pulled away from the hot object.

In both the above arrangements the pathway is short and the number of synapses small; hence the shortest possible time elapses between the application of the stimulus and the reaction. Such mechanical responses do not need to be learned by the organism but are an essential part of its anatomy; as such, they are passed down from generation to generation. Often such simple reflex arcs are held up as a model of all nervous activity and in this capacity have some value. But it must be emphasized that the simple action outlined above probably rarely if ever occurs. Even the simplest reaction is complicated by the fact that when one muscle contracts another must relax to an equal degree, otherwise no movement of the part could result. And at least in somatic reactions many appear to be subject to modification by the brain.

Modified Direct Route.   In the reflexes

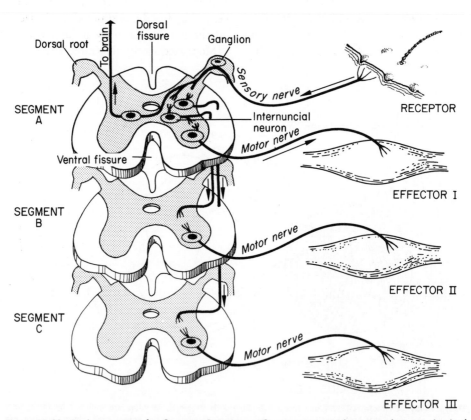

Figure 14–22. An intersegmental reflex arc. Sometimes reflex arcs can involve more than one level of the central nervous system. In the diagram, a stimulus from a single receptor is shown to be transmitted to three muscles, each of which is thereby induced to contract; sensory impulses simultaneously are transmitted to the brain.

just described the impulses along the motor neuron leave the spinal cord at the same level as they enter over the afferent nerves. But there are many reflex arcs in which different spinal cord levels are involved; these are known as *intersegmental reflex arcs*. For example, if the skin on the posterior portion of the thorax of a dog is irritated, the ipsilateral hind leg reflexly scratches the area. If the stimulus is sufficiently strong and the ipsilateral leg is prevented from scratching the part, often the contralateral leg may be provoked into action.

Indirect Route. Although in the direct route, whether modified or simple, the synapse between the afferent and efferent fibers lies within the spinal cord, other reflex arcs involve synapses in the brain. Since the junction of the afferent and efferent fibers is thus at some distance from the point of contact with the stimulus and a number of neurons are involved, the route may be said to be indirect. As an illustration of this type of reflex route we cite the increase in the flow of saliva when some substance is tasted. The impulses arising in the taste buds are transmitted first to the thalamus and thence to the ventral portion of the cerebral cortex. Next the impulses reenter the thalamus and appear to be distributed to the lateral portion of the cerebral motor cortex (Figure 14-23), which in turn transmits impulses to the several salivary glands, thereby stimulating them to increase their production of saliva. It must not be assumed that all indirect reflexes involve so many distribution centers; some, particularly the visceral, may be relatively simple. Others undoubtedly are far more complex.

The Mediation of Somatic Responses

Again it must be emphasized that reflex arcs of the various types account for only a small proportion of the total responses of a vertebrate and do not form the model of a typical response pattern. The large majority of responses of such an animal are far too complex to be explained in terms of reflex arcs. For one thing, vertebrates, like most higher animals, have a brain in which information garnered from previous experience may be stored and drawn upon on future occasions. How impulses reach this central organ from the numerous receptors has already been shown; now it remains to be seen how responses are mediated and coordinated by its several parts.

The Cerebrum. On each hemisphere of the cerebrum, largely anterior to the central sulcus but extending posterior to it as well, lies the *principal motor area* (Figure 14-23) of the cortex. In the sequence of the representation of bodily parts in this area a close correspondence will be noticed to that of the somatic sense area (compare Figure 14-13), the arrangement being contralateral and inverted from top to bottom. In fact, these two areas overlap and intermingle quite extensively; that is to say, the anterior area is *largely* motor but partly sensory, and an opposite statement is true for the posterior area. Furthermore, similar conditions prevail in the representation of the individual bodily parts; none is represented solely in its given section of the sequence, but only most strongly. For example, electrical stimulation of the motor area in which the thumb is most strongly represented will at first cause the contralateral thumb to move, but continued stimulation will later result in movement of the index finger. Still further stimulation of the same area produces activity in all the fingers, followed by bendings at the wrist! Hence it appears that although the thumb in this example is the chief part represented in this location other nerve endings representing associated structures are found here too, enabling coordination of movement to be brought about.

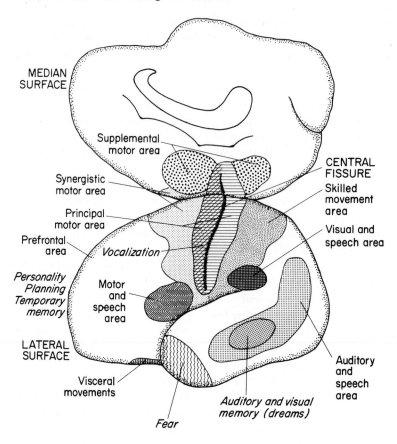

Figure 14–23. The motor areas of the cerebral cortex. Many areas of the cerebrum are involved in motor activities. The one labeled principal motor area is located largely anterior to the central fissure but extends posterior to it to some degree as well.

In addition to the principal motor area, there are several others concerned with motor activities. The *supplementary motor area,* surrounding the sensory motor area within the longitudinal fissure (Figure 14–23), appears to have definite representation for the various bodily parts. Chiefly, it acts contralaterally, but it can act bilaterally as well. For example, stimulation of a particular point in this area of the left hemisphere may cause the right thumb to move strongly while the left thumb moves to a lesser degree. It may well be found, when further studies have been made, that this supplementary area helps

especially to coordinate the activities of the two sides of the body. A second additional region, the *synergistic motor area,* is involved in movements of the whole trunk or of the entire contralateral arm or leg; its activities become apparent when parts of the principal motor area are damaged or removed. Should the region respresenting the arm and hand, for example, be lost, and the patient thereafter desires to bend a finger on the contralateral side, all the fingers on that hand will bend, the hand will turn downward (pronate), the lower arm will flex, and the upper arm abduct. Or, if he attempts to bend his elbow, the same series of movements takes place, or opposite ones if extension of the lower arm is attempted. All fine and individual movements have been lost; only synergistic ones remain. A fourth motor area, poorly defined and even more poorly explored, is located behind the principal sensory area; this area apparently is occupied with *skilled movements,* as of the throat, tongue, and mouth in speaking and of the hands, arms, and legs in such activities as playing the piano, typing, and so on. It is closely tied to the principal motor area, on one hand, and with vision, on the other. In short, it serves as a visual-motor coordination center.

While thus it appears that the cerebrum is well fitted to play the dominant role in the neural control of the organism's responses to incoming stimuli, it actually may perform in a more subordinate manner. In recent years it has been found that the thalamus also possesses motor and sensory areas, each provided with sequences of body part representation, quite comparable to the more thoroughly explored ones of the cerebrum. As knowledge accumulates, the point of view is becoming increasingly popular that the two cerebral hemispheres possibly may represent mere extensions of the thalamus and serve much as branch switchboards. Just as additional telephone switchboards or even exchanges are needed to provide the enlarged number of interconnections required by increased populations, so the higher vertebrates' increment in body size and complexity of musculature places demands for more space in the brain because each additional set of muscle fibers needs its individual representation there. So it may eventually prove that the thalamus is the main center of conscious activity but calls upon the cerebral cortex to provide the points of contact between the many parts it coordinates.

The Cerebellum. This structure is implicated in motor responses to stimuli in several diverse ways. In one of its major responsibilities gravitational stimuli arising in the muscles, inner ear, and so on, are received and bodily reflex movements are augmented or inhibited as occasion demands. In the anterior lobe of this organ, the neck muscles and each appendage have individual representation ipsilaterally.

Although the cerebellum receives stimuli from the skin, particularly that covering the appendages, they are not consciously received; hence the nature of the sensations is not known. As a whole, the cerebellum adjusts motor impulses arising in the cerebrum, strengthening or inhibiting them to accord with the action's requirements. When extensive damage has occurred or much of it has been surgically removed, it is difficult for the patient to judge distances. In leaping, cats and dogs, for example, will often overshoot the mark and leap or even walk or run against doors and walls.

Complex Movements

The performance of a volitional act concerns not just one part of the cerebrum, plus another part of the cerebellum, as may be implied in the foregoing discussion. In actuality it requires much of the central and peripheral nervous systems as well as the entire locomotor system. Only in conjunction with one another can either the locomotor or the nervous system produce a motor response, no matter how strong the stimulus may be. Let us take two different kinds of bodily actions as illustrations of what really happens in such ordinary activities as throwing a ball and talking.

Throwing a Ball. Let us suppose that you are quarterbacking the varsity team and that you have just received the ball from the center and have dropped back to throw a pass. Over to the right you see that a receiver is open and you get set to make the throw. Exactly what is involved in the succeeding action? First of all the image of the receiver on the retina of each eye stimulates the retinal cells to transmit impulses to the occipital lobe of the cerebrum and possibly to the superior colliculus; these impulses are evaluated against previous experience and an estimate is made of the distance between yourself and the planned receiver. At the same time, in the skin of the hand holding the football, nerve endings are receiving stimuli relating to its hardness, smoothness, and wetness and transmitting them to the brain. Muscles, tendons, and joints of the throwing arm send impulses to the cerebellum regarding their position, tautness, and the weight of the ball, all of which are compared against previous experience. In fact, every part of the somatic region is sending similar impulses concerning changes in position, gravitational pull, and tone, and proper adjustments are being mediated constantly by the cerebellum. Impulses, your "will," possibly from the thalamus, initiate the act of throwing the ball by the mediation of the proper portions of the several motor areas of the cortex. Here the impulses—whole series of them—are modified by the impulses received through the somatic sense area, coordinated by the skilled movement area in accordance with visual stimuli, and sent thence to the cerebellum. In this organ some impulses are strengthened, others are inhibited to a greater or lesser extent in accordance with experience gained by training and practice. They are then sent by way of the brainstem and spinal cord to the numerous muscles of the upper and lower arm, trunk, and legs, one set after another, and you throw the ball! In addition to these voluntary and involuntary movements of somatic parts, it should be borne in mind that equally complex adjustments of visceral parts, such as heart rate, tension on the individual arteries, blood pressure, and depth and rate of breathing, have also been made unconsciously.

Speech. In the dominant hemisphere of the cerebrum three areas directly concerned with speech are to be found (Figure 14–23). One is motor in function and mediates the actual muscular movements necessary in talking; damage to this area results in impairment of speech. A second one is a continuation of the skilled-movements area of the parietal lobe and appears to be associated with the visual portion of the cortex. In cases of damage to this area the patient has difficulty in correctly naming objects shown to him. When shown a tree, for example, he may say "chair" or use some other entirely erroneous word. The third area is close to the auditory cortex; damage to this part produces inaccuracies of pronunciation and erroneous responses to spoken words. Hence it is clear that in speech, visual, auditory, and motor memory centers are drawn upon. In addition, two vocalization centers in the cortex are required to produce the basic sound in the first place, these centers being parts of the principal and secondary motor areas—the basic sound is simply a long continuous cry. Furthermore, the thalamus probably wills the act and, finally, the cerebellum is necessary to modulate the motor impulses in order to adjust and to coordinate the muscular movements.

MISCELLANEOUS RESPONSES

Some of the "responses" to be described here are not clearly responses in the ordinary sense of the term—that is, reactions to incoming stimuli. In the case of consciousness, for example, it can scarcely be said that this property of the nervous system arises from stimuli from any source. Yet consciousness manifests itself only through somatic and visceral activities, and hence can well be considered a part of the efferent nervous system.

Consciousness. It is difficult enough to attempt even an exact definition of consciousness, let alone discuss the neural mechanisms involved in its production. As a definition, it may be suggested that consciousness is a state of being in which stimuli of normal strength can be detected and reactions to them elicited. At one time it was believed that the cerebrum was its center, but, in view of the fact that both cerebral hemispheres can be removed without unconsciousness resulting, it is now generally held that the thalamus is its probable seat. As long as a person is conscious, it is believed his thalamus sends out impulses to all centers; when this flow of impulses ceases, loss or diminution of the ability to receive stimuli follows. However, at present this belief is without any supporting evidence.

Sleep. In sleep the person or organism loses the ability of detecting stimuli of normal strength and of reacting to them; however, stimuli of more than usual strength will bring the individual back to full consciousness. The level of usualness in the stimuli varies with the individual and with his experience. A city dweller may sleep with ease through all the roar of trucks, howling police sirens, and bright lights flashing through his window but may lie wakeful on a country visit, unable to sleep because of the soft chirping of a cricket or because of the complete darkness. Obviously, adaptation to incoming stimuli is involved, so a sleeping person is conscious, only less so than when awake. Since during sleep metabolic activities, such as heart rate

and body temperature, are decreased and since the hypothalamus controls all such activities, it is to be expected that it mediates this lowered state of consciousness. This has been found to be the actual case.

Behavior and Emotions. Personality traits, behavior, and emotions are so closely interrelated that they must be discussed together; because the emotions are best known, they will be taken up first. The emotions of man and other mammals are numerous and diverse, yet in many of the stronger ones there are common elements. Not infrequently, especially in fear, anger, and disgust, a heavy feeling in the stomach is noted; pain, sorrow, anger, and even joy can initiate weeping. Likewise, blushing or quickened heart beat can be aroused by several emotions, and a feeling of weakness and exhaustion follows in the wake of others. All of these physical states are the result of the activities of the two divisions of the autonomic system; hence we can deduce that the hypothalamus is implicated in their production. Some also result in part from the actions of chemicals secreted by certain glands, discussed in the next chapter. In addition to the hypothalamus, the actual mediating center appears to lie largely in the cerebral cortex, particularly in the temporal lobes and lower mesial surface. Electrical stimulation of certain areas of the temporal lobes (see Figure 14–23) produces fear, sorrow, and depression. Similar stimulation of the lower mesial surface elicits signs of anger, anxiety, surprise, and marked concentration. Apparently, control of hunger and sexual response also center in this region.

Other emotions and behavior traits seem to be in part regulated by the anterior part of the frontal lobes of the cerebrum. These "prefrontal" lobes appear largely blank on our diagrams, for not one area on them anterior to the motor areas can be assigned a definite function. Yet their removal can have marked effects on the behavior of the individual. In cases of removal of larger portions of both lobes the patient may laugh unduly, both too loudly and at things that are not amusing, or may become completely placid, showing no emotions of any sort. In addition, there may be loss of the ability to plan activities and a large decrease in drive. In short, the arousing of such emotions as anger, awareness, and desire and the suppression of other emotions are centered here; it is looked on as the personality integration center in the brain.

Memory. Memory is largely a function of the cerebral cortex, but it must not be supposed that a single area carries this responsibility. Visual, auditory, and motor centers seem to have their individual neighboring regions to serve this purpose. In the case of motor activities it would appear that it is the synergistic motor area, not the principal one, that stores information about motor activities. The auditory sense has a broad area surrounding it which seems to accumulate both auditory and visual knowledge.

Since we are able to remember and recognize such things as odors and tastes, it is not unlikely that memory areas will eventually be found for them; however, none has been detected up to the present. Indeed, it is not unlikely that there are memory centers for many visceral experiences of which we are entirely unaware.

There are, moreover, two types of memory, those of recent and of remote events; all the above-mentioned areas are concerned with memory—things that have happened in the past which are of sufficient importance to preserve for future use. But there are events which need to be remembered for only a short period; for example, where you laid your pencil a few moments ago. When the prefrontal lobes are excised in rats, for instance, these animals are unable to recall even the simplest facts, such as in which of two cups food had been placed. Nor can they learn anything that requires mastery of a sequence of events, though they can recall complex activities that they had been taught before the lobes were removed. Undoubtedly, future studies of the prefrontal lobes will cast much light on the processes of learning in the human being.

Questions for Review and Thought

1. During what period or periods of life, if any, is the body not exposed to sudden changes in the external environment?

2. In what ways do organisms differ from inorganic substances in their reactions to stimuli?

3. What is the structure of the basic unit of the nervous system? What theories explaining the conduction of nervous impulses have been advanced? How are impulses possibly transmitted across a synapse?

4. Under the three major subdivisions of the nervous system list all the principal parts that compose each.

5. List the major parts of the brain and then summarize the principal functions of each.

6. Which sense receptors other than those of taste and smell appear really to be chemoreceptors?

7. One afternoon you see across the street a person you recognize as a friend who has been out of town for several years. Describe all the events necessary in this simple process, beginning with the light reflected from your friend and continuing through the action that takes place in the brain.

8. Being as specific as possible, name the structure or structures in the eye engaged in the following:

(a) Four structures required to focus the image on the retina.
(b) Absorbing stray light.
(c) Helps you see red!
(d) Reading the fine print.
(e) The retinal part that sees nothing.
(f) The parts through which light passes before striking the rods or cones.
(g) Supporting the retina.
(h) Feeding the lens and iris.

9. Outline all the events in collecting and hearing a sound.

10. What, if any, clear evidence is there that sugar can "take the bitterness" out of foods?

11. List all the senses found in the human.

12. What two effects can motor impulses produce?

13. Tell how the three types of reflex arcs differ from one another.

14. From a functional standpoint, why do you suppose the principal somatic sense and motor areas have a corresponding sequence of representation?

15. Suppose the stimulus received in question 7 causes you to respond by calling the friend's name. Describe all the steps in this procedure.

16. Through what means has knowledge of the function of the brain parts been garnered?

17. What function of the synergistic motor area probably explains why the motor speech center is really a continuation of it rather than of the principal motor center?

18. When a person becomes absentminded, what area of the cerebrum might be affected? Can you suggest a reason why emotionally disturbed persons often are forgetful? Why might it be difficult for you to study when you are emotionally upset?

19. In the final analysis, what structural unit carries out the functions of the nervous system, sensory, motor, memory, and all?

20. What evidence is there that "cramming" for examinations perhaps does not actually provide one with knowledge on a permanent basis?

Supplementary References

Busnel, R. G. *Acoustic Behavior of Animals*. New York, American Elsevier, 1963.

Fantz, R. L. "The Origin of Form Perception." *Sci. Amer.*, May 1961.

Gardner, E. *Fundamentals of Neurology*, 4th ed. Philadelphia, Saunders, 1963.

Katz, B. "The Nerve Impulse." *Sci. Amer.*, November 1952.

Matthews, L. H., and M. Knight. *The Senses of Animals*. New York, Philosophical Library, 1964.

Miller, W. H., F. Ratliff, and H. K. Hartline. "How Cells Receive Stimuli." *Sci. Amer.*, September 1961.

Pavlov, I. P. *Conditioned Reflexes*. New York, Dover, 1960.

Pfeiffer, J. *The Human Brain*. New York, Harper, 1955.

Ruch, T. C., *et al*. *Neurophysiology*. Philadelphia, Saunders, 1961.

Sherrington, C. S. *Integrative Action of the Nervous System*. New Haven, Yale Univ. Press, 1947.

Snider, R. S. "The Cerebellum." *Sci. Amer.*, August 1958.

von Békésy, G. "The Ear." *Sci. Amer.*, August 1957.

The Control of Metabolic Activities

Strictly speaking, the majority of the vertebrates' responses to the environment are instrumented through the neural control mechanisms described in the preceding chapter, so that the whole organism is kept alerted to the changes in the surroundings, and its parts are coordinated to perform intricate responses. As a whole each such response is of short duration, so that it may be stated on a good basis that the nervous system provides short-term control over the immediate activities. An entirely different set of controls exists in the body that largely govern long-term responses to the environment, reactions to the ecological conditions that in most instances have required eons of time for their acquisition. In these regulatory devices, chemical agents are secreted directly into the blood stream without the assistance of ducts; hence the organs concerned

with these activities are referred to both as *ductless glands* and as *endocrine glands,* the latter term meaning "internally secreting." (In contrast, ordinary glands which, like the salivary glands, possess ducts are said to be of the *exocrine type*.) The secretions of the endocrine glands, called *hormones,* are carried by the blood from their point or points of origin to cells or organs often quite remotely situated from the glands, and here they induce a reaction. Sometimes a hormone may even affect several different systems, and in fact, in many cases, they may have a strong influence upon the organism as a whole. As a rule, the action of any given hormone will be seen, in the following pages, to be of long duration; others, however, will be noticed to parallel closely the nervous system in inducing immediate and short-term responses. Also it will become apparent that these two major coordinating systems are not sharply separated from each other; more than one overlap in their activities will appear during the course of this chapter. Organisms, as will be seen more than once, tend to be greater than the sum of their parts, contrary to the ordinary physical and chemical laws though this may be.

The Endocrine Glands

Since many of the endocrine glands are narrow in their range of activities and instigate perhaps only one particular response in a single organ, all do not function as a unit to form a system in the strict sense of the term. For example, in the walls of the intestine are ductless glands that secrete the hormone *secretin,* which excites the pancreatic cells into releasing their juices into the intestine but which has no known action on any other organ of the body. Since these glands are thus concerned solely with digestion, they are treated later in the discussion of the appropriate system, and others likewise limited in function are placed correspondingly with the system of which they form an essential part.

Here, it is with those glands through which the body as a whole is controlled that we are concerned. Often these organs are subject to disease, so that they either become overly active (*hypersecretive*) or fail to secrete a sufficiency of their product (*hyposecretive*). Such malfunctionings frequently result in pronounced defects of bodily growth or appearance as well as in physiology, and it is tempting to accentuate this phase of the subject. However, abnormalities and diseased states, being really medical topics, will be cited only when they aid in elucidating the natural activities, which are the proper concern of a zoology textbook.

THE GLANDS OF THE THROAT AND CHEST

In the neck and thoracic regions are three sets of glands, two of which are of the highest importance in regulating general bodily activities and one, the *thymus,* of such doubtful nature that it need not receive further attention.

The Thyroids. Possibly the best known of all the endocrine glands is the one called the *thyroid,* lying in the lower portion of the neck (Figure 15–1); this moderately large gland is nearly completely divided into two lobes. These, however, are narrowly interconnected by a straplike isthmus. Although their cells actually secrete a globular protein called *thyroglobulin,* this product breaks down into a number of molecules of a special amino acid called *thyroxin* before entering the blood stream; hence, this substance is the true hormone. Each of its molecules contains four atoms of iodine attached to a derivative of the simpler amino acid tyrosine. Normally, thyroxin is involved in controlling the rate at which metabolic activities proceed and in regulating body temperature and growth by processes to be presented later. Moreover, in amphibia the hormone exercises control over the development of the larva into an adult. Triiodothyronine is the 3-iodine relative of thyroxin that also is made in the thyroid. In action it is similar to thyroxin but is somewhat more energetic (Figure 15–2).

In areas in which iodine is deficient in the soil, as in many inland regions of all continents, locally grown vegetables do not supply an adequate amount of this element in the diet of human beings. As a consequence, the thyroid becomes enlarged and appears as the prominent growth on the neck known as *simple goiter*. When the thyroid is inactive from birth, as happens in occasional individ-

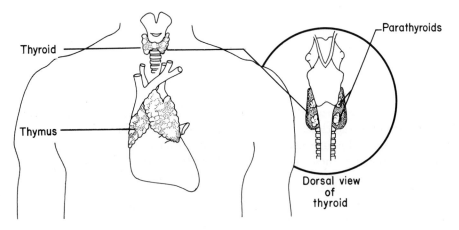

Figure 15-1. Glands of the thoracic region.

uals, a peculiar type of dwarf results from the failure of the child to grow and function normally. Such dwarfs, called *cretins,* are deformed, typically having proportionately short legs and arms, swollen abdomens, thick tongues, and low mentality. In cretinism, if commenced sufficiently early, thyroxin administration produces phenomenal results, restoring the individual to complete normality. Occasionally, too, the thyroid may become overly active, so that metabolism is strongly accelerated; in extreme instances it proceeds at a rate twice that of normal. In cases of this sort the tonus of the muscles is greatly increased, the body temperature is elevated, and a state of nervous excitement, accompanied by a

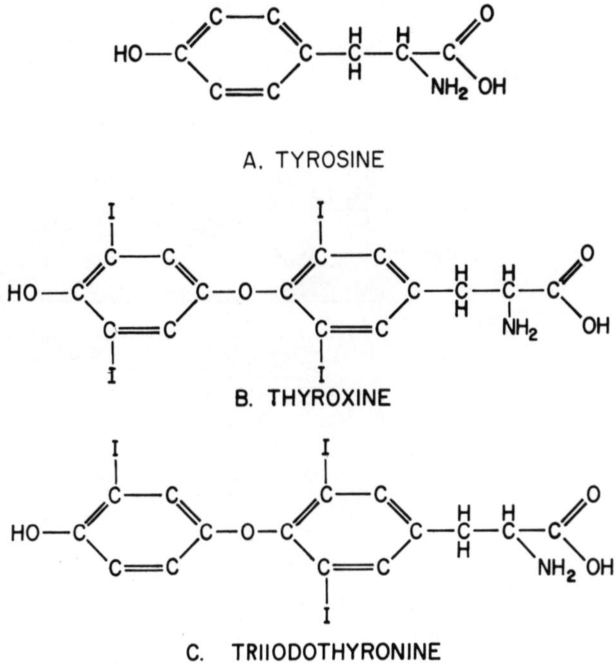

A. TYROSINE

Figure 15-2. Thyroid hormones. Tyrosine (A) is speculated as forming the chief ingredient from which the thyroid glands synthesize thyroxin (B) and triiodothyronine (C).

B. THYROXINE

C. TRIIODOTHYRONINE

protrusion of the eyeballs, is maintained. The prominent eyeballs are the most pronounced external evidence, and the disease is accordingly referred to as *exophthalmic goiter*.

The Parathyroids. Human beings possess two pairs of *parathyroid glands,* each gland the size of a pea, closely associated with the thyroids. Although insignificant in size, functionally these glands are highly important, for their removal results in death within a few days because of the ensuing deficiency of calcium in the blood. Without calcium the muscles of the body gradually lose their ability to relax and ultimately enter a state of tetany, thus producing a general convulsive condition. The secretion of the glands, called either parathyroid hormone *(PTH)* or *parathormone,* thus is seen to

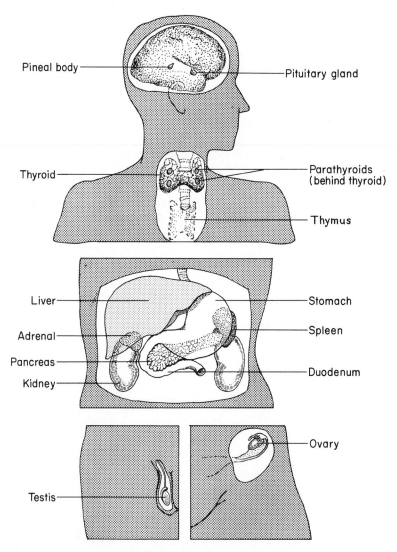

Figure 15–3. The endocrine glands of a human. In the abdominal section the glands of both a male and a female are shown.

be involved in the metabolism of calcium. In addition, it is known to affect phosphate and citrate metabolism and the activities of the intestines and kidneys, as described later in greater detail. Furthermore, in birds it plays an active role in regulating the formation of the calcareous eggshell. Chemically, PTH is a protein with a molecular weight of around 8,600; hence it is relatively simple as protenoid substances go.

Occasionally, through enlargement of the glands or by a tumorous growth on them, an excess of PTH is secreted, the over-all effects of which are not clear-cut, being complexly interwoven with other control factors. Generally, defects in the skeletal system may be noted, especially in advanced cases of hypersecretion, as calcium is withdrawn from the bones. As withdrawal proceeds, the bony tissues are reduced essentially to their flexible organic matrices so that distortions, as well as fractures, are frequent.

THE GLANDS OF THE ABDOMEN

Within the abdomen of the vertebrates are a number of glands of known endocrine activity, whose secretions influence a large variety of physiological functions of the body. Some are specialized portions of exocrine glands, while others secrete hormones secondarily in conjunction with products of a more basic nature. Nonetheless, several of the glands located here are strictly confined to hormone secretion, as are those in the neck region studied above (Figure 15–3).

The Islet Cells. Scattered through the pancreas are numerous patches of tissue called the *islet cells,* found in recent years to be of two cellular types, designated simply as *alpha-* and *beta-cells.* Each of these secretes a distinct and important hormone. Especially as manifested by the

not too infrequent occurrence of hypoactivity, the effects of the beta-cell secretion have been known for some time and consequently have received more thorough study than the product of the alpha-cells. Beta-cells produce *insulin,* a protein, the exact chemical constituency of which has been worked out in full detail, including the sequence of amino acids which comprise its two chains. It is notable as the first protein for which this feat has been accomplished. In insulin occur 17 different amino acids united in various proportions by a total of 50 peptide bonds; the amino acids are arranged into two major chains, lying parallel to one another and coupled by the sulfur components contained in the amino acid cystine (Figure 15–4). Principally, this hormone centers its activities around the control of carbohydrate metabolism, but it is also required in protein and lipid metabolism and in body growth. When the supply of this hormone is cut off, by removal of the pancreas, for example, the level of sugar in the blood rises, whereas the amount of glycogen in the liver and muscles decreases. Upon administration of insulin to an animal so treated, the blood sugar is restored to normal and the glycogen in the liver increases. In contrast, too much insulin lowers the blood sugar concentration and results in convulsions, coma, and death unless a carbohydrate is supplied. Similarly, without insulin the synthesis of fatty acids ceases, and with an oversupply deposition of fat results. Hypoactivity of these beta-cells in humans produces the disease *diabetes mellitus,* popularly known as "sugar diabetes"; this condition in recent years has been found to be much more complex in its nature than formerly suspected. For instance, it has become evident that the diabetes mellitus appearing in youth is caused by the actual inability of the beta-cells to produce insulin; on the other

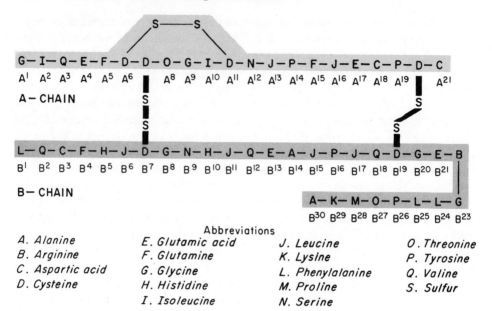

Abbreviations

A. Alanine	E. Glutamic acid	J. Leucine	O. Threonine
B. Arginine	F. Glutamine	K. Lysine	P. Tyrosine
C. Aspartic acid	G. Glycine	L. Phenylalanine	Q. Valine
D. Cysteine	H. Histidine	M. Proline	S. Sulfur
	I. Isoleucine	N. Serine	

Figure 15–4. The molecular structure of insulin from the horse. Basically the molecule consists of two chains—one of 21 amino acid links, the other of 30; these two chains are coupled by the sulfur atoms in cysteine. This is the first protein whose molecular structure had ever been determined; now the composition of several other proteins has been worked out in full detail.

hand, in the type that first appears in older persons, even though an adequate amount of insulin may be secreted, the tissues of the body are unable to utilize it properly.

The alpha-cells of the islets secrete the hormone *glucagon,* which is similar to insulin in being both a protein and involved in carbohydrate metabolism. Its chief action seems to be concentrated in the liver cells and is the reverse of that of insulin, for it effects the release of glycogen from that organ by promoting the formation of a phosphorylase. In this manner it secondarily influences the sugar level of the blood, for as the glycogen is broken down the resulting glucose passes rapidly into the blood stream.

The Gonads. Although the principal function of the *gonads* (the ovary and testis) is that of producing gametes, the organs also secrete a number of hormones, most of whose actions are concerned with reproductive functions in one

way or another. Since this is the case, a full discussion of the hormonal activities must await the appropriate chapter; nevertheless, some of the hormones possess aspects that require treatment with those of the remainder of the body.

As a whole, the endocrine products of the gonads are lipids of the class called *steroids,* to which cholesterol (page 20) belongs. Since so many other hormones also belong to this category, it might be well to describe the chemical nature shared by all the members. First among these is the highly characteristic basic molecular structure or *nucleus,* derived from a chemical called CPP for simplicity's sake, its full name being of no immediate value to the student. As may be seen in the diagram (Figure 15–5), the molecule consists of three carbon "rings" joined to an incomplete ring in a unique fashion; all the gonadal and other steroid hormones result from modifications in the radicals adhering to this

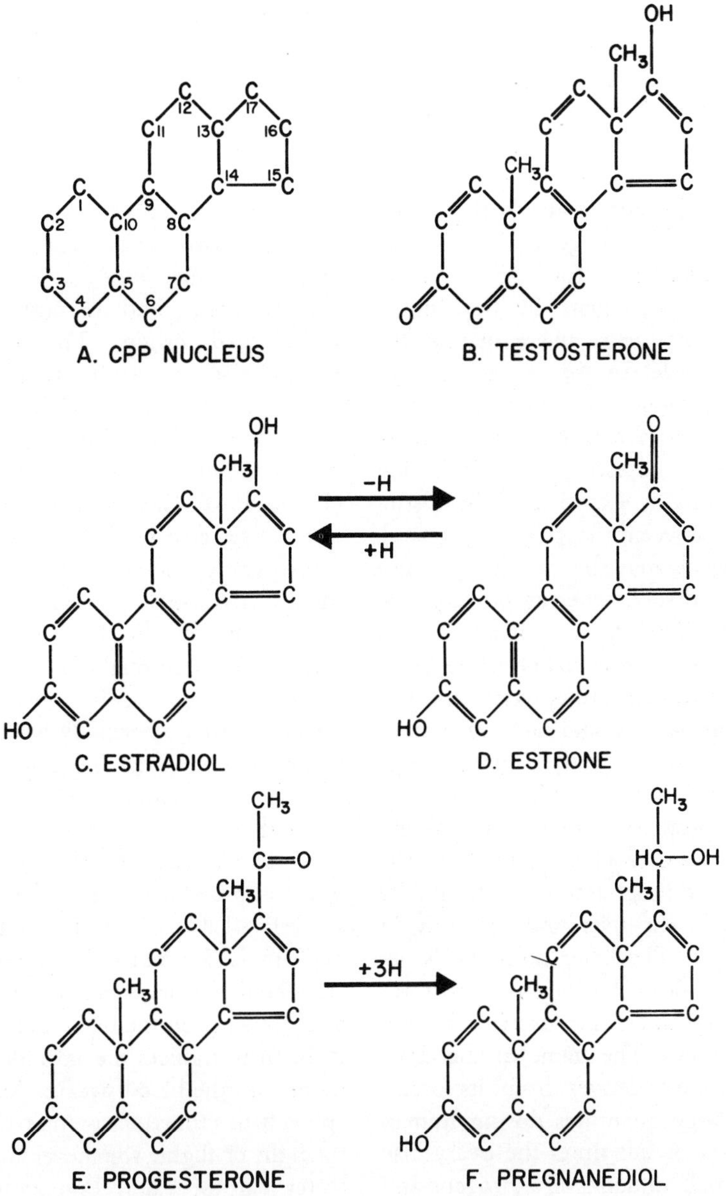

Figure 15–5. The principal sex hormones of mankind. Numerous variations in detail exist among the sex hormones and other steroles, all of which are built on the CPP nucleus (A). The numerals there refer to the sequence of the carbon atoms as arbitrarily assigned by chemists.

nucleus. The testes secrete a group of sterols called *androgens*, principal among which in human beings is *testosterone* (Figure 15–5). Aside from participating to some extent in the anabolism of proteins and carbohydrates, all the activities of this hormone center around reproduction and in the control of secondary sexual traits of the male.

In the female two general types of sexual hormones, classed as *estrogens* and *progestogens*, are especially secreted. Two estrogens are normally produced by the human ovary, namely, *estradiol* and *estrone;* since each can be converted into the other by the enzymatic action of DPN or TPN, their effects on the body are identical (Figure 15–5). Generally speaking, they correspond to the androgens of the male in governing the secondary sexual traits; furthermore, along with the progestogens in the higher primates, they assist in regulating the menstrual cycle. In the second class of ovarian hormones the most important member is *progesterone;* it is so closely correlated to the estrogens in its action that difficulty is experienced in distinguishing between the two. In general, the estrogens may be said to produce growth of tissues, whereas progesterone influences differentiation. In addition to their effects on the reproductive processes, the estrogens are powerful mitosis-influencing agents and act on almost every organ of the body. Indeed, sometimes they are suspected of having *carcinogenic* properties—that is, the ability to promote cancerous growths. Both the estrogens and progesterone are eventually destroyed in the liver and probably in other organs. The latter hormone is deactivated by being hydrogenated to form *pregnanediol* and is then excreted by way of the kidneys. The name of the deactivated product derives from its occurrence in large quantities during human pregnancies. At all times the ovary also secretes small amounts of androgens and during pregnancies a proteinaceous hormone called *relaxin* (page 395).

The presence of androgens in females should cause no particular concern, for testosterone is an intermediate product during synthesis of the estrogens. Similarly, progesterone is a side-product in males in the process of testosterone formation; moreover, the testes normally secrete a small amount of estrogens.

What roles these minute quantities play, if any, has not been clearly determined to date.

The Adrenal Glands. Lying dorsally closely associated with the kidneys are the pair of *adrenal glands,* composed of two different types of tissues. In mammals the two tissues are arranged in layers, an inner *medulla,* derived from nervous tissue, and an outer *cortex* of mesodermal origin. The medulla is known to secrete two hormones, *epinephrin* (adrenalin) and *norepinephrin* (noradrenalin), both of which are rather simple compounds called "catechol amines" (Figure 15–6). Closely related compounds also are secreted by the ends of neurons; consequently, the activities of these hormones frequently parallel those of the nervous system and have similar widespread effects throughout the body. Secretion of these two hormones is under neural control, principally by the sympathetic system, with integration centers lying in the thalamus, hypothalamus, and cerebral cortex. Chiefly norepinephrin appears to assist in the routine regulation of blood pressure but has other functions as well (Table 15–1). In contrast, epinephrin is secreted only in response to emotional factors; pain, fright, anger, and stress act on the nervous system, and it, in turn, induces the flow of this hormone into the blood stream. As a whole, epinephrin's functions prepare the animal for fight or flight, whichever may be the better part of valor. Preparation is accomplished by increasing blood pressure, heart action, and respiratory rate and by redistributing the blood supply; alterations in the pattern of redistribution include a decreased flow to the skin and internal organs and a greatly enhanced flow to the skeletal muscles and brain. Moreover, muscle tone is increased and the level of sugar in the blood is raised; even the ability of the blood to form

TABLE 15-1

ACTIONS OF ADRENAL CORTEX SECRETIONS

Epinephrin	Activity	Norepinephrin
3+	Carbohydrate metabolism	2+
2−	Intestinal wall activity	−
	Vascular system	
3+	heart rate	+
2+	blood pressure (systolic)	3+
0	blood pressure (diastolic)	2+
Dilation	peripheral blood vessels	Constriction
Dilation	coronary arteries	Dilation
+	eosinophil count	0
2+	Pupil dilation	+
2+	Mental anxiety	0

Slight increase (+) or decrease (−); moderate increase (2+) or decrease (2−); strong increase (3+) or decrease (3−); no effect (0).

clots is augmented. Besides thus serving as a whip for emergencies, the hormone also assists when needed in carbohydrate metabolism and is mentioned later in that connection. Finally, it has an effect on the brain in human subjects, producing a sense of anxiety and fatigue or restlessness; in contrast, norepinephrin has no known effects on the central nervous system (Table 15-1).

Within the cortex of the adrenals a number of hormones are produced, many of which are sex hormones, including androgens, estrogens, and progestogens. All the products, about 40 in number, are steroids related to the hormones secreted by the gonads. Only about seven, however, have been fully explored functionally; on the basis of their activities, these secretions fall into three principal groups. In the first group are placed those steroids that have an atom of oxygen attached to carbon 11; its four known members, of which *cortisone* and *corticosterone* are

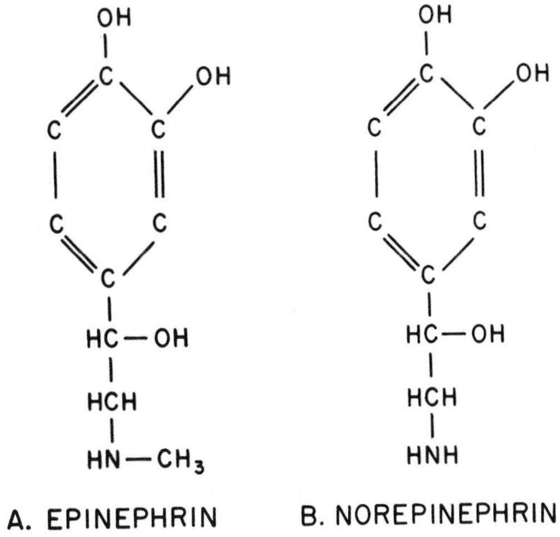

Figure 15-6. The secretions of the adrenal medulla.

A. EPINEPHRIN   B. NOREPINEPHRIN

most eminent, are especially potent in influencing carbohydrate and protein metabolism. In the second group are found most of the cortical secretions that lack an atom of oxygen on carbon 11 and that manifest their chief effects on salt and water metabolism. Placed in it is *cortexone,* also known as *DOC* as well as one other of less general importance. The third group contains only *aldosterone,* which has an aldehyde radical ($^-$CHO) on carbon 13 in place of the usual methyl ($^-$CH$_3$) (Figure 15–7); it plays an active role in regulating the metabolism both of salts and of carbohydrates. As far as the sex hormones are concerned, at present it is not possible to differentiate the normal

parts played by the cortical products from those of the gonads.

A number of malfunctioning effects are known for the adrenal cortex, but since it is not feasible to distinguish the relative importance of each of its principal secretions in their production they must be treated as a unit. Complete absence or severe deficiency of the cortical hormones results in *Addison's disease,* characterized by a bronzing of the skin, lowered blood pressure, improper carbohydrate metabolism, dehydration of the bodily tissues, and weakness; in extreme deficiencies death may even occur. Overactivity of the cortex is often reflected in female human beings by the acquisition

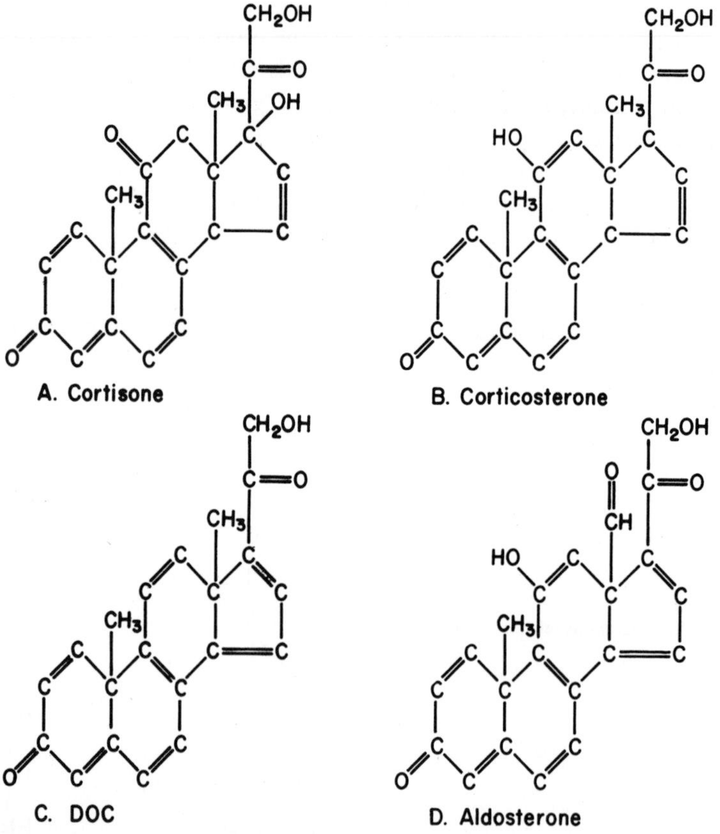

Figure 15–7. Some secretions of the adrenal cortex. A few of the better known adrenocortical hormones alone are diagrammed here.

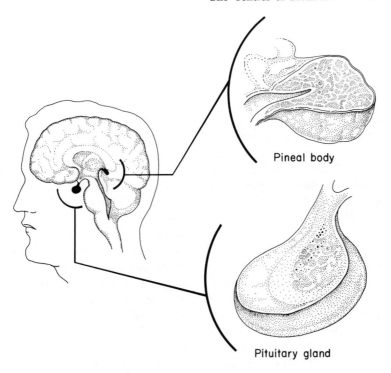

Pineal body

Pituitary gland

Figure 15–8. The endocrine glands of the head.

of male characteristics, such as growth of beard and deepening of the voice, whereas similar effects can occur in very young boys if hypersecretion commences at an early age.

THE GLANDS OF THE HEAD

In the heads of vertebrates only one gland of known endocrine function exists, although one other structure is frequently suspected of playing a hormonal role. The single proven gland, the pituitary, however, makes up in importance for what this region lacks in numbers (Figure 15–8).

The Pituitary Gland. The importance of the *pituitary* can scarcely be measured by its size, for in a fully mature individual it weighs but 0.6 gram (= 0.02 ounce). When sectioned longitudinally, it is found to contain three distinct parts,

often called lobes, each of which has had a different origin evolutionarily. Two parts, the anterior and middle, have their earliest traces in the form of a pouch lying in the roof of the mouth in the tunicates and lancelets. Although the pouch in these animals is principally concerned with the control of feeding, it also is involved in the detection of the species' eggs or sperm in the water. When such gametes are detected, it secretes a hormone that acts on a nearby ganglion, instigating an impulse that triggers the release of the animal's own eggs or sperm, as the case may be. Hence, even in these simple chordates, the gland is partly concerned with the control of reproductive functions. In all the vertebrate embryos these two portions of the pituitary form first as a pocket in the mouth cavity, the anterior from the front face, the intermediate from the posterior.

As a whole the *anterior lobe* is the most active endocrinal portion, secreting at least six distinct hormones, all of which are proteins. Quite as in the lower Chordata, two hormones participate in the control of the reproductive system and are referred to as *gonadotropins* because of their influence on the growth and functioning of the gonads. One gonadotropin, called "follicle stimulating hormone" (*FSH*), regulates the production of eggs and sperm, whereas "luteinizing hormone" (*LH*), also called "interstitial cell stimulating hormone" (*ICSH*), affects the production of progesterone and testosterone. In mammals a third secretion concerned with reproductive physiology, known as *lactogenic hormone,* controls the development of the milk glands and secretion of progesterone during pregnancy as well as during periods of normal activity. The three remaining hormones are concerned with the regulation of metabolic processes, either directly or by influencing other endocrine glands. "Thyrotropic hormone" (*TSH*) and "adrenocorticotropic hormone" (*ACTH*), respectively, act on the thyroid and adrenal cortex. When injected into the animal, TSH produces an enlargement of the thyroid (goiter) and signs of hyperactivity, whereas removal of the anterior pituitary has the opposite set of effects. Conversely, there are indications that in normal animals the level of thyroxin in the blood influences the rate at which TSH is produced. A parallel arrangement between ACTH and the cortical hormones also is known to exist, the productivity level of one controlling the secretory activity of the other. Such *feedback* mechanisms probably are oversimplifications, for they suggest fixation of secretion in both glands concerned, a status quo that does not normally exist in actuality. In the last of the metabolically active secretions, the "growth hormone" or, better, the *somatotropic hormone* (*STH*), the effects are direct and influence the entire body of the organism. Most striking among its activities are those that act on the growth of the body as a unit, undersecretion producing a *normal dwarf*—that is, one whose proportions are similar to those of the ordinary individual, whereas hypersecretion results in *gigantism* if it commences in the young. In older persons or specimens, after growth has ceased, an overabundance of STH causes the bones to increase in diameter, the lower jaw and cheek bones, especially, becoming enlarged and producing a bulldoglike effect known as *acromegaly*. Principally, four other activities of this hormone have been established. First of all, it acts on the pancreatic alpha-cells, stimulating them into greater production of glucagon; second, it suppresses the functioning of the other islet cells, the beta-cells, and can, if present in too large amounts, bring about their total destruction and result in diabetes mellitus. A third effect is found in the anabolism of proteins, in which it serves especially to increase the amount of nitrogenous substances retained in the cells and to retard the production of urea. Finally, it has a pronounced influence on lipid metabolism by accelerating the removal of fats from the adipose tissues and their transportation to the liver, activities that result in an increase of lipids in the blood and liver.

Sharply contrasting with the complexity of the anterior lobe, the *middle lobe* is extremely simple, for it is known to generate only one hormone. Its sole product, "melanocyte-stimulating hormone" (*MSH*) or *intermedin,* a protein, has long been known to act on the black pigment bodies or melanophores in the integument of fish, amphibia, and reptiles. When present in the blood stream, this substance induces the pigment to

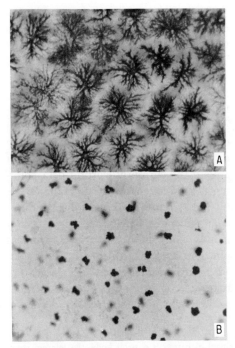

disperse throughout the melanophores so that the body coloration is darkened (Figure 15-9). Although diverse metabolic activities have at times been suspected to be influenced by this hormone, no other than that described has yet received confirmation.

In all the vertebrates the third part of the pituitary, the *posterior lobe* or *neurohypophysis*, develops as an outpocketing of the lower surface of the brain. Consequently, there is an intimate association between this structure and the area of the midbrain, the *hypothalamus*, to which it is attached. Indeed, it has recently been demonstrated that the posterior lobe functions chiefly as a storage vessel for secretions actually produced by the hypothalamus. For example, if the tract between the hypothalamus and posterior pituitary is partly severed, the hormonal secretions of this lobe accumulate above the cut, clearly indicating their origin in the midbrain (Figure 15-10). Be that as it may, two hormones are known to be released by this portion; both are simple proteins, composed

Figure 15-9. Melanophores in a toad. *A.* In this larval tail of a South African toad called *Xenopus,* the melanophores have the pigment fully dispersed, causing the skin to darken. *B.* When the pigment is contracted as here, the skin becomes light in color. (Courtesy of Dr. Joseph T. Bagnara and the Managing Editor, reproduced from the *Biological Bulletin,* Vol. 118, 1960.)

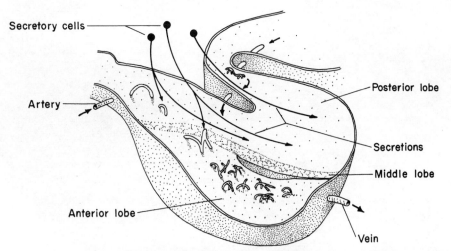

Figure 15-10. Relationships of the hypothalamus and posterior pituitary lobe. The hypothalamus secretes hormones, but sends them to the posterior lobe of the pituitary to be released into the blood as needed by the body.

of eight different amino acids each, similarly arranged. The first, *oxytocin,* is especially potent in inducing contractions of the uterus and release of milk from the mammary glands. On the other hand, the second, *vasopressin,* is particularly active in the control of blood pressure, causing the constriction of all blood vessels except those leading to the kidneys; moreover, it has strong influence over water metabolism and its excretion by the kidneys. In deficiencies of vasopressiñ the rate of urine production is strongly enhanced and results secondarily in an increment of thirst. In cases of this disease, called *diabetes insipidus,* patients have been known to drink as much as 10 gallons of water daily.

The Pineal Body. Lying on the upper surface of the midbrain is a projection only one third of the mass of the pituitary, called the *pineal body.* This body is known to be a remnant of a third eye (Figure 15–11) that many terrestrial vertebrates formerly possessed and is still found in the peculiar tuatara of New Zealand (Figure 12–14). Although its origin is clear enough, little has been discovered about its function. Chief among the currently existing data pointing toward an endocrine function are the facts that removal of the pineal induces enlargement of the adrenal and pituitary glands along with the ovaries, whereas pineal extracts retard growth of the gonads. Furthermore, when the gonads are removed, the pineal first undergoes growth which is followed by degenera-

Figure 15–11. The pineal body of a frog. Within the pineal of a frog is a small body, the internal structure of which is seen under the electron microscope to resemble that of retinal photoreceptors, such as the rods and cones. Magnified 13,800×. Compare with Figure 14–16. (Courtesy of Dr. Douglas E. Kelly, *American Scientist,* Vol. 50, 1962.)

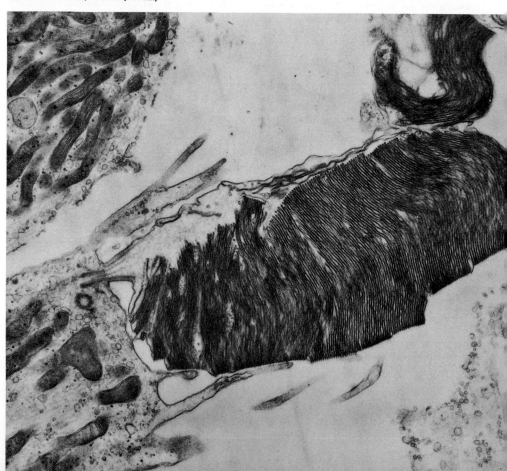

tion. Thus the evidence points to some kind of interrelationship between the pineal and the reproductive organs. Moreover, a substance called *melatonin* has recently been extracted from the cow pineal body. When this extract is applied to frog skin that has undergone chromatophore expansion so that its surface is darkened, a pronounced lightening effect can be noted as the chromatophores retract. Just what role this hormone plays in cattle has still to be determined.

The Vitamins

Although at first glance there appears to be nothing in common between vitamines, which are part of the diet, and hormones, which are bodily secretions, a closer examination reveals that many similarities exist. Particularly is this true from a functional point of view, for in many cases hormones act in an enzymatic capacity, either in the cells or tissues, bringing about total bodily effects through the accumulation of cellular reactions repeated untold trillions of times. Similarly, many vitamins are converted by the cells into chemicals which serve either as enzymes or coenzymes; thus in such cases, too, the result of the vitamin's presence is the accumulation of cellular effects. Since both classes of substances participate directly or indirectly in fundamental cellular processes, it is inevitable that both should sometimes find themselves sharing in the same chemical activities, though in different roles. Hence it is requisite that the vitamins too be discussed before the intricacies of bodily metabolism and its control can be presented.

The term *vitamin* may be defined as those substances of heterogeneous chemical structure that are required in the diet to maintain health. Since diets and physiologies of animals vary widely, a compound that is a vitamin for one species may not be for another; consequently, most of our attention is devoted to the vitamins of man and other mammals.

The Oil-Soluble Vitamins

Four diverse groups of substances soluble in oil and organic solvents are recognized as important vitamins. As in each case several distinct though closely related chemical compounds produce exactly the same reactions within the body, it is simpler to refer to the present vitamins by their letters rather than by a whole series of technical names. In several instances certain substances chemically allied to a given vitamin are immediately synthesized into it upon entrance into the body; compounds that can thus be readily converted into vitamins are referred to as *provitamins*.

The Vitamins A. At least five different *vitamins A* are known, the most important of which in mammals is that designated as vitamin A_1 or acerophthol. This is taken in either as the vitamin or as the common plant pigment beta-carotene (Figure 15–12); this yellow pigment is broken into two vitamin A molecules as it passes through the intestinal wall and therefore may be considered a provitamin. Since it is abundant in green and yellow vegetables and yellow fruit, as well as in egg yolk, butter, and milk, deficiencies (referred to in general as *avitaminoses*) of this present vitamin are not frequently encountered. However, by controlled diets avitaminosis A has been artificially produced in man and in many experimental animals, and some uses made of this vitamin by the body have been uncovered. First of all it is found to be essential to growth, for it

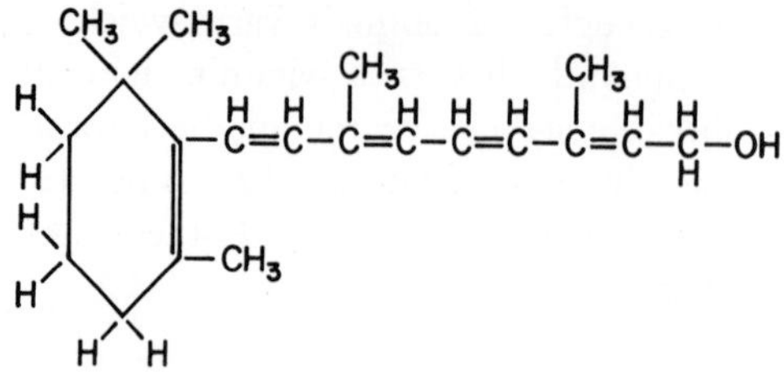

A. Vitamin A₁

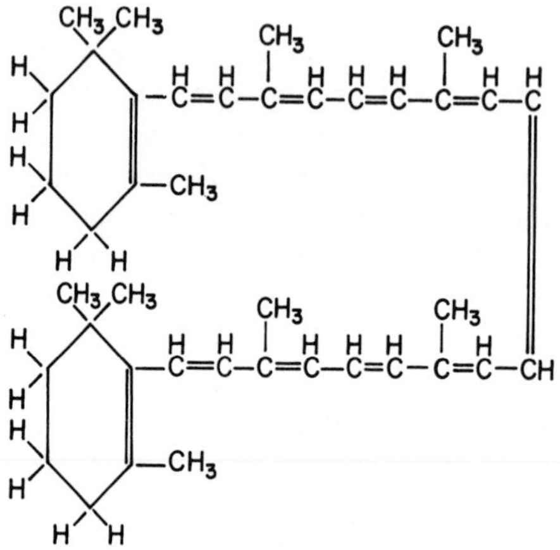

A. Vitamin A_1

Figure 15–12. Vitamin A_1 and its source. As a rule the body cells obtain their vitamin A_1 by splitting the common pigment of plants, beta-carotene, into two.

B. Beta–carotene

enters into the organic matrix of the skeletal parts, an effect particularly noticeable, of course, in young animals. Second, it is concerned with sulfur and carbohydrate metabolism and, indirectly, as a consequence, with the secretion of mucus and the deposition of keratin in epithelial coatings—keratin is the compound that constitutes claws, nails, and horn and occurs in the outer layer of the skin. In mammals, too, this vitamin is necessary for tear gland activity; and finally, it is the chief ingredient in visual purple, the pigment found in the rods of the retina. As will be recalled, the rods are employed chiefly in dim light, and in the decreased production of this pigment, so-called *night blindness* results —an overly strong descriptive term for a lessened ability to become adapted to small quantities of light. In cases of ex-

treme avitaminosis A, keratin is deposited on the conjunctiva, and this deposition, in combination with the decreased flow of tears, produces a dry-eyed condition called *xerophthalmia* (Figure 15–13). In prolonged deficiencies the cornea may ultimately become dry and wrinkled. Overdosages of this vitamin may also be detrimental, for they have been found to damage the liver, skin, and particularly the skeleton. In fact, on the basis of a recent X-ray study, it appears likely that hypervitaminosis A is more frequent in the United States than the condition caused by a deficiency.

The Vitamins D. As in the above, the *vitamins D* occur as several different compounds, vitamin D_2 and D_3 being the most active. Vitamin D_2 (calciferol) can be derived from its provitamin ergosterol, and D_3, from provitamin D_3 by

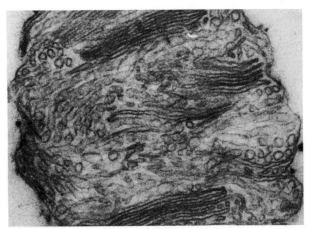

Figure 15–13. Role of vitamin A in the retina. In this electronmicrograph the membranelles of an outer rod segment from rats made nightblind by vitamin A deficiency, the membranous disks are seen to break down. Compare to Figure 14–16B. (Courtesy of Dr. John E. Dowling, *Vitamins and Hormones*, Vol. 18, 1960, The Academic Press.)

irradiation. In natural diets it is these provitamins that are normally taken into the body to be converted into the vitamin by the action of sunlight, for the actual vitamins D rarely occur as such. The liver and fat of fish and of those animals that feed largely on fish are important sources of these essential foods, as are eggs and milk. In the body the vitamins D influence the deposition of calcium in the bones and the level of citrates in the blood, but largely secondarily through their primary role in assisting in the absorption of calcium. In *avitaminosis D* calcium deposition in the bones is in a disorderly fashion, so that the weight of the body and stresses of muscular con-

traction distort the shape of the organic matrix, characteristic of the disease called *rickets*. Although rickets can also result from an insufficiency of calcium or phosphates in the diet, most commonly it occurs as a deficiency of these vitamins, frequently as a consequence of underexposure to sunlight.

The Vitamins E. At present seven variations of *vitamin E* are known, ranging from alpha- through eta-*tocopherols* (Figure 15–14), all of which have the same fundamental properties and actions in the body. They occur dissolved in the lipids of seeds and leaves and in small amounts in foods of animal origin, particularly beef liver. Although in human

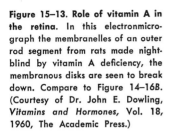

Alpha - tocopherol

Figure 15–14. One of the vitamins E.

beings no deficiency effects are known, some can be produced in other mammals experimentally, the most noticeable defect being the reduction of fertility. In male animals *avitaminosis E* decreases the motility and viability of the sperm, followed eventually by degeneration of the testes and permanent sterility, and in pregnant females the developing young frequently die or are resorbed. Normally within the cells, these chemicals serve as *antioxidants,* preventing the oxidation of other substances (vitamin A, for example) by becoming oxidized themselves. Moreover, recent studies reveal that they are essential in the cytochrome series of cellular chemicals, acting in the transfer of hydrogen from cytochrome *b* to *c.* Transaminase activity too is retarded in the absence of these essential foods, and creatine utilization in muscular activity is adversely affected.

The Vitamins K. Although only two *vitamins K,* referred to as K_1 and K_2, are known, a number of varieties of K_2 have been found in recent years (Figure 15–15). Normally, vitamin K_1 occurs abundantly in the leaves of seed plants, where it is believed to play an unknown role in photosynthesis, while K_2 is produced by microorganisms, including those that live in the digestive tracts of vertebrates. Since humans thus have two abundant sources, *avitaminosis K* occurs

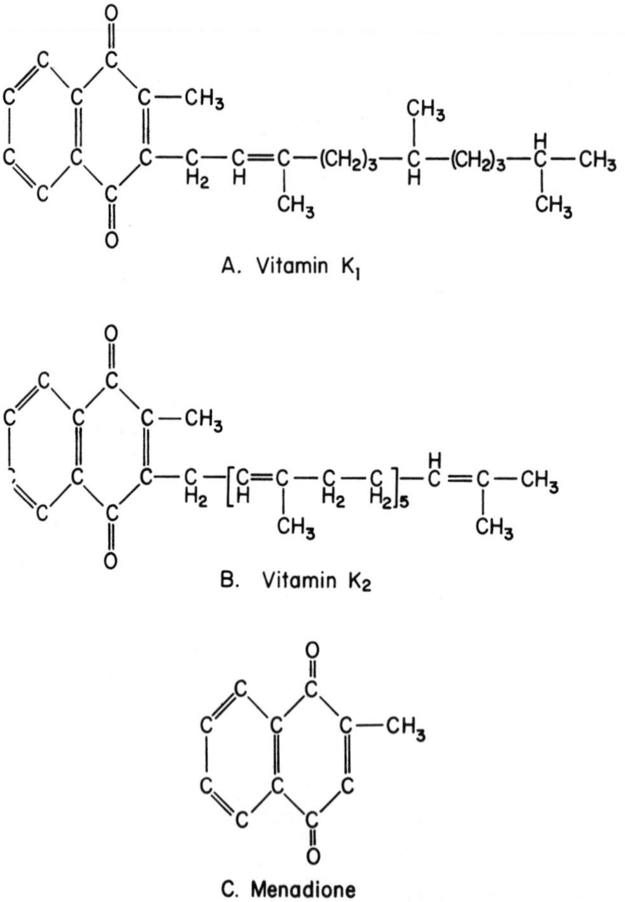

A. Vitamin K_1

B. Vitamin K_2

C. Menadione

Figure 15–15. The vitamins K.

only in cases in which difficulty in absorbing the material exists, as in obstruction of the bile duct. When the condition does arise, its principal manifestation lies in the occurrence of *hemorrhage,* for in a deficiency of these vitamins the liver is unable to secrete prothrombin, a substance essential to the clotting of blood. As newborn infants do not acquire intestinal bacteria for several days after birth, occasionally avitaminosis K is found in them. Characteristically appearing on the second or third day following birth, the resulting *hemorrhagic disease* may cause death either from loss of blood or by hemorrhage in the brain. If a fatality does not result after a few days, the intestinal bacteria increase to a number sufficient to supply the necessary quantity of vitamin K_2 and the symptoms disappear. For clarity's sake, it must be pointed out that avitaminosis K does not instigate bleeding, only the failure of clotting in wounds from other causes, although the damage may be so trivial that it would be unnoticeable were it not for the occurrence of hemorrhage. In most animals the normal function of K_1 appears to lie much as the vitamins E in the cellular respiratory activities.

The Water-Soluble Vitamins

Ascorbic Acid. Formerly called vitamin C, *ascorbic acid* is widespread in its natural occurrence, being found in citrus fruits and tomatoes in especial abundance but in almost all fruits and vegetables to some degree. Only in the primates and in the guinea pig is this substance known to be a true vitamin, since all other organisms are capable of secreting their own supply as required. Chemically, this compound is not too unlike the simpler sugars (Figure 15–16). As it readily yields two hydrogen atoms, it is an active

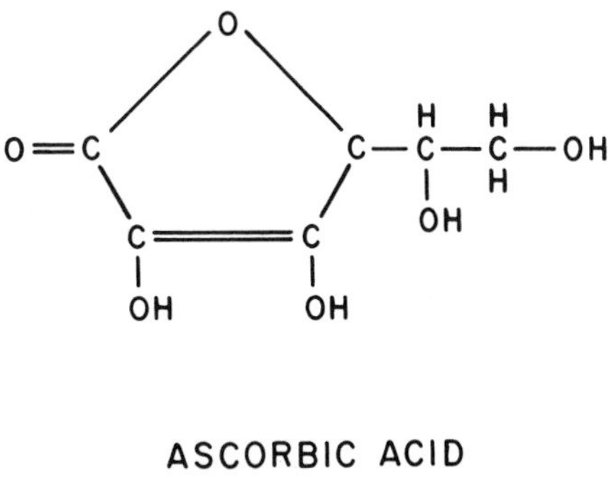

ASCORBIC ACID

Figure 15–16. The molecular structure of ascorbic acid.

reducing agent and possibly acts in this capacity in certain of the cellular processes; however, its chief function in the body appears to center around the formation of the matrix of connective tissues. In a deficiency new connective tissue, as in wounded areas, fails to form and existing tissues begin to degenerate. Especially noticeable is the degeneration in the walls of capillaries, so even in mild cases of *avitaminosis C* bleeding of the gums and under the skin in the form of bruises is frequent. Severe deficiencies result in *scurvy,* characterized by the foregoing effects, with the addition of emaciation, painful and swollen joints, and general weakness.

Thiamine. Known in former years as vitamin B_1, *thiamine* is the first of the vitamin B complex to be outlined here but by no means the last. The members of this group have little in common, chemically or otherwise, except that originally they were obtained in the bran from the polishing of rice grains. Thiamine is the chief constituent of the coenzyme cocarboxylase (or TPP; Figure 15–17) that acts on pyruvic acid in its preparation to enter the citric acid cycle and aids in the removal of CO_2 or ^-COOH; thus it is of fundamental importance in cellular metabolism, as are the other B vitamins. Although occur-

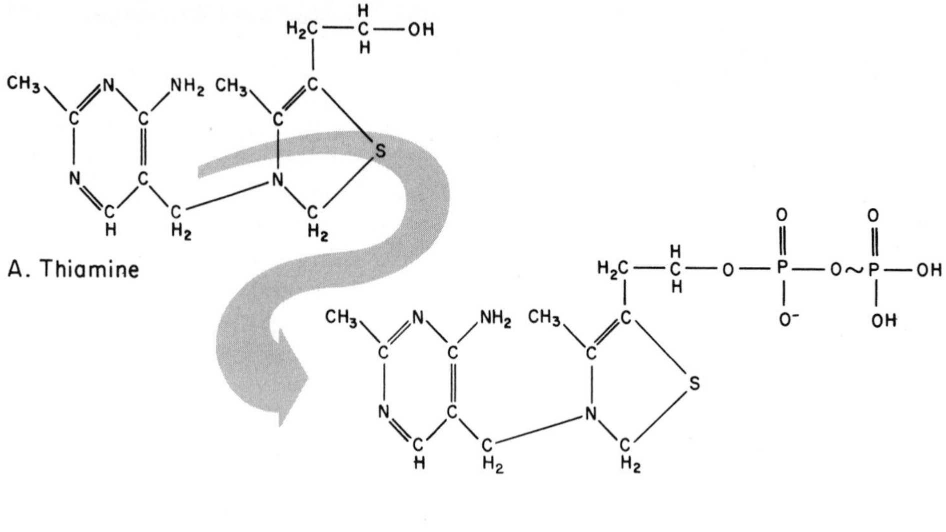

A. Thiamine

B. Cocarboxylase (TPP)

Figure 15–17. The molecular structure of thiamine.

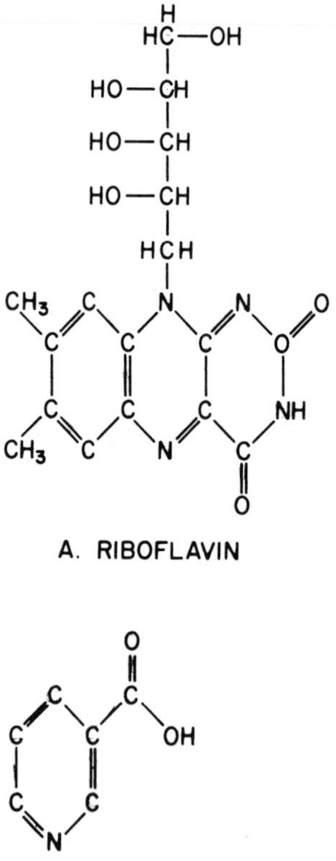

A. RIBOFLAVIN

B. NICOTINIC ACID

Figure 15–18. Two important vitamins B.

ring widely in vegetables and fresh fruits, some thiamine is found in meats, pork being the best supplied; however, whole grains and fortified and whole wheat breads are probably the foods richest in this vitamin. Mild deficiencies cause an increase in the pyruvic and lactic acid content of the blood and a concomitant feeling of fatigue. In more severe instances heart disease may result. At the onset of deficiency the heart may quicken its rate of contraction, and in a continuation of the condition enlargement and reduced blood pressure follow. *Neuritis* is another product of *athiaminosis.* Prolonged insufficiencies of the substance result in *beriberi,* typically a disease of eastern Asia, where polished rice forms the principal dietary staple; however, it is prevalent also among alcoholics the world over.

Riboflavin. The second member of the B-complex, *riboflavin* (vitamin G or B₂) in the cell serves as the basis (Figure 15–18) for a large variety of coenzymes, including a number already familiar to the student, such as FM (flavin mononucleotide) and FAD (flavin adenine dinucleotide). Hence in deficiencies of this substance among young animals there is cessation of growth, accompanied by an extensive inflammation of the skin and spread of blood vessels across the cornea to form a characteristic cataract. Furthermore, the tongue assumes a deep magenta color and becomes deeply fissured, and sores develop around the mouth. Among everyday foods, milk is probably the best source of the vitamin, but goodly quantities also occur in leafy vegetables, fruits, eggs, and meat, with wheat germ serving as a rich supplement.

Nicotinic Acid. As in the other B vitamins, *nicotinic acid* (Figure 15–18) enters into the structure of fundamental cell coenzymes; with ribose, adenine, and phosphate, it forms three of the essential compounds, namely, DPN, TPN, and coenzyme III. As may be imagined from the importance of these products, a deficiency has widespread effects on the body. Principally in human beings *pellagra* results, a disease most frequently associated with alcoholism or poverty or a combination of the two. Doubtlessly this is the commonest avitaminosis in the United States, for it is prevalent in the southeastern states where "meal, molasses, and meat"—the last item in the form of dried or smoked pork— form the chief articles of diet. Briefly stated, the disease is characterized by "dermatitis, diarrhea, and dementia." The skin becomes inflamed, especially in exposed areas, the diarrhea is severe and often the chief cause of death, and the mental derangement may range from mild neurosis to extreme mania or stupor. All symptoms quickly disappear when nicotinic acid is supplied the patient. Among the principal natural sources are fresh meat and liver, fish, eggs, and whole grains.

Pyridoxine and Pantothenic Acid. In humans and most other vertebrates three substances similar to *pyridoxine* (Figure 15–19) are interconvertible within the cells and are together referred to as the vitamins B_6. As a rule, they are components of important coenzymes, particularly in transaminases and in those involved in sulfur metabolism. Hence deficiencies result in abnormalities of amino acid metabolic processes, especially of tryptophane. Similarly, *pantothenic acid* is a basic ingredient of CoA. The chief dietary sources of both vitamins are the same as the others of the B group: fresh meats and vegetables, liver, eggs, and whole grains.

Biotin and Folic Acid. Two B vitamins, *biotin* and *folic acid* (Figure 15– 19), are secreted in such abundance by the bacteria of the intestines that deficiency effects are difficult to produce in mammals. In the case of the first substance, diets containing large quantities of raw egg white, perhaps to the extent of one third of the total caloric intake, are capable of producing deficiencies by their property of adsorbing the vitamin. Biotin appears to be a constituent, not of a coenzyme, but of an enzyme (carboxylase) that assists in carboxylation (the addition or subtraction of $^-$COOH or CO_2), such as in the attachment of carbon dioxide to an amino acid. On the other hand, folic acid enters into the formation of the coenzyme CoF, which is concerned in the transfer of one-carbon units, such as $^-CH_3$ (the methyl radical), from one molecule to another. In humans serious disturbances of the intestinal tract and occasional cases of pregnancy produce a type of anemia in which the red blood cells are large and rich in hemoglobin; however, the cells are so few in number that the blood is actually deficient in its total hemoglobin content. Usually this disease, named *macrocytic anemia,* results from folic acid deficiencies in the body, but other factors may occasionally be involved in its production.

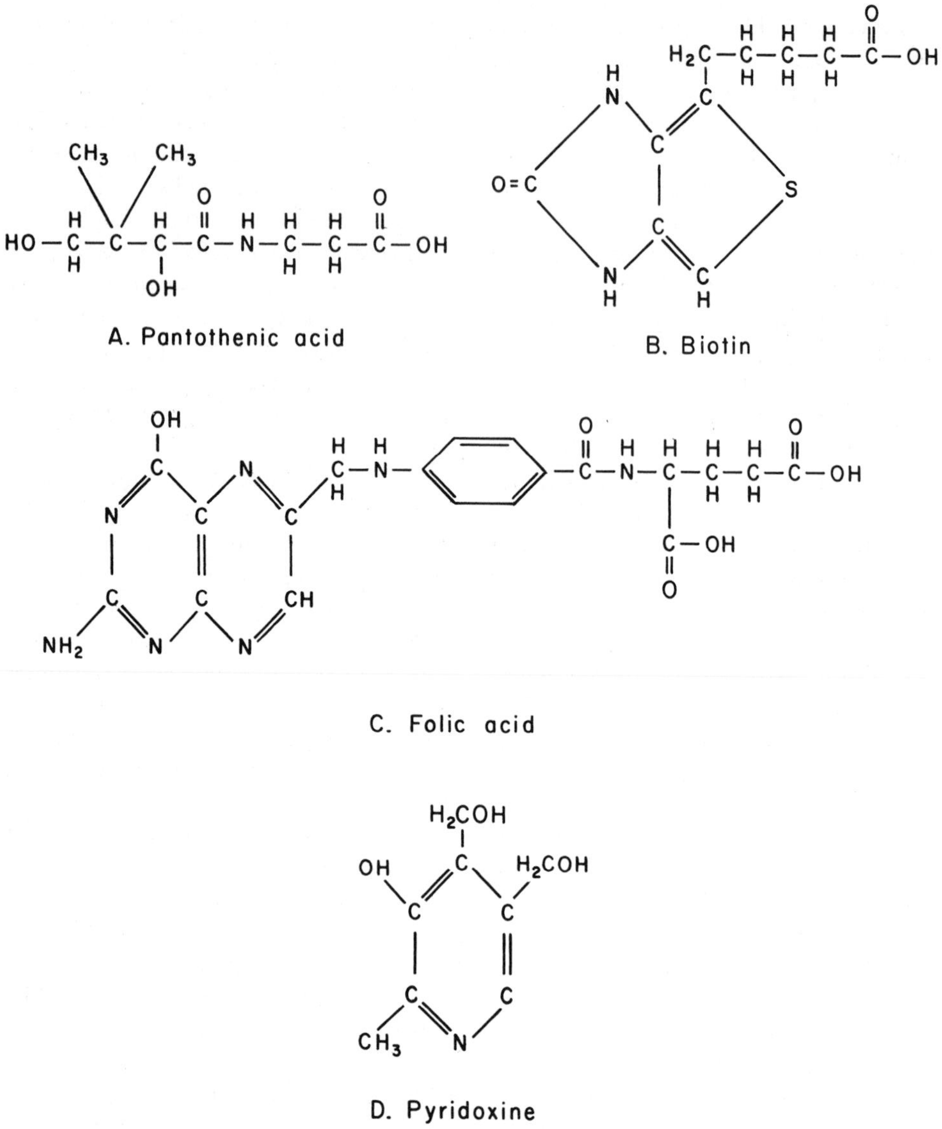

A. Pantothenic acid

B. Biotin

C. Folic acid

D. Pyridoxine

Figure 15–19. Additional members of the vitamin B complex.

The Cobalamines. The *cobalamines* (vitamin B_{12}) have large complex molecules built around an atom of cobalt; these compounds are secreted in ample supply by the bacteria of the intestines. Although the supply is always sufficient, occasional individuals lose the ability to absorb it and develop *pernicious anemia,* in which disease the body is unable to produce red blood cells. Dietary sources include liver and other fresh meats, fish, milk, and eggs.

The Regulation of Body Metabolism

To appreciate the organization of organisms as complex as the vertebrates, an insight into the processes of the bodily metabolism must be gained. Although currently scarcely more than a good beginning has been made in understanding the participating mechanisms, what has been unraveled will perhaps suffice to provide some appreciation of the intricacies that exist. In connection with this discussion, a brief review over the essentials of the cellular metabolic activities may prove helpful (Chapter 4).

The Regulation of Energy Mechanisms

All of the activities of an animal, whether at the level of the cell or of the whole organism, in the long run are dependent on the provision of energy. To ensure that a sufficient supply of fuel materials be constantly at hand, adequate storage mechanisms must be provided. Although other processes, such as the intake of foods and the transport of materials to and from storage and utilization centers, form part of the over-all picture and should be borne in mind, their details can be better presented separately in a later chapter. In the present account the regulation of the supply and utilization of the fuels, with associated phenomena, are the main points of interest.

The Storage of Fuel Materials. As the student already knows, much fuel required for bodily functions is stored in the liver and fatty tissues, as well as in the muscles themselves. Since energy materials are stored chiefly as glycogen, a quite insoluble substance, it must be converted into a soluble carbohydrate, principally glucose, before the supply can be drawn on. Thus this conversion of glycogen into glucose and the reverse process provides a place in the chain of fuel activities in which a measure of control can be applied. Just as the speed of an automobile engine is dependent on

the quantity of gasoline fed into it by way of the carburetor, so the rate of muscular activity cannot exceed its supply of energy materials. After its formation, glucose is transported by means of the circulatory system and may enter the muscles. Upon entering, it is reconverted to glycogen and here in the enzymatic processes is provided a second point of control. Similarly, the lactic acid produced by a muscle during contraction can be reconverted into glucose and glycogen. To these reactions a third set of regulatory activities may be applied, which proceed to a small extent in the organs forming the lactic acid but for the greater part in the liver after being transported there by the blood stream.

Mechanism of Control. In the processes of carbohydrate and lipid utilization, as might be anticipated from their importance, a number of hormones and the vitamins A are concerned with control. Only at one locus in the cyclic activities do all ingredients play a role; at others duplication is minimal. As all components show some effects in the liver on the conversion of glucose into glycogen or the latter's breakdown into the former, the metabolic activities of this organ can well serve as the starting point of our discussion.

Since energy utilization and its control are composed of many small steps, it may be helpful to follow the diagram (Figure 15–20) closely as the processes are outlined. First, in the liver epinephrin and glucagon serve to accelerate the breakdown of glycogen and also to facilitate the deposition of the resulting glucose into the blood stream, so that the net result is a rise in the level of the blood glucose. In this same organ the activities of the two substances are opposed by insulin, the vitamins A, and the cortisones; all 11-oxygenated products of the adrenal cortex together are referred

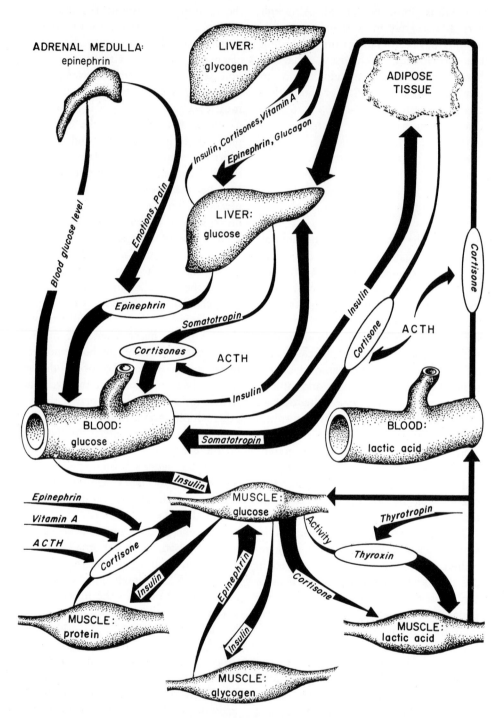

Figure 15–20. Energy control mechanisms. That energy control is highly important in animal functioning is indicated by the complexity of this diagram showing processes known to exist among the mammals. Arrows which increase in width toward the point are used to indicate a stimulatory action, whereas those which decrease in width apically suggest an inhibitory effect.

to here as cortisones for the sake of brevity. Hence the direction in which the glycogen-glucose reactions proceed depends largely on the hormone being secreted most abundantly at any given moment. As far as the interchange of glucose between the blood and the liver is concerned, not all of the glycogen-producing hormones have identical actions, for the cortisones act in a direction opposed to that of insulin, whereas the vitamins A play no known role. In the conversion of blood glucose into fat, or the opposite, insulin and the cortisones again act antagonistically, whereas the cortisones are paralleled functionally by somatotropin. As a generality, it may be pointed out that insulin decreases blood sugar by stimulating its entrance into the cells of the entire body, apparently by involvement in a mechanism that transports glucose through cell membranes. After its entrance into the cell the carbohydrate may be employed for energy or stored as fats, proteins, or glycogen, depending on the organ. On the other hand, the cortisones tend to raise the level of blood glucose through accelerating conversion of adipose tissues into glucose and by removal of glucose from the liver. Moreover, the blood sugar level is under control of a feedback mechanism involving epinephrin. After the level has risen, as under increased epinephrin flow instigated by injury or emotional stress, the supply of the hormone is later diminished again because of the restrictive action of high blood-glucose concentration. Similarly, a drop in the level, initiated by an increased presence of insulin, for example, stimulates the adrenal medulla into greater production of epinephrin, and the normal level is restored. Hence one hormone counterbalances the other.

At the utilization end of the cycle the muscles and other metabolically active parts of the body (hereafter all such parts are referred to merely as "muscles") have a net effect of depleting the blood of its glucose content. As already stated, insulin accelerates the entrance of the sugar into the organ and also tends to stimulate its conversion into glycogen or protein. In the first process it is opposed only by epinephrin, whereas in the second the cortisones alone have a reverse effect. However, epinephrin, not to mention ACTH and the vitamins A, indirectly enter into protein breakdown by stimulating the adrenal cortex into secreting more of the cortisones. In the processes that actually utilize glucose the cortisones have a retarding action, whereas thyroxin (under the control of thyrotropin) and muscular activity (regulated by the central nervous system) increase cellular respiration and the formation of lactic acid. Most of the lactic acid is removed by the blood stream and conducted to the liver for reconversion into glucose; these steps are influenced by the cortisones and indirectly by ACTH.

THE REGULATION OF BODILY GROWTH

In the following discussion, as in the foregoing, the term "muscles" is used to denote all metabolically active structures of the body, for together these organs constitute the most abundant representative type. Out of the processes of nitrogen metabolism new proteins, and thus protoplasm, are formed, so that bodily growth is one of the net outcomes, at least in young animals. Although the deamination of amino acids is also a part of nitrogen metabolism, that aspect is closely associated with the elimination of waste by-products; hence it is presented with the rest of the excretory processes later.

The Control of Protein Formation and Growth. As the replacement of cytoplasmic proteins is of constant importance in all the cells of the body, linking of amino acids to one another in peptide formation proceeds to a large extent uncontrolled by extracellular influences. As long as amino acids are supplied to the blood stream and the B vitamins are present in sufficient quantities, the cells' enzymatic systems are capable of carrying on peptidization autonomously. Only a relatively few hormones appear to be directly involved in the organism's control of the processes (Figure 15–21). However, it must not be forgotten that the anabolism of any substance, including the proteins, requires energy from the respiratory processes; hence secondary but highly effective regulation can be supplied by those intricate hormonal controls over carbohydrate catabolism that were just discussed.

Directly affecting the formation of proteins are the two opposing hormones which act on the conversion of glucose into amino acids and the reverse reaction. The antagonistic chemicals are *insulin*, which stimulates amination, and *cortisone*, which facilitates deamination. Whereas insulin secretion is under an unknown control mechanism, cortisone is influenced by epinephrin, ACTH, and the vitamins A. Supplementing insulin in protein formation after puberty, the *androgens* display a restrictive influence over the breakdown of blood amino acids by the liver and exert a strongly stimulatory one in building proteins, especially in muscular tissue in a strict sense.

In contrast, *somatotropin* is the chief regulator of growth in the organic matrix of bones, as shown by the production of dwarfs and giants when abnormalities of secretion occur; how this hormone exerts its influence, however, is presently unknown. Another set of hormones, namely the androgens, probably by their effect on protein formation in general, for a time after sexual maturity enter into bone matrix growth, as shown by the rapid development of youths. By themselves, however, these sex hormones have no force; STH and *thyroxin* must also be present. Nor is thyroxin useful by itself; only in the presence of somatotropin does it induce protein formation. On the other hand, it greatly enhances the activity of somatotropin, the two hormones together being nearly twice as effective as the latter alone. From the deformities of cretins it must be concluded that thyroxin plays a selective role, for whereas in cases of early hypothyroidism some bones attain normal proportions, others, particularly the appendicular, are greatly retarded in growth. The anterior pituitary thus exerts a dual control over growth, directly through the secretion of somatotropin and indirectly by way of thyrotropin's influence on thyroid activity. Thyrotropin and thyroxin, in fact, are mutually controlled by a feedback arrangement through the level of thyroxin in the blood. Finally, it must be recalled that vitamin C is important too in the formation of connective tissue, including the matrix of bone, and that growth is impaired unless an adequate supply is available. Since many animals produce their own ascorbic acid, in light of this fact might not this material be looked upon also as having in such cases a hormonal control over bone growth?

THE REGULATION OF BONE FORMATION

Although bone growth is chiefly a function of protein metabolism, unless calcium deposition accompanies elongation of the organic matrix, deformation of the skeletal parts will quickly develop.

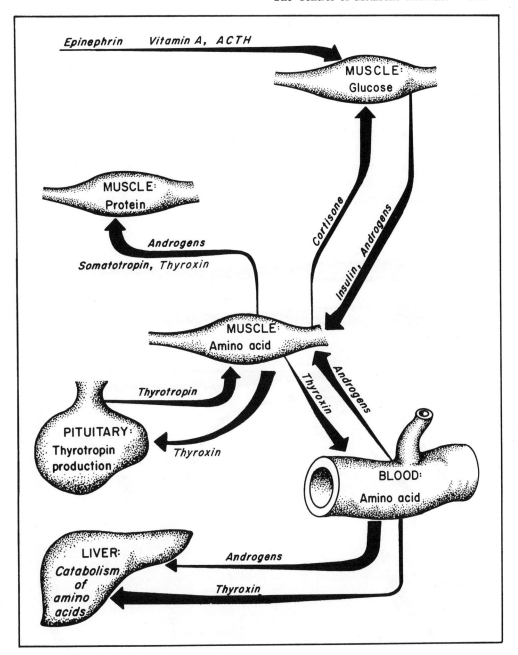

Figure 15–21. Protein metabolism control mechanisms. Stimulatory activities are indicated by arrows increasing in width toward the point, while inhibitory effects are shown by those of the opposite shape.

Essential Ingredients of Calcification. Important to normal deposition of bone are the vitamins A and D, certain hormones including parathormone, such inorganic constituents as calcium phosphate, and lactic acid (lactates). As stated earlier, the *vitamins D* are essential to the formation of the bony tissue, acting largely on the absorption of calcium from the digestive tract. In their absence the calcium of ingested foods passes out of the intestines with the other undigested remains; hence their real role is in making this mineral available to the body as a whole rather than in serving the skeleton. In fact, an excess of these vitamins in the body induces a resorption of calcium from the bones. The *vitamins A* are necessary for resorption and appear to react principally with the phosphate

constituents rather than the calcium. In a deficiency the dermal bones of the skull and long bone shafts become thick because of the failure of the osteoclasts to carry out their normal functions. In connection with the inorganic constituents of bone, it must be pointed out that the skeletal parts, in spite of appearances to the contrary, are actively metabolic throughout life. Bone is not just deposited once and for all, but both the calcium and phosphate ions are removed and re-

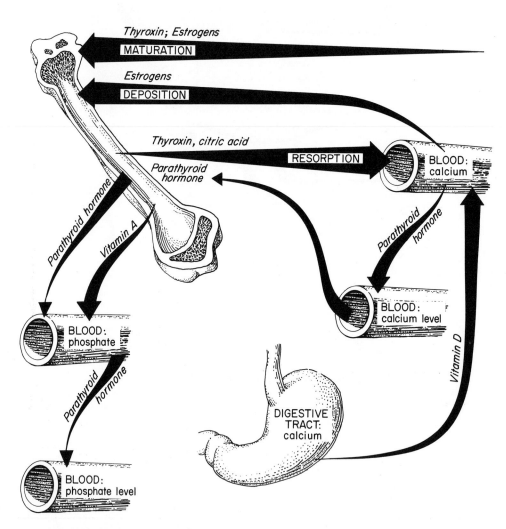

Figure 15–22. Principal controls over bone growth. Inhibiting actions are indicated by apically tapering arrows and stimulatory effects by expanding ones.

placed continually. By the use of radioactive materials it has been shown that both elements are incorporated quickly even into mature bones.

The Control of Bone Formation. Much of bone formation centers around the organic matrix, and hence control over bone deposition is secondary to controls that form the skeletal parts through heredity and hormones. Nevertheless, a degree of hormonal control is exercised over the activities involved (Figure 15–22). In addition to those substances such as parathormone and excessive vitamins D that draw on the constituents of the bones when supplies from the digestive tract are insufficient, only two types of hormones participate directly in governing deposition. Of the two, namely thyroxin and the estrogens, the first is by far the most important, for it acts to check further bone elongation by inducing the epiphyses to become fused with the shaft

by processes referred to as *maturation*. Hence it is seen that thyroxin, although subordinate to somatotropin during the actual growth of the organic matrix, nonetheless has final control over the length of skeletal parts by inducing cessation of growth. When only STH is present, bones continue to elongate indefinitely, but once thyroxin has induced maturation, even heavy secretory activities by the pituitary cannot bring about additional elongation. Along with the thyroid secretion, the estrogens also serve to instigate maturation of bones, but whether they act directly in this capacity or by way of the thyroid or anterior pituitary is unknown. Nor is it known why thyroxin does not bring about maturation before puberty; apparently there is an interplay of the thyroxin and estrogens, along with still undiscovered factors essential to the control of the processes.

Questions for Review and Thought

1. Define the following terms: *endocrine gland, hormone, hypersecretion, hyposecretion, cretin, diabetes,* and *acromegaly.*

2. Name the endocrine glands of the neck and thorax. List the hormones of each and give as many as possible of their functions.

3. In this text a morphological scheme is employed for the classification of the endocrine glands. Classify the glands in two other ways: (1) on the basis of the chemical nature of their secretions and (2) on the function of their hormones. In which scheme is the name of any given gland most frequently repeated? According to your second scheme, which set of organs or which processes of the body are under the influence of the greatest number of hormones?

4. Distinguish between the two types of diabetes.

5. List the endocrine glands that are at least in part under the control of the pituitary and those which are not.

6. Which hormones appear to have an important influence on the central nervous system, either functionally or developmentally?

7. Distinguish between vitamins and provitamins.

8. Prepare a scheme of classification of the vitamins based upon their functions and a second one based upon sources.

9. Make a list of the known effects of vitamin deficiencies.

10. Outline the mechanism and substances involved in:

(a) the regulation of fuel usage by the body
(b) the regulation of protein anabolism
(c) the governing of bodily growth

11. What is meant by a "feedback" mechanism? List as many activities as you can in which such a mechanism is known to exist.

Supplementary References

Baldwin, E. *Dynamic Aspects of Biochemistry,* 4th ed. Cambridge, Cambridge Univ. Press, 1963.

Fieser, L. F. "Steroids." *Sci. Amer.,* January 1955.

Green, D. E. "The Metabolism of Fats." *Sci. Amer.,* January 1954.

Hall, P. F. *Functions of the Endocrine Glands.* Philadelphia, Saunders, 1959.

Jenkin, P. M. *Animal Hormones—A Comparative Survey.* New York, Macmillan, 1962.

Kimber, Diana C., *et al. Anatomy and Physiology,* 14th ed. New York, Macmillan, 1961.

Rasmussen, H. "The Parathyroid Hormone." *Sci. Amer.,* April 1961.

Schmitt, F. O. "Giant Molecules in Cells and Tissues." *Sci. Amer.,* September 1957.

Stein, W. H., and S. Moore. "The Chemical Structure of Proteins." *Sci. Amer.,* February 1961.

Turner, C. D. *General Endocrinology,* 3rd ed. Philadelphia, Saunders, 1960.

Walker, B. S., W. C. Boyd, and I. Asimov. *Biochemistry and Human Metabolism,* 3rd ed. Baltimore, Williams & Wilkins, 1957.

West, E. S. *Textbook of Biophysical Chemistry.* New York, Macmillan, 1962.

Woodward, J. D. "Biotin." *Sci. Amer.,* June 1961.

CHAPTER 16

The Supply
of Metabolic
Materials

As THE STUDENT already knows, the cells of the body need a constant supply both of basic foodstuffs and oxygen in order to carry out the metabolic activities described in the preceding chapter or any comparable ones to be discussed later. In the vertebrates the provision of these two classes of necessary substances is the duty of three separate systems, the digestive and respiratory doing the actual procuring while the circulatory delivers them to the cells. Although thus working toward one end, the three are highly specialized for different roles and require separate discussions as a consequence.

The Digestive System

Although the food habits of the vertebrate groups are greatly varied and often highly specialized, the basic pattern of the digestive system is strikingly uniform throughout. Essentially it consists of the following organs, in sequence beginning anteriorly: mouth, pharynx, esophagus, stomach, small and large intestines, and cloaca (Figure 16–1). Although the last-named structure is absent from most adult mammals and many fishes, it is always present at least during the developmental stages; it is a structure that serves as a conduit for the reproductive and excretory systems in addition to the present one. As a rule, three principal roles are played by the digestive tract: the procurement and swallowing, or *ingestion,* of food; the breaking down and absorption of food materials, classed as *digestion* proper; and the elimination of the indigestible remains, called *egestion.*

PROCUREMENT AND
INGESTION

The Mouth. Although the original function of the mouth, as exemplified in

325

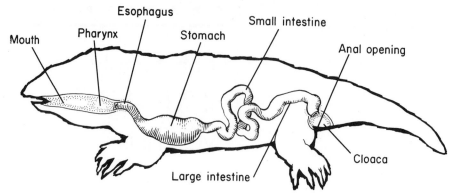

Figure 16–1. The digestive tract of a typical vertebrate.

the cyclostome larva, was probably the passive one of permitting food to enter the body or perhaps of acting as a filter, to this function have been added in the terrestrial vertebrates definitive roles in ingestion and often, to a limited extent, in digestion. To assist in its activities, the cavity of the mouth is well provided with *tongue* (Figure 16–2) and *teeth* in all vertebrates above the cyclostomes, except in those forms such as turtles and birds that have lost these structures secondarily. But only in the mammals is specialization made into grinding types, such as molars and premolars, tearing types (canines), and chopping types (incisors). In these animals the modifications of the dental equipment of the mouth are so closely correlated with the food habits of each species that a good picture of the nutritional habits of fossil forms can be drawn from a study of the teeth alone.

The Glands of the Mouth. Only in terrestrial vertebrate groups is the mouth assisted in its functions by *salivary glands,* for, since their chief activity is that of moistening food in preparation for swallowing, none is needed by organisms whose nutrients are taken in water. Although in amphibians only one or two

Figure 16–2. The use of the tongue in food procurement. In this unusual photograph contact of the frog's tongue with the meal worm released the flash control mechanism and exposed the film. Note the anterior attachment of the tongue within the mouth. (University of Colorado Museum. Van Riper photo.)

pairs may be present, such strictly terrestrial reptiles as the snakes and lizards have four pairs of these glands, frequently modified to secrete venom, as in rattlesnakes and cobras. However, it is in the mammals in which best development of the salivary organs is to be found. Among the members of this class, although much variation exists, typically three pairs are present—namely, the *parotid* lying near the ear and opening laterally to the upper molars, the *submaxillary* placed beneath the lower jaw and opening posterior to the incisors, and the *sublingual* located below the floor of the mouth and opening near or with the submaxillary. Chiefly all these glands secrete a watery substance containing *mucin,* a protein with mucuslike properties that give the saliva its lubricating qualities; in many mammals the secretion from the parotid contains in addition the enzyme *amylase* (formerly called ptyalin) which acts on starches to hydrolyze them into maltose. Contrary to an existing concept, this is the sole digestive activity that occurs in the mouth.

Control of Ingestion. The body's control over the procurement and ingestion of food to meet its needs is largely provided by the sense of *hunger,* those vague feelings of emptiness in the stomach that prompt the animal to seek nourishment. Closely associated with this sensation is *appetite,* which can be defined best as the mental desire for food, whether or not a real need or hunger exists in the body. Where one of these nervous activities ends and the other begins is not always readily discernible; however, the appetite appears to increase in direct relation to the increment of hunger. To most humans, for example, sweets appeal to the appetite at almost any time; even after a heavy meal one can usually find room for a mint candy, whereas bread then holds no attraction

at all. In contrast, under extreme hunger even a dried crust appears attractive. Hence while hunger can be viewed as the drive that compels the animal to seek nourishment, appetite aids in the selection of the material taken in and thus assists in the procurement of foodstuffs for which the species is most adapted.

The importance of appetite in the procurement of food may be illustrated by the recent experimental analysis of the American raccoon's feeding behavior carried out by the British zoologist M. Lyall-Watson. As is well known, this animal is noted for its peculiar habit of "washing" its food, at least in captivity. In the wild state it normally feeds on crayfish, fish, pond snails, and other aquatic animals, but when an aquatic situation is not available it also captures mice, insects, earthworms, and small reptiles on dry land. These "dry" foods are apparently at no time carried to water for "washing" under natural conditions. When food hunting along streams, after locating prey visually, the raccoon *dabbles* it in the water, using the sensitive palms of the forepaws to feel and rub the surface, while staring vacantly into space (Figure 16–3). These activities continue for several moments until the animal's appetite for the captured object has been sufficiently aroused, whereupon it feeds. Only among captured specimens does the so-called "washing" of dry foods appear; this behavior, according to Lyall-Watson's results, seems to be a learned response that apparently substitutes for the normal dabbling activities and serves to stimulate the appetite in its stead. So while the raccoon can now no longer be cited as the meticulously clean animal that even "washes" its food before eating, it nevertheless remains the same fascinating creature.

In the control of ingestion two pairs of centers in the hypothalamus are

Figure 16–3. "Food washing" by a raccoon. Dabbling food, as behaviorists call this activity, appears to be part of appetite arousal behavior in this North American mammal. (Photo by Norman Langley, courtesy of Dr. Malcolm Lyall-Watson and the Zoological Society of London, *Proceedings,* Vol. 141, 1963.)

involved: one set, the *feeding centers,* initiate food seeking and ingestion; the second, the *satiety centers,* induce a cessation in such activities. Although the mechanisms through which these centers act have not yet been clearly established, one substance in the blood, namely glucose, has been shown to act in this capacity. In experiments involving implantation of delicate electrodes in the rat hypothalamus the satiety center was found to react strongly to an elevated level of this carbohydrate; whether other factors have a similar reaction remains to be determined. Activation of the feeding center—that is, the initiation of the

sense of hunger—also seems to be in response to the blood glucose level, this time a lowered one, despite the fact that often it is suggested to arise from contractions of the stomach walls. When the nerves to the stomach are severed or even when the entire stomach has been removed surgically, the sense of hunger still is aroused normally.

DIGESTION AND ASSOCIATED ACTIVITIES

Because the actively digestive portions of the alimentary tract are complex in their organization and physiology, closer attention must be given them than was requisite for the ingestive parts. Accordingly, it is convenient to subdivide this section into discussions of the anterior and posterior regions.

The Anterior Organs

The Pharynx and Esophagus. From the mouth the food, in the form of a ball or *bolus* of particles held together by the saliva, is conducted to the stomach by a continuous tube consisting of the *pharynx* and *esophagus*. When the bolus or liquid is pushed into the pharynx by the tongue, swallowing reflexes are initiated by the sympathetic system, which force the substance down the tube's length into the stomach. In many birds an enlargement of the esophagus known as the *crop* serves as a temporary storage place; in it, too, foods are moistened until released at intervals into the stomach.

The Stomach. Basically, the vertebrate stomach is a croplike dilation in the esophagus for the temporary storage of foods, and in many of the lower vertebrates, including some of the fishes, it serves solely in this capacity; only commencing with the amphibians does it consistently play an active part in digestion. Since its activities have been most thoroughly investigated in mammals, detailed discussion is confined to that group. Although the essential features of the mammalian gastric morphology are sufficiently clear in the diagram (Figure 16–4), a brief explanation may be in order concerning the part called the *fundus*. This term merely refers to that portion of the stomach prolonged anterior to the entrance of the esophagus; it is a region with no special function, save in the instigation of the wavelike contractions of the stomach wall.

In carrying out its digestive functions

the stomach secretes several substances, the most outstanding of which is *hydrochloric acid,* believed by most workers to be formed by the *parietal cells.* These glands are found in the *mucosa* lining the organ in close association with others called the *chief cells;* these cells seemingly produce *pepsinogen,* a type of "proenzyme"—that is, the forerunner of an actual enzyme. In the presence of the hydrochloric acid, pepsinogen is converted into *pepsin,* the principal ingredient of the gastric secretion, which acts on certain peptide linkages of proteins, and hence is a protease. Besides these two types, there are four other glands active in the formation of the mucus which constitutes the remainder of the stomach's secretions, known collectively as *gastric juice.* Only one other enzyme, a *lipase,* has been accurately determined as existing in the gastric juice of humans; but since it functions only under nearly neutral conditions, its effectiveness in active breakdown of fats is probably highly restricted. Another substance of possible enzymatic activity, *rennin,* is found in abundance in cattle and other hoofed

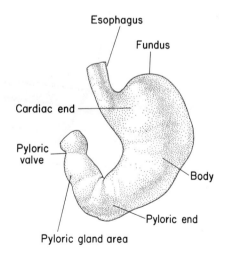

Figure 16–4. The structure of a typical mammalian stomach.

forms that consume large quantities of milk as young. Principally, this compound serves to coagulate the milk, perhaps slowing its passage through the stomach, but it may also affect the digestion of milk proteins in some still undetermined fashion.

Control of Secretion. Considerable success has been achieved in investigations of the mechanisms controlling gastric secretion. In the first place, it has been learned that the flow of the gastric juices is initiated by stimuli received in the pyloric area during the processes of ingestion. When food is placed in the mouth, impulses are sent to the brain, and are thence relayed over the vagus nerve to the pyloric area of the stomach. As long as acid is more or less absent, this region is thus induced to release a hormone called *gastrin* into the blood stream, which, on reaching the parietal cells, instigates production of hydrochloric acid (Figure 16–5). Second, after food

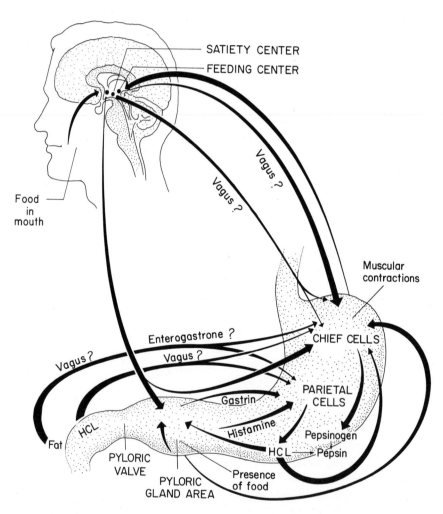

Figure 16–5. Control of stomach action in human beings. The interlocking mechanisms that control gastric action are indicated in this diagram as far as present-day knowledge permits. Arrows that taper to the point indicate inhibition, while those that expand apically suggest a stimulatory influence.

has actually been swallowed, the mechanical stimulus provided by the bolus in this same end of the stomach continues the release of gastrin until the contents have attained a fairly low degree of acidity. It also appears likely that *histamine*, derived from the cells of any animal food taken into the stomach or perhaps secreted by the mucosa cells, may activate the production of hydrochloric acid after gastrin secretion has ceased or become diminished. During the gastric digestive processes several types of muscular movement in the walls churn the mixture of swallowed food and gastric juice referred to as *chyme*. Initially, the contractions begin in the fundus with the first feelings of hunger and become augmented in frequency and extent by the mechanical presence of ingested foods. For some time they continue unabated but cease when the chyme has attained a suitable acidity; hence hydrochloric acid is seen to have an inhibitory action in this instance.

In former years it was postulated that a similar degree of acidity in the pyloric region initiated the opening of the pyloric valve; recently, however, this has been found not to be the actual case. Emptying appears to be largely by means of muscular contractions of the wall that move wavelike throughout the entire organ, called *peristaltic* movements. When a peristaltic wave moving along the stomach reaches the pyloric region, it closes the valve, which at other times apparently remains open; however, when the upper portion of the intestine is emptier than the stomach, the resulting pressure gradients permit the valve to remain open even during peristalsis, so that chyme is then pumped into the duodenum. In the upper portion of the small intestine the entrance of the acid chyme activates a mechanism that retards the activities of both the stomach muscles and its glands, as the pressure

gradient diminishes. Similarly, the presence of fats in the same part of the intestine has an inhibiting effect. So long as lipid materials remain unabsorbed in the duodenum, a sense of hunger fails to develop.

The Posterior Organs

From the stomach the chyme enters the posterior portion of the alimentary tract composed entirely of the *intestines*. Although, in the cyclostomes no such differentiation exists, as a rule the organ is subdivided into small and large parts, the distinction being based on relative diameter, not on length.

The Small Intestine. By far the most important digestive organ in all vertebrates is the small intestine, for in it the bulk of the digestive activities are carried to conclusion. Frequently it is variously modified, depending on the group and on the food habits of the species; differences in length especially reflect the type of nutrition, herbivorous forms having much longer intestines than the carnivorous, a fact that is strikingly illustrated by the frog during the course of its life history. As a tadpole the amphibian is strictly vegetarian and accordingly has long coiled intestines; after metamorphosis, however, it acquires a carnivorous habit of feeding and the intestines are short. Not only are they short relatively but on actual comparison they prove shorter, despite the fact that the tadpole itself may be less than half the body size of the adult. In man, with his mixed diet of flesh and vegetables, the organ is intermediate in proportionate length, ranging from 11 to 26 feet and being somewhat shorter in women than in men, generally correlated to body height. Modifications in features other than length also exist, but specialization into separate regions is found only in the mammals. In these animals three subdivisions, named the *duodenum, jejunum,* and *ileum* in sequence beginning anteriorly, carry out particular aspects of the digestive processes.

Small Intestinal Secretions.   Within the cavity of the small intestine a number of secretions are formed or received that enable the organ to perform a variety of tasks. In addition to breaking down nutrients by enzymatic action, it dilutes hypertonic solutions and concentrates the hypotonic. Moreover, it emulsifies lipids, thus facilitating their digestion and absorption; and, finally, it exercises a considerable degree of selectivity over the absorption of its contents into the body. Assisting it in these functions are the products of the two large glands, the *liver* and *pancreas,* as well as the secretions of a number of small types within its own walls; among them, in addition to numerous *mucous glands,* is a type known as the *crypts,* which secrete *enterokinase,* a substance needed to activate a pancreatic proenzyme. Finally, various epithelial cells produce other constituents of the *intestinal juice,* as all the secretions of the intestine together are

called. Known to be contained in the juice are numerous enzymes, including intestinal *amylase,* several that act on simpler saccharides, and a small number of *peptidases* and *polynucleotidases,* which break down peptides and nucleotides, respectively (Table 16–1).

Although the secretion of the liver, called *bile,* is highly important in the small intestine, it contains no digestive enzymes. Principally it acts through its alkalinity, both in neutralizing the acidity of the chyme as it arrives from the stomach and in emulsifying lipid materials. Furthermore, bile contains several derivatives of cholesterol known as *bile acids* which are especially significant in the absorption of fats.

In contrast to the bile, the exocrine product of the pancreas, the *pancreatic juice,* is rich in enzymes and proenzymes. Among these materials are *trypsinogen* and *chymotrypsinogen,* which are converted, respectively, into two proteases; the first develops into *trypsin* in the presence of the enterokinase mentioned above, and the second is converted into *chymotrypsin* by action of the trypsin

Figure 16–6. Microvilli on intestinal villi. When examined under the electron microscope, intestinal villi are found to be densely covered by projections called "microvilli." That these minute structures perhaps assist in absorption into the villi is suggested by the apparent pinocytotic fold indicated. (Courtesy of Drs. Sanford L. Palay and L. J. Karlin, Journ. Biophys. Biochem. Cytol., 5:363–372, Pl. 150, Fig. 3, 1959.)

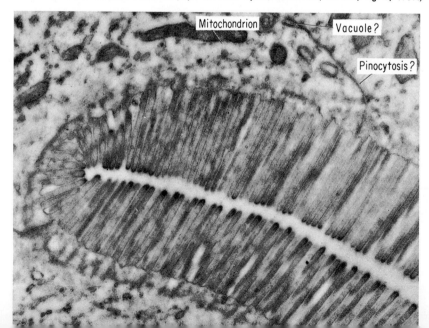

TABLE 16-1

THE DIGESTIVE ENZYMES OF MAMMALS

Food Class Acted Upon	Source	Proenzyme	Activator of Proenzyme	Enzyme	Food Acted Upon	End Products
carbohydrates	salivary glands	—	—	amylase	starch	maltose
	pancreas	—	—	amylase	starch	maltose
	intestinal glands	—	—	maltase	maltose	glucose
	intestinal glands	—	—	sucrase	sucrose	glucose, fructose
	intestinal glands	—	—	lactase	lactose	glucose, galactose
lipids	gastric glands	—	—	lipase	fats?	glycerol, fatty acids?
	pancreas	—	—	lipase	fats	glycerol, fatty acids
	intestinal glands	—	—	lipase	fats	glycerol, fatty acids
proteins	gastric glands	pepsinogen	hydrochloric acid	pepsin	proteins	proteoses, peptones
	gastric glands	—	—	rennin	proteins	(in ruminants only)
	pancreas	trypsinogen	enterokinase	trypsin	proteins	peptides
	intestinal glands					
	pancreas	chymotryp-sinogen	trypsin	chymotrypsin	proteins	peptides
	pancreas	—	—	carboxy-peptidase	peptides	amino acids
	pancreas	—	—	amino-peptidase	peptides	amino acids
nucleic acids	intestinal glands	—	—	ribonuclease	RNA	nucleotides
	intestinal glands	—	—	deoxyribo-nuclease	DNA	nucleotides

thus formed. Another enzyme active on nitrogenous products exists in pancreatic juice, one named *carboxypeptidase,* which acts on the end peptide link of proteins by breaking off amino acids one by one, so to speak. Finally, two other important enzymatic compounds are produced in the pancreas, *pancreatic amylase* and *lipase.*

Absorption in the Small Intestine. Over the inner surface of the small intestine are innumerable fine projections called *villi,* which are active in the processes of absorption of the products formed by enzymatic action. Within these projections are fine networks of blood capillaries and lymph vessels into which digested materials are absorbed for transport to other parts of the organism; the surface is shown by electron-micrographs to be covered with fine microvilli that may aid absorption by pinocytosis (Figure 16–6). Carbohydrates are absorbed only in the form of monosaccharides, with the exception that sucrose or other disaccharides can be absorbed when present in large amounts; however, whenever disaccharides are thus absorbed, they are promptly conducted to the kidneys and excreted. During the processes of absorption, certain sugars such as fructose are first converted to glucose by the mucosa. Even the absorption of glucose itself is not a simple osmotic procedure, for there exist much data indicating that this sugar is phosphorylated as it enters the cells of the mucosa and that perhaps its absorption involves some sort of ionic "pump" or enzyme system (page 57).

Proteins appear to be absorbed only in the form of their amino acid constituents, and these are transported through the mucosal cells at different rates of speed, probably by active transport mechanisms. Glycine is absorbed most rapidly, followed in turn by alanine, cystine, glutamic acid, valine, and so on. In the case of some amino acids, conversion to simpler ones occurs first; for example, glutamine is changed into glutamic acid by the mucosal cells before absorption.

In lipid absorption the products for the most part enter the lymph vesels rather than the blood capillaries as in the two foregoing types of nutrients. According to studies under the electron microscope, fats may enter the mucosal cells in droplet form by processes not unlike those of pinocytosis. On the other hand, it is frequently believed that lipids cannot penetrate the cell membrane until made soluble by union of the fatty acids with the bile acids. After entering the cells, the bile acids are believed to be broken off the fatty acids and are either returned to the intestinal cavity directly or carried by the blood stream to the liver to be reincorporated into bile.

Control of the Small Intestine.   When chyme enters the duodenum from the stomach, a number of control mechanisms are set into motion. First of all, the presence of acid in this part of the digestive tract releases into the blood three hormones that activate the liver and pancreas. Whereas one of these, *secretin,* increases the production of bile and the watery portion of pancreatic juice, the second, *pancreozymin,* produces an increment in the enzymatic content of secretin, while the third, *cholecystokinin,* stimulates contraction of the gallbladder in which bile is temporarily stored and initiates flow into the intestine. In addition, an endocrine secretion called *duocrinin* instigates the pouring out of an alkaline mucus into the duodenum that assists in counteracting the acidity of the stomach. Some evidence points to the failure of this last mechanism or of some related activity, as being involved in the formation of *peptic ulcers,* which typically arise in the upper portion of the duodenum.

Egestion and Associated Functions

For all practical purposes, the digestion and absorption of foods ends with the small intestine; all that appears to remain for the more posterior organs in the system is the elimination of the undigested remnants. However, there are some other less obvious, although still important, functions conducted here along with the egestive ones.

The Large Intestine.   In most vertebrates the large intestine consists solely of the *colon* and leads directly to the cloaca from the small intestine; however, beginning with the reptiles, it is modified somewhat by the addition of a pouch, known as the *caecum,* close to its juncture with the ileum. As it is best developed in herbivorous forms and in those that frequently swallow woody particles, this structure appears to supply a relatively undisturbed region where bacteria can carry out initial digestive processes on hard or resistant foods. In some mammals a portion of the caecum is reduced to an inactive remnant known as the *vermiform appendix* (Figure 16–7). In addition to man, this condition is found in the other higher primates, certain carnivores, and a few rodents. In contrast to this reduced state of affairs, the caecum may be greatly elongated in other mammals, as in some marsupials and most rodents; in fact, in several ungulates the sac is so enormous it exceeds the body in length. Moreover, in the mammals the posterior end of the large intestine may be modified into a muscular *rectum,* but a *cloaca* is present only in the egg-laying species and in certain distant relatives of rabbits, the pikas. The outermost opening of the tract, whether preceded by the rectum or the cloaca is the *anus,* which is closed by sphincter muscles.

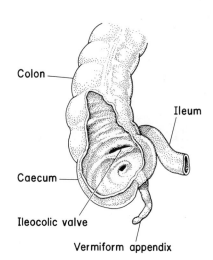

Colon

Ileum

Caecum

Ileocolic valve

Vermiform appendix

Figure 16–7. The vermiform appendix of man. In the diagram, part of the wall of the colon and caecum has been removed to expose the ileocolic valve.

The Activities of the Large Intestine. Upon its entry into the colon, the chyme consists of 75 to 80 per cent water, in which is suspended a number of lipid and proteinaceous products, including excess digestive enzymes. Consequently, one of the most important activities of the colon is that of conserving water by absorbing it into the blood, thus concentrating the chyme into the form of feces. In this organ, too, are found most of the bacterial symbionts. These organisms feed on the protein contents of the chyme, breaking them down into simpler substances, some of which are absorbed into the body; during these metabolic activities they produce biotin, folic acid, vitamin K, and other vitamins as by-products, which, as indicated earlier, are utilized by the mammals. Moreover, the wall of the large intestine absorbs many inorganic chemicals from the body and deposits them within the intestinal cavity to be eliminated with the feces. Principal among these substances are the salts of calcium, magnesium, iron, and copper, but sodium and potassium salts are also egested to a small degree by the same processes.

The Respiratory System

As a rule, the fuels supplied by the foregoing activities of the digestive system are of little value to the cells of the body unless an adequate quantity of oxygen is also available. The provision of this chemical is the function of the *respiratory system*. Often its organs are classed together as the "breathing" or "ventilation system" in an effort to avoid the dual implications of the term respiration, for, as the student already knows, this word can be employed for the cellular use of carbohydrates as well as for the processes of breathing in (*inspiration*) and breathing out (*expiration*). To distinguish them, currently it is the vogue to refer to the two types of processes as *internal* and *external respiration,* respectively. Since the internal has already received sufficient attention, discussion here is confined solely to the organs and activities involved in the external.

TYPES OF ORGANS

Among the vertebrates, chiefly two sorts of structures, gills and lungs, are employed in the actual processes of gaseous exchange between the blood and the atmosphere. In addition, basically similar parts or "accessory organs" assist in these activities.

The Accessory Organs. Since the principal *accessory* parts of the external respiratory system in the human are already familiar to the student, they need not be described in detail here; Figure 16–8 will suffice to recall the particulars to mind. In most fishes and in the cyclostomes *nostrils* leading into the mouth cavity are wanting, but in some forms their appearance is foreshadowed by the formation of *labial grooves* in the lips; however, only at the level of the Choanichthyes are true nostrils first found. Since the outer nostrils in the lungfish are covered by the lips, they are not visible when the mouth is closed. Nor are these passageways employed in breathing atmospheric air but solely in chemoreceptive activities; only in the terrestrial classes do they become functional for breathing. Among higher reptilians a bony partition (palate) is formed which

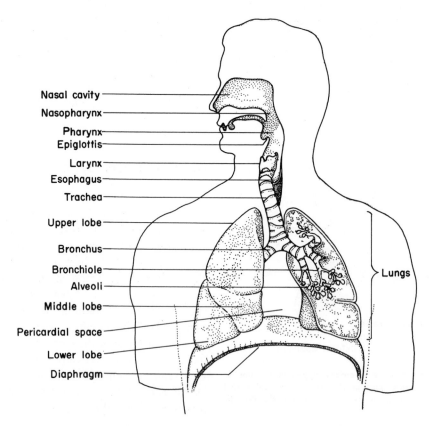

Figure 16–8. The respiratory tract in man.

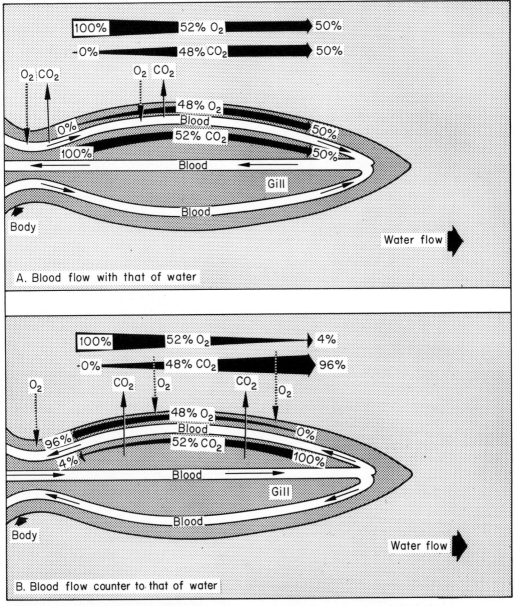

Figure 16–9. The principle of counterflow in gills. **A.** If the surface blood within a gill flows in the same direction as the water passing over the gill's surface, a state of equilibrium is reached at about 50 per cent of saturation. **B.** However, if the blood flows in the opposite direction (counter to the water), no equilibrium is reached prior to saturation.

separates the internal openings from the mouth cavity, and it is this state of affairs that exists in both the birds and mammals.

The Gills. In all strictly aquatic vertebrates the gill slits lead directly out from the pharynx, the walls between the openings being supported by skeletal structures called *visceral arches*. From the fleshy portions of the walls extend the actual *gills* as well as the blood vessels which are among their most essential components. Two main vessels are present, an *afferent artery* which conducts blood to the tip of the gill and an *efferent* which returns it from the gill to the rest of the body; a dense network of fine capillaries is between these two, ramifying through the entire body of the respiratory organ. Thus on the surface the blood flows from the tip to the base of the gills, in a direction counter to that of the water. Only by circulating the blood in a direction opposing the flow of water can such structures function efficiently. This fact may be best understood from the diagram (Figure 16–9), in which it is assumed for simplicity's sake that 100 per cent of saturation of oxygen can be either lost or gained by both the blood and the surrounding water. As may be seen, although a greater degree of difference (that is, a higher gradient) exists initially between the two fluids if both

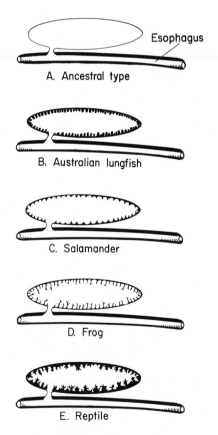

A. Ancestral type

B. Australian lungfish

C. Salamander

D. Frog

E. Reptile

Figure 16–10. Lung structure in various vertebrates. In the amphibians the structure of the lungs is very simple; with the passage of time, the terrestrial classes became better equipped to absorb atmospheric gases.

flow in the same direction, an equilibrium is reached at 50 per cent of saturation, making further exchange impossible. On the other hand, if the direction of blood circulation is opposite to that of the water, smaller gradients exist but persist throughout the length of the gill, avoiding equilibrium until saturation is virtually complete.

The Lungs. Only in the terrestrial vertebrates and their ancestral stocks are true *lungs* to be found. The first such organs, like the lungs of the lungfish and amphibians, are simple saclike structures, carrying numerous blood vessels but forming such an inefficient mechanism that the main respiratory activities, as will be recalled, are carried out by gills and skin in the lungfish and by the skin in adult frogs and salamanders. In the reptiles and other higher vertebrates the lungs have attained a complexity of construction that permits efficient operation (Figure 16–10). Among all these groups the respiratory organs proper commence with a *trachea* leading out from the pharynx, the tracheal opening being guarded from nongaseous substances by a trapdoorlike covering, the *epiglottis.* At its inner end the trachea branches into two *bronchi,* and these, in turn, are subdivided and redivided into numerous *bronchioles,* to the ends of which are attached saclike compartments called *alveoli* (Figure 16–8). Around each alveolus is a dense network of capillaries through which the exchange of gases actually occurs. It is this complex mass of bronchioles, alveoli, and capillaries together that forms each lung.

THE MECHANICS OF BREATHING

Although, in general, the basic mechanics of breathing in mammals are simple enough, investigations of certain details form one of the most active areas in respiratory biophysics today. Fundamentally, inspiration involves the enlargement of the thoracic cavity by contraction of the skeletal muscles which lift the "cage" made of the ribs and sternum, whereas expiration comprises the opposite set of movements. Accompanying these activities are the similar ones on the part of the diaphragm, which separates the thoracic and abdominal cavities. When this muscular organ contracts, it flattens, while during relaxation it bulges upward or forward into the thorax in dome fashion; thus it increases and decreases the volume of the chest and accordingly assists in inflating and deflating the lungs.

Gas Exchange. In order to understand the processes of gas exchange between the atmosphere and the blood, a few facts must be brought to mind. First it must be recalled that the atmosphere around us, if its water contents are overlooked as of no pertinence here, consists almost entirely of nitrogen and oxygen, with the addition of a small fraction of carbon dioxide (Table 16–2). Since the total pressure of the atmosphere at sea level is 760 mm of mercury (abbreviated as Hg) and its normal content of nitrogen is 79.02 per cent, the total pressure due to the nitrogen is equal to 79.02 per cent of the whole, namely, 600.6 mm Hg under the stated conditions. If, as at higher elevations, the total atmospheric pressure is reduced, say, to 500 mm Hg, the contribution of nitrogen is still 79.02 per cent and amounts to 396 mm Hg. This and similar fractional pressures exerted by the components of gaseous mixtures are referred to as *partial pressures* of the gases concerned; hence the partial pressures of oxygen and carbon dioxide in the atmosphere are equal to their respective percentages of the whole. These partial pressures provide the basis for the movement of the gaseous constituents between the air and the dissolved content of the blood, the direction of movement always being away from a higher pressure of a given substance to a lower one.

Second, it should be borne in mind that the gases within the alveoli of the lungs are not identical in composition with those of the atmosphere, even though they seemingly are derived directly from

TABLE 16-2

GAS CONTENT OF AIR, ALVEOLI, AND THE BLOOD

		Nitrogen		Oxygen		Carbon Dioxide		Water Vapor	
		Per Cent	Partial Pressure	Per Cent	Partial Pressure	Per Cent	Partial Pressure	Per Cent	Partial Pressure
Atmosphere	Dehydrated	79.02	600.6	20.94	159.1	0.04	0.3	0.0	0.0
	20% humidity at 37°C	78.07	593.4	20.69	157.2	0.04	0.3	1.20	9.1
	100% humidity at 37°C	74.16	563.5	19.63	149.2	0.04	0.3	6.17	47.0
Alveoli	Normal breathing	74.56	567.0	13.90	106.0	5.26	40.0	6.17	47.0
	Forced breathing	72.13	548.0	19.73	150.0	1.97	15.0	6.17	47.0
Blood	Arteries	75.71	576.0	12.79	97.0	5.33	40.5	6.17	47.0
	Veins (at rest)	82.13	627.0	5.60	40.0	6.10	46.0	6.17	47.0
Body tissues (at rest)		83.31	633.0	3.94	30.0	6.58	50.0	6.17	47.0

it. The alveolar cavity is always fully or virtually saturated with moisture at body temperature (37°C), at which temperature water vapor exerts a partial pressure of 47 mm Hg. Furthermore, the alveolar gas contains a relatively high percentage of carbon dioxide, and since the proportional content of nitrogen is more or less constant in the alveoli and blood as well as in the atmosphere, a lowered percentage of oxygen ensues. The contents and partial pressures given in Table 16–2 are averages except for those of the atmosphere.

Upon examination of the table it may be noted that, on the basis of partial pressures, whereas a gradient exists between the alveolar oxygen during normal breathing and the atmosphere, it is not nearly so pronounced as that existing between the carbon dioxide of the alveoli and the atmosphere. In contrast, the gradient between the oxygen content of venous and arterial blood is much sharper than that of the carbon dioxide. Hence, as blood circulates over the alveoli in the capillaries, it gains much oxygen but loses little carbon dioxide. In light of the high carbon dioxide content of the alveoli, this latter fact is not difficult to understand; what cannot be readily perceived is the basis for this high alveolar concentration of the gas. Even in forced breathing, when the oxygen of the lung compartments becomes exactly equal in percentage to that in the atmosphere, the carbon dioxide remains at a partial pressure of 15 mm Hg in comparison to 0.3 in the air. Yet, in spite of these points, which are incomprehensible at the moment, it can be readily seen that the direction of gas exchange is from the highest concentration, expressed either in percentage or as partial pressure, toward the lowest. In the case of oxygen the flow is constantly from the atmosphere to the body tissues; the course of carbon dioxide is in the opposite direction, from the body tissues to the atmosphere (Figure 16–11).

CONTROL OF BREATHING

The control of the rate and depth of respiration engages the action of gaseous concentration of the blood and mechanical conditions of the lung, the interplay of which act on respiratory centers in the brain. Although the essentials are thus readily summarized, the actual processes involve delicate devices that are extremely sensitive to change, for, as can readily be understood, the functions, and often the survival, of the animal depend on a constantly adequate supply of their respiratory needs and a rapid removal of the chemical by-products.

The Respiratory Centers. In the medulla of the brain, just behind the middle of its length, lie two closely interconnected areas together referred to as the *respiratory centers*. Each has sole control over one phase of the respiratory cycle; that placed more anteriorly regulates expiration, and the other, inspiration. During the last few years the fact has been uncovered that the fibers which run between the two have inhibitory action one upon another. Hence, when the inspiration center is "excited" or active, it sends impulses to the expiration center which inhibit its action for the moment; then, when the inspiration center ceases to be stimulated and the expiration center becomes activated, it in turn suppresses the first, and so on. In addition, there is a higher level of involuntary control situated in the hypothalamus and a voluntary center in the cerebral cortex. It is believed that the cerebrum functions by bringing its influence to bear upon the respiratory area in the hypothalamus and that this exerts the actual control by suppressing or stimulating the medullary centers.

Regulatory Stimuli. The normal stim-

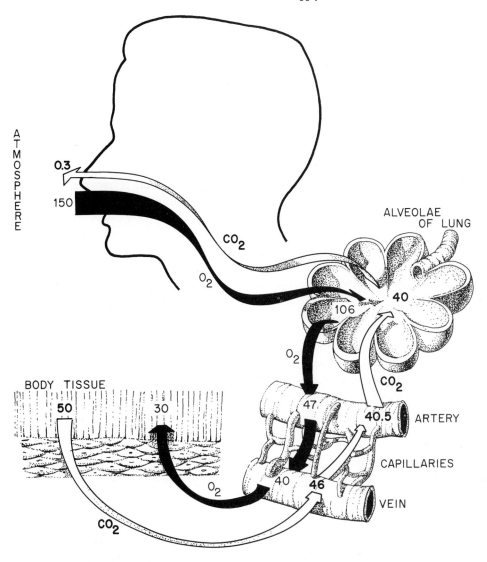

Figure 16–11. Gas exchange in the lungs and body. The direction of flow of both oxygen and carbon dioxide follows the path of their successively lowered partial pressures.

uli that activate the respiratory centers of the medulla are of two chief types—namely, chemical and mechanical. Among the *chemical* changes either known or conjectured to serve as stimuli are the levels in the blood of carbon dioxide and acidity changes of the blood plasma, in part correlated to the CO_2 level. Principally, it is the carbon dioxide that displays the greater influence on the central nervous system. Elevated concentrations of the compound stimulate the respiratory centers and thus have an accelerating effect on the rate of respiration, and the reverse is equally true. During sleep, however, the hypothalamus acts to inhibit the medullary centers, and, in spite of a rise in the CO_2 level in the blood, the respiratory rate remains retarded.

In regard to the *mechanical* stimuli that may be present, several have been postulated but none is universally accepted as actually existing. The most popular one suggests that there are stretch receptors embedded upon the wall of the alveoli, which inhibit inspiration and expiration, respectively, when the alveoli are distended or collapsed. These receptors form a sort of neural feedback mechanism, in which the vagus nerve serves to transmit the impulses to the medullary centers. Under this concept, the inspiration center initiates and continues both the raising of the ribs and the contraction of the diaphragm until impulses sent out by the stretch receptors indicate that the lungs are filled. Then inspiration is halted and expiratory actions are commenced which proceed until a second set of receptors indicates that the lungs are emptied. However, much evidence regiments against the acceptability of the hypothesis. For instance, in a mammal in which the brain has been completely removed above the level of the medullary respiratory centers respiration proceeds normally even after the vagus has been severed.

The Circulatory System

In animals of the size and complexity of vertebrates the internal cells are of necessity out of direct contact with the environment. Their sole means of obtaining and releasing metabolic materials is the indirect one provided by the *circulatory system,* composed of a fluid carrier mechanism in the form of the blood and the organs needed to keep the fluid moving, such as the heart and vessels. But over the eons of time the blood stream has acquired other functions than carrying food, oxygen, and waste products to and from the cells. Its services in the control of the metabolic processes have already been described; furthermore, it has acquired the chief responsibility for bodily maintenance in guarding against the assaults of parasites and, among warm-blooded groups, in helping to regulate the body temperature.

THE BLOOD AND LYMPH

The blood and lymph consist of two main portions each, a fluid matrix and the formed elements, which include both whole cells and fragments. Since lymph is in reality only a modified form of blood, its essential features can be pointed out as the components of the blood stream proper are discussed.

The Nature of the Plasma. In the blood the fluid matrix is known as the *plasma,* the main constituent of which is water. As the amount of this material is directly correlated to the total volume of blood in the organism, its level must be carefully controlled; hence the intake is counterbalanced by excretion of excess through the skin, lungs, and kidneys. In this aqueous part are dissolved or suspended inorganic salts and a large variety of organic compounds. Some of the compounds, such as the plasma proteins, are more or less constant in concentration and are essentially constituents of the plasma itself. On the other hand, the quantities of foodstuffs, waste products, and hormonal secretions fluctuate widely during the day in accordance with the activities of the individual and therefore may be looked on as materials being carried; that is to say, these ingredients represent work being done, not the tissue carrying it out.

The Formed Elements. Contained in the fluid matrix are three principal types of formed elements: red blood cells (erythrocytes), white blood cells (leucocytes), and platelets (thrombocytes), as already briefly outlined in Chapter 9. Of the three varieties the *erythrocyte* is by far the most numerous and most important in the transport of the respiratory gases. Except among the mammals, these cells in vertebrates are nucleated and ovate but vary in size considerably from group to group. Only in the mammals are they circular in outline and with an impression centrally, so as to be more or less doughnut-shaped (Figure 16–12). In this class, too, the nucleus is removed from each cell before it is deposited in the blood stream. The functional basis for the denucleation is not clear, for it can scarcely be stated that the gas-carrying efficiency of mammalian red blood cells is greater than that of birds. Besides the important and well-known pigment *hemoglobin,* all erythrocytes contain various inorganic ions.

The *leucocytes* are a highly diversified type of blood cell, showing two principal variations, each of which is represented by several subtypes. One of the chief subdivisions is known as the *granulocytes*

on the basis of the existence of numerous granules in the cytoplasm of its members. In addition to this trait, the class is marked by the apparent subdivision of the nucleus into segments, the number of segments being correlated both to the subtype and the age of the individual cells. Although each cell starts life with a nucleus of normal shape, before it enters the blood this organelle has become ribbon-shaped or, more frequently, divided into two segments or lobes. As the cell increases in age, the number of lobes enlarges, as a rule to five, but very old members of one subtype (the neutrophils) may have as many as seven. Classification into subtypes is based on the chemical nature of the granules as shown by their reaction to standardized staining techniques; the usual stains employed for the purpose are essentially mixtures of two dyes, a pink one, *eosin,* and a blue one, known as *hematoxylin.* By these means three subtypes are distinguished on the traits illustrated in Figure 16–12.

In the second main subdivision of

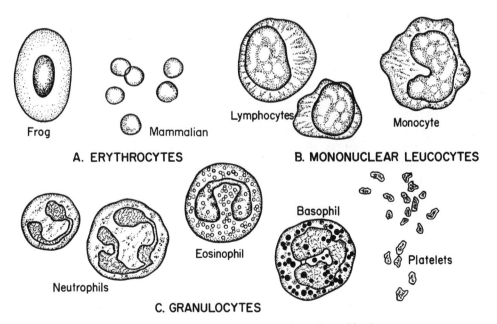

A. ERYTHROCYTES

Frog   Mammalian

Lymphocytes   Monocyte

B. MONONUCLEAR LEUCOCYTES

Neutrophils   Eosinophil   Basophil   Platelets

C. GRANULOCYTES

Figure 16–12. The formed elements of vertebrate blood.

leucocytes, the *mononuclear* class, granules of a neutral nature may or may not be present in the cytoplasm but the nucleus is never multisegmented. Its two subtypes are distinguished largely on size and on the characters of the nucleus and cytoplasm (Figure 16–12).

As they actually occur in the blood, the final type of formed elements, the blood *platelets* or *thrombocytes,* are not cells but only cytoplasmic fragments of certain blood-forming cells containing neutral granules. These bodies are scattered, individually or in clumps, throughout the blood, and are active in the formation of clots.

The Lymph. Probably the chief distinction between blood and lymph is the absence of red blood cells from the latter, for this circulating material is really only a collection of the fluid matrix and white blood cells that seep from the blood into the body tissues. Hence it is identical with the so-called *tissue fluid* that bathes all the internal cells of the organism. Aside from minor deviations in relative concentrations of several components, a second important difference is found in the lower concentration of protein contained in lymph than in plasma (50 to 70 per cent of that in the plasma).

The Formation of Blood Cells. Under the general term *hemopoiesis* are included the processes of secreting all the various formed elements of the blood; these take place chiefly in the lymph nodes and marrow and to a smaller extent in the spleen and liver. The hemopoietically active marrow is located principally near the ends of long bone shafts, the tips of the ribs, and spongy portions of flat skeletal parts such as those in the skull, pelvic girdle, and sternum. In adult mammals *red-blood-cell formation* (erythropoiesis) is confined almost solely to those cells of the marrow called *reticular cells,* which undergo mitotic cell division constantly throughout life. Although many of the cellular products thus formed develop into other reticular cells, a certain portion undergoes processes of specialization, the early steps of which, accompanied by cell division, involve the formation of the oxygen-carrying pigment *hemoglobin*. Among the first steps in the synthesis of this protein is the accumulation of an iron compound called *ferritin* in the mitochondria of the young cells; after these organelles have been filled with this substance, they burst and release their contents into the cytoplasm, where four long peptide chains are coupled to the ferritin to form the actual hemoglobin (Figure 16–13). In newborn mammals the cells with their nuclei still intact are then capable of functioning and enter the blood stream as *normoblasts;* after a few days, however, newly

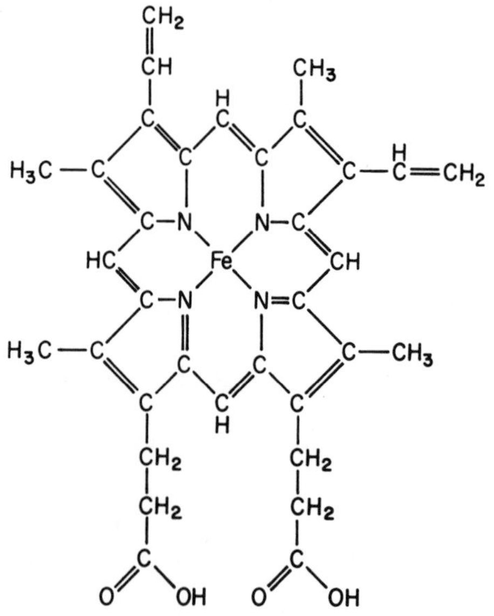

Heme

Figure 16–13. A distinctive constituent of hemoglobin. Heme is the iron-bearing unit of the hemoglobin molecule that is directly involved in the conduction of oxygen.

formed normoblasts before being placed into the blood are modified into erythrocytes by removal of the nucleus, except in certain types of disease. Once in the blood, the erythrocytes survive an average of 120 days.

As the *granulocytes,* and perhaps the *monocytes,* also are products of the bone-marrow reticular cells, they have their origin from the very same reticulocytes which produce the foregoing. During their formation, however, no ferritin is accumulated in the mitochondria, but the granules that characterize these varieties of leucocytes are deposited within their cytoplasm. On the other hand, the remaining variety of white blood cells, the *lymphocytes,* as their name implies are formed almost exclusively in the lymph nodes of the body but occasionally may be manufactured in the marrow. As far as the life-span of the leucocytes is concerned, there is little agreement among biologists; however, a generally accepted value is that of three to eight days. On the average, one variety of leucocyte, the lymphocytes, appears to remain within the blood stream for three or four days, then penetrates the walls of the capillaries and, after a period of activity in the body tissues, perishes and is digested there.

Regulation of Hemopoiesis. The production of blood cells by the hemopoietic tissues of the body must equal their normal rate of destruction; otherwise a deficiency or excess in the blood stream would soon result. Moreover, stress of various sorts, diseases of the blood cells, or loss of blood through wounds create emergencies that require a compensatory change in the production rate to meet the new needs. Since red blood cells are concerned especially with the transport of oxygen, it might be anticipated that control over their synthesis be tied to the total oxygen-carrying power of the blood stream, and such has proven to be the

actual case. Oxygen deficits from any source, including the low atmospheric partial pressures that exist at high altitudes, bring about an increment in erythropoiesis. When a person spends even a few days on a high mountain, an over-all increase in the number of red blood cells per unit volume of blood can be noted. Moreover, a lack of blood oxygen may result from an insufficiency of erythrocytes due to a poorer survival rate than usual on the part of the cells. In diseases in which the life-span of these formed elements may be reduced to a period as short as 20 days the speed of production is found to be greatly enhanced. Not only disease but the basal rate of the body heat production has a like effect, for an increase in body temperature is accompanied by a decrease in the life-span of the erythrocyte, with an increment in erythropoiesis to compensate.

Just as in the red blood cell, the lymphocyte has its life-span greatly shortened by elevated body temperatures, with comparable increases in production to compensate. Moreover, emotional stress, including that elicited by subject-matter studies on university students, and especially by the prospects of rigid examinations, can cause a heightened level of lymphopoiesis. In one segment of a student body confronted by an approaching examination in a difficult subject lymphocytes increased from a mean of 24 per cent under normal conditions to 52 per cent—more than double—under this stress. Attacks by bacteria also result in the outpouring of white blood cells; lymphocytes are typically produced in excess numbers in cases of injury and chronic infection, whereas neutrophil levels rise in acute infections, severe hemorrhages, and heavy exercise.

The Transport of Materials. Without doubt the earliest and probably still the chief activity of blood is that of transporting the materials involved in metabolism to and from the tissues. In the blood many such metabolic compounds, including glucose and lipids, require no especial treatment but merely dissolve in the plasma until employed by some organ of the body; however, in a number of other cases the material being carried is coupled chemically to a constituent of the blood. For an illustration of the processes involved, the well-studied reactions in oxygen transport may be utilized. As the student doubtlessly knows, this gas is united to the hemoglobin of the erythrocytes as it enters from the lungs; were it merely in solution in the plasma instead of being chemically united, a volume of plasma 75 times as great as now exists would be required to carry the same quantity of oxygen. Its mode of attachment to the hemoglobin is a finely adapted one, firm enough so that it freely enters the blood within the respiratory organs, and at the same time sufficiently loose that it readily detaches to enter tissues in which lower partial pressures exist. Nevertheless, the dissociation of oxygen from the erythrocyte's pigment is not unassisted, for the presence of carbon dioxide or the increased acidity resulting from carbon dioxide is required. Similarly, this latter gas is not in a state of simple solution in the blood but is carried chemically combined in three different states. First, it unites with water to form *carbonic acid*. Whereas a portion of the gas is transported in this form, the remainder either reacts with salts to produce *bicarbonates* ($^-HCO_3$) or unites with hemoglobin to form *carbamino hemoglobin* ($HHbCO_2$). As the blood passes through the capillaries of the lungs, the increase in partial pressure of the oxygen assists in the release of carbon dioxide into the alveoli just as this chemical aids in the freeing of oxygen within

the tissues. With Hb employed as an abbreviation for hemoglobin, the chief reaction in the lungs can be written as follows:

$$HHb + O_2 \rightarrow HHbO_2 \rightarrow {}^-HbO_2 + {}^+H$$
Reduced
hemoglobin

$$^+H + {}^-HCO_3 \rightarrow H_2CO_3 \xrightarrow{\text{carbonic anhydrase}}$$
$$H_2O + CO_2 \uparrow$$

As shown in the foregoing equations, the carbon dioxide end product is given off in the lungs; in tissues the equations are exactly reversed, with oxygen liberated as an end product.

The Formation of Blood Clots. During the life-span of any vertebrate it is inevitable, through accident or attack by a predator, that a wound should be experienced. Should the animal be fortunate enough to escape with its life, if it is to survive the bleeding of the injury must be halted before an excessive amount of blood has been lost. To this end, the processes of *clotting* have evolved. Although on the surface, the formation of a clot appears to be a simple matter, such is far from the case in actuality—no fewer than 15 different products and intermediates are currently recognized as essential, and the list is still not complete.

In fact, its incompleteness is shown at the onset of clotting, for the very first ingredient is still undiscovered—namely, one conjectured to be produced by the injured surface of the body. This supposed factor appears to have two effects, one that activates clotting and a second that elicits the production of pain. Since this effect is now attributed to peptone formation, it is postulated that the unknown factor initiates the breakdown of plasma proteins into a substance of this nature. As for the remaining factors, the account of clot formation that follows

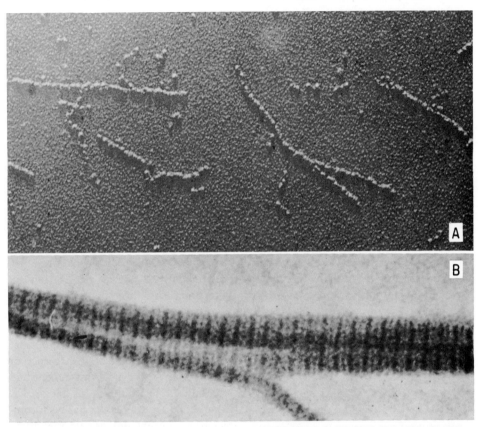

Figure 16–14. The structure of fibrin.   A. An intermediate stage in the production of fibrin is shown in this electronmicrograph to consist of end-to-end aggregates of fibrinogen molecules brought into combination by thrombin. Magnification 100,000×.   B. A single fibrin fibril, fully developed, is seen by electron microscopy to consist of alternating dark and light bands when stained with phosphotungstic acid. Magnified 180,000×. (Courtesy of Drs. Cecil E. Hall and H. S. Slayter, *Journ. Biophys. Biochem. Cytol.,* 5:11–16, Pl. 1, Figs. 2, 4, 1959.)

has been simplified by the omission of those substances of unascertained activities. Perhaps it will be more lucid if the end products, the only really visible evidence in the entire chain of reactions, are listed first.

The actual network that serves to block the bleeding consists of a complex protein called *fibrin,* composed of a series of molecules of a globulin named *fibrinogen* placed end to end (Figure 16–14). In circulating blood this substance is a constant ingredient of the plasma and is possibly secreted by the liver. The polymerization of fibrinogen to form fibrin is brought about only by the action of a third protein, named *thrombin.* Currently, thrombin is accepted as serving in an enzymatic capacity, possibly splitting off certain segments of fibrinogen and thus enabling polymerization to occur. Although its activities seem to be generally agreed upon, its origins certainly are not, aside from the fact that it arises from *prothrombin* secreted by the liver in the presence of vitamin K, which serves to catalyze the reaction.

Only a few steps and requirements of thrombin formation are sufficiently well established to be generally accepted. First of all, the requirement for *calcium chloride* is clear-cut, but since it is a normal constituent of the plasma, no problem arises in its connection. Formerly a second required substance was postulated to exist and was given the name "thromboplastin," a compound variously supposed to be secreted by the platelets, the injured tissue, or the brain. Now it is realized that this hypothetical material is not a single compound but a whole chain of interacting substances, and it is on its links that most investigations in the area are currently focused. In this intricate chain factors V, VII, VIII, and IX interact, together with calcium and the platelets and more than likely with three additional factors not yet identi-

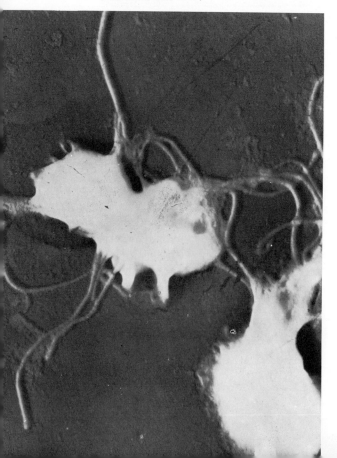

Figure 16–15. Blood platelets undergoing viscous metamorphosis. During clot formation, the platelets actively participate by undergoing great changes in their structure. (Reproduced by permission of Dr. R. G. Macfarlane and Academic Press, from *Functions of the Blood*, R. G. Macfarlane and A. H. T. Robb-Smith, eds., 1961.)

fied. However, no agreement has been reached regarding the manner in which these substances act. Nevertheless, a few details of the over-all picture have been established. For example, platelets at one time were suspected of playing a secretory role in clotting, usually that of forming the so-called thromboplastin. Now it is known that during the activation of prothrombin these formed elements increase in mass by swelling, become sticky, and form clumps; moreover, they discharge numerous granules and filaments (Figure 16–15), which activities together are termed "viscous metamorphosis." Unless platelets are present, clotting proceeds slowly or not at all. During investigation of "thromboplastin" formation, it was discovered that two types of hereditary diseases exist in which blood is unable to clot. *Hemophilia,* the more common, is the result of the absence of factor VIII; the second is infrequent and is produced by the lack of factor IX. Finally, shortly after a clot has been completed in normal individuals the quantity of thrombin in the blood stream decreases rapidly under the influence of an enzyme called *antithrombin,* which destroys it. Figure 16–16 depicts the whole of clot formation as presently known.

Protection Against Injuries. During the normal course of living the vertebrate body may receive other types of injuries than cuts or wounds; concussion against hard objects in the environment can produce bruises, and friction caused by rubbing against rocks or logs can result in burns. All of these injuries are accompanied by a set of reactions generally known as *inflammation* (Figure 16–17). Bruised and rubbed skin may also be broken, and bacteria or other microorganisms may penetrate into the underlying tissues. In response to the inflammation and invasion, the white blood

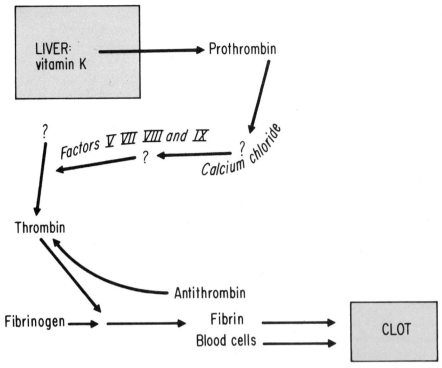

Figure 16–16. The processes known to be involved in clot formation.

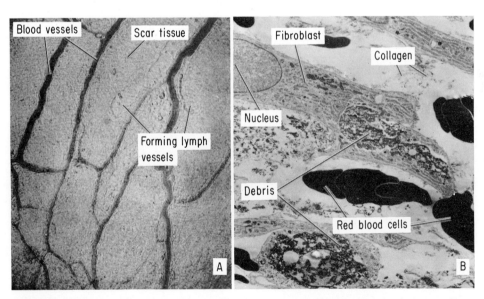

Figure 16–17. Scar tissue formation. Part of the healing processes of a wound involve formation of scar tissue. While many steps make up the whole, two principal ones, after bleeding has been stopped, include the invasion of the hemorrhaged area by new blood and lymph vessels (A). Magnified 100×. B. Later fibroblasts enter the area and begin the processes of secreting connective (scar) tissue, such as the collagen fibers in the upper right. Magnified 6,000×. (Courtesy of Dr. W. J. Cliff and the Royal Society of London, *Philos. Trans.*, Vol. B246, 1963.)

cells show two reactions. First, they exhibit *chemotaxis,* a reaction to the chemicals liberated by the injured area and by the invaders; since the cells migrate toward this chemical stimulus, their response is seen to be of a positive nature. At present, neutrophils, eosinophils, and monocytes, but not lymphocytes, are known to react in this manner. Movement toward the foreign substance is by pseudopod formation, the monocyte being much slower in locomotion than the granulocytes. Upon arrival at the locus of injury, all leucocytes engage in a second activity, namely *phagocytosis,* engulfing the invading organisms and bits of tissues by amoeboid processes. Although lymphocytes do not respond to chemicals, they are nevertheless phagocytic but confine their attentions to small organic particles scattered about the cells of the bodily tissues rather than to any invading organisms.

Antibody Formation. In addition to the phagocytosis of foreign objects by the formed elements, the blood carries out protective functions by means of the plasma. When any organism enters the blood stream, directly or indirectly, it yields proteinaceous compounds peculiar to the species, for as stated in Chapter 2, certain chemicals of this class are unique to each form of living thing. Such introduced foreign proteins are referred to as *antigens.* Upon being contacted by an antigen, many tissues of the body react by secreting a second protein, the *antibody,* which couples with the first and inactivates it, often by causing it to become an insoluble precipitate. Each antibody acts specifically on one kind of antigen, which in turn is derived from only one species of organism. The processes of producing any given antibody are, in a sense, "learned" by the cell, for antibody formation against any antigen not previously encountered by the organism proceeds at a slow rate at first. Hence, in an invasion of large numbers of an antigen-producing virus or bacterium, the body of the host is at a disadvantage during the early stages and can become diseased. During the course of the disease, however, it acquires the ability to form the proper antibody, and if it does so before death ensues, it is enabled to bring about the destruction of the pathogen. Once this particular antibody has been secreted, its formation is often a permanent acquisition, and subsequent invasions by the same species are quickly repelled. Thus the individual gains *immunity* against the various diseases. Already familiar to the student is the fact that immunities can be artificially produced by introducing either controlled amounts of the pathogen or dead organisms, or a serum containing antibodies into the tissues of an individual, whose cells thereby "learn" to produce the antibody themselves, sometimes permanently, sometimes only for a short period. Particularly against the proteins of the more complex forms of life, especially the pollen of seed plants, occasional persons are incapable of producing the corresponding antibody; and, as a consequence, the functioning of many tissues is thrown off balance. Such *allergies* may show up as rashes, swellings, "hay fever," asthma, or in other form. Although the fluid matrix of the blood is the most active portion in the transport of these antibodies, certain blood cells are concerned with their production. These cells are the *plasmocytes,* normally present in the blood solely during severe and chronic infections and then only in small quantities, for they chiefly remain in the hemopoietic tissues where they appear to be concerned exclusively with the secretion of antibodies. There is some evidence to indicate that both lymphocytes and monocytes may be converted into plasmocytes, but the facts have not been established.

Blood Groups. Although the existence of four different types of blood is common knowledge, the details of the processes involved in producing these variations may not be familiar. Basically, the blood groups stem from diverse inherited abilities to secrete two different antigens, *A* and *B*, and corresponding antibodies, *anti-A* and *anti-B*. *A* and *B* are carried upon the surfaces of red blood cells, whereas the *anti-A* and *anti-B,* as with most antibodies, are found in the plasma. How the four groups result from the differing combinations of these factors may be seen by examining Table 16–3. From the table can also be garnered the fact that on intermixing the blood of any two different types, as in blood transfusions, a reaction between an antigen and an antibody results in a clumping of the blood cells, blockage of the vessels, and death. Hence only bloods of like groups are compatible. Although those listed are given as they occur in human beings, similar ones are known to exist in many other species of mammals and birds.

In addition to the letter of the human group, usually designations of blood groups include symbols representing *positive* or *negative*. This symbolism pertains to the *Rh* (rhesus) blood groups, of which a large number are known. Although many factors have been discovered, only three, *C, D,* and *E,* are usually considered, typically treated together as one under the name *Rho*. *Rho* is active in two ways in human relations—in blood transfusions and parenthood—and knowledge of the groups to which each party belongs is of vital importance to those contemplating marriage. In cases of transfusion the receipt of blood from a negative donor by a positive recipient, for example, induces the cells of the recipient to form antibodies; however, these have no, or only a mild, effect in the first transfusion, for by the time an ability to secrete them in quantities has been acquired most of the introduced cells will have died. If a second similar transfusion is received, however, the antibodies of the recipient cause an immediate clumping of the blood cells, with death as a consequence. Likewise, the marriage between a male who is positive for *Rho* and a female who is negative carries a certain degree of danger unless proper care is exercised preceding conception. Ordinarily, the first pregnancy is normal, as is the child at and following birth. Nevertheless, because the *Rho* positive type of blood may be produced in a child from matings between positive and negative persons, while it is being carried in the mother's body, its presence initiates the formation of antibodies in the mother's blood stream. Hence, if a second pregnancy is commenced before these antibodies have had opportunity to disappear, death of the fetus may result either from the failure of blood cells to form or from their clumping and blocking the vessels if they actually do develop. Usually a period of two years is sufficient for the antibodies to disappear, but because of individual variation, their absence from the wife's blood should be definitely established by a competent physician before a second child is contemplated. With due exercise of these precautionary measures, no risk exists

TABLE 16–3

BLOOD GROUPS AND FACTORS IN THEIR
PRODUCTION

Blood Group	Red-Blood-Cell Antigens	Plasma Antibodies
O	none	anti-A and anti-B
A	A	anti-B
B	B	anti-A
AB	A and B	none

TABLE 16–4
THE BEHAVIOR OF THE Rh_0 FACTOR

Father	Mother	Child	Reaction
Rh_0+	Rh_0+	Rh_0+	None, as the child is like the mother
Rh_0+	Rh_0-	Rh_0+	First child sets up antibody formation; second one can be killed by the reaction
Rh_0-	Rh_0-	Rh_0-	None, as the child is like the mother
Rh_0-	Rh_0+	Rh_0+	None, as the child is like the mother

in marriage between mixed types. Nor is there any danger if the male is Rh_0 negative and the female Rh_0 positive, for the baby's blood, being positive like the mother's, will not set up antibody formation (Table 16–4).

THE CIRCULATORY ORGANS

In brief, the organs of the circulatory system of the vertebrates may be summarized as consisting of vessels through which blood flows and a pumping organ in the form of the heart, along with the spleen and other glands. Although the external relations of the system are largely borne by the circulating blood, that tissue is internally dependent on these organs for its own activities.

The Arteries and Veins. While *arteries* are, first of all, distinguished from veins in conducting blood away from the heart instead of toward it, further distinctions are found in the construction of the walls. In arteries three layers of tissue (*tunics*) occur in the walls, each provided with elastic connective tissue. In addition to this material, the innermost of the three includes an endothelial lining, whereas the middle one is made almost entirely

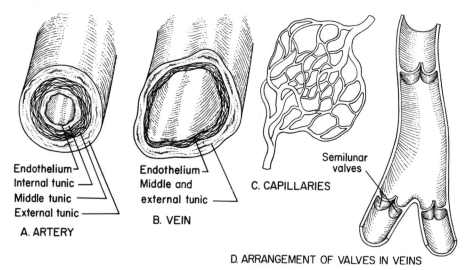

Endothelium
Internal tunic
Middle tunic
External tunic

A. ARTERY

Endothelium
Middle and
external tunic

B. VEIN

C. CAPILLARIES

Semilunar valves

D. ARRANGEMENT OF VALVES IN VEINS

Figure 16–18. The structure of blood vessels. *A, B.* Whereas arteries have three distinct layers (tunics) in their walls (*A*), the bulk of the venal wall (*B*) consists of the outer tunic to which the middle one is fused. *C.* Capillaries consist solely of the endothelial layer, or intima. *D.* In veins of legs and arms, semilunar valves, typically placed before and after the confluence of branches, assist in preventing backflow.

of smooth muscle fibers arranged to encircle the walls. The outer tunic is also composed principally of muscle, but the fibers are placed lengthwise (Figure 16–18). Physiologically, these thick but elastic walls are highly significant, for when blood is forced into the arteries by the beating of the heart the vessels are greatly distended. Upon being dilated, the circular muscles in the middle tunic contract and, since backflow is prevented by valves in the heart, force the blood along the length of the vessels. By the ensuing waves of contraction much of the movement of the blood is accounted for. Moreover, the muscles of the walls also regulate the quantity of blood supplied to a given region by varying the diameter of the arteries.

Although veins also have three tunics in their walls, they differ from arteries in that the circular muscle in the middle tunic is greatly diminished, so that the external tunic makes up the bulk of the walls. In addition, among birds and mammals with long appendages, the in-ner tunic is folded in the form of crescentic pockets, arranged in groups of threes. These *semilunar valves,* as they are called, are important in preventing backflow of the blood in the veins and are generally located in tributaries just below the point at which entry is made into larger vessels (Figure 16–18).

The Capillaries. By far the most abundant of the blood vessels are the *capillaries,* for approximately 2,000 of them are present in each cubic millimeter of human muscle alone. In fact, someone has estimated that were all the capillaries of the human body placed end to end they would form a line encircling the globe six times at its greatest circumference. Contrasting to those of other vessels, the walls of this type are extremely thin and consist solely of the endothelium. In diameter, too, the capillaries are very fine, averaging close to 0.009 millimeter. As the diameters are small and the vessels numerous (Figure 16–19), blood courses more slowly through the beds of capillaries than

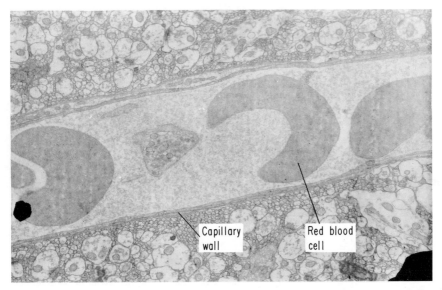

Capillary wall

Red blood cell

Figure 16–19. Blood cells passing through a capillary. The diameter of a capillary is so small that the red blood cells in many cases must become folded to pass through the vessels. Magnified 5,100×. (Courtesy of Drs. K. A. Siegesmund, C. A. Fox, and S. K. Dutta.)

elsewhere; so, with the delicate walls, these structures are well adapted for their functions. By the combination of these factors, white blood cells can readily enter the tissues by penetrating the vessels' walls between their cells, and the various gases are able to flow in directions according to their respective partial pressures. Many of the plasma constituents also enter and leave by these same routes.

The Lymphatic Vessels.   Since the lymph flows solely from the tissues toward the heart, no arteries are represented in the lymphatic system, only capillaries and veins. *Lymph capillaries* are somewhat larger and less uniform in diameter than those that carry blood; at their closed ends are small saclike knobs which assist in collecting the lymph from the tissues (Figure 16–20). Networks of the capillaries combine to form larger *lymph vessels,* the walls of which are not unlike those of veins, except that still fewer muscular elements

are evident. In the larger vessels, especially those that run vertically, are series of *semilunar valves,* differing from the corresponding structures of the veins in their arrangement as pairs rather than triplets. Along the course of the vessels are found *lymph nodes* (Figure 16–20), which are active in secreting lymphocytes and in phagocytosis; near the heart all vessels empty into the larger veins.

The Heart.   As shown by its condition in the lower chordates, the heart is really a highly modified blood vessel, for in the tunicates, lancelets, and other forms this pumping organ is little more than a pulsating artery. Even in the cyclostomes and fishes its tubular construction is still evident, although in these groups it is subdivided into a number of compartments (Figure 16–21). In all primitive vertebrates only two of the four subdivisions present, the *atrium* and *ventricle,* are considered to be true *chambers;* the other two, the *sinus venosus* and *truncus arteriosus,* are classified as accessory

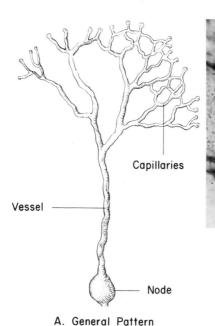

Capillaries

Vessel

B. Section through a valve

Node

A. General Pattern

Figure 16–20. Lymph vessels.   A. Because lymph vessels conduct lymph only toward the heart, the collecting capillaries are closed at one end.   **B.** Semilunar valves, resembling those of veins, assist in preventing backflow of the vessels' contents. (B, courtesy of the General Biological Supply House, Inc., Chicago.)

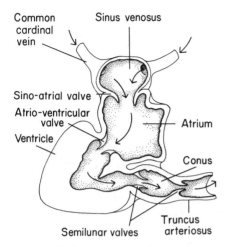

Figure 16–21. **Hearts of some lower vertebrates.** Fish of all kinds, except lungfish, have only two pumping chambers (A). Amphibians, as well as lungfish, have added a second atrium which helps to keep oxygenated blood received from the lungs separated from the deoxygenated blood returned from the body.

chambers. In higher forms the accessory parts disappear, for the sinus venosus becomes incorporated into the atrium and the truncus into the ventricle. As the vertebrates undergo adaptation for a terrestrial mode of life, the two-chambered condition of the fish is modified to three chambers in the amphibians

by the subdivision of the atrium into right and left components. Here the former of these receives blood from the body, whereas the latter receives that from the lungs; however, both empty their contents into the single ventricle, whence it circulates to the entire body, including the lungs. With still further advancement in the reptiles, the ventricle also becomes subdivided into separate right and left components; while in the lower reptilians the subdivision is only a partial one, the chamber is completely partitioned in the crocodilians as well as in both the birds and mammals. With the establishment of four separate chambers, the oxygenated blood coming from the lungs is entirely prevented from mixing with the deoxygenated material arriving from the rest of the body, thus increasing the efficiency of the blood stream extensively.

Among all vertebrates except the mammals the openings between the atria and the ventricles are closed by muscular valves; in the mammals, except the egg-laying varieties, these straps are replaced by membranous folds. Since, in man, the membranous valve on the right half of

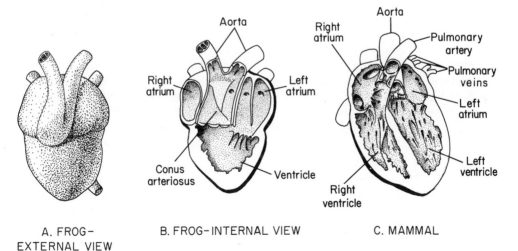

A. FROG–EXTERNAL VIEW

B. FROG–INTERNAL VIEW

C. MAMMAL

Figure 16–22. **Structure of the mammalian heart.**

the heart has three projections, it is known as the *tricuspid valve,* while that on the left half is the *bicuspid* for a similar reason (Figure 16–22). To these projections extend numerous fine *tendinous cords* often attached to the wall of the interior by muscular processes called *papillae.* When the ventricles contract, such great pressures are exerted on the valves by the blood that they would turn inside out, as it were, if these cords did not support them and assist in maintaining their position. To prevent the backflow of the blood into the ventricles after it has been pumped into the main arteries, a single set of three *semilunar valves* guards the entrance of both the aorta and the pulmonary artery. On the outer walls of the heart is a series of blood vessels, which supplies the wall with nourishment and oxygen; the *coronary arteries,* as the arterial set of these organs is called, open into the aorta just above the semilunar valves. Blood clots or other occlusions blocking these entrances are a frequent source of heart disease, for the wall of the heart is highly active metabolically and cannot function without a liberal supply of the necessary substances.

Even when completely removed from the body, as long as it is supplied with the necessities of life, the heart continues to beat, its contractions (but not rate) being entirely independent of the nervous and endocrine systems. Contractions of all parts of the heart do not occur simultaneously but in a rhythmic fashion. By means of slow motion pictures, a wave of contraction can be seen to pass obliquely over the heart, beginning with the right atrium, followed in turn by the left atrium and right ventricle, and finally the left ventricle. As a result, blood is squeezed from one compartment into another and into the arteries. This wave is coordinated by means of the *pace-maker,* a bundle of modified muscle cells lying in the sinus venosus, or in the right atrial wall when the former compartment is absent. When a change in pumping rate is required in intact animals, nerves bring impulses to the pacemaker from a center in the brain.

Regulation of the Heart. Ordinarily, the heart beats at a rate between 60 and 64 times per minute in healthy men when at rest, but the range of variability lies between rates as low as 40 and as high as 110. In women the rate averages seven to eight beats a minute faster. Depending on the activities of the individual during the course of the day, the heart beat may vary widely from somewhat below normal to a maximum near 200 under strenuous exercise. Even when operating at its maximum rate, the heart does not beat continuously. Although each contraction (*systole*) is followed immediately by relaxation (*diastole*), before the next systole occurs there is a brief recovery or *refractory period* in which no activity occurs.

Two sets of nerves of opposing function lead to the heart and influence its beat. One, the *vagus,* retards cardiac actions by secreting acetylcholine from its axon endings. Largely this nerve supply involves reflexes; for example, on the carotid, the large artery supplying the head, is an enlargement called the *carotid sinus,* the walls of which contain a number of nerve fibers leading to the medulla of the brain. When an increase of pressure occurs in the sinus, impulses are sent to the medulla where they are relayed to the terminals of the vagus in the pacemaker, releasing acetylcholine and thereby depressing the heart beat rate. Secondarily, this retardation then lowers the general blood pressure, including that within the carotid sinus, and removes the stimulus that initiated this chain of activities.

On the other hand, the second set of neural connections to the heart, in the form of *sympathetic fibers,* has a stimu-latory action, eliciting an acceleration of beat and a shortening of the refractory period. Largely sympathetic effects are

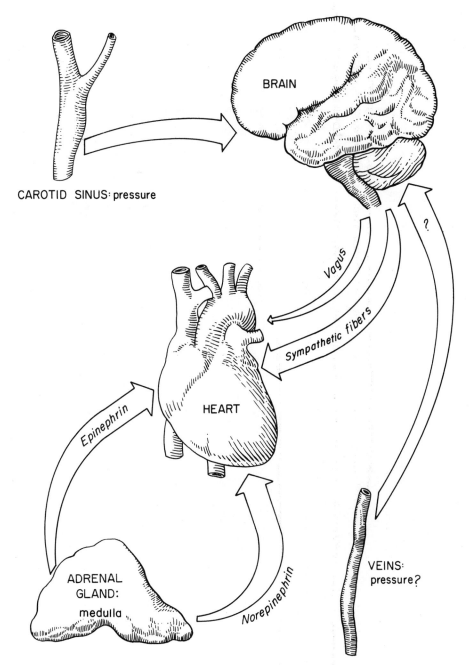

CAROTID SINUS: pressure

BRAIN

Vagus

Sympathetic fibers

HEART

Epinephrin

?

VEINS: pressure?

ADRENAL GLAND:

medulla

Norepinephrin

Figure 16–23. Regulation of heart activity. The rate of heart beat is controlled by both nervous and hormonal mechanisms. Whether changes in distention of veins plays a role in neural control is still unde-termined. Expanding arrows suggest a stimulatory activity, contracting ones an inhibitory effect.

produced by the secretion of sympathin. That sympathetic reflex controls which increase heart beat during exercise probably exist is generally accepted; however, no universal assent exists in regard to the mechanisms involved. In one theory it is suggested that increment of pressure in the veins induced by exercise initiates impulses that ultimately produce sympathetic activation of the heart, but evidence supporting the concept is relatively meager. Moreover, much control over heart rate is mediated by the adrenal medulla, for both its hormones have an action counteracting that of the vagus. Although epinephrin

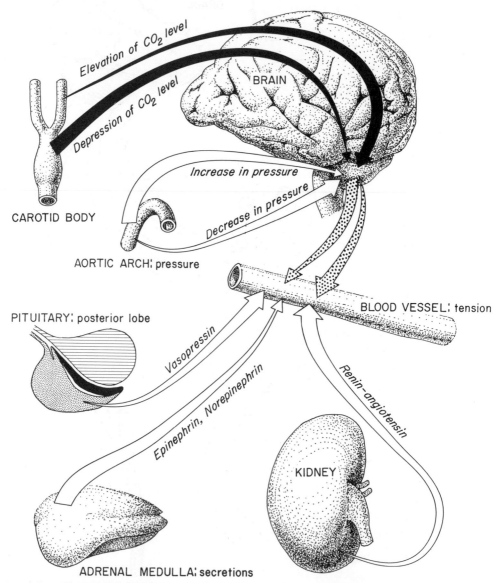

Figure 16–24. Regulation of blood pressure. Both the pressure on arterial walls and the CO_2 level of the blood arouse neural control mechanisms, while secretions of the adrenal medulla, the hypothalamus (via the posterior pituitary), and the kidneys act directly upon the arterial walls.

is the more potent, it is used only in emergencies, whereas norepinephrin appears to serve in more normal situations (Figure 16–23).

Control of the Vessels. As in the heart, the muscles of the arteries are under the control to a large extent of two opposing sets of nerves. One set, entirely of sympathetic fibers, induces constriction of the blood vessels and its members hence are named *vasoconstrictors*. On the other hand, the *vasodilators* are a curious mixture of sympathetic, parasympathetic, and somatic elements. Both groups are regulated by a vasomotor center in the medulla, consisting of closely adjacent *pressor* and *depressor* units not unlike those of the respiratory center in their basic nature. As their names imply, these areas are responsible, respectively, for vasoconstriction and vasodilation. Their activities are modified in accordance with impulses received from the vessels themselves, in addition to those from the carotid sinus, the organs of the body, and the cerebral cortex and hypothalamus. Among the chief receptors for vasodilating stimuli are a number located in the wall of the aortic arch and the principal arteries of the head and arm. Increases of pressure within the vessels are detected by these receptors, and impulses from them instigate a series of activities that result in the slowing of the heart and a relaxation of the arterial walls so that normal pressure is once more restored. Similar *depressor receptors* appear to be located within the tissues of the various body parts and effect a decrease in tension in local arteries by reflex mechanisms. In a like manner there are *pressor receptors* which have the opposite action, for they initiate an increase of pressure in the vessels either on a local or general body basis, depending upon the size and location of the artery in which they are embedded (Figure 16–24).

In addition to these receptors, which are stimulated by the mechanical tension on the walls of the blood vessels, there are several sets that are responsive to changes in carbon dioxide and oxygen partial pressures. A rise in the carbon dioxide level or a fall in that of oxygen increases the rate at which these receptor organs send impulses to the medulla, whereas the reverse retards their activities. Principally, these receptors appear to lie in bodies adjacent to the aorta and carotids; increases in their rate of impulse transmission to the brain induce both an increment of heart beat and a constriction of the arteries.

Questions for Review and Thought

1. Outline the mechanisms that are involved in the control of all aspects of the alimentary tract, including procurement of food.
2. Define the following terms:

   (a) satiety center
   (b) egestion
   (c) bolus
   (d) appetite
   (e) hunger
   (f) chyme
   (g) proenzyme
   (h) feces
   (i) cloaca

3. As far as possible, make a chart of all the structures contained in the digestive tract of vertebrates, indicating their presence or absence and the chief modifications in the various classes.

4. List the *active* digestive enzymes of each principal subdivision of the digestive tract, indicating the substrate and end products in each case as far as is feasible.

5. Compare the accessory respiratory organs of a fish with those of a mammal. How are respiratory activities controlled?

6. Explain why it is more efficient in gills to have the surface blood flow in a direction opposite to that of the water.

7. What is a partial pressure of a gas and how is it usually calculated in respiratory problems? Using the chart, state the direction of flow for each of the four chief gases of the atmosphere. Explain your results as thoroughly as you can.

8. List the various types of blood cells and the chief functions of each. On what basis are the three granulocytes differentiated? In what ways do monocytes resemble lymphocytes and how do they differ?

9. Name some factors that effect a change in rate of hemopoiesis.

10. Briefly outline the methods and blood constituents employed in the transport of oxygen, carbon dioxide, salts, and water.

11. Outline the essential steps involved in the formation of blood clots. Why is it essential that an antithrombin be present in the blood?

12. By what methods does the blood defend the body against invasion by microorganisms? What are antibodies and antigens? List the various blood groups of human beings. Of what importance is a knowledge of the Rh_0 factor?

13. Describe the beating of the heart and the mechanisms of its control.

Supplementary References

Andresen, P. H. *The Human Blood Groups*. Springfield, Ill., C. C. Thomas, 1952.

Anthony, C. P. *Textbook of Anatomy and Physiology*, 6th ed. St. Louis, Mosby, 1963.

Burnet, M. "The Mechanism of Immunity." *Sci. Amer.,* January 1961.

Easton, D. M. *Mechanisms of Body Functions*. Englewood Cliffs, N. J., Prentice-Hall, 1963.

Eaton, T. H. *Comparative Anatomy of the Vertebrates,* 2nd ed. New York, Harper, 1960.

Fenn, W. O. "Mechanism of Breathing." *Sci. Amer.,* January 1960.

Laki, K. "The Clotting of Fibrinogen." *Sci. Amer.,* March 1962.

Short, A. R. *Synopsis of Physiology*. Baltimore, Williams & Wilkins, 1961.

Weichert, C. K. *Anatomy of the Chordates,* 2nd ed. New York, McGraw-Hill, 1961.

Wiggers, C. J. "The Heart." *Sci. Amer.,* May 1957.

Wilson, T. H. *Intestinal Absorption*. Philadelphia, Saunders, 1962.

Wood, W. B. "White Blood Cells vs. Bacteria." *Sci. Amer.,* February 1951.

Youmans, W. B. *Human Physiology*. New York, Macmillan, 1954.

The Elimination
of Metabolic
Wastes

SINCE the end products of destructive metabolism are so diversified, ranging from such innocuous compounds as water to ones so highly toxic as ammonia, each type must be treated by the body in a different manner to ensure the maximum conservation of desirable compounds and the most rapid elimination possible of those that are poisonous and otherwise objectionable. In the processes of eliminating excess and undesirable substances, many organ systems are concerned, some of which, like the respiratory tract, have already been discussed, but two other systems that participate in these activities still remain to be described. One of these, the integumentary, plays many other roles in the vertebrate in addition to that of present concern, but a second, the urinary, is confined solely to the function of *excretion*—that is to say, the elimination of the end products of catabolism.

The Integument and
Its Activities

As indicated above, the *integumentary system,* including the skin and its derivatives, engages in many activities aside from excretion, for, lying as it does between the remaining parts of the organism and the environment, it serves both as a buffer against the surroundings and as a provision for contact with it. Thus the skin must be highly selective to permit the ready egress of certain substances into the environment and to resist the entrance and exit of others, depending on the needs of the body and the conditions of the surroundings. In hot climates, for example, excess body heat must be lost, whereas in cold ones, as much as possible needs to be conserved. To meet the fluctuating demands made on it, the integument has become developed to a much greater extent than is

361

readily perceived on superficial examination, as will be seen as its structure is studied.

THE MORPHOLOGY OF
THE INTEGUMENT

In general, the integument consists of two major subdivisions, an external layer largely of epithelial tissue, called the epidermis, and a deeper portion composed of connective tissues, known as the dermis. Within the latter, blood vessels, nerves, and other associated structures are embedded, whereas on the surface of the epidermis are a number of products derived from the skin itself, including nails, claws, hair, feathers, and scales (Figure 17–1).

The Epidermis. Briefly, the *epidermis* is a stratified epithelium which covers the entire outer surface of all vertebrates. Although the epithelium is of the stratified squamous type in the terrestrial forms, the earlier aquatic groups usually lack the outer flattened cells. In the amphibians and higher classes the squamous cells of the surface contain deposits of the tough horny protein called keratin and form a *cornified layer* (Figure 17–2). As these cells die and their hardened contents wear out, they are flaked off, and replacements are continually made from below; thus there is a steady movement of cells, accompanied by changes in structure, from the innermost layer to those on the surface. Although the region immediately beneath

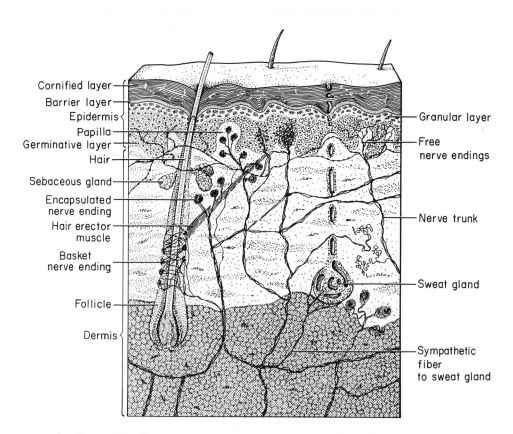

Figure 17–1. The structure and innervation of human skin. (After Woollard.)

Labels (left): Cornified layer, Barrier layer, Epidermis, Papilla, Germinative layer, Hair, Sebaceous gland, Encapsulated nerve ending, Hair erector muscle, Basket nerve ending, Follicle, Dermis

Labels (right): Granular layer, Free nerve endings, Nerve trunk, Sweat gland, Sympathetic fiber to sweat gland

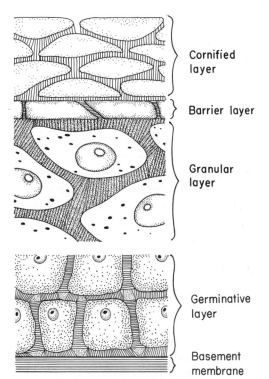

Cornified layer

Barrier layer

Granular layer

Germinative layer

Basement membrane

Figure 17-2. The principal layers of the epidermis.

the cornified stratum has for many years been known as the "transparent layer," since electron microscope studies have revealed its real nature its name has been altered to the *barrier layer*. These recent researches show that, before passing to the surface and undergoing cornification, the cells become more compact and closely united and hence appear to form a region that strongly resists the passage of materials either into or out of the body. Only when breaks in the skin are deep enough to rupture this layer are bacteria and foreign chemicals able to penetrate freely through the rest of the skin (Figure 17-2). In the region next below the barrier the cells contain cytoplasmic grains and become less and less flattened toward the interior. Finally, beneath this *granular layer* at the innermost portion of the epidermis, in part resting on the basement membrane, is a stratum that largely forms new cells to

replace those successively above its own; the cells of this layer range from columnar at the bottom through cuboidal to somewhat flattened forms at its top. Variously known as the *Malpighian* or *generative layer* (Figure 17-2), this is the only layer present in the several classes of fishlike organisms.

Though the cells of the cornified layer are denucleated, much in the same manner as the erythrocytes of mammals, they are not dead, although often described as being so. Recent investigations show that these cornified cells secrete several hormonal substances, one of which represses the mitotic activities of the generative layer. When the cornified layer is removed without injury to the cells beneath, mitotic activities in the Malpighian layer proceed at an accelerated pace.

The Dermis. The connective tissue portion of the integument, called the *dermis*, provides nourishment for the epidermal part and for the skin derivatives

Figure 17-3. Prickle cells. In the epidermis at the upper portion of the germinative layer, the electron microscope shows the cells to possess numerous cytoplasmic projections (intercellular bridges), so that they look quite prickly. The function of these projections is still unknown. Magnified 9,000×. (Courtesy of Drs. K. A. Siegesmund and C. A. Fox.)

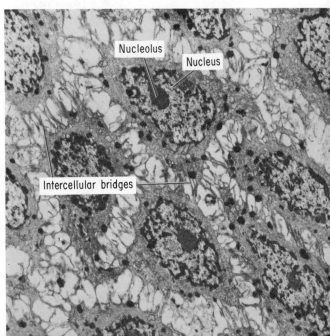

Nucleolus

Nucleus

Intercellular bridges

and seems also to serve in guiding the growth and differentiation of the outer constituents. Just below the epidermis is the first of two dermal divisions, a relatively thin *papillary layer,* composed of collagen and elastic fibers interspersed with a capillary network. The name of this portion is derived from the fact that its outer boundary meshes with the epidermis through a series of small projections or papillae, as well as by less prominent hills and valleys. However, the greater part of the dermis is contained within the boundaries of the *reticular layer,* which consists almost exclusively of collagen and elastic fibers. In both layers are found numerous blood vessels, nerves, smooth muscle fibers, and glands of the many sorts to be discussed shortly.

The Scales.   While the bodies of many vertebrates are covered with scales, these structures are far from being identical in all groups except in their common function of providing protection. Two major types are found, one derived from the dermis, the second from the epidermis. Of these two types, *dermal scales* are by far the more primitive, for they form the thick armor found on the oldest fossil fish. These first coverings were constructed of two varieties of bone overlaid with dentine, ending with a thin coat of enamel on the surface (Figure 17–4). From these very thick originals the thinner ones of present-day fishes have been derived through loss of some layers and modification of others. Several principal variations exist. Among the

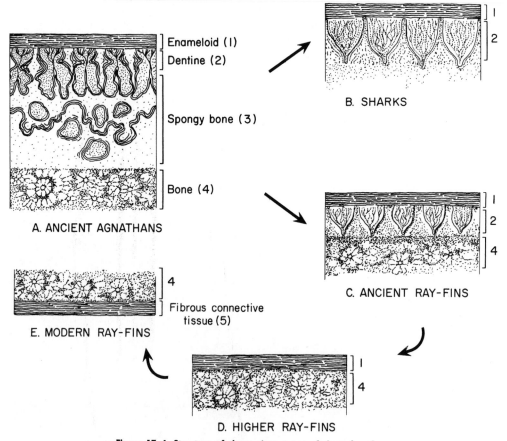

Enameloid (1)
Dentine (2)

Spongy bone (3)

Bone (4)

A. ANCIENT AGNATHANS

B. SHARKS

C. ANCIENT RAY-FINS

Fibrous connective tissue (5)

E. MODERN RAY-FINS

D. HIGHER RAY-FINS

Figure 17–4. Structure of the various types of dermal scales.

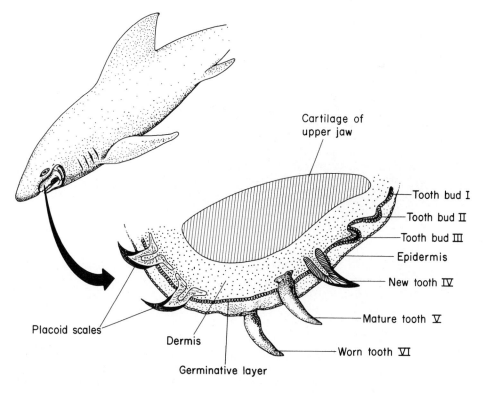

Cartilage of
upper jaw

Tooth bud I

Tooth bud II

Tooth bud III

Epidermis

New tooth IV

Mature tooth V

Worn tooth VI

Placoid scales

Dermis

Germinative layer

Figure 17–5. Development of sharks' teeth. Because of the similarities in structure and development, sharks' teeth are looked upon as having been derived from their dermal scales.

sharks and rays, *placoid scales* are the typical form and consist of a bony basal plate from which a dentine spine projects outward through the epidermis (Figure 17–4). Often this spine is erroneously described as being covered with enamel like that of our teeth, but recently it has been shown actually to consist of a hard modified dentine called "vitrodentine." Nevertheless, as the interior of the spine contains a pulp cavity ramified with blood vessels, the construction of these scales is quite similar to that of the higher vertebrates' teeth. Indeed, such an origin of our own dental equipment is suggested by the development of that of modern sharks (Figure 17–5). More advanced fish have thin plates made of very little bone and an equally thin layer of connective tissue (Figure 17–4). Two variants among teleosts are recognized, based on

shape and on the presence or absence of fine teeth. If rounded and unarmed the scales are classed as *cycloid*, whereas if they are scalloped and have one end covered with denticles, they are referred to as *ctenoid* (the initial letter of this term is silent; Figure 17–6).

Following the evolutionary loss of dermal scales in the ancestral stock, possibly as shown among the Amphibia of today, higher forms developed an entirely new type derived from the cornified layer of the epidermis. These *epidermal scales* are continuous with one another at their bases and in reality represent series of hardened folds in the outermost layer of skin (Figure 17–7). In addition to forming the scales of snakes, turtles, and lizards and the scutes of alligators, this type occurs on the legs of birds and often on the tails of mammals. As already indi-

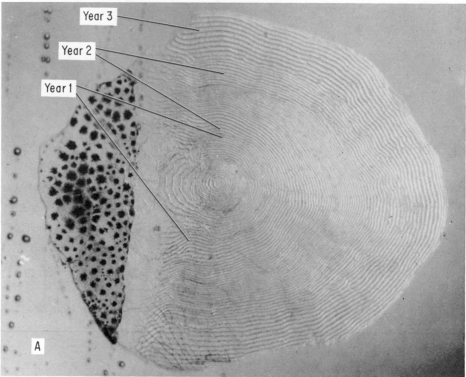

Figure 17–6. Dermal scales of ray-finned fish. A. The ridges of this cycloid scale from coho salmon (*Oncorhynchus kisutch*) are growth lines. Using them, experienced fish biologists can read much of the fish's life history; this one, for example, went to sea in its second year and returned to its home in the Lewis River, Washington, in its third year to spawn. At the base on the left can be seen a cluster of melanophores. (Courtesy of M. E. White, Pacific Power & Light Co.) B. A ctenoid scale. (Courtesy of General Biological Supply House, Inc., Chicago.)

cated, the scales develop first as folds of the entire skin. While the folds are deepening, the cornified layer increases in thickness, so that after folding and thickening have progressed to some extent a

series of flattened backward-pointing projections are formed (Figure 17–7). Following their formation, the germinative layer and dermis retract and the folds flatten to become scales, each continuous at its point of origin with the preceding one. In a manner not too unlike snake scales, the feathers of birds develop first as folds of the entire skin, and it is believed that these skin derivatives are highly modified adaptations of the old reptilian scale. Although the hair of mammals is believed to have had the

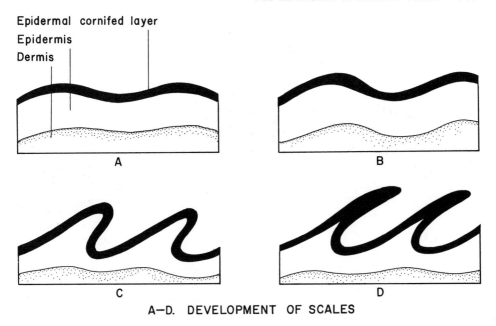

Epidermal cornifed layer
Epidermis
Dermis

A

B

C

D

A–D. DEVELOPMENT OF SCALES

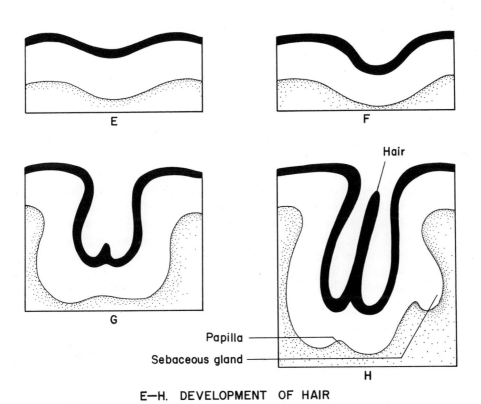

E

F

Hair

G

H

Papilla

Sebaceous gland

E–H. DEVELOPMENT OF HAIR

Figure 17–7. The development of scales and hairs.

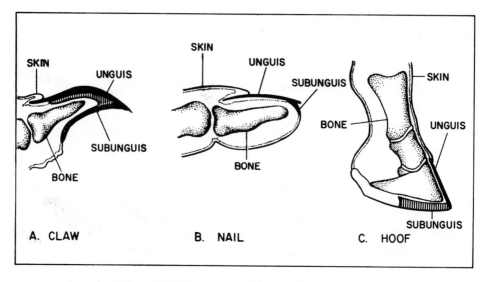

Figure 17–8. The structure of claws, nails, and hoofs.

same origin, it has become even more removed from the ancestral form and develops as a follicle embedded in the skin.

Both in construction and origin claws are not too unlike scales, and they, too, first put in an appearance among the reptiles. As a whole, they may be described as the products of the germinative layer and as being modifications of the transparent and cornified strata (Figure 17-8). The nails and hoofs of various mammals are in turn modified claws. All of these derivatives of the skin consist largely of *keratin,* the protein of the cornified layer. This protein, an albuminoid, is characterized by containing a large number of molecules of cystine, 15 to 20 per cent of human hair being comprised of that amino acid.

THE ACTIVITIES OF THE SKIN

The diverse activities of the skin in general fall into two classes, those in which it acts as a *barrier* and those in which it performs as an agent of *transfer*. Although the differences appear to be

sharply marked, in practice the distinctions are less readily detected, for there exists a large amount of overlap and complicating circumstances.

Secretory Activities. Many of the skin's transferring activities, including excretion, are carried out by glands. Since glands form their secretions in a number of ways, most of which are represented by those of the integument, the several types must first be described.

1. In *holocrine glands* the secretion is formed within the cells, where it accumulates. After a sufficient quantity has collected, the cells die and are discharged through the duct along with their contents. These processes are continued by constant replacement of new cells.

2. In *merocrine glands* the secretion also collects in the cells of the gland, but as it is periodically released by the rupturing of the cell membrane the individual cells, virtually uninjured in the process, remain functional for long periods.

3. *Apocrine glands* are intermediate between the two foregoing types, for the secretion involves the release of a portion of the cell and the maintenance of

single cells over long periods. In this type, when sufficient secretion has collected, a bit of the cytoplasm breaks off along with the product, the lost portion being subsequently replaced by anabolic metabolism.

4. The *eccrine glands* are closely similar to the apocrine but differ chiefly in that the cytoplasm is broken down before fragmentation occurs.

It is important here to differentiate between two similar activities of the organism—namely, secretion and excretion—for in the skin the distinctions are not clear-cut. As generally defined, the term *secretion* applies to those processes that form substances of further use to the organism, the product being completely distinct from the material supplied to the gland by the blood plasma. On the contrary, *excretion* involves the ridding of the body of substances either of no further use to it or present in excessive quantities. In excretory processes the products are not chemically changed but are eliminated in the same form in which they occur in the plasma. However, as shall be seen, excretion in the vertebrate skin involves secretory processes; hence the present definitions leave much to be desired. Clarity can be better attained if the term "secretion" is extended to include all the processes that result in an accumulation of materials in the cells of multicellular organisms, whether they are used by the cell itself or are released by it regardless of their value to the organism.

Among the numerous glands found in the mammalian integument are the *sebaceous glands* which occur over the entire body except in the soles of the feet and palms of the hands. As a whole, these glands are placed about 100 per square centimeter, with their ducts for the greater part connected to hair follicles; on the forehead, cheeks, and chin of man, however, on which 400 to 900 of these glands occur per square centimeter, most are not associated with hairs. Produced by holocrine methods, their secretion is oily, for it contains much cholesterol, fatty acids, and waxes and serves especially to maintain pliability in the skin. In addition, there is much evidence to support the point of view that the formation of the vitamins D by action of sunlight occurs in these glands.

Sweat glands are one of the most characteristic integumentary glands of mammals, although not all species possess them. Two principal types are found, *eccrine* and *apocrine* (Figure 17–9), the first of which is the more abundant in human beings and related primates, but in most other mammalians it is confined to the soles of the feet. On the average, man has more than 2 million of the eccrine variety scattered over the body, the glands being most numerous on the palms and soles where more than 400 per square centimeter are found. In contrast to the eccrine, which are functional from birth, the apocrine become active only with puberty and are closely associated with hair follicles. In relation to the eccrine variety in man they are few in number and are concentrated in the armpits, on and around the external reproductive parts, and on the nipples. Most mammals, particularly horses and swine, in which they are abundant, possess this type rather than the eccrine.

The products and methods of functioning are also quite distinct in the two sweat-gland types. Apocrine secretion is milky and viscid and contains large amounts of proteins, carbohydrates, iron, and ammonia; its flow is slow and scanty and is emitted largely in response to epinephrin production. Since apocrine sweat is rich in organic matter, bacteria frequently attack the deposit on the skin, and a distinct odor is the result. In the

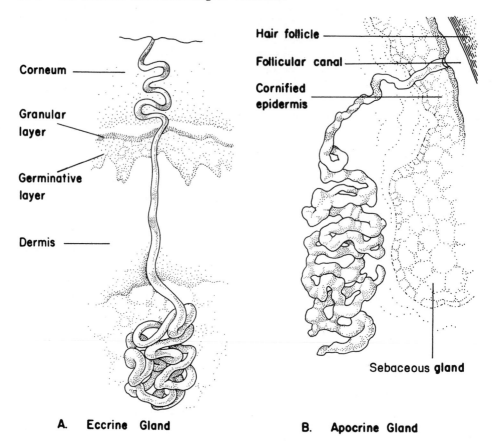

Corneum

Granular
layer

Germinative
layer

Dermis

Hair follicle

Follicular canal

Cornified
epidermis

Sebaceous gland

A.   Eccrine Gland   **B.   Apocrine Gland**

Figure 17–9. The two types of sweat glands.

eccrine variety some of the secretory activities also respond to emotional stress.
Particularly active under such conditions
are those on the soles of the feet and
palms, but for the greater part the eccrine glands respond to thermal stimuli
under neural control, with the chief center in the hypothalamus. Although varying greatly from region to region and
under the varying demands of thermal
regulation, eccrine sweat contains a large
proportion of water, in which sodium
and potassium salts and urea are dissolved. The concentration of the sodium
salts in the sweat is usually lower than
that of the blood plasma, whereas that
of the potassium is higher.

The Urinary System

Although other systems may serve to
eliminate wastes and hence are excretory to a degree, only the urinary system is capable of being regulated in response solely to the concentrations of
the excreted substances present within
the organism. For example, although the
skin and lungs excrete water, the rates
at which they give off the substance depend not on the quantity contained in
the interior of the body but on external
temperatures and humidity as well as on
body temperature. Furthermore, in the
long run, the urinary system eliminates
the largest portion of metabolic wastes

and therefore carries the principal burden of excretion.

THE MORPHOLOGY OF THE URINARY SYSTEM

Generally speaking, in all vertebrate groups this system consists of kidneys, a set of tubes leading into the urinary bladder, and either a cloaca or a tube which carries the contents of the bladder to the outside.

The Kidney. Among the several classes, the *kidneys* vary somewhat in location and in details of construction, but the essential features remain fairly constant. Basically, the organs consist of masses of fine tubules or *nephridia*, to each of which a knot of capillaries called the *glomerulus* is closely associated. In the cyclostome larva the nephridia open at one end directly into the body cavity, near which opening a glomerulus is located, and although the organs actually

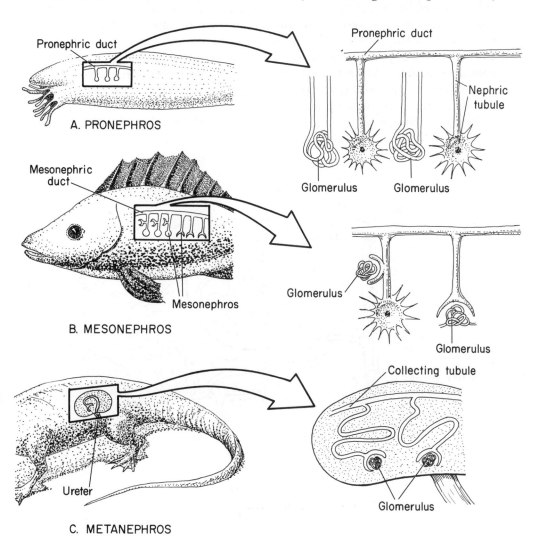

Figure 17–10. The types of kidneys found among vertebrates.

filter the fluid of the coelom, the blood stream is indirectly filtered simultaneously. As in these larvae the kidneys are located in the neck region, this type of renal structure is referred to as the *head kidney,* or *pronephros* (Figure 17–10). In most fishes and in amphibians this basic construction is improved somewhat by attachment of the glomerulus to the tubule, so that filtration of the blood is direct. In the anterior part of the *midkidney,* or *mesonephros,* as this modification is called because of its location behind the head kidney, connection with the coelomic cavity is still maintained; however, in the posterior portion the openings into the coelom are lost. In the reptiles and warm-blooded vertebrates the midkidney is replaced by the *hind kidney,* or *metanephros,* a structure in which only the blood stream is filtered, since no openings into the coelom are present (Figure 17–10). Usually, in mammals, the collecting tubules of this type of organ are highly coiled (convoluted) at both ends, whereas the middle portions are comparatively straight (Figure 17–11). Both the convoluted sections as well as the glomerulus are covered with a capillary network. Since all the tubules lie in the same direction, the interior of the kidney appears to consist of two regions, the *cortex,* containing the network of convolutions and blood vessels, and the *medulla,* which consists of the straighter portions and the larger *collecting tubules.* As their name implies, these tubules serve to collect the filtrate of the nephridia and to conduct it to the hollow neck, or *pelvis,* of the kidney. The

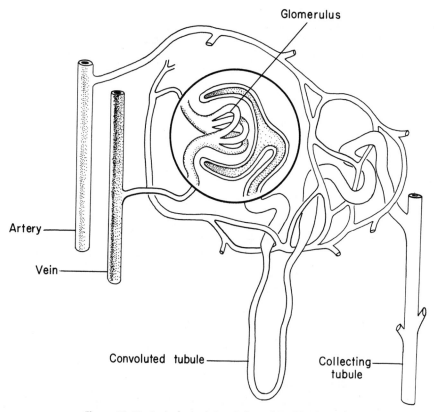

Figure 17–11. A single nephric tubule and its blood supply.

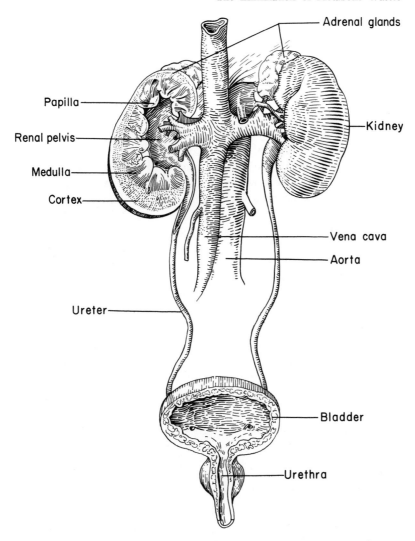

Figure 17–12. The human excretory system.

capillaries within the glomerulus do not connect an artery to a vein, as is usually the case, but recombine as a continuation of the original arteriole, from which the blood flows through a second network of capillaries surrounding the convolutions of the nephridia. Only after it passes through this network does it enter a venule.

The duct that carries the urine from the kidney also varies somewhat, depending on the type of excretory organ present. When head kidneys or midkidneys are present, tubes variously called the *pronephric* and *Wolffian ducts* serve in this capacity, whereas *ureters* accompany the hind kidneys. Although the storage organ, the *urinary bladder,* to which these tubes lead, varies considerably in location and construction, it is uniformly present in the terrestrial groups and constantly absent in lower forms. In the amphibia and modern reptiles it is attached to the cloaca, but in mammals a separate duct, the *urethra,* serves to conduct the waste products to the outside of the body (Figure 17–12).

THE FORMATION OF URINE

In the processes of urine formation, all of which occur in the kidneys, three distinct steps are involved. One of these, *filtration,* is confined to the region of the glomerulus, whereas the other two, *reabsorption* and *tubular secretion,* take place chiefly in the tubules.

Filtration. As the *efferent* arteriole, which leads from the capillary knot, is normally of slightly smaller bore than the *afferent,* which leads into it, considerable pressure is exerted upon the blood within the glomerulus. This pressure, it is believed, is an important factor in the *filtration* processes, for it discourages the return of the fluid and dissolved substances into the blood vessels and encourages its exit through the walls.

In the liquid thus obtained through the capillaries the materials and proportionate concentrations are virtually identical with those of the blood, except that formed elements and the complex proteins are uniformly absent. Among the contents, in addition to water, may be listed sodium and potassium salts, glucose, phosphate, creatinine, urea, amino acids, and a few peptides. In carrying out its functions the glomerulus is highly efficient, for filtration across its membranes occurs at a rate nearly 100 times greater than it does across an equal area of capillaries in muscles or other organs. Perhaps some of this efficiency stems from the intimate association that exists between the capillary walls and those of the glomerulus, as revealed by electronmicrographs (Figure 17–13).

Reabsorption. After the filtrate leaves the glomerular region, it enters the cavity of the tubule and flows along its length. As it does so, much of its orig-

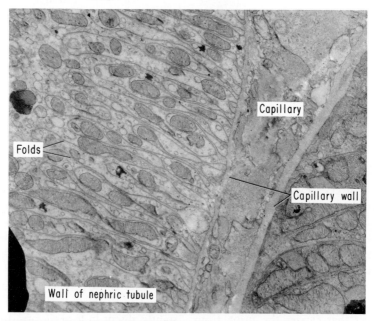

Figure 17–13. **Electronmicrograph of a nephric tubule.** A very intimate relationship is shown to exist between the tubules and the enveloping capillaries by the presence of numerous interlocking folds in the respective cell membranes. Magnified 10,000×. (Courtesy of Drs. K. A. Siegesmund and C. A. Fox.)

inal contents undergoes *reabsorption* by means of two processes, *back diffusion* and *cellular transport*. Through use of back diffusion, involving simple osmosis, much of the resorbed water and urea re-enter the capillaries, whereas the remainder of the water and all the salts, sugars, and amino acids require energy for reabsorption, indicating the existence of an active cellular transport mechanism. Normally, all glucose and amino acids originally filtered out are restored to the blood stream by active transport, so that the urine in its final form contains none of these compounds. Only when the blood level of glucose is unusually high, as in diabetes mellitus, is any of this substance eliminated.

Tubular Secretion. As the forming urine is passing through the tubules and is becoming altered by the several reabsorptive processes, additional substances are added to it. These additions are made by secretory activities of the tube's cells. Only a few naturally occurring materials thus enter the urine, most important among which are creatinine, potassium, hydrogen ions, and ammonia. Furthermore, drugs injected into the body, such as penicillin, are often eliminated by the kidneys through activities of this nature.

CONTROL OF EXCRETION

Aside from the regulation of the diameter of the main blood vessels entering and leaving the organ, no control over kidney function is directly under the nervous system but is performed solely by the action of several hormones. Although some of these hormones act directly on the kidneys, others regulate excretion indirectly by influencing the circulatory system or even the liver.

Excretion of Nitrogenous Products. In the processes of nitrogen excretion the liver plays an important role, for it re-moves amino acids from the blood stream and converts them into carbohydrates by processes of deamination. Since ammonia, a highly toxic substance, is one result of deamination, this end product must be either eliminated rapidly or converted into a less poisonous compound. In fishes its elimination presents no problem, for ammonia readily diffuses into the surrounding waters, but terrestrial organisms are differently situated. Among the mammals the problem has been solved by converting ammonia into *urea* by the action of enzymes in a series of chemical reactions which occurs only in the liver. Following the release of ammonia by deamination, the principal steps involved in urea production are, first, the formation of arginine by uniting carbon dioxide and ammonia to ornithine (by way of an intermediate product) and, second, the breakdown of arginine into ornithine and urea in the presence of the enzyme arginase (Figure 17–14). The energy in each case comes from the conversion of one molecule of ATP into ADP. In actuality the carbon dioxide, ammonia, and one unit of energy are first applied to an entirely different amino acid, one named glutamic acid; only after a complex series of steps are these substances finally united to ornithine to form citrulline. However, these details, while of much importance to a biochemist, are of no concern to the student at present.

After its formation in the liver by the above processes, the urea is then conducted in the blood stream to the kidneys. Here the bulk of this material is filtered out in the glomeruli, but later, as the forming urine is passing through the convoluted tubules of the nephridia, a large fraction is reabsorbed into the blood. No control over the processes of urea formation is exercised by the organism, the rate of its synthesis being

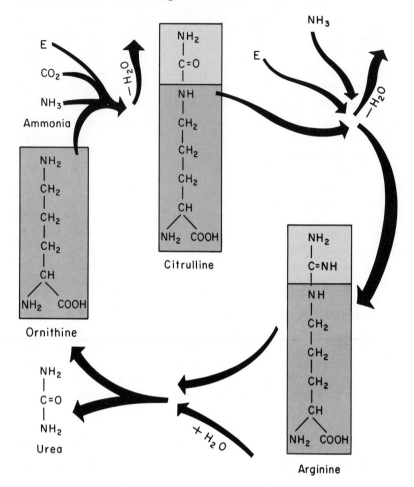

Fig. 17–14. The cycle of urea formation.

correlated solely to the protein intake of the mammal, at least to that quantity over and above the minimal maintenance requirements of the body. If the protein contents of the diet are doubled daily, the total production of urea is likewise doubled, and so on.

Another class of nitrogenous compounds that needs to be eliminated from the body are the nucleic acids; especially is their removal important among flesh-eating species, for meats are far richer in these substances than are foods of plant origin. Prior to excretion the nucleic acids

are first split into their chief constituents. Although the sugar fraction presents no problem, for it can eventually be catabolized by way of glycolysis and the citric acid cycle, the pyrimidines and purines are quite different matters. Concerning the fate and processes in the catabolism of the pyrimidines little is known, aside from the fact that the single "ring" of which each basically consists is broken during the reactions. In contrast the breakdown of purines is well known. Both guanine and adenine appear to have several alternative routes through which

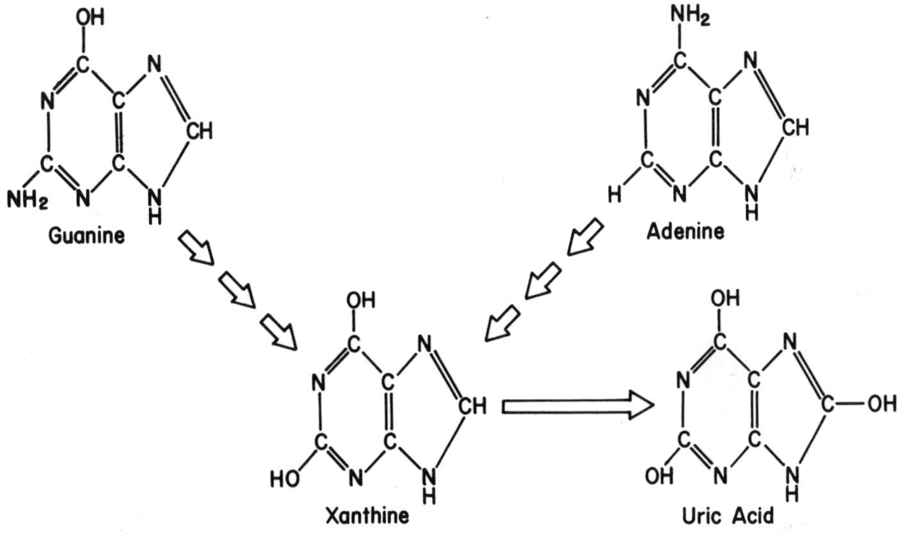

THE CATABOLISM OF PURINES

Figure 17–15. Steps in the breakdown of purines.

they may pass during the catabolic processes in the liver, but all involve the formation of *uric acid* by way of another purine called xanthine (Figure 17–15). As in elimination of urea, the uric acid thus formed is transported from the liver in the blood to the kidneys where it is excreted in the urine. But uric acid differs from urea in being soluble only to a limited extent and hence is eliminated slowly. Consequently, in diets with an overabundance of meats or in persons with faulty hormonal controls, uric acid may reach too high levels in the blood and subsequently become deposited as crystals within connective tissues of the body. Particularly susceptible to such accumulations are the ligaments of the big toe, deposits here characteristically giving rise to the very painful disease known as gout.

Excretion of Water. In the primitive vertebrates, which consistently live in aquatic media, there is little need for complex mechanisms to rid the body of nitrogenous and other wastes, as they can readily be diffused into the environment. Hence it comes as no surprise to learn that the kidney in these groups is principally concerned with the elimination of the excess water absorbed into their bodies osmotically. In terrestrial groups, in which other excretory responsibilities have been added, the chief concern of the kidneys, nevertheless, is that of maintaining the water balance. As already pointed out, the lungs, skin, and digestive tract excrete water from the body, but only in the present organs is its removal controlled solely from the standpoint of water balance.

In the total water of the body are included the quantity in the blood plasma and that within the cells, plus that surrounding the tissues. No doubt the mechanism controlling the distribution among

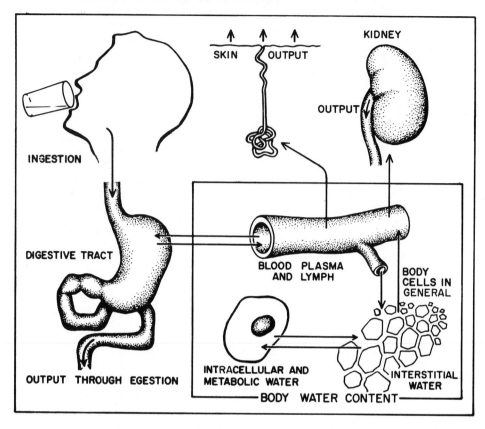

Figure 17–16. The water relations of the mammalian body.

the several parts is complex, but it is known to be influenced by thyroxin to some extent. In a deficiency of thyroxin the water level within the tissues increases, whereas the blood volume is considerably reduced; an excess of this hormone, however, results in an increase of water lost through the kidneys, probably at the expense of the tissues. But the adrenal cortical hormones have even more of an effect on water distribution and elimination. In a deficiency of either aldosterone or DOC, water shows an increased tendency to remain within the cells and thus becomes immobilized, so that the volume both of tissue fluid and of blood decreases. As the blood volume is lowered, blood pressure falls and, with it, renal excretion. Finally, one more hormone is known to be concerned with water regulation—namely, vasopressin, often called the antidiuretic hormone (ADH). Principally, its presence activates the reabsorption of water in the distal convolutions of the kidney tubules; hence it acts to reduce the volume of urine while increasing its concentration. Possibly it also influences other cells of the body and encourages the retention of intracellular water. In the absence of this hormone excessive urination occurs, as has already been pointed out, accompanied by an elevation in the quantity of extracellular fluid (Figure 17–16).

Questions for Review and Thought

1. Clearly differentiate between excretion and secretion. List as many methods used in excretion as you can.

2. Define the various types of glands based on the processes employed. Which of these types occur in the skin?

3. Describe the organization of the urinary system and the structure of the kidneys in general. How do the three types of kidney differ from one another?

4. Name and describe the functional unit of the kidneys. What is unique about the capillaries of the glomerulus? Discuss fully the processes generally involved in excretion in the kidneys.

5. What steps are found in the excretion of proteinaceous substances and what controls are found? In water metabolism?

6. Briefly state the roles, nil or otherwise, played in excretion by each of the following:

(a) liver	(g) adrenal cortex
(b) thyroids	(h) convoluted ducts
(c) heart	(i) adrenal medulla
(d) muscles	(j) parathyroids
(e) pituitary	(k) glomerulus
(f) thalamus	(l) intestines

7. In mammals what is the source of the uric acid excreted by the kidneys? What causes gout? Why is gout rarely found among persons with a relatively low level of income?

Supplementary References

Cantarow, A., and B. Schepartz. *Textbook of Biochemistry,* 3rd ed. Philadelphia, Saunders, 1962.

Jones, I. C., and P. Eckstein. *Hormonal Control of Water and Salt-Electrolyte Metabolism in Vertebrates.* Cambridge, Cambridge Univ. Press, 1956.

Montagna, W. *The Structure and Function of the Skin.* New York, Academic Press, 1956.

Rothman, S. *The Human Integument.* Washington, Amer. Assoc. Advance. Sc., 1959.

Ruch, T. C., and J. Fulton. *Medical Physiology and Biophysics,* 18th ed. Philadelphia, Saunders, 1960.

Smith, H. W. "The Kidney." *Sci. Amer.,* January 1953.

———. *Principles of Renal Physiology.* New York, Oxford Univ. Press, 1956.

Walker, B. S., W. C. Boyd, and I. Asimov. *Biochemistry and Human Metabolism,* 3rd ed. Baltimore, Williams & Wilkins, 1957.

Wolf, A. V. *The Urinary Function of the Kidney.* New York, Grune and Stratton, 1950.

Reproduction in the Vertebrates

ALTHOUGH in the lower chordates asexual propagation by bud-ding is not of infrequent oc-currence, among the vertebrates only sex-ual methods of reproduction are found. Consequently, no alternation of genera-tions, such as characterizes many plants and simpler metazoans, exists among these animals. At the cellular level of the reproductive processes, nothing among the present animals is distinctive, for ga-metogenesis is by meiosis, and the result-ing gametes are not especially remark-able, either structurally or in behavior. Only in the structure of the organs and in the nature of the control mechanisms are unique features prominent. The mor-phology and regulation of the system, then, will form the central topics of the present chapter, while the development of the zygote will be followed in an en-suing one.

The Reproductive System

In a strict sense, no separate system can be said to carry out the processes of reproduction, for the entire organism, in one way or another, is involved in the perpetuation of the species. Courtship, selection of a mate and nesting site, care of the eggs and young—all are aspects that are far beyond the capabilities of any single set of organs to perform and require the presence of fully integrated individuals, whether fish or snakes or human beings. Only when attention is confined to the organs engaged in the routine activities of forming the gametes and of bringing the sperm and egg cells into contact can one truly speak of a re-productive system, a procedure that will be followed here.

THE MALE REPRODUCTIVE SYSTEM

Morphology. Except for the hermaph-roditic hagfish, all vertebrates are dioeci-ous, with the two sexes quite frequently sharply distinguished by secondary sexual characteristics. Among primitive forms like the lamprey, however, the male re-productive system contains remarkably few organs, nor does the number and complexity greatly increase until the level of the amphibian has been attained. In the cyclostomes, *testes* are present and little else; the sperm form in these organs, and after maturity has been attained, they emerge through a rupture of the testicular wall into the coelom, from there passing to the cloaca through the nephridial tubules and the pronephric duct. As fertilization of the eggs takes place in the watery surroundings, no secondary sexual parts are required. With evolutionary advancement as represented by the elasmobranchs, better provision is made for the conduction of the sperm, for in this class, the testes are provided with fine tubules that connect to those of the anterior portion of the midkidney. In this way a direct route is formed that leads the spermatozoa into the cloaca (Figure 18–1).

This same basic pattern, variously modified, persists throughout all lower groups including the amphibians. Higher in the scale of vertebrate life, beginning with the reptiles, the testes are provided

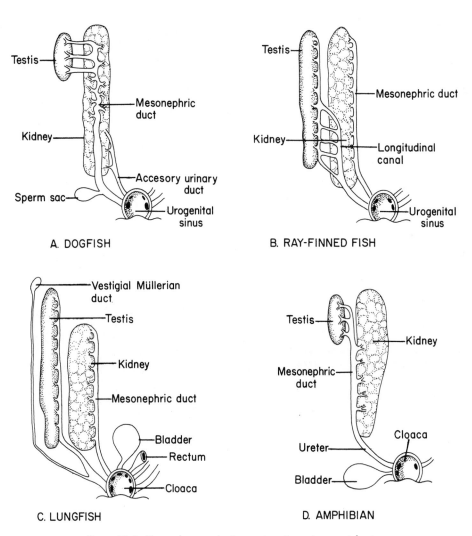

Figure 18–1. The male reproductive system in various vertebrates.

with long *seminiferous tubules,* in which the sperm develop, and the former pronephric duct, now called the *vas deferens* or *sperm duct,* leads the sperm to the cloaca. Since fertilization in the highest vertebrates occurs within the body of the female instead of in the water, a copulatory mechanism, varying with the different representative types, is usually present, save in most birds.

In mammals, the testes are typically enclosed in an extension of the coelom called the *scrotum* (Figure 18–2), but important exceptions to this general condition are found among the monotremes, elephants, whales, and dugongs. In a number of forms, including most rodents, the testes undergo cyclic movements, remaining in the abdomen except during the breeding season, when they migrate into the scrotum. Moreover, the path of the sperm has become more elaborate in this class. First, while an *epididymis* is present among certain reptiles and

all birds, it is a constant feature of the mammals and is uniformly well developed throughout the class. Basically this organ is a long, highly convoluted tubule enclosed within a sac, in which sperm are stored. Although here the sperm remain in an inert state, as their flagella are not capable of movement, they appear to mature physiologically in some way while passing through the organ, for sperm removed from the anterior portion are found less effective in fertilizing eggs than those from the terminal section. From the epididymis the *vas deferens* leads to a gland called the *seminal vesicle.* While the name of the latter implies the storage of sperm, it serves in no such capacity, its sole function being the secreting of a portion of the seminal fluid in which the sperm become suspended. Beyond the junction with this gland, the wall of the vas deferens is provided with muscles until it ends at the *urethra,* an adaptation that aids in eject-

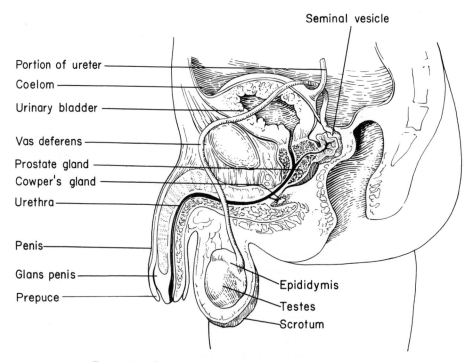

Figure 18–2. The male reproductive system of the human being.

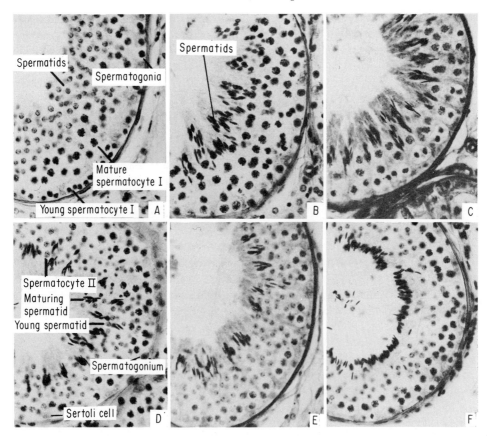

Spermatids

Spermatids
Spermatogonia

Mature
spermatocyte I

Young spermatocyte I   A

B

C

Spermatocyte II
Maturing
spermatid
Young spermatid

Spermatogonium

Sertoli cell   D

E

F

Figure 18–3. Development of sperm. In this series of bull seminiferous tubules, the cellular changes that occur during the formation of a spermatozoan are shown. At the onset (A), no sperm are visible; only the stages in which the first steps in meiosis occur (primary spermatocytes) and the precursors of sperm (spermatids) can be seen. B. The spermatids are elongating and commencing to assume the form of sperm. C. The spermatids have now become arranged in distinct bundles. D. More spermatids have formed and still more will be formed as the secondary spermatocytes (spermatocyte II) undergo division. E. The spermatids begin to move toward the cavity (lumen) of the tubule as maturation approaches completion. F. The mature sperm are now arranged around the lumen, ready for passage into the epididymis. (Courtesy of Dr. R. P. Amann, Dairy Research Center, Pennsylvania State University.)

ing semen. Beyond this point the urethra conducts the sperm through the length of the *penis* and thus subserves both the urinary and the reproductive systems. Along it are found a number of accessory sex glands, the first of which is the *prostate,* located at the neck of the bladder, followed by *Cowper's* (bulbo-urethral) *gland* and a number of *urethral mucous glands,* all of which contribute to the seminal fluid.

The Seminal Fluid. As might be anticipated, the exact nature of the secre-
tion of the several glands that contribute to the seminal fluid varies from species to species. In man the *seminal vesicle's secretion* contains proportionately large amounts of fructose, its concentration in the semen exceeding that of glucose in the blood; apparently this substance serves as the principal energy source for the spermatozoa. Also abundant in the product of the vesicles is a chemical precursor of *choline,* a compound lipid with strong alkaline reactions. While the full significance of this substance is unknown,

it is suspected to assist in neutralizing the acid secretion of certain areas in the female genital tract. Chief among the constituents of *prostate secretion* are citric acid, calcium, acid phosphatase, other enzymes, and proteins. Although the components are well known, their respective functional roles are not. Citric acid has been suggested to serve in facilitating sperm motility, but the fact has not been established. When the secretions of the seminal vesicles and prostate become intermingled, coagulation occurs; after about 15 minutes, however, the mixture again liquefies under the influence of prostatic enzymes. So long as one or the other of these glands is present, sperm are capable of fertilizing the egg, but absence of both interferes with the processes.

The Physiology of the Male Organs. It will be recalled that the testes in vertebrates consist of *tubules,* in which spermatogenesis occurs (Figure 18–3), surrounded by *interstitial tissue.* While the latter's cells are claimed to be active in hormone secretion, the point has still not been indisputably established. There exists an equal possibility that the male hormones are produced by the cells lining the tubules. Whatever the source may eventually prove to be, the chief hormone is testosterone, but other androgens are produced too, not to mention small amounts of estrogens. These hormones have a pronounced effect on the growth and maturation of the accessory sex organs, for the entire system is reduced and nonfunctional until puberty, nor can spermatogenesis proceed to completion in their absence. Then as the testes mature and commence secreting androgens, the epididymis, seminal vesicles, and other glands and parts increase in size and assume an active role. In turn, the development of the testes is under the control of the anterior pituitary through the secretion of *gonadotropins.* These hormones are the same in both sexes and include *follicle-stimulating hormone (FSH)* and *luteinizing hormone (LH),* although the latter in the male is more appropriately called *interstitial cell–stimulating hormone (ICSH).*

In the present sex with the approach of puberty and the initiation of its production, FSH acts on the testicular tubules, inducing their enlargement and the commencement of spermatogenesis. Similarly ICSH stimulates development of the interstitial cells and possibly the secreting of testosterone; in turn this hormone has a suppressing action on the pituitary production of FSH but only a slight stimulatory one, if any, on the secreting of ICSH. Estrogens have an activity paralleling that of testosterone but are more pronounced in their effects; hence, assistance in influencing the pituitary may be the normal role of these hormones in the male. Thus the production of sperm and the sex hormone is regulated by a delicate mechanism involving the interstitial or tube-lining cells and the pituitary (Figure 18–4).

THE FEMALE REPRODUCTIVE SYSTEM

Morphology. As in the male tract, the female reproductive parts are few in number among the lower classes of vertebrates. In the agnathans there is a single *ovary* (really a fused pair) lying medially below the notochord, and almost nothing more. When fully mature, the eggs break through the ovarian walls, enter the coelom, and leave the body by way of a posteriorly placed pore that leads through a genital sinus to the outside, fertilization being external.

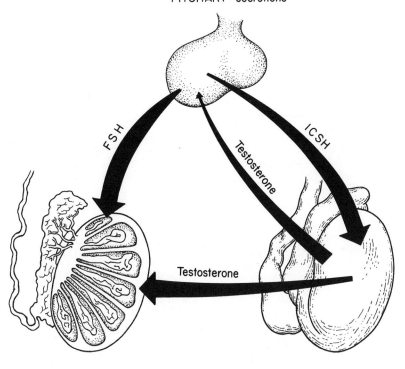

PITUITARY : secretions

FSH

ICSH

Testosterone

Testosterone

TESTES : sperm production

TESTES : hormones

Figure 18–4. The regulation of testicular function. Arrows that widen toward their tips signify a stimulatory action, while those that narrow in that direction indicate inhibition.

While to the student this reproductive pattern may appear very primitive, it is nonetheless essentially the one found throughout the Vertebrata, for in all classes the eggs follow the same early procedures, including development within the ovary, escape through the ovarian wall when ripe, and entrance into the coelomic cavity. In place of a simple pore, however, almost all vertebrates above the lampreys except some bony fish possess a pair of tubes that assist in conducting the eggs to the outside. This set of *oviducts* (or Müllerian tubules) occurs first in the elasmobranchs and persists throughout the remainder of the subphylum (Figure 18–5). Whenever present, as is usually the case, the inner end opens by means of a porelike or funnel-like *ostium* into the coelom; around the borders of the opening are a number of cilia, which move the eggs into the duct. Once within the tubules the gametes are propelled along by either ciliary action or muscular contraction. In the simplest condition each oviduct is uniform in diameter, but this state of affairs is frequently modified. Among the sharks, for example, the two ducts are fused at the ostial ends, so that only a single funnel-like opening is found there; however, the tubes soon separate and proceed along normal courses. Further modification is found near the ends of each in the form of a *shell gland* that provides the egg after fertilization with a tough covering,

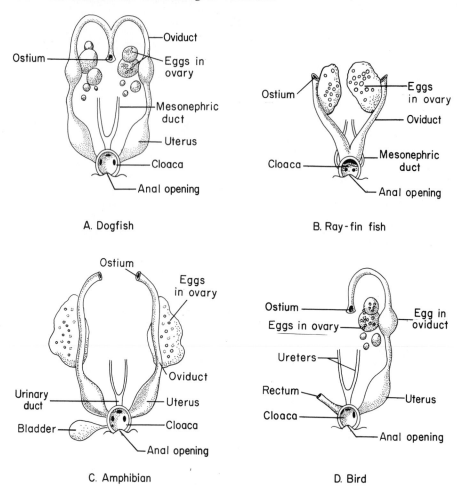

A. Dogfish

B. Ray-fin fish

C. Amphibian

D. Bird

Figure 18–5. The female reproductive tract in various vertebrates.

for fertilization is internal in this group. The resulting egg cases (Figure 18–6) bear tentacles, which become ensnared in seaweeds and prevent the cases from washing ashore. Depending on the species, each case contains one to four eggs; the resulting embryos, on becoming matured, leave by rupturing the walls. On the other hand, some sharks retain the eggs within the body and enclose them with only a thin, membranous case. The eggs in this envelope develop within an enlargement of the oviduct called the *uterus,* sometimes requiring the better part of two years for the process. While most of the teleost fish are *oviparous* and lay eggs, some are *ovoviviparous* like the sharks, retaining their eggs within the body until hatched. It should be noted that the retention of an egg does not in itself imply giving birth to young, for the latter term is applied only to species that are *viviparous*—that is, that nourish the embryo by way of a placenta, not on yolk contained in the egg. In ovoviviparous fish, a uterine enlargement is present, too, that serves as a temporary depository for the eggs; to effect internal fertilization in these species, certain fins of the male are especially modified for introduction of

Figure 18–6. Egg cases of some sharks. Certain species of sharks enclose their eggs in buoyant capsules; the tentacles become entangled in seaweeds and prevent the capsules from washing ashore.

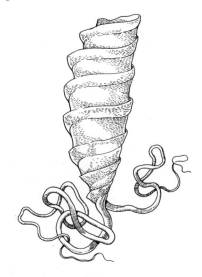

A. Dogfish

B. Bullhead shark

the sperm into the female genital tract.

Although, as a whole, the lungfish are little more advanced in structure of the female reproductive tract than the teleosts, glands are found in the oviducts that provide the eggs with a gelatinous covering. At least in the Australian species, the eggs are deposited singly on the underside of water lily pads or other aquatic vegetation, with fertilization being external. Nor do the Amphibia show any advancement as a class; however, among the salamanders, internal fertilization is the rule, although males do not have special copulatory organs. In these forms, the sperm are enclosed in small packets called *spermatophores* and are deposited randomly in the water or even on land by the males. Subsequently these are placed into the cloaca by the female, where the spermatozoa leave the packet and unite with the eggs.

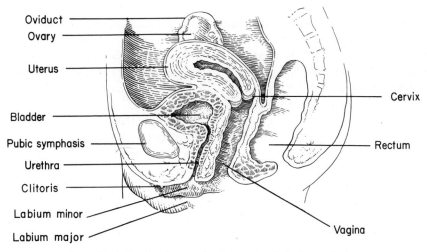

Figure 18–7. The female reproductive system of the human being.

Commencing with the reptiles, the higher classes have the oviduct greatly modified (Figure 18–7), especially in those forms like birds and most reptiles that envelop the egg with several successive deposits before the protective covering is applied. Structurally the organs of birds differ from those of the modern reptiles principally in being present only on the right side of the body, those of the other side having been lost. In both groups, the ovum, after maturing and being fully equipped with yolk, by ciliary action is moved through the oviduct's ostium, which lies closely associated with the ovary. Once inside the oviduct, at the upper end of the tubule the egg may be fertilized and then is moved along the tract by the beating of cilia and by muscular contraction. As it moves, *oviducal glands* apply albumin in layers until, finally, after a double membranous coat has been acquired, the *shell gland* is reached and its characteristic shell is deposited around the whole. The nature of the shell varies from group to group, being leathery and pliable in turtles, snakes, and most lizards, but as hard and brittle in crocodiles and a few lizards as it is in hens or other birds. While quite a few snakes and lizards are ovoviviparous, the remaining reptiles and all the birds are egg-laying species. Contrariwise, the mammals are nearly entirely viviparous and form the largest group of animals with this type of reproduction. Only the duck-billed platypus and the several species of echidna, confined to Australia and New Guinea, are oviparous (Figure 12–19). In the platypus the eggs are provided with a membranous shell quite similar to that of the turtle and are laid in subterranean nests and cared for by the female. Those of the echidna, in contrast, are provided with only a vestige of the shell; the eggs on being deposited are placed within a pouch located ventrally on the female's abdomen and are carried about until hatching occurs.

In all higher mammals, however, the egg never develops a shell but becomes attached to the walls of the oviducts; often portions of these oviducts are enlarged and modified into *uteri,* several types of which are found. In the *duplex* type, only the very lower ends of the tubes are fused, as in the rodents (Figure 18–8), whereas in the *bicornuate* variety of cattle and horses, the fusing is more extensive and involves the entire lower half of the organs. Finally, in the *simplex* uterus of primates including human beings, the fusing is complete and forms a single central organ, to which the oviducts join. Beyond the uterus of whatever variation is a muscular tube, the *vagina,* in which the sperm are deposited. At its lower end, a portion of the uterus usually protrudes into the vaginal tube, the protrusion being known as the *cervix.*

The Physiology in the Mammal. As the processes involved in the production of the egg and other reproductive activities have been most thoroughly investigated in the mammals, they will be employed to illustrate the functioning of the female tract in vertebrates in general. While doubtlessly the details differ from class to class, the essential features are fundamentally similar in all. Two basic steps are concerned—namely, the formation and maturation of the egg within the ovary and the periodic preparation of the uterus for reception of the fertilized ovum.

Seemingly the activities within the ovaries parallel those of the testes quite closely, but some distinctive features can be noted. As in the male, at puberty the anterior pituitary commences secreting the two gonadotropins, *FSH* and *LH,* plus one called *prolactin*. The first of these stimulates growth and development of the ovaries, and also under its influence

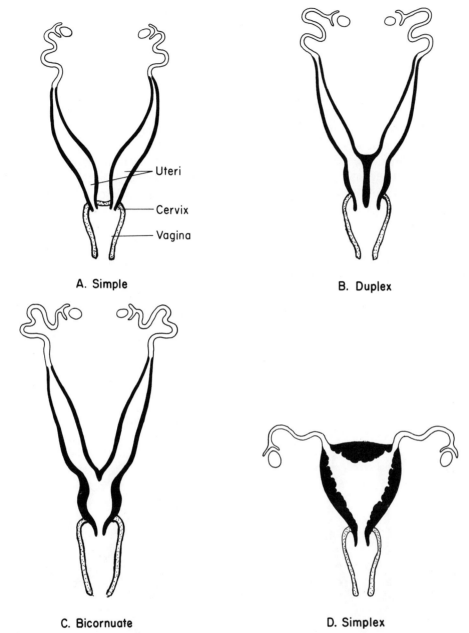

A. Simple

B. Duplex

C. Bicornuate

D. Simplex

Figure 18–8. Types of mammalian uteri. Usually in mammals the bases of the oviducts are swollen to form uteri; each uterus may be separate (A) or fused into a single unit to a greater or lesser degree (B–D).

the follicles begin to mature. One difference from the male should be noted here: no meiotic processes accompany the development of the follicles, nor do any occur elsewhere within the ovaries after the fetal period, for it has recently been established that the female mammal has a predetermined number of follicles in each ovary at birth, and once these are exhausted, the processes cease. Such, undoubtedly, is not the case with all vertebrates. At any rate, as follicular increment proceeds, the cells lining the follicle initiate the production of *estrogens,* the presence of which in the blood stream induces the maturation of the remainder of the genital tract.

As in the testes, the complete maturing of the ovaries, too, depends on their own hormonal secretions, as do many other parts of the body not related to reproduction. With the advent of the estrogens the vagina and the uterine walls acquire their full size, and the external genitalia assume their adult form. Once these hormones are present even in small amounts in the blood stream, the anterior pituitary is stimulated to generate LH, which in turn leads to an enhanced production of the various secretions. Furthermore, this luteinizing hormone brings about events

in ripened follicles that lead to *ovulation,* the release of the egg into the coelomic cavity; however, the presence of FSH is requisite, too, for ovulation to occur. Whether one or both ovaries discharge an egg or eggs each cycle depends largely on the species. In human beings, while the ovaries alternate in this matter monthly in general, no strict adherence to this practice is to be expected.

After the discharge of the egg, the old follicle and its enclosed blood clot are converted into a body of endocrine activity called the *corpus luteum,* a term meaning "yellow body" in reference to its color in the human. The hormone formed by this body is *progesterone,* which like the estrogens has a strong impact on the growth of the uterine walls. As the level of progesterone in the blood increases, a retarding action on the

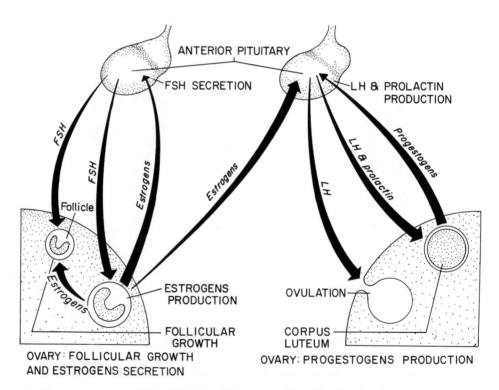

Figure 18–9. The regulation of ovarian function.

production of LH can be noted. While the latter hormone brings about the conversion of the follicle into the corpus luteum, the active synthesis of progesterone is induced by *prolactin*. As yet, however, little more than this fact is known about the effects and regulation of this latter endocrine secretion. Nevertheless as far as the over-all picture has been established, it can be perceived that a four-way feedback system is involved in the development of the ovaries and in the governing of their activities (Figure 18–9). From the interplay of the hormones, cyclical changes in the uterus and other reproductive organs result, two main patterns of which occur as described below.

CYCLICAL FUNCTIONINGS IN FEMALE MAMMALS

Among placental mammals a unique feature is found in the females in the form of marked cycles. Although in the cold-blooded reptiles and the birds periodic fluctuations of sexual functionings occur too, they are not so sharply pronounced as in the higher mammals. In the birds the rhythms are manifest largely in behavioral changes and will be discussed in the following chapter. Here the anatomical and physiological cycles in mammals alone shall receive attention.

The Estrous Cycle. Most typically among mammals an *estrous cycle* is found, which can be briefly characterized as a period of "heat" in which copulation is permitted, followed by a season in which it is not. Many variations in pattern and length of period exist, since almost each species possesses its own peculiar modifications; for our purposes, the periodic changes in the rat will serve as an example, as the processes involved

have been most thoroughly explored in this animal.

The cycle is divisible into four stages, of which the heat phase proper, spelled *estrus* to distinguish it, can be employed as the starting point (Figure 18–10). During this phase within the ovaries a number of follicles, perhaps 12 or more, undergo rapid development under the influence of FSH. As these structures grow, the blood level of estrogen becomes more and more strongly elevated, and through this hormone's presence, the uteri are induced to enlarge. Simultaneously, the cells of the vaginal lining undergo active mitotic divisions, and as this tissue increases in thickness, its outer layers become squamous and cornified, quite like the surface of the skin. Sometime after the middle of this stage, which endures for 9 to 15 hours, *ovulation* occurs, followed by a gradual lowering of the estrogen level and loss of the cornified vaginal layers. Shortly after ovulation, the second stage, called *metestrus*, commences; it is 10 to 14 hours in duration and is characterized by the presence of corpora lutea in the ovary. Moreover, in the vagina the mucous lining begins to decrease in thickness through loss of the outer cells. The third phase, *diestrus*, is by far the longest, lasting 60 to 70 hours. During its entire length the corpora lutea gradually diminish in extent as they become resorbed, while the uteri likewise regress in size. At this time the vaginal lining is reduced to a membrane so thin that it is readily penetrated by the neutrophils and other cells of the blood. *Proestrus* precedes the next estrus and occupies the remainder of the four or five days included in the entire cycle. Its characteristic features are found in the complete loss of the corpora lutea and the initiation of follicular growth within the ovaries, the beginning of uterine

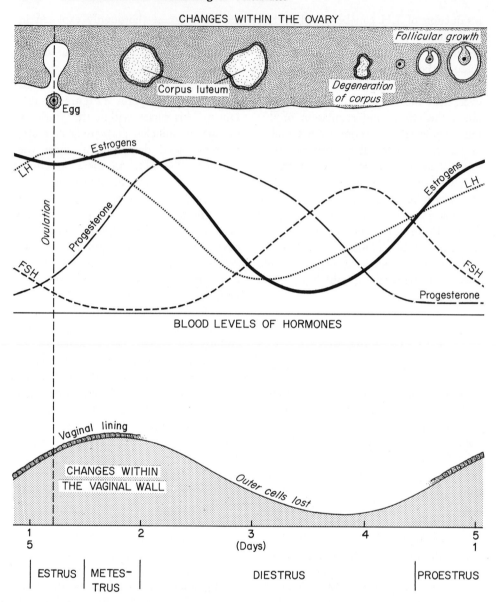

CHANGES WITHIN THE OVARY

Follicular growth

Corpus luteum

Egg

Degeneration of corpus

Estrogens

LH

Ovulation

Progesterone

FSH

Estrogens

LH

FSH

Progesterone

BLOOD LEVELS OF HORMONES

Vaginal lining

CHANGES WITHIN THE VAGINAL WALL

Outer cells lost

1 5	2	3 (Days)	4	5 1

| ESTRUS | METES- TRUS | DIESTRUS | PROESTRUS |

Figure 18–10. The principal events in the rat's estrous cycle. Although other parts of the reproductive tract, especially the uterus, are also involved in the cycle to a lesser degree, chief events center around the ovary, vagina, and several hormones.

enlargement, and the augmenting of the vaginal epithelium (Figure 18–10). After its close and the advent of the next estrus, the cycle is completed.

The Menstrual Cycle. At the higher levels of the order Primates, represented by several monkeys, the lesser and great apes, and the human being, a peculiar modification of the estrous cycle exists. Outstanding among the features of the *menstrual cycle,* as this distinctive variation is called, is the lack of a definite heat period, sexual activity occurring at any stage of the cycle. Furthermore there exists a second prominent characteristic in the form of a *menstrual flow,* which consists of the shedding of lining cells, mucus, and blood from the uterus at definite intervals. In the following discussion attention will be devoted to the processes as they occur in human beings, for which a period of 28 days is generally accepted as normal (Figure 18–11).

Since the menstrual flow is a marked feature whose inception can readily be observed, it is usually employed as the beginning of the cycle. At the onset of this flow, or *menstruation,* a number of follicles commence increasing in size within the ovaries. While several enlarge, only one egg completely ripens during any one period; so observations can be confined to a single developing ovum. By the end of the eighth day, the follicle has attained a size that permits the production of relatively large

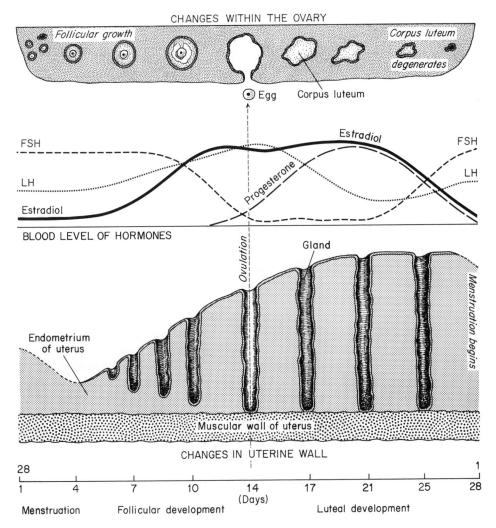

Figure 18–11. The chief features of the menstrual cycle in humans. In higher primates the estrous cycle has undergone modification to include a series of drastic changes within the uterus. It is interesting to compare the hormonal and ovarian events shown in Figure 18–10 with those diagrammed above.

quantities of estrogens, which act on the anterior lobe of the pituitary in the manner already described, stimulating the production of LH and retarding that of FSH. With the advent of LH, the follicular cells secrete small amounts of progesterone, followed at the fourteenth day by *ovulation* and the subsequent formation of the *corpus luteum*. As the latter comes into existence, the blood level of progesterone is considerably elevated under the influence of prolactin, whereas that of estrogen is continued at its former maximum. Toward the close of the period, after the twenty-second day, the corpus luteum begins to regress in size, and as it does so, the production of ovarian hormones gradually is retarded, until by the close of the cycle, their original blood levels have been restored.

While nothing of a unique nature, aside from the timing, is to be noted among the foregoing events within the ovaries and pituitary, more distinctive features can be found in the recurrent changes undergone by the uterus. Most of the alterations take place within the lining of the organ, called the *endometrium*. After the menstrual flow ceases, about the fourth day, growth is inaugurated in the endometrium even in the low concentration of estrogens then present. As the level of the hormones increases, mitotic divisions in the lining occur at a more rapid pace, so that 10 days later at ovulation, a considerable thickness has been acquired. Within the endometrium, capillaries and other small blood and lymph vessels develop, and glandular infoldings of the epithelial coat are formed. At first the latter are shallow and simple, but as the endometrium increases in extent, the inpocketings deepen, reaching to the muscular portion of the wall. After ovulation and the subsequent increase in progesterone production, while increment in thickness continues, elaboration of the glandular pockets occurs under the inducement of the present hormone, so that they become highly convoluted. Furthermore, the nature of these glands' secretion changes. Whereas in earlier stages their product is thin and contains no glycogen, it now is more viscid and is rich in that carbohydrate. With the degeneration of the corpus luteum and the consequential lowering of the ovarian hormone level in the blood, growth and elaboration of the endometrium at first cease, and then at the twenty-eighth day, disintegration sets in, inaugurating the menstrual flow. The menstrual fluid consists of blood and plasma along with the endometrial tissues. With the advent of menstruation, the cycle also commences once more (Figure 18–11); it should be noted that thus day 28 of one cycle is day 1 of the succeeding.

Other Aspects of Mammalian Reproduction

As reproduction is of such fundamental importance to the survival of the species, it can readily be understood why many peculiar adaptations have been acquired by the various types of vertebrates in response to the demands of their environments. Particularly outstanding among these are two specializations of the higher mammals—namely, the retention within the uterus of the developing embryo and the establishment of mammary glands to provide nourishment for the young after its birth. While both these features are striking, the fact that comparable adaptations are found in other vertebrates too—and indeed in invertebrates—should not be overlooked. The mammalian processes discussed below might well be looked upon mainly as types exemplifying specializations for reproductive purposes by animals in general. Here only the parental aspects are outlined; the development of the young is part of a later account.

INTERRUPTION OF
THE CYCLES

Normally the cyclic activities of the female mammal repeat themselves indefinitely during adulthood until interrupted by the fertilization of the egg or by relatively advanced years. The interruption brought about by the former is referred to as a pregnancy, whereas that caused by the latter is, in humankind, called the menopause.

Pregnancies. As noted earlier, fertilization of the ovum can only transpire in the upper region of the oviduct; if sperm are absent there in mammals, after a day or two the ovum degenerates while being moved along the tubule and ultimately is resorbed. Should sperm unite with the egg, however, a number of changes in the usual female reproductive cycle are initiated while the zygote continues toward the uterus. Most important among these is the perpetuation of the corpus luteum, so that its secretory activities are considerably prolonged; in human beings this body remains functional till the twelfth week of a pregnancy. So long as it is present and active, progesterone stays at a high level in the blood, and the endometrium is maintained intact. In the meanwhile, the zygote has moved into the uterus, developing continually, and has become embedded on the uterine lining. By the twelfth week, the vascularized region attaching the growing young to the uterus, the *placenta,* has attained a fair size and has commenced endocrinal activities. Among its earliest secretions is *chorionic gonadotropin,* a hormone that closely resembles LH in its actions; through its influence the corpus luteum persists through pregnancy, although it becomes relatively nonfunctional after three months. The placenta also secretes various estrogens and progesterone, all of which assist in maintaining the endometrial lining intact throughout the term. Another important feature of pregnancy is the formation of a third type of hormone by the ovary, one known as *relaxin* in reference to its actions on the pelvis. Under its influence the union (symphysis) of the pubic bones becomes loosened through a softening of the connective-tissue ground substance, while the other pelvic bones similarly become less rigid, and the vagina becomes enlarged. Hence, in brief the action of the hormone is that of facilitating *parturition,* i.e., the birth processes.

While the mechanisms controlling the maintenance of pregnancy appear clear enough, the question arises as to the agency that inaugurates the retention of the corpus luteum intact in the first place. Largely this must remain unanswered at present. However, it is known that the sexual act instigates neural impulses which trigger hypothalamic stimulation of the anterior pituitary productivity. Perhaps it is this reaction in some species, perhaps in none or in all. At any rate, it is also known that, after fertilization of the eggs, prolactin is produced in larger amounts, and its presence is the factor that prolongs the life and activities of the corpus luteum. Moreover, the elements involved with the instigation of parturition at the termination of pregnancy are poorly known. While the length of a pregnancy, the *gestation period,* is a species trait and is determined by genetic means, most of the hormonal agents are not evident, but possibly are secreted, at least in great part, by the placenta and ovaries. Progesterone has a negative influence, and parturition cannot occur in its presence; on the other hand, estrogens have an enhancing effect on uterine contractility. Hence, it is probably of some significance that the first-named hormone decreases in concentration and the second one increases as labor approaches. In addition it is not unlikely that oxytocin plays an important role in the birth processes and that neural activities enhance its production through the hypothalamic paths. So although much is postulated, all that is clear at the moment is that a large number of factors are involved.

The Menopause. Though in the human male there is no definite period in which the reproductive functions draw to a close, in the female the cessation of reproductivity is quite marked and is accompanied by a number of other changes. The actual time of onset of the *menopause,* as the interval of alterations is called, varies considerably. At the earliest, it may commence at 40 years of age and at the latest at 50, but the average in temperate climates is close to 45. Essentially the processes are the reverse of those of puberty, with two phases characteristically appearing. Briefly, in the first phase, the menstrual cycle becomes irregular and finally ceases; after this is a post-cessation phase, in which disturbances of the various bodily systems are of frequent occurrence. The whole period endures for approximately five years.

In greater detail, the two phases are as follows: As the ovary approaches the close of its functioning, the follicles, which are nearing exhaustion of their original numbers, develop to completion sporadically, in part causing the irregularity of the monthly flow. Still later after several years, when ovulation and menstruation end permanently, the first stage is brought to a close. During the remaining phase, the estrogens and progester-ones decrease in concentration in the blood, the latter disappearing entirely; concordantly, the amount of FSH becomes elevated, since the repressive actions of the estrogens are diminished, and continues at an accelerated level through the remainder of life. Also in response to the disappearance of the estrogens, the reproductive organs retrogress, the uterus becoming reduced to one fourth of its normal size, the ovaries and oviducts to a lesser degree. Frequently the closing stage is marked by vascular upsets, manifested as "hot flashes" in which the skin becomes flushed, accompanied by profuse sweating and sometimes by a feeling of suffocation. At this period palpitations of the heart or digestive tract malfunctionings also occur in some persons. More frequently, emotional and other psychic disturbances appear, and mental instability is not infrequent at the change of life. After these sensitive periods have ended, with some alteration in personality occasionally, the individual resumes normal behavior.

THE MAMMARY GLANDS

Among the unique accessory reproductive features in mammals are the *mammary glands,* on the secretions of which the young are nourished for a period after birth. Usually these organs are considered to be derivatives of the apocrine type of sweat gland, for in the egg-laying species they are similarly constructed, are always likewise in close asociation with hair follicles, and secrete in the same fashion.

Morphology. Although variations exist among the numerous species of mammals, essentially two basic patterns of organization exist, the differences between which concern the mode of opening at the surface. In the simpler type,

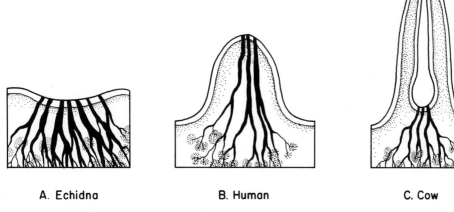

A. Echidna   B. Human   C. Cow

Figure 18–12. The organization of milk glands. No nipple is present in the echidna or platypus; the milk simply flows along tufts of hair which surround the openings.

represented by the condition in the human being, each compound gland opens through a separate duct, whereas in the more advanced type, found in the cow, the individual ducts lead first into a collecting sac, or *cistern,* whence the milk is conducted through a single tubule to the surface (Figure 18–12). The structure of the actual glands, as well as of the surrounding areas, changes materially during the postnatal life of the individual and also during the reproductive cycle and pregnancy. As the changes have been studied more thoroughly in man, that species will serve as typical.

At birth the glands are simply tubules, radiating about the nipple and numbering between 16 and 25. While present in both sexes, they undergo further development, as a rule, only in females (Figure 18–13). With the approach of puberty, the ducts become extensively branched and arborescent under the influence of estrogens and progesterone, and much deposition of fat occurs in the breasts. As further maturity is attained, the branching becomes even greater; only during pregnancies, however, do the actual secretory alveoli develop (Figure

18–13). This development appears to be largely in response to the high levels of estrogens and progesterone secreted by the placenta. While growth is completed in this fashion, functioning does not commence until parturition.

Physiology. Because of the evident interrelationship of sexual maturity and growth of the mammary glands, it soon was established that hormones concerned with the reproductive functioning controlled development of the breasts. As pointed out in part above, the roles played by the ovarian secretions have been well worked out and found to include influences by the gonadotropins as well; in contrast, the processes by which milk secretion is regulated have not been clearly established. At first it was believed that prolactin alone initiated the flow of milk, i.e., *lactation,* because the impure extracts of this hormone originally available elicited milk production when injected into test animals. Since purified forms of prolactin have been obtained, however, this substance, either by itself or with ovarian hormones, has proven ineffectual. In fact the latter have an inhibiting action, and it is not unlikely that

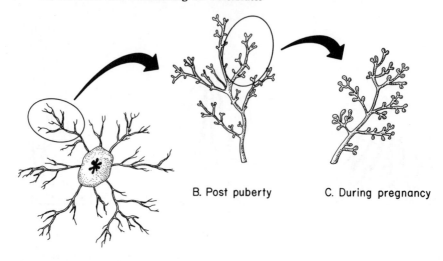

B. Post puberty   C. During pregnancy

A. Prepuberty condition

Figure 18–13. Development of the milk glands in the human female. A. In early childhood, the milk glands are simple tubules without any real glands. B. Following puberty, the tubules become more complex but still lack glands. C. Only during pregnancies do the milk-secreting glands develop; their formation is accompanied by a great increase in the intricacy of the tubules.

only when the blood level of estrogens diminishes after birth of the young is lactation able to occur. Along with prolactin, still other factors are involved, including somatotropin and the adrenal cortical secretion, probably under the mediation of ACTH. Moreover, the mechanical activities of the uterus, during and after parturition, appear to arouse stimuli within its wall which are transmitted to the hypothalamus; the latter region then possibly induces the pituitary anterior lobe to increase its secretory activities and thus lead to the formation of milk. In addition a similar neural path might also be involved in an associated release of oxytocin by the posterior lobe, for this hormone too plays a part, not in milk formation but in its liberation. Typically only when this hormone is present in the blood is the milk ejected from the glands into the ducts. That the production of the endocrine secretion is brought about by a reflex mechanism in which the act of nursing serves as the stimulus has been demonstrated by a simple experiment centering around the anes-

thetization of a lactating female animal. If a young animal is permitted to nurse such a female, only the milk stored within the ducts or cistern can be withdrawn in the absence of assistance by this reflex arc. Apparently the milking stimulus instigates hypothalamic activities that result in the outpouring of oxytocin, and in turn, the presence of this hormone in the blood brings about alveolar contractions in the mammary glands, liberating their contents into the ducts and thus providing nourishment for the young. However, nursing mothers are occasionally known to liberate milk without such a stimulus.

A similar situation is known to exist in the cow. Often the udder of these animals is conceived of as being a simple sac which becomes filled with milk during the day and which must be periodically drained by milking. In actuality this is far from being the case, for the udder is in no way a hollow organ, but instead is quite solidly filled with adipose and other connective tissues through which the mammary glands and their ducts ramify.

Were a dairy cow that has been producing many quarts of milk per day to be killed just before the usual milking time, in all likelihood not more than a pint of milk would be obtainable from the udder. As in human beings, during life, the milk is ejected from the alveoli by stimuli on the teats by the processes of milking or of nursing by a calf.

The Milk. Although often acclaimed as a "nearly ideal food," in actuality milk fluctuates widely in the proportions of its constituents from species to species. For example, the milk of seals contains 4 times the amount of proteins of cow's milk and 12 times that of fat, but carbohydrates are completely absent. In contrast, the product of rabbits is rich in both proteins and carbohydrates but low in fat. As a whole, human milk is relatively dilute, as may be shown by the fact that doubling of birth weight in man requires 180 days, whereas in a seal only 5 days are required and in a calf 47 days. Most probably the correlation of growth rate is with protein content, for human milk has 1.9, cow's 3.3, and seal's 11.9 per cent protein on a total weight basis. Aside from the organic constituents, calcium is an important ingredient. Among human beings since nursing mothers thus supply the young with a considerable quantity of this material, unless their supply of calcium is replenished from outside sources such as cow's milk, damage to the parents' teeth and skeletal parts may result as a consequence of this element's being withdrawn from them.

SEXUAL DUALITY

Among the vertebrates the most usual condition in all the classes is the dioecious one, in which separate male and female individuals exist; however, the monoecious state of affairs is not entirely precluded from these animals. The normal or occasional presence of both types of reproductive organs in the same individual, called *hermaphroditism,* should not be confused with a condition that occurs as an abnormality or freak, usually differentiated by the term *gynandromorphism.* In the latter case, reference is chiefly to the external appearance of sexual duality, with secondary sex traits principally involved. While the sporadic production of these atypical specimens is not without biological interest, it is of little importance as far as the species as a whole is concerned.

Hermaphroditism. As might be anticipated, almost all instances of hermaphroditism are confined to the lower classes among the vertebrates. In the agnathans, for example, the hagfish is a true hermaphrodite, with but a single gonad. This organ is a combination of male and female parts, the anterior portion being ovarian and the posterior testicular in function; at any one time, however, only one gonadal region is active so that a given individual is either male or female on a functional basis. Some reports on these organisms state that a single specimen first serves as a male for a time and later as a female.

In the bony fish very few consistently bisexual species are known. One form, the daurade (*Chrysophrys auratus*), is normally hermaphroditic and has eggs and sperm ripening within the gonad in an alternating fashion. Some of the sea bass of the genus *Serranus* are habitually of a similar nature and have even been known to fertilize their own eggs. As a rule, however, the condition is a sporadic one arising in normally dioecious forms, occasionally reported among commercial fish, including mackerel, herring, ling, and cod. Among all the higher groups, hermaphroditism is either accidental or entirely absent. Only about 25 cases of true bisexuality in which both types of gonads exist have ever been reported for human beings in the whole body of medical literature.

Gynandromorphism and Sex Reversal.
Only rarely are examples of *gynandromorphism* encountered and reported in the literature, but occasionally it may appear in any of the classes. Among birds, for example, it has been recorded to have occurred in pheasants, chickens, and certain European finches. In each instance one side of the body was covered with the plumage of the male, while the other had that of the female. When dissections of these freaks are made, it is often found that a testis is present on the male side of the body and an ovary on the other, although usually female birds have reproductive organs on one side of the body only. How conditions of this sort are produced in the developing individual is still completely unknown.

A correlated reproductive phenomenon, *sex reversal,* is even more infrequent in occurrence than the foregoing. As the term implies, the state of affairs concerns the change of sex in an individual during the course of life. Among chickens one example of the sort has been reliably established. The fowl, it appears, laid eggs regularly for a time and had reared several broods, but, later, it was found to have developed into a functional rooster, for it mated with a hen and fathered two chicks. There now exists one widely noted case of sex reversal in human beings, but in this illustration, the subject commenced as a male. The person, a British citizen with the given name Robert, saw much active service with the Royal Air Force during World War II, but a number of years later underwent a spontaneous series of changes that culminated with his being declared a female by the courts, now to be called Roberta.

Questions for Review and Thought

1. List in sequence the organs of the male mammal through or near which sperm passes on its journey from the testes to the outside. Which of these are present in the lamprey, in the amphibians, and in the reptiles?

2. Give the function or functions of each part of the male mammalian reproductive tract. What glands contribute to the seminal fluid? What activities are assigned to the more important chemical ingredients of semen?

3. Compare the effects of the gonadotropins in the male and female mammal. How do the secretions of the respective gonads differ in the regulation of pituitary activities? Describe the hormonal control of sperm production. What other controls are involved in the functioning of the male reproductive parts?

4. Describe the female reproductive tract in human beings, and briefly state the function of each part. Specifically where are eggs produced? How do the tracts of birds and reptiles differ from the human being?

5. Outline the hormonal controls and changes in the ovary that occur through the time of ovulation. Trace the path of the egg in mammals beyond the ovary and the mechanisms involved in its movement. What happens to it if fertilization does not occur?

6. Distinguish between oviparity, viviparity, and ovoviviparity and between hermaphroditism and gynandromorphism.

7. Give a synopsis of the changes in the egg that have occurred between the lower and higher vertebrates.

8. State the changes that occur in the ovary and other organs during a typical estrous cycle and during the menstrual cycle. What in your opinion are the major differences between the two types?

9. What alterations in the reproductive cycle occur when the egg is fertilized? Summarize the controls over the maintenance of pregnancies in the mammal. What factors are involved in the control of parturition and of lactation?

Supplementary References

Bullough, W. S. *Vertebrate Sexual Cycles.* London, Methuen, 1951.

————. *Hormones and Reproduction.* London, Methuen, 1952.

Burrows, H. *Biological Action of Sex Hormones,* 2nd ed. Cambridge, Cambridge Univ. Press, 1949.

Carlson, A. J., *et al.* *Machinery of the Body,* 5th ed. Chicago, Univ. Chicago Press, 1961.

Corner, G. W. *Hormones in Human Reproduction.* New York, Atheneum, 1963.

Csapo, A. "Progesterone." *Sci. Amer.,* April 1958.

Nalbandov, A. V. *Reproductive Physiology.* San Francisco, Freeman, 1958.

Raven, C. P. *Outline of Developmental Physiology,* 2nd ed. New York, Macmillan, 1962.

Riedman, S. *Our Hormones and How They Work.* New York, Abelard-Schuman, 1954.

Stone, A. "The Control of Fertility." *Sci. Amer.,* April 1954.

Turner, C. D. *General Endocrinology,* 3rd ed. Philadelphia, Saunders, 1960.

PART V

Development
and
Inheritance

I MMEDIATELY UPON FERTILIZATION of the egg, the resulting zygote begins to develop into a new individual, a development that does not cease with hatching or birth, as the case may be, but is continuous throughout life. Within the zygote's protoplasm are contained controls which determine those details of physical features and physiological traits which the individual animal ultimately comes to possess; these controls are properly the object of study for the science of genetics. However, in obtaining its adult features, the zygote passes through a whole series of stages which bear no resemblances externally or internally to the final product. While embryology, the biological science that concerns itself with these developmental processes, is a discipline separate and distinct from genetics, the two are so closely interrelated that it is well to discuss them together. For our purposes the metazoans as a whole will provide the basis, although of necessity stress must be placed upon the vertebrates, particularly the mammals and, of these, frequently the human being.

Many a time ere now I have stopped to think and wonder—I fancy the marvel will never grow less—why it is that we Greeks are not all one in character, for we have the same climate throughout the country and our people enjoy the same education.

THEOPHRASTUS

CHAPTER 19

Reproductive
and
Cyclic Behavior

As one progressed through the vertebrate physiology, perhaps preceding chapters devoted to it was noted that while digestion or respiration, for example, may be principally the function of a single set of organs, in no case does any one system perform its tasks entirely by itself. By and large the subdivision of the body into the various systems is a man-made device, that, although admittedly extremely useful, is nonexistent in the actual organism. Quite obviously the digestive tract could do very little toward digesting foods were it not assisted by circulatory and nervous elements. And how much breathing could be accomplished by the lungs and its associated parts if muscular, skeletal, and neural mechanisms were inactivated? Likewise excretion depends, not on the kidney and the urinary ducts alone, but on the blood

stream and liver, along with endocrinal secretions and nervous activities, and similar statements may be made regarding each of the compartmentalizations.

Reproductive Behavior

In all probability nowhere is this participation by the whole organism in functioning more clearly perceptible than it is in the reproductive processes. While some interrelationships of certain organs in these functions have already been shown, others on a larger scale of performance need to be outlined briefly. These activities and comparable ones which obviously involve the entire organism are known in general under the term *behavior*. To understand truly the nature of reproductive behavior, our main topic here, a look at other aspects of

405

the subject must also be taken. But these must wait until a summary of propagative habits has made clear the nature of the problems involved.

INTERNAL INFLUENCES ON REPRODUCTIVE BEHAVIOR

Although a vast quantity of available information indicates that the internal secretions involved in reproduction in the narrow sense of the term also have a marked effect on the outward activities of the individual, for the greater part the behavior patterns stem from the hormonal actions on the nervous system and, consequent to the cyclic courses inherent in each species, fluctuate in accordance with the internal events. Since the rhythmical changes are especially typical of the female, more has been learned of internal influences on the members of that sex than is the case with the male. As the regulation of sexual behavior patterns is both complex and poorly understood, only the most salient aspects of the topic can be presented here.

Endocrinal Influences. Some of the endocrine effects on behavior in the female have already been noted, such as, in nonprimate vertebrates, the inacceptability of the male's attention except during estrus. In female rats that have had the ovaries removed, the same state prevails, as it does also in those with just the pituitaries removed; thus in one way or another the lack of ovarian secretions prevents normal response to sexual stimuli. Typically during the estrus phase, there is a general increase in physical activities on the part of the female. While at other times relatively quiescent, rats of this sex show a sudden tendency to run, exercise in this manner reaching a peak at ovulation and then gradually subsiding. Similar bursts of activity, sometimes accompanied by emotional stress, often occur in the higher primates including human beings just prior to the onset of menstruation.

Patterns of mating, as well as behavior preceding and following the act (Figure 19–1), are highly influenced by the presence of endocrine secretions. Usually such patterns disappear after removal of the testes or ovaries and are restored to normality when the appropriate hormones are administered. Although these hormones must be present, differences in concentrations have little effect; most of

Figure 19–1. A reproductive adaptation in a toad. Among the specialized reproductive habits of amphibians, numerous as they may be, probably none are more striking than this one possessed by the Surinam toad. The eggs, after being deposited upon the back of the male, sink into the body after they have formed pockets; here they remain until the embryos have developed into tadpoles. (Photo by Dr. George B. Rabb.)

Figure 19–2. Display in birds. *A. Courtship in birds often involves stereotyped patterns of behavior, such as the display of colorful ornaments—in this case by the American spruce grouse. (Photograph by Dr. Harry G. Lumsden, reproduced, with permission, from the* Canadian Field Naturalist, 75:155, 1961.) *B. Stereotyped reproductive behavior can involve protection of the nest or young. Here the European ringed plover is displaying in an effort to distract attention from the nest to itself. (Courtesy of Dr. Edward A. Armstrong.)*

the actual activity depends principally on inherited traits and instincts of the species concerned. While the patterns are largely of a genetic nature, the modes of transmittal and the mechanisms through which they become manifest are not known. As a whole, sexual behavior is only slightly flexible in the vertebrates and is particularly stereotyped among birds. Nests and nesting sites, "displays" (Figure 19–2), and other courtship activities—all are rigid and predetermined; only the final selection of a mate on the part of the female is typically not entirely mechanical (Figure 19–3). In contrast, the mammals are quite flexible. It would seem that, as the cerebral cortex developed in the latter animals and permitted finer thalamic control of some aspects of body functioning, the hormonal and other mechanistic devices regulating reproduction diminished in importance (Figure 19–4). Especially is this true in the human being, where it is difficult to perceive any pattern of sexual behavior that is the product of any single hormone, for while the reproductive hormones probably influence the strength

Figure 19–3. Nesting behavior in birds. Almost without exception, each species of bird has its own inherited pattern for building a nest. These patterns range in complexity from the simplicity of the American killdeer's (A), in which a hollow is made among small pebbles or gravel, to the huge mound made by the brush-turkey (B) in the rain forests of New South Wales. The former species incubates its eggs in the usual manner, but the latter makes use of the heat of the decaying vegetation for development of the eggs. These are deposited in its depths. However, the temperature must be carefully controlled, so the male makes checks at frequent intervals and removes or adds vegetation as needed. (B, courtesy of the Division of Wildlife Research, CSIRO, Australia.)

of the sex drive, they do not govern the means by which it is expressed nor do they determine the direction it takes.

Nervous Influences. Though the hormones influence the nervous system and thus bear weight on the actions of the individual, that system can similarly sway the activities of the endocrine glands.

For example, animals that have been captured in the wilds and placed in captivity are often unable to breed because of the nervous disturbances thus set up. Female wild rats, when brought into the laboratory, do not show any estrous cycling and, consequently, reject males. However, if a portion of the lateral cerebral

Figure 19–4. Reproductive behavior in two species of mammals. A. Family groups, often of considerable durability, are of not infrequent occurrence among mammals. These lions, photographed in their native habitat in Kenya, East Africa, also illustrate *sexual dimorphism*—i.e., marked morphological differences between male and female. (Courtesy of Alan Root, Nairobi.) B. Patterns of nest building are much less elaborate as well as less fixed among mammals than is the case with birds. Here an American opossum uses its tail to carry leaves to its nest in the hollow log. (Courtesy of Oscar B. Greenleaf.)

cortex involved in emotions is removed surgically, regular cycles soon appear. Separate centers for control of the estrous rhythm and the mating response have been found in the rat, located in the hypothalamus.

EXTERNAL INFLUENCES

Not all the influences on reproductive behavior are innate within the individual, as either hormonal or neural mechanisms. The surroundings, too, have their effects.

Figure 19–5. A murre rookery in Newfoundland. "Standing room only" could well be the caption for this photograph! Such crowded conditions appear to be required by many sea-birds for breeding to occur normally. (Photo by Bernard L. Jackson, Newfoundland Department of Mines, Agriculture, and Resources.)

Although undoubtedly many forces are active to a greater or lesser degree, attention will be given to only the three factors—biological, temperature, and light—that have been more thoroughly studied.

Biological Factors. The most pronounced of the biological factors is the presence or absence of other members of the same species. In female rats, even during estrus, no typical mating behavior can be noted so long as the male is absent; while the mere presence of a male individual elicits the pattern, it has not been established whether olfactory or visual stimuli produce the response in this species. The possible involvement of the former, however, appears indicated, because when the olfactory bulbs are removed, the corpora lutea do not form, and the vagina becomes subnormal in size. On the other hand, in many birds visual stimuli are the dominant factor. If female pigeons are caged in such a fashion that they can hear and smell others of their own species but not see them, they do not lay eggs; when mirrors are provided so that they can see their own images or if provision is made for them to perceive other pigeons directly, they deposit eggs quite normally. Similarly the glands that secrete pigeon milk only become functional in the male dove or pigeon if he is able to see a female of his own species incubating eggs.

The numbers of other individuals in the immediate vicinity often have impact on reproductive activities, particularly in social species. Especially has the effect of numbers been noted in sea birds. On the arrival of terns, shearwaters, or gannets at their rookeries in spring, the sounds and excitement of the wheeling birds appear essential in physiological preparation for breeding (Figure 19–5) as well as for the intricate behavior patterns of nest building, incubation, and caring for the young. If too few birds happen to occupy a nesting site, no eggs are laid; this lack of productivity may continue for several years until, by the chance addition of individuals from other areas, the colony is increased to an essential minimum. When only minimal numbers are present, reproduction proceeds but in a less-coordinated manner. Typically in crowded rookeries, egg laying in all individuals occurs almost simultaneously, so that the period of propagation is concentrated, whereas under dilute situations, egg laying is prolonged much longer and at a diminished rate (Figure 19–5). As an extreme example of the need for multiplicity of individuals the case of the guano birds (cormorants) that live off the coast of Peru may be cited. On one island a minimum approximating 10,000 of these birds, resulting in an average density of three nests per square yard, is required for normal reproduction; at lesser concentrations egg laying is entirely inhibited. Although birds have been

more thoroughly studied as far as these effects are concerned, species concentration is known to be important in mammals too. For instance, muskrats, while far from being social, fail to breed at population densities of less than one pair per mile of river or per 85 acres of marshland.

Temperature Effects. In spite of the fact that the body temperature is maintained at a uniform level in birds and mammals, breeding activities in many of these animals vary in accordance with external fluctuations in heat. Cattle, by way of illustration, reproduce at a diminished rate during the summer months, and milk and butterfat production also are highly retarded. Similarly in warm climates sheep produce lambs at an average rate only 60 per cent of that in cool climates. With rising temperatures, the testes of male ground squirrels cease functioning, while with the return of cooler weather in fall, they become reactivated. To investigate whether a correlation to seasonal changes in light intensity or day length is involved, males of this species were maintained at a constant temperature of 40°F for an entire year. Throughout the period the testes were found to remain active, with the normal cyclical cessation of functioning during the summer months failing to appear. In other species such as the prairie dog, on the contrary, temperature has no visible effect.

In some groups, particularly among cold-blooded forms like the frogs, experiments are making it clear that the amount of heat present in the environment is not so important as the direction in which mean temperature changes occur. By way of illustration, *Rana temporaria* of Europe has been found to undergo sexual maturation under the influence of increasing temperature, as normally would be found in the spring of the year. On the other hand, decreasing temperatures have no effect, even when within the same range as the effective ones.

Effects of Light. Conceivably light might affect organisms in three different manners: first, by its relative intensity, second, by changes in the periods of its presence, and finally, by changes in the periods of its absence. Since 1925, when the American biologist W. Rowan first published results of experiments involving light effects on the common North American bird, the eastern junco (Figure 19-6), this topic has developed into a fertile and active field of investigation. Rowan's original work showed that if captive juncos of either sex were exposed to electric illumination to prolong the period of light in fall when the day was decreasing in length, the gonads commenced to mature as they usually do only in spring. Since his studies, many researches have been conducted, with the outcome that numerous diversified patterns of response to light have been found.

Especially important, it seems, are the *photoperiod* effects—that is to say, the length of the daylight period relative to

the dark. Numbers of fish, reptiles, birds, and mammals have been subjected to experimentation and found responsive to alterations of day or night length. Particularly responsive to daylight changes are birds of the temperate zones. In a number of such species not only the reproductive cycles but their characteristic annual migrations toward the opposite hemisphere apparently are regulated by photoperiodic influences. Almost exclusively in these forms an increasing length of daylight is effective, as is also the case with numerous mammals, including the horse and ferret. On the other hand, in several mammals, among which can be mentioned deer and sheep, a decrease in the number of daylight hours provides the stimulus. However, light is not universally required in the governing of annual cyclic patterns. Some tropical bats, for instance, have a marked breeding season in spite of the fact that the number of daylight hours is nearly constant throughout the year. Even birds of temperate deserts are known to be insensitive to photoperiod effects but are induced to breed by the sporadic rainfalls.

The mechanism through which photo-

Figure 19–6. The slate-colored junco. This common bird of cold forests, such as those of Alaska, Canada, and the northern United States, was the first bird studied for photoperiod effects. (Courtesy of Oscar B. Greenleaf.)

periodic effects act on the organism has not been clearly demonstrated in most cases. If the optic nerves are severed in the ferret, no response to light can be noted; nevertheless, the blinded animal undergoes periodic changes in gonadal development under an innate rhythm that seems to be present in the body cells. After the severing of the optic nerves or removal of the eyes, ducks on the contrary continue to respond to increases of daylight hours, even when these are artificially produced. Responses are elicited, in fact, when the light is applied directly to the hypothalamus. Among some lizards, the median eye or even its remnant appears to be acted on by the light rays. As a result of these experiments, biologists generally are in accord on the fact that the light stimuli affect the central nervous system, either directly or through various acceptor organs, and that these transmit impulses to the hypothalamus. Beyond this, much discussion but almost no agreement is to be found regarding the paths involved.

Cyclic and Related Behavior

Both in the chapter on reproduction and in the foregoing discussion, frequent mention has been made of the existence of cycles, including such out-and-out rhythmic patterns as estrous and menstruation and more subtle ones like annual breeding habits and migration. *Cyclic behavior,* as periodic changes in habits are called, currently is an important and active field of zoology, and some extremely pertinent and interesting discoveries have been made. To discuss the subject with any degree of clarity, strict adherence to vertebrate representatives must be temporarily laid aside and a number of invertebrates included in the

discussion. One might as well try to comprehend the history of any given nation without a single reference to a foreign power as to attempt to understand completely the vertebrates or any other taxon by themselves alone. Related forms, even species totally different in outward appearance, frequently can throw light on a subject difficult to illuminate from studies solely of the group concerned. As an example of this might be mentioned the fact that much knowledge of the biochemistry of vertebrate cells has been garnered first by studies made on bacteria and fungi. So the student should not be at all surprised to encounter mention of crabs or bees along with birds and mammals in the present topic.

DAILY CYCLES

That some animals are active chiefly at night and others during daylight is common knowledge, as is the fact that these daily patterns of activities are designated as *nocturnal* and *diurnal,* respectively. But a third type exists that includes those cases when greatest activity is displayed during the transition between light and dark, at dusk and dawn, organisms with such habits being called *crepuscular.* Daily rhythms of any sort are known as *circadian* (from *circa* plus *diem*).

External Controls. Very frequently, the external factors themselves provide the stimuli that initiate activity and bring it to a close. For example, fireflies begin to flash only when the day is changing to darkness and at a light intensity that is constant for each species. Hence, in these insects commencement of flight is timed, as a rule, by the degree of darkness following sunset, hastened somewhat on occasion by such weather conditions as heavy cloud formations. But because of the requirement of direction, i.e., from light to dark, fireflies are not active at dawn.

Under experimental conditions, many other insects show similar direct response to the physical factors; if the favorable condition, illumination or darkness depending on the species, is prolonged, activity is continued correspondingly; if the unfavorable one is extended, the period of quiscence is similarly lengthened. Many vertebrates also show comparable direct responses. In the continual day of the arctic summer when the sun remains above the horizon weeks on end, many avian species fly until fatigued, then after a varied period of rest, resume flight; hence, some individuals are active and others are asleep at almost any hour of the day. Likewise in a number of mice,

variations in the length of night and day in experiments failed to show anything except reaction to the presence and absence of the light factor. Not only terrestrial forms but aquatic ones, too, show similar daily cycles of activity. Many plankton remain at depths during the daylight but rise to the surface at night, returning to deeper water at the advent of dawn. In response to this rhythmic set of changes, especially in the seas, the fish in the area adjust their own location to that of their food source (Figure 19-7).

Biological Clocks. In contrast, a number of other animals show the presence of a built-in clock mechanism of some sort. Among the scorpions, for instance, many Italian and North African varieties have been shown to continue a marked 24-hour periodicity in the laboratory even when

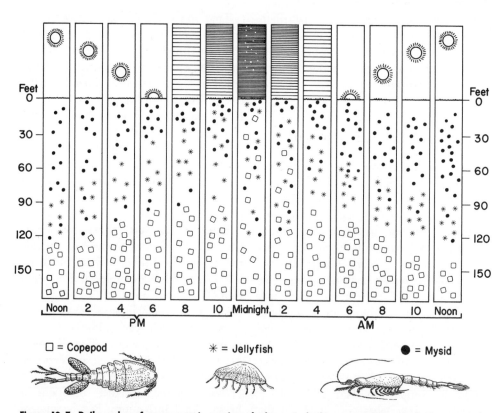

Figure 19-7. Daily cycles of movement in marine plankton. Each day most species of plankton ascend toward or retreat away from the surface, adjusting their level constantly in a cyclic pattern.

they are maintained in constant darkness or light week after week. Among the Crustacea particularly striking observations have been made. In nature many members of the group show a daily fluctuation in coloration, the pigments of the chromatophores dispersing and contracting regularly every 24 hours. When maintained even in total darkness or in bright illumination and at constant temperatures, the rhythm is found to remain unaltered. In the fiddler crab (*Uca*) no change in periodicity occurs even after 30 days of uninterrupted darkness. If the animal, however, is exposed to temperatures lower than 32°F, the pattern is resumed when the specimen is restored to normal conditions but is out of phase by a period corresponding to the time of exposure to the low temperature. For illustration, if a crab is thus treated to below-freezing conditions for six hours and then returned to its usual environment, the color change in either direction reaches the maximum state six hours later than it had previously and continues to do so; in other words, the whole cycle is six hours out of phase. Whereas maximum darkening of the body in untreated specimens may be reached at 2 P.M. daily and maximal lightening 12 hours later, the former now occurs at 8 P.M. and the latter at 8 A.M. After exposure to the usual diurnal changes of light and darkness for a while, the treated crab's *biological clock,* as such adaptive devices are called, automatically readjusts itself and eventually comes back into phase.

Honeybees, too, have been shown to have ability to time events regardless of the environment. By use of attractive foods, these creatures are first trained to visit the same feeding place either once, twice, or three times per day at regular intervals. After being placed in an experimental room in which humidity and temperature as well as light are held at constant levels for long periods, the spacing and circadian rhythm continue undisturbed. One set of such experiments, in fact, was conducted in a deep salt mine where all environmental fluctuations were eliminated. Even individuals reared from eggs in a dark chamber and never permitted to contact the normal alternations of day and night are able to be trained and show the same periodicity. When, after a training regime has been completed, bees or wasps are given certain drugs that retard metabolism, they are found to be at first perhaps four hours behind phase; later, as the effects wear off, the delay is reduced to three hours and then two, and in the end, normality is regained. So it appears that the timing is basically a metabolic activity of some unknown sort.

Similarly as investigations proceed, an increasing number of birds, bats, and other vertebrates are being found to have biological clocks. Let us use man as an illustration of the mammalian pattern. Recently it has been discovered that, in addition to the obvious diurnal pattern of alternating activity and rest, heart rate and body temperature also show a daily rhythm. Normally these latter two aspects are so closely correlated that in bygone years before thermometers, physicians estimated the height of a fever by the rapidity of the pulse; moreover, administration of thyroxin has a concomitant effect on both. To determine whether the two aspects are inseparably coupled, an American biologist, N. Kleitman, lived with his wife and two young adult daughters in Norway for a nine-week period during the arctic summer months when the sun never set. For periods of three weeks each, 18-hour, 24-hour, and 28-hour schedules of activity, eating, and sleeping were maintained. While both the shortened and lengthened "days" disrupted the body temperature patterns in the young women, none of the regimes had any effect on the temperature of the middle-aged man. However, in all of the individuals, the heart soon conformed to the new periodicity, no matter whether the cycle was a shortened or lengthened one. Hence, it is obvious that these two factors are not products of one another.

Moreover, it has been shown that activity and heart rate are mutually independent by another set of experiments in the continuous sunlight of the arctic. In this series, special wrist watches were provided for the experimental human beings, with normal timepieces for controls; some of the watches were designed to complete a "day" in 21 hours, whereas others were adjusted to require 27 hours. Each person ate, worked, relaxed, and slept according to the time indicated by the instrument he wore. Within a few days, the subjects became established in their respective routines, and body temperature patterns soon adapted likewise; however, the excretion of certain products did not change correspondingly. While normally the excretion of water, potassium, and chloride is the same, under the abnormal schedules, although water and chloride elimination became adapted, potassium excretion failed to do so. Hence, it may be possible that the hypothalamus controls water and chloride excretion, along with body temperature and sleep, as has already been seen, but that potassium is under the control of a separate rhythm possibly centered in the adrenal cortex. In other animals the presence of more than one clock mechanism also is suggested by existing evidence.

Even more striking results have been obtained in recent years, some of which indicate that an organism may be quite different, say, at noon than it is at midnight. For instance, certain bacteria secrete a toxin that is extremely deadly when injected into mice during the daylight hours, but which is ineffective when administered in the same doses after midnight! Furthermore Pittendrigh, an animal ecologist at Princeton, and his students, by making analyses of the proteins of mammalian liver, heart, kidney, and other organs at hourly intervals during the day, have uncovered cyclic patterns of changes existing in certain of these most characteristic compounds of the protoplasm. Perhaps these changes in the metabolic processes within the cells of the body may eventually be found to provide the actual basis for daily timing mechanisms. Be that as it may, with one exception, all organisms, unicellular or multicellular, plantlike or animal-like, are known to possess biological clocks. The sole exception is found in the blue-green algae, which group has been suggested to be the most primitive form of life. If this is so, it is then possible that the rhythmic pattern was established only after the cell had evolved toward a higher level, such as that represented by the bacteria perhaps.

TIDAL AND LUNAR CYCLES

Rhythms in response to tides are, of course, entirely confined to marine organisms, and those related to the full moon are largely so. Since the tides have a 12.4-hour cycle, very often it is difficult to distinguish the effects of two such rhythms from a single diurnal one. Moreover, in some species of fiddler crabs, the circadian pattern of color changes is modified in relation to tidal fluctuations too. While darkening always occurs during daylight and hence is a diurnal cycle, the time of maximum darkening varies in accordance with the low tide, occurring from somewhat before to somewhat after noon. Whenever darkening takes place early in the day, there is a second maximum at evening. Other marine forms respond solely to the ebbing of the seas. For example, flatworms of the genus *Convoluta* live in the intertidal zone just above low-tide boundary, within the sand while the tide is in but on the surface when it is out. When emerged onto the surface, they are often so abundant as to form green patches on the sand, the green resulting from the symbiotic algae contained in their digestive tracts. This rhythmical change apparently has an innate control mechanism, only indirectly influenced by the tide, for as the tide recedes the patches gradually increase in extent until all have surfaced, but then the areas slowly become diminished until the tide commences to return. Consequently, before the rising water comes within a few feet of the worms, the last of them has disappeared into the sand. In the laboratory this same rhythm exists even though the worms are entirely without the influence of changing water levels.

Among marine animals a *lunar cycle* frequently governs breeding activities. One polychaete worm of the West Indies, a luminescent species, emerges from the ocean bottoms in large numbers during the full of the moon. In the shallow waters the luminous organs apparently are employed to attract mates; after mating activities have been completed, all retreat into the ocean bottom for another lunar month. While lunar cycles are typical of marine species, a somewhat similar pattern has been suggested to exist among a few terrestrial forms too. Besides several bird and mammalian instances of doubtful validity, certain mayflies in Africa in the region of Lake Victoria seem to swarm at regular intervals;

the swarms always occur within five days of the full moon, and the greatest number of swarms can be counted on the second night after the full of the moon.

ANNUAL CYCLES

Although flowering plants are most notorious for their annual rhythmic cycles, some animals too are known to have yearly patterns of activity governed largely by the number of daylight hours and the direction of change in day length. Among metazoans, internal mechanisms seemingly play a quite important role. Frequently in the birds, the gonads, governed by the hypothalamus by way of the pituitary, appear largely involved as the activating mechanism, as has already been shown in the discussion of reproduction, with the number of daylight hours forming the principal stimulatory factor. Along with these alterations in the size of the gonads, birds become restless, in many cases the restlessness intensifying until migratory flight is inaugurated. Only rarely in birds are the patterns of the nature of biological clocks in a strict sense. Chief among the exceptional instances are a few south-temperate species, including the common lovebird, or budgerigar, which retains a fixed cycle even when transported to northern latitudes, breeding from September to November regardless of whether this be the spring or the fall of the year. As to the actual character of the metabolic clocks that regulate seasonal activities, there is at present no generally accepted hypothesis.

NAVIGATIONAL MECHANISMS

The mechanisms employed by various motile organisms to orient themselves geographically are no less remarkable than those used in timing their activities. For the most part the mechanisms have been studied more extensively in insects and in birds than in other groups, although migratory fish are currently receiving close attention too. As one instance of the latter can be cited the salmon of the Columbia River basin in western North America, which die after spawning in the headwaters of the river system. After hatching and some degree of growth, the young fish migrate down the streams to the seas, where they reach maturity several years later. If the young are marked before they leave their home territory on the seaward journey, it has been found that they return as adults to precisely the same headwaters in which they were hatched several years earlier. Since landmarks in rapidly flowing waters of mountain streams are apt to change frequently, it has been suggested that visual stimuli are probably of limited value in helping the salmon regain their original homes. Recent experiments, in fact, seem to indicate that orientation is largely through olfactory memory and that each rivulet has a slightly different odor that distinguishes it from others.

Insect Navigational Mechanisms. While a large number of studies of orientation have been made on a variety of insects, including bees, wasps, ants, termites, and roaches, not to mention other arthropods, such as spiders and sandhoppers, the general principles can be sufficiently illustrated by those devoted to the honeybee. Doubtlessly, the Austrian entomologist von Fritsch has been the leader in the investigation of this interesting form. To understand the nature of the mechanism, however, it is first necesary to examine bee behavior briefly.

When a worker bee discovers a new source of nectar, she returns to the hive and, inside, performs a "dance" on a comb with myriads of other workers watching her. This dance is essentially a rapid walk in a figure-of-eight pattern, on one straight stroke of which the abdomen is waggled rapidly from side to side. Over and over again the ritual is repeated. While this behavior had been noted many years ago, only recently has its significance been made clear. The direction of the waggling movement of the dance, von Fritsch has found, indicates the direction of the food source from the hive in relation to the sun, while its length is correlated to the distance from the colony. Moreover, the dance's intensity evidences the richness of the new source. By means of the communications thus transmitted, the onlookers are able to fly directly to the patch of freshly opened flowers or whatever the newly discovered supply may be.

As stated above, the instructions for direction are relative to the sun. On the vertical comb when the waggling movement is performed on the upstroke, the location of the new source is toward the sun, whereas when this movement is rendered during a downward run, the opposite is intimated. Positions between these two extremes are indicated by the angle of deviation from these points (Figure 19–8). However, it should be recalled that the information is received by the watching insects, first, within the confines of the comb removed from sight of the sun and that, as a rule, it is both imparted and obtained in a vertical position, whereas actual flight is horizontal. Moreover, not only is the communicated pattern remembered, it is adjusted for changes in time. For instance, von Fritsch set out a supply of food in late afternoon and permitted a worker bee to find it and return to the hive, where the information was passed to others of the colony by means of this unique "language." But

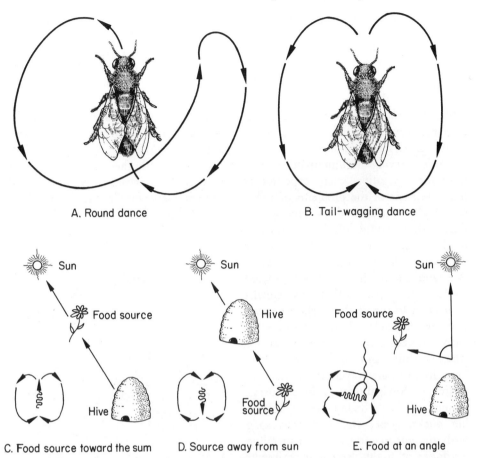

A. Round dance

B. Tail-wagging dance

C. Food source toward the sum

D. Source away from sun

E. Food at an angle

Figure 19–8. The "dance" of the bees. A. The round dance is employed to indicate the presence of a food source less than about 100 yards distant from the hive. B. The tail-wagging dance is used when the food source is more remotely located. The direction of the wagging phase of the dance provides information regarding the direction of the food relative to the sun, the intensity suggests its richness, and the length of the wagging run indicates the distance—simple language, indeed, but one that requires considerable intelligence both to transmit and to comprehend.

before other workers had an opportunity to visit the food, the entrance was blocked and the whole hive moved to a new location three miles distant. When the bees, properly marked for identification, were released in the new situation the next morning, they flew to a point corresponding precisely to that where the food supply would have been located the night before. This was accomplished in spite of the difference in time of day, the sun now being to the east instead of to the west as when the dancing occurred; the new location of the hive, of course, eliminated all possibility that familiar landmarks were employed in these operations.

Only when the sunlight is polarized, as by passage through clear atmosphere, can the bees communicate instructions; hence since clouds depolarize the rays, the dances do not occur when the sun is obscured. On a cloudy day if an opening over the comb is covered by a sheet of polarizing plastic, the bees dance as usual if the sheet is placed in a position that yields a pattern similar to that of a clear day at the same hour; if the pattern differs from that of a corresponding time of day, however, dancing does not take place. Presumably the bees associate the artificially produced "time" pattern with their memory of that which would ordinarily appear in a clear sky.

Besides serving to illuminate adaptations for navigation, these experiments illustrate some of the problems of precision flight encountered by any species during the daytime. While the sun is a bright enough beacon, there are rainy or cloudy periods when it is unavailable, on one hand, and on the other, even in good weather, its apparent daily movements in relation to the earth's surface necessitate compensatory timing devices—devices that need constant readjustment for seasonal shifts and for latitude where long distances are traversed.

Bird Navigational Mechanisms. Among the birds, many species, including ducks, geese, and numerous song birds, migrate to and from their breeding territories at night. Recent experiments conducted on certain European warblers (relatives of the American kinglet) suggest one mechanism that may be used in navigating under nocturnal conditions. Although in one experiment the birds were hatched and reared in soundproof, completely enclosed chambers under constant illumination, so that nothing suggestive of an annual cycle of climatic changes ever contacted these birds, yet in autumn and spring they underwent periods of nocturnal restlessness. Instead of sleeping at night, they flew constantly from perch to perch throughout the time when they normally would have been migrating. When placed in a glass-topped cage out of doors at night, the animals oriented themselves by the stars and

fluttered in the normal direction of migration. At other times they were caged in a planetarium. Here the "stars" could be adjusted to north-south or east-west positions so as to mislead the birds as to their actual location. In every case the creatures responded and made the correct directional shifts in their movements according to the changed pattern of the stars. Apparently there exists a hereditary mechanism by means of which the birds can automatically find directions by a mere glimpse of the starry sky, coupled

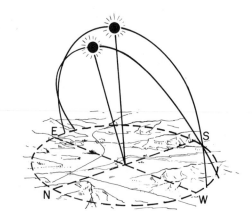

A. SOUTH OF THE EQUATOR

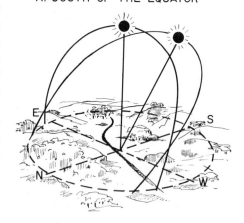

B. NORTH OF THE EQUATOR

Figure 19–9. A theory of bird navigation. One current concept proposes that birds utilize the movement of the sun in its daily arc across the sky in orienting themselves.

with a daily and seasonal biological clock, which assists in making the necessary adjustments for time of day and year, as well as latitude. The employment of stars in nature, too, is suggested by the fact that, on cloudy nights, birds become confused and tend to lose their way.

Homing. Closely correlated to migrational navigation is the ability of an animal to return home when taken to a remote point and released. While the *homing instinct* in the pigeon has been a familiar phenomenon for years, it is emphatically not confined to that species. Starlings, warblers, and other song birds, as well as gulls, shearwaters, and similar seabirds have experimentally been shown to possess remarkable powers of returning home. In one concept currently widely accepted, it is suggested that a bird makes use of the sun together with its own metabolic clock in orienting itself in a strange locality. According to this theory, it is not so much the position of the solar body that is involved as it is the arc in which the sun moves across the sky. With the progress of the year the solar arc constantly alters its angle relative to the horizon, but this angle is also correlated to latitude. Toward the poles the arc becomes lower, although it contacts the horizon further northward as one travels toward the Arctic Circle and southward as the antarctic region is approached. On the contrary, the arc becomes more and more vertical toward the equator, and contacts the horizon at points placed almost at absolute east and west (Figure 19-9). The concept proposes that in the home territory, the bird memorizes the arc and the seasonal changes and keys the pattern to its own metabolic clock; hence, when it finds itself in a strange territory, whether it is flying or perching, it first observes the sun's arc. Should the arc be lower in the sky than in the home range, it "knows" to fly southward; if the arc is higher than ordinary, a northward path is indicated. Moreover, the bird's biological clock indicates whether the sun's location is behind or ahead of its home schedule. If the former is the case, the bird is west of its home range and flies eastward or in the opposite direction in the latter case. Having "decided" on its direction, the bird flies until it arrives within a few miles of its familiar grounds, and then, by recognizing landmarks, it regains its original home.

Questions for Review and Thought

1. Which two systems appear to be especially active in reproductive behavior in contrast to the actual reproductive processes? Are these internal influences completely free of external factors? Why or why not? Where does the ultimate control of all behavior center, and what facts support your answer?

2. Give some examples of external biological factors that influence reproductive behavior. In what different ways does temperature affect organisms?

3. What is meant by photoperiod effects? Can photoperiodism be better classed as a daily or an annual cyclic pattern? What is the basis for your reasoning? Why is photoperiodism not a common phenomenon in tropical species?

4. By what means are photoperiod changes detected by the organism?

5. Define the term *circadian rhythm*. If fireflies are crepuscular, why do they fly only at dusk and not at dawn? In what regions of the earth do daily cycles frequently break down, if they actually do exist in organisms there?

6. Illustrate the existence of biological clocks in as many invertebrates as you can. Do likewise with some vertebrates.

7. What cycles other than daily seem to exist among living things? List the types and give examples of each.

8. By what means do bees communicate with one another? Describe the various elements contained in their "language." Being as specific as possible in your answer, what provides the point of reference that enables bees to navigate with precision? What evidence exists that indicates the involvement of internal factors in their navigation?

9. Compare the navigational mechanisms of birds with those of insects, giving the basic resemblances as well as the distinctions. How does "homing" behavior differ in its essentials?

Supplementary References

Beach, F. A. *Hormones and Behavior*. New York, Hoeber, 1948.

Blond, G. *The Great Migrations*. New York, Macmillan, 1956.

Cloudsley-Thompson, J. L. *Rhythmic Activity in Animal Physiology and Behavior*. New York, Academic Press, 1961.

Fraenkel, G. S., and D. L. Gunn. *The Orientation of Animals*. New York, Dover, 1961.

Klopfer, P. H. *Behavior Aspects of Ecology*. Englewood Cliffs, N. J., Prentice-Hall, 1962.

Lincoln, F. C. *Migration of Birds*. Garden City, N. Y., Doubleday, 1952.

Matthews, G. V. T. *Bird Navigation*. Cambridge, Cambridge Univ. Press, 1955.

Milne, L., and M. Milne. *Paths across the Earth*. New York, Harper, 1958.

Roeder, K. D. *Nerve Cells and Insect Behavior*. Cambridge, Mass., Harvard Univ. Press, 1963.

Shaw, Evelyn. "The Schooling of Fishes." *Sci. Amer.*, June 1962.

Tinbergen, N. "The Curious Behavior of the Stickleback." *Sci. Amer.*, December 1952.

Von Fritsch, K. *Bees, Their Vision, Chemical Senses, and Language*. Ithaca, N. Y., Cornell Univ. Press, 1956.

———. "Dialects in the Language of Bees." *Sci. Amer.*, August 1962.

Withrow, R. B., *et al. Photoperiodism and Related Phenomena in Plants and Animals*. Washington, Amer. Assoc. Advance. Sc., 1959.

The Development
of the Individual

HAPTER 18 undertook the discussion of the reproductive processes as they occur in the adult animal, but there are other aspects, largely concerned with the development of the fertilized egg, which still remain to be considered. Many variations in detail exist in these developmental stages among the various classes, mostly arising from differences in egg structure and especially in yolk content. Here, three examples, the frog, the chicken, and the human, serve to show the fundamental concepts of embryology as a whole and some variations in expression that are found in the Vertebrata.

Embryological Development

Since in most vertebrates provision is made, sometimes by an abundant supply of yolk, to nourish the developing young far beyond ordinary embryological stages until they have, in fact, achieved some substantial growth, it is necessary to distinguish between a true embryo and a fetus. As a rule, the stages of the *embryo* are considered to commence with the fertilization of the egg and to persist until all the foundations, or *primordia,* of the body organs have been established. Those of the *fetus* carry through development and continue until hatching or birth and largely involve growth of the primordia. Here the embryonic period is our first concern.

THE EGG AND ITS
FERTILIZATION

More is involved in the union of the sperm with the egg than the mere fusion of two cells. First of all, the sperm must

423

reach the egg and penetrate any protective coats that the egg may possess. Furthermore, since numerous sperm may contact a single ovum, devices must exist to permit the entrance of only one male gamete or at least to prevent the fusion of more than one sperm nucleus with that of the egg. Since investigations of these matters have been carried out only in recent years and are still actively continuing, the basic processes are not entirely clear. But to understand what has been learned, a knowledge of the structure of the vertebrate egg must first be garnered.

The Vertebrate Egg. Generally speaking, the vertebrate egg shows a steady increase in diameter from the lower forms to the more advanced, much of which increment results from an accumulation of yolk within the egg cell. Only the higher mammals are exceptional, and they have acquired a secondary means of nourishing the fetus. Around the egg and its yolk contents is a *vitelline membrane* in addition to the cell membrane which covers all cells. Beyond this fact, the structure varies in accordance with the group being considered. In contrast

to the other classes, in which deposits of gelatinous material or albumen and often a shell surround the egg cell proper, the mammalian ovum is devoid of any protective covering; however, it does retain two follicular structures, the *zona pellucida,* a colorless transparent zone, and the *corona radiata,* a highly irregular coating containing numerous cells (Figure 20–1).

Fertilization. As the processes of fertilization have been more completely studied in mammals, that group alone will receive attention here. In these animals, subsequent to their being deposited in the vagina, sperm have a life-span of no more than 24 hours. This fact, coupled with their small size and the relatively great length of the reproductive tract, indicates that their locomotive equipment in the form of a flagellum can scarcely be sufficient for their needs. Moreover, the latest evidence shows that sperm arrive at the upper end of the oviducts within a few minutes after insemination, and since even dead sperm and particles of carbon or dye arrive as rapidly as the live gametes, some assistance in the sperm transport can safely

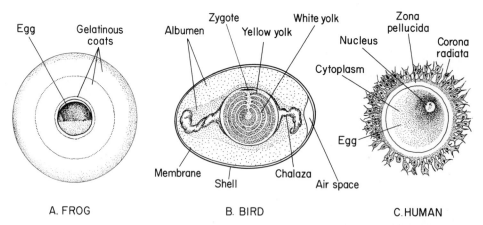

Figure 20–1. The eggs of representative vertebrates. A. In gross structure the eggs of many fish do not differ greatly from this one of an amphibian. B. Except in certain details, the eggs of the cold-blooded reptiles and of the egg-laying mammals do not depart greatly from the structure shown in the chicken egg. C. The human egg illustrated is quite similar to that of most other mammals.

be assumed to be present. More than likely, muscular contractions of the uterus and oviducts may be involved; however, the sperm appear first to enter the uterus through the cervix by means of their flagella alone and only from there receive assistance.

Although the sperm arrive at the site of the eggs shortly after insemination, they are not immediately capable of uniting with the female gametes but must first undergo some changes. Although the nature and production of the phenomenon of change, called *capacitation,* are virtually unknown, it is clear that sperm must be exposed to the secretions of the uterus and oviducts for a minimum of six hours before fertilization is possible. On the other hand, sperm contained in the tubes for longer periods, up to the maximal survival time of 24 hours, tend to produce embryos of decreasing viability, for there is a strong negative correlation between the age of the sperm and the survival of the resulting embryo. Moreover, the same statements are equally true of the egg.

When a sufficient number of sperm have been capacitated and a freshly ovulated egg is present, the coverings over the egg, particularly the corona radiata, begin to disintegrate. The explanation of how this breakdown might be induced is still largely hypothetical, but much evidence points to the involvement of an enzyme called *hyaluronidase* secreted by the sperm. Once through this layer, the male gametes must traverse the zona pellucida, in which process the hyaluronidase of the sperm head perhaps assists, perhaps not. At any rate, after this zone has been penetrated, the first sperm to arrive adheres momentarily to the vitelline membrane by its anterior end and finally makes its entry into the egg's cytoplasm. Immediately following its entrance, in many mammals, the

membrane thickens and forms the so-called *fertilization membrane* that blocks passage of further sperm.

All this time the egg has been traversing the length of the oviduct under the influence of the ciliary beating of the tube's cellular lining. At first its progress is rapid, so that the upper half of the tubule is passed through in perhaps two hours; however, the rate soon diminishes, for, depending on the species, two to five days are required for it to reach the uterus. En route, the pronuclei of the gametes fuse and fertilization is consummated, subsequent to which, development of the zygote proceeds without delay.

DEVELOPMENT OF THE ZYGOTE

To illustrate the processes of embryological development in a simpler condition, one of the invertebrates must first be drawn upon. Although not really typical of the metazoans as a whole, the development of the echinoderms is usually taken as the model, a custom that is followed here. In them, as in all animals, the single-celled *zygote,* diploid in chromosome number, is the point of departure; its subsequent development, too, is universal in nature and involves not growth in mass but subdivision into finer and finer cells by mitotic cell division, processes referred to as *cleavage.* In some groups the products are nearly entirely separate cells (*blastomeres*), marked off on the surface by grooves called *cleavage furrows.*

Embryology of the Starfish

As division is initiated, the zygote first divides into two cells and, after a further mitotic division of each component, into four smaller cells, and so on, all within the confines of the fertilization membrane. These *early cleavage* stages

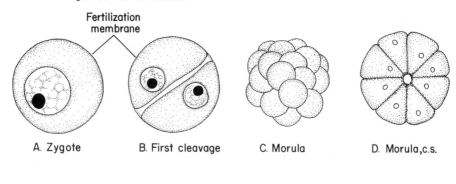

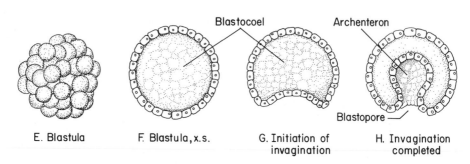

Figure 20–2. Early development of the starfish. Although not actually typical of metazoans as a whole, the embryological development of the starfish is widely accepted as a model of the principal events.

proceed until a solid ball of cells, the *morula,* is produced. Although the term is loosely applied, a morula generally possesses around 32 to 64 cells and in cross section shows no internal cavity (Figure 20–2). By the time it is formed, the fertilization membrane has disintegrated and disappeared, so that now the embryo is without this protective coat. As cleavage continues and the number of blastomeres increases, the cells become aligned in a single layer around a cavity, the *blastocoel,* thus producing a hollow ball, an embryological stage designated as the *blastula.* After cell division has proceeded still further, an infolding or *invagination* results in a flattened ball, now composed of two layers which surround a new cavity, the *archenteron* or embryonic digestive tract. This tract opens on the underside of the embryo by means of the *blastopore.* Within

this two-layered early *gastrula* a third layer of cells forms, and it is in its formation that perhaps the greatest divergency of details is found, varying highly from species to species. Sometimes the walls of the archenteron outpocket and develop into sacs on each side, where, as in other echinoderms, a flat sheet of cells grows from the internal portion around the blastopore, and in still others is produced externally. By whatever processes, the *late gastrula* comes to possess the three primary germ layers mentioned in an earlier discussion, named in sequence, beginning externally, *ectoderm, mesoderm,* and *entoderm* (Figure 20–2). During the remainder of the embryonic period each germ layer undergoes a series of modifications so that eventually the primordia of all the organs are brought into existence. The procedures of establishing the individual early organs form a fascinating study but are far beyond the scope of this text.

The Development of the Frog

Basically, the early embryological history of the frog is no different from that of the starfish. The starting point is the zygote, the processes are by cleavage, and the embryo passes through the same early stages, including the morula, blastula, and gastrula. However, the details of formation of the embryonic stages

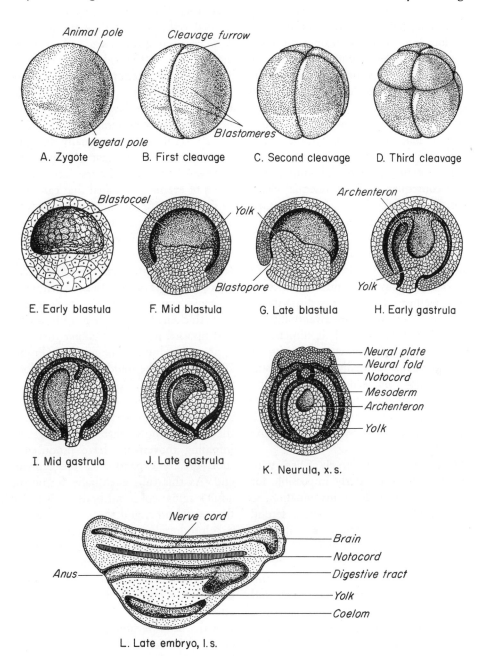

A. Zygote   B. First cleavage   C. Second cleavage   D. Third cleavage

E. Early blastula   F. Mid blastula   G. Late blastula   H. Early gastrula

I. Mid gastrula   J. Late gastrula   K. Neurula, x. s.

L. Late embryo, l. s.

Figure 20–3. The embryology of the frog.

and the germ layers are highly distinct, the distinguishing traits resulting especially from the presence of a moderate yolk deposit. As shown in Figure 20–3, the frog egg is paler at one end than at the other, the difference in color arising from the yolk at the lower *vegetal pole*. Eventually, only the darker *animal pole* develops into the tadpole, since the vegetal end is completely digested during the later stages. Following fertilization, the first *cleavage* forms two complete and equal blastomeres, as does the second; the third cleavage, however, in which the four long cells are split transversely, does not take place at the center, but instead, occurs closer to the animal pole. As a consequence of the unequal cleavages, the vegetal cells are, from this time on, larger than the animal counterparts, aided by the fact, too, that in the lower region cell division occurs at a slower rate. During the following stages the inequality of division and difference in rate together effect a great disparity of cell size at the two poles. Eventually the animal blastomeres, as their dimensions decrease, form a thin layer that grows down over and gradually completely surrounds the yolk cells. Accompanying these envelopmental steps, a small blastocoel develops within the ball and a well-marked *blastula* is established (Figure 20–3).

With its interior largely filled with vegetal cells, it is utterly impossible for the frog egg to undergo invagination, so in place of infolding to form a second layer, a simple expedient is employed. In this substitute method those animal cells enveloping the yolk migrate in sheets into the interior when they attain a point marking the blastopore and continue movement within the interior. Finally, the migrating layers meet at the top within the egg cavity and become continuous to form the *early gastrula*.

On its completion, the yolk-laden cells are considered to form a part of the *archenteron,* and hence are entodermal. As a rule, in the frog a middle germ layer in part migrates inward as the archenteron is formed and within the blastocoel gives rise to a plate of mesodermal cells. At this time the *late gastrula* begins to grow in size and a marked elongation of the body can be noted, while definite anterior and posterior ends become established. No longer is the blastopore on the lower side, for it has now assumed a posterior location (Figure 20–3); however, eventually this pore narrows and becomes completely closed.

Toward the end of these activities a series of events is initiated that can serve to illustrate how complex organ systems are derived from a simple layer of cells. On the dorsal surface, broadening at the anterior end, the ectoderm becomes flattened somewhat to form the *neural plate*. Next, the edges of the plate thicken while a groove appears along the median line. The thickened edges then roll inward and upward in such a manner that they approach and touch one another (Figure 20–4), first at the middle and then along the entire length. After the edges have become contiguous, a fusion takes place, so that now a transverse section through the embryo shows that the rolling and infolding movements have produced a tube, greatly expanded at the cephalic end. As this tube eventually forms the adult's spinal cord and brain, it is called the *neural tube,* and the stage in which it is produced in the vertebrate embryonic development is referred to as the *neurula.* Thus the chordates uniformly have an additional embryological stage beyond the gastrula that occurs in no other metazoan. Obviously, much growth, multiplication, and elaboration of the relatively few cells now present in the neural tube are necessary before it can be perfected into the functional organs of adulthood, but this simple neural tube may be considered the primordium of the nervous system. Hence any further development it undergoes would be a part of the fetal stages, not of the embryonic ones. Comparable developments in each of the remaining germ layers, not to mention additional ones within the ectoderm, are proceeding concurrently with the laying down of the nervous system, so that by the time that primordium is completed the neurula has attained a fair degree of complexity as a whole. Within a short period, it completes fetal development and breaks free of the protective gelatinous coats of the egg as an active but minute tadpole.

Principal Features of Bird Development

If a frog's embryo experiences difficulty in carrying out the normal processes of development because of the relatively small amount of yolk present, the obstacles to the embryo provided by the abundance of stored foodstuffs in a bird's egg can well be imagined. Nevertheless, the zygote undergoes stages comparable to those of the other animals, although in highly modified states. During this discussion if the fact is kept in mind that the actual embryo in the bird is a mere island of dividing cells floating on top of a mass of stored food material, the correlations of the embryonic stages will be readily perceived, for it can be visualized that the little isle can no more surround the yolk to become spherical than a coral atoll can engulf the world. Hence the chief distinctions of bird embryology lie in the flattening or, better still, the spreading out of the cells to form disks in contrast to the formation of spheres found in the preceding examples. After a number of cleavages have occurred, in section the *morula* is seen as a disk of blastomeres closely applied

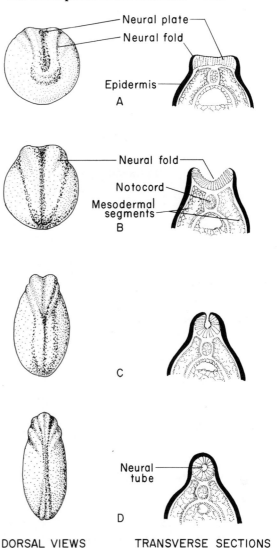

DORSAL VIEWS   TRANSVERSE SECTIONS

Figure 20–4. Steps in the formation of the neural tube. In the vertebrates the nervous system begins as a dorsal thickening of the ectoderm (A), the neural plate. Later the edges of the plate thicken to form folds (B, C) and finally fuse to form the neural tube.

to the yolk mass throughout (Figure 20–5). Almost as soon as this phase becomes established, the dividing cells realign themselves to change the single-layered tissue into one composed of two rows of cells, beneath which there now appears a cavity, the *blastocoel*. As in

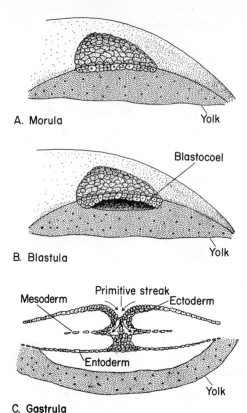

A. Morula   Yolk

B. Blastula   Blastocoel   Yolk

C. Gastrula   Mesoderm   Primitive streak   Ectoderm   Entoderm   Yolk

Figure 20–5. Early developmental stages in the chick. Because of the great quantities of yolk that are present, bird embryos develop as disks rather than spheres.

the frog, the presence of this cavity marks the *blastula* stage. Since invagination was seen to be an impossibility in the amphibian, it can be no less out of the question in avians. Although the frog retained a blastopore that ultimately elongated as it migrated to a posterior location, even the formation of a definitive pore cannot occur in the present forms. Nevertheless, the establishment of the second germ layer is accomplished by comparable means of an inward movement of cells. A thickening over a broad area occurs in the chick at the posterior end of the blastula. The cells of this thickened region then flow posteriorly and toward the midline to produce what appears as a streak along the median line. This *primitive streak* corresponds essentially to an unopened blastopore in

a greatly elongated condition, and, just as in the frogs, cells on the surface move toward it and then downward to assume an internal location, thus establishing a second germ layer and, with it, the *gastrula* stage. Between these two layers the mesoderm is produced as a thin sheet of cells on each side. Later, on the upper surface, a neural plate develops in the ectoderm as the primitive streak gradually shortens and eventually disappears. Similar increments along the edges of the plate, followed by an inward and upward rolling to establish the neural tube, can be noted. As the tube is forming, a series of transverse blocks begin to appear behind it; these blocks are the *somites* of the mesoderm which give rise to the body cavity and the muscles, both of the skeleton and internal organs as well as other parts. With increase in age, more and more of the somites are added posterior to those existing until a total of 45 has been attained. If the series of photographs of the developing embryo is followed (Figure 20–6), a general concept of the changes in the growing young before hatching may be gathered.

Principal Features of Mammalian Embryology

On the surface of the matter, since the mammalian egg contains no yolk while the bird's has so much, one would anticipate little correspondence between the two; the actual state of affairs is just the opposite, however, for most of the essential details are closely alike in the two groups. When it is recalled that the existing primitive mammals have eggs not unlike those of reptiles, replete with yolk, it might be conceivable that the resemblances to the birds found in the higher mammals stem from the fact that the loss of yolk has occurred only recently, so that the embryo develops as though an ample supply were still at hand—a retention of an old habit, as

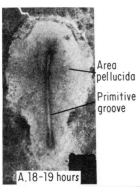

Area
pellucida

Primitive
groove

A. 18-19 hours

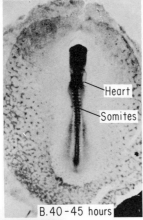

Heart

Somites

B. 40-45 hours

it were, originally essential but now totally useless. Nevertheless, differences can be noted. In the first place, the *early cleavages* show more resemblances to those of the starfish than to anything else, for the blastomeres are equal in size and arranged spherically within the zona pellucida of the original egg. Even through the *morula* stage nothing distinctive can be observed (Figure 20–7), but when the morula becomes altered into a *blastula* several atypical features are perceptible. Instead of a central blastocoel being formed, the cells withdraw more to one region than to others, so that a mass is established at one end, and the whole of the blastocoel is surrounded by only a thin single-cellular layer. This layer originally had a nutritional function and is referred to as the *trophoblast;* the enlarged mass on it ultimately develops into the embryo and is accordingly named the *formative tissue.* Combined, the two parts are the whole blastula, commonly called the *blastocyst,* in mammals. Beyond this point, the processes of forming the *gastrula* and *neurula* are not unlike those of the bird (Figure 20–5).

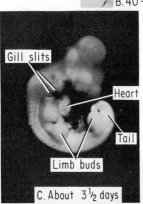

Gill slits

Heart

Tail

Limb buds

C. About 3½ days

Figure 20–6. Selected stages in the chick's development. Within the short span of 21 days, the unicellular zygote develops into an active chick. Some of the steps passed through are shown along with the characteristic features that distinguish each stage. (Courtesy of Drs. V. Hamburger and L. Hamilton, *Jour. Morph.,* Vol. 88, 1951.)

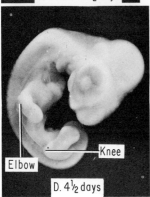

Elbow

Knee

D. 4½ days

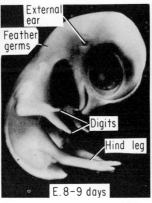

External
ear

Feather
germs

Digits

Hind leg

E. 8-9 days

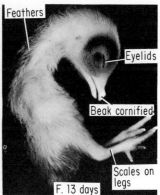

Feathers

Eyelids

Beak cornified

Scales on
legs

F. 13 days

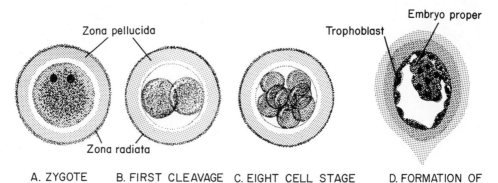

Figure 20–7. Early steps in the development of the mammalian embryo.

THE EMBRYONIC MEMBRANES

In birds, reptiles, and mammals, in which, at least primitively, the embryo develops within a protective shell, a series of mechanisms is required to make existence possible within such confines. To this end a whole series of membranes is formed, completely surrounding the embryo and providing it with oxygen and other essentials. Four sets are normally present in the higher vertebrates, the amnion, chorion, yolk sac, and allantois; since they are not part of the embryo proper, they are together referred to as the *extraembryonic membranes.* Of these the *yolk sac* is found in most vertebrates, including lower forms, and is really an extension of the archenteron containing yolk. Apparently its stored foodstuffs are not passed into the digestive tract but are digested by the lining cells and absorbed into blood vessels on its wall to be conducted to the embryo. Two membranes, the *chorion* and *amnion,* are formed simultaneously by a saclike outpocketing on the entire lower surface of the embryo; this outpocketing should be envisioned as occurring on all sides of an ellipse and as growing outward as well as downward at first (Figure 20–8). On the other hand, after the

sides and ends of the developing vertebrate have been surpassed, subsequent growth is upward and inward, with all edges of the sacs approaching a common point, much as a pouch is drawn closed by strings. As the edges meet, they fuse, and the final result is the formation of the amnion from the inner walls of the former sacs and the chorion from the outer. Between the two membranes is the chorioamniotic cavity, and around the embryo within the amnion is the amniotic cavity, filled with a fluid that probably serves to absorb mechanical shocks and to permit the growing individual freedom to move and change shape. Within its walls, too, is unstriated muscle tissue, which by contraction and relaxation gently agitates the amniotic fluid, thus preventing the embryo from adhering to its surroundings and becoming maimed. On its part the chorion increases in extent and frequently surrounds the entire contents of the egg in shelled species; functionally it is of value as protection and in aiding the exchange of respiratory gases through the shell. In the reptiles and birds a similar role is played also by the *allantois,* an outgrowth of the digestive tract located near the posterior end of the body. Although it is concerned also with absorpticn of albumen in birds, its chief function is that of storing the waste products excreted by the kidneys.

THE PLACENTA

Even in the higher mammals whose eggs lack a heavy covering the same series of extraembryonic membranes develops, some of which serve in identical, others in distinctive capacities, such as entering into the formation of the placenta. Since the placenta is an important feature of mammalian reproduction, it may be well to give close attention to its structure and physiology. For our purposes, the human embryo provides the example, and we begin the account where

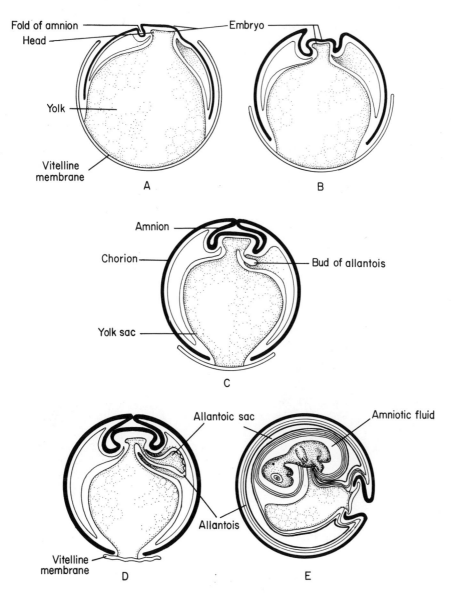

Figure 20–8. Membrane formation in the chick embryo.

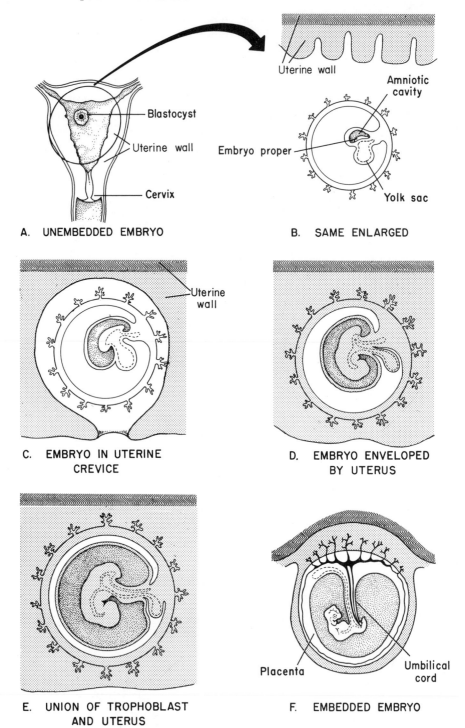

Figure 20–9. Implantation of the human embryo. At first free in the uterine cavity, the embryo soon contacts the wall and becomes embedded in a crevice. By combined activities of both the trophoblast and the uterine wall, the embryo becomes completely surrounded with tissue.

that describing fertilization left off, with the zygote passing through the length of the oviduct. Probably about three days are required for complete passage, during which time the zygote undergoes development, so that by the time it has arrived in the uterus it has attained the blastocyst (blastula) stage. For several days after its arrival it remains free within the uterus, all the while developing into the gastrula and initiating formation of the embryonic membranes, but still within the trophoblast. After this short free period, the embryo on the sixth day after ovulation becomes embedded in the uterus, the endometrium of which has been maintained in its

thickened, glandular state by progesterone. How embedding or implantation of the embryo within a glandular pocket actually occurs is unknown except for the fact that progesterone must be present. In man and some other mammals the pocket closes over the embryo during the next nine days, so that it and the placenta develop entirely within and surrounded by the uterine wall. The first intimate contact with the parent's body is provided by the trophoblast, on the surface of which irregular folds called *villi* are formed, while within the blastocyst's cavity the amnion, chorion, and yolk sac are developing (Figure 20–9). In the mammals under discussion, as

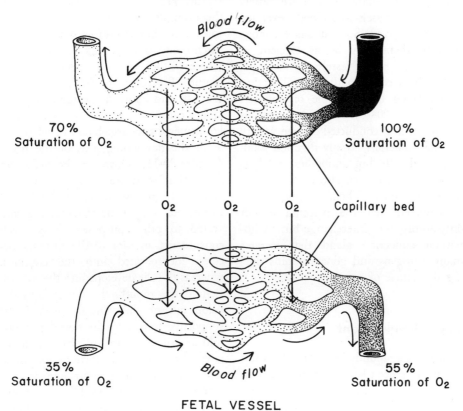

MATERNAL VESSEL

Blood flow

70% Saturation of O_2

100% Saturation of O_2

O_2 O_2 O_2 Capillary bed

35% Saturation of O_2

Blood flow

55% Saturation of O_2

FETAL VESSEL

Figure 20–10. Exchange of oxygen in the placenta. In the placenta partial pressures and the principle of counterflow are utilized just as in gills.

well as in many others, the chorion does not arise as a part of a sac conjointly with the amnion, as it does normally, but is produced mitotically by the trophoblast. Consequently it forms a lining over the entire inner surface of the trophoblast with which it thereafter is constantly associated. Within a few days the allantois grows out of the body and joins the chorion in making contact with the uterine wall; hence, ultimately the trophoblast, chorion, and allantois all participate in the formation of the placenta.

A *placenta* is best defined as the structure in which intimate fusion of fetal and parental organs is made for the physiological exchange of metabolic wastes and supplies. In making this association between mother and young, although the organs of each are closely applied, the vessels and blood never become intermixed. So that gas exchange between them may be as efficient as possible, the blood vessels are arranged in a manner corresponding to gill design in following the principle of counterflow (Figure 20–10). Between the uterus and placenta is conducted a large variety of other materials, mostly digested foodstuffs and salts, but antibodies and hormones are exchanged also by the opposing blood vessels. Then, too, it must be remembered that the placenta is not only an organ of interchange but an important endocrine gland that secretes many estrogens and gonadotropins during the course of pregnancy.

Later Development

After the foundations of all adult organs have been laid down and the embryonic period ends, many changes already initiated in the embryo continue into the ensuing fetus. Because of this continuity, certain characteristics found in the embryo can best be treated with the fetal preiod in order to show them as the uninterrupted processes they actually are.

DEVELOPMENT OF ORGANS

Although innumerable variations exist in the developmental processes of the many organs and systems, essentially three general methods are principally followed, as outlined in the following examples.

Gill Clefts and Derivatives. The gill clefts serve admirably to show how parts originally of one function are altered to assume quite diverse roles. In all higher vertebrates the essential alterations are the same, so it matters little whether a reptile, bird, or mammal is employed for the example. As a rule, four *gill clefts* form in the higher groups, some of which extend into the pharynx and are open, whereas others may be closed by a thin septum. Preceding the first cleft, behind the last, and between the remainder are arches comprised of skeletal and muscular elements and large blood vessels, quite as in the developing gills of the fishes (Figure 20–11). However, the clefts and supporting structures never acquire an active role in respiration in the higher forms, but instead the elements are converted to other purposes. Those arch constituents anterior to the first slit become incorporated into the cranium, whereas the slit develops into the mouth. Behind the mouth, the lower jaws develop out of the ventral cartilaginous supportive rods, and the dorsal portions fold or grow forward to form the upper jaws. In mammals portions of these same elements also contribute to the bony ossicles of the middle ear. Similarly, during the course of the embryonic stages the second gill cleft becomes modified and moves inward to constitute

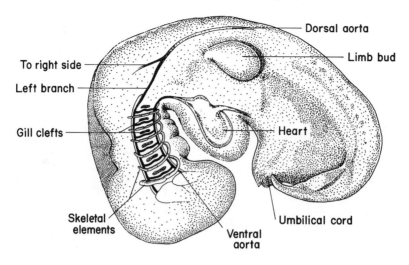

To right side
Left branch
Gill clefts
Dorsal aorta
Limb bud
Heart
Skeletal elements
Ventral aorta
Umbilical cord

Figure 20–11. The gill arches and gill clefts of a vertebrate.

the Eustachian tube while the supportive structures behind it ossify into the third ear ossicle (the stapes), the hyoid apparatus that supports the tongue and pharynx, and the supportive cartilages of the larynx and trachea. As to the associated blood vessels, many of them disappear or become highly modified to form various components of the anterior circulatory system, including the aorta.

The Heart. Although the heart actually appears early in the embryonic period, it is not completed until well into the fetal stages; this illustrates how an originally simple structure can become quite elaborate. When first established, it is in the form of a straight tube and pumps blood forward, chiefly to the arteries of the yolk sac and other embryonic membranes. From these outer extensions as well as the body's interior the venal blood returns to the heart's posterior end to be circulated once more. Later in the embryology the pumping vessel twists into a loop, so that its former posterior end becomes located to one side (Figure 20–12). In this lateral position a separate sinus venosus, atrium, ventricle, and conus arteriosus develop,

in the form of a four-compartmental, two-chambered organ similar to that in fishes. Later, as the looping processes resume, the atrial end moves to an anterior position, as the sinus becomes partially fused to the atrium and the conus to the ventricle. From this two-chambered condition, one of four chambers is developed by ingrowing septa, which divide the atrium and the ventricle into right and left halves. However, the septum of the atrium is not completely closed until hatching or birth, for between the atria an opening known as the *foramen ovale* is left, a feature that is given more attention later.

The Kidneys. The kidneys of the higher vertebrates serve to illustrate a third method by means of which complex organs are formed from the simple germ layers of the gastrula, one in which replacement of simpler by more advanced structures is made. Early in the embryonic period a pair of head kidneys (pronephros) develops from two mesodermal ridges along the middorsal line of the coelom, at a time when only 9 or 10 pairs of somites are present (about the tenth day of existence). This set of kid-

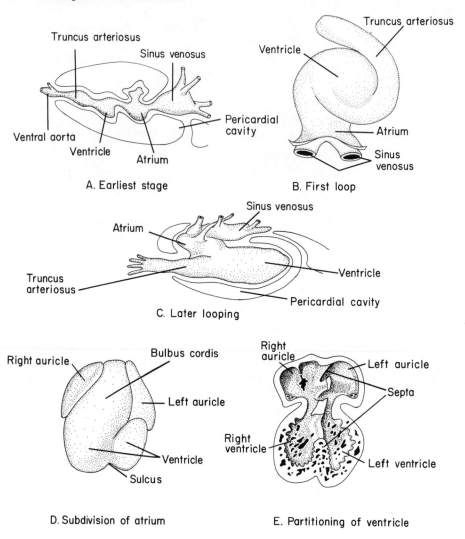

Figure 20–12. The development of the mammalian heart.

neys, constructed like those of the cyclostome larva, never becomes functional and degenerates after surviving only five or six days. Before it disappears entirely, however, its successor in the form of a pair of midkidneys (mesonephros) commences development from the same ridges but is located more posteriorly (Figure 20–13). These midkidneys, built like the anterior portion of those of the frog, are functional and make use of the ducts of the now degenerate pronephros to conduct wastes to the cloaca, whence they are carried to be stored in the allantois. Like the pronephros, the life of this set of kidneys is relatively short, but in the present case they remain functional at least into the earlier months of the fetus. Gradually, beginning late in the embryonic period, the third and final pair of kidneys comes into existence. These, the hind kidneys (metanephros),

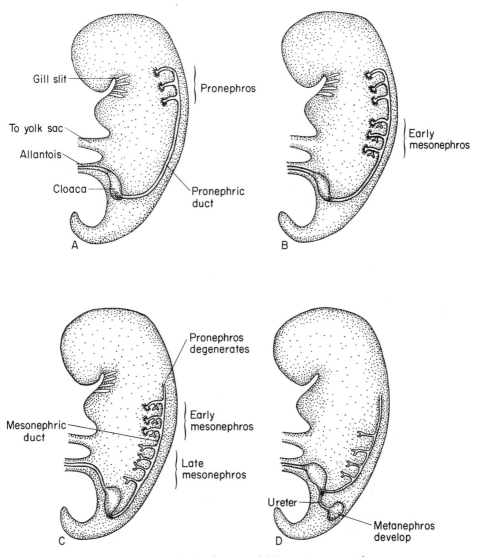

Figure 20–13. The development of kidneys in a mammal.

are of definitive structure except that they do not contain complete nephric tubules until the sixth month of development, by which time their predecessors have completely degenerated. As these kidneys must keep pace with the rapidly growing fetus, they greatly increase in size and develop functional tubules during the remainder of the fetal life. In fact, growth continues even for 10 days after birth, during which period new nephridia and glomeruli are added.

DIFFERENTIATION AND ITS CONTROL

As the foregoing illustrations suggest, the embryonic and fetal stages in an individual's life are periods of great activity, with new parts being added here

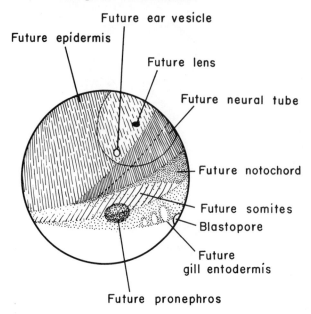

Future ear vesicle

Future epidermis

Future lens

Future neural tube

Future notochord

Future somites

Blastopore

Future
gill entodermis

Future pronephros

Figure 20–14. Map of the early gastrula of a frog. After the gastrula stage has been attained, the cells of the various regions have commenced specialization and the future of each region has become established.

and old ones undergoing modifications or destruction elsewhere. Yet, as the entire embryo and fetus arise from a single cell, in a sense the kidneys, heart, nervous system, legs, and all the rest are products of one original protoplasmic mass of microscopic size, the zygote. How, it may well be asked, do the various subdivisions of the fertilized egg become so diversified and how do they know to become arranged into their respective positions? And how are the events synchronized so that the embryo develops in an orderly and coordinated fashion? The answers to these questions are difficult to find, and, though embryologists have been seeking them for many years, only a few glimmerings of light have been cast upon the actual processes that govern the observed changes.

Chemical Aspects. Much experimentation on embryos involves the removal of one area and its transplantation into a different region of the same or another individual. By such means it has been determined that up to the blastula stage

of development none of the cells has become specialized in any way. In other words, the area that eventually becomes the general ectoderm (the presumptive ectoblast), for example, has in no manner become distinguished from that which later forms the neural plate and tube (presumptive neuroblast), for cells or pieces of tissue transplanted from one region to another develop quite like the surrounding ones of their new location. As the gastrula is formed, however, the situation changes, and the cells in various areas become specialized. Following gastrulation, transplants no longer develop as their surrounding tissues do but produce parts corresponding to those from which they were removed. The noted embryologist H. Spemann showed that the differentiation of these regions results both from their geographic location on the egg and the influences of an organizing tissue situated at the dorsal lip of the blastopore (Figure 20–14). This governing tissue is the chordoblast that ultimately grows inward and develops into the notochord. As long as this *organizer* is present, the other areas around it become specialized normally, but in its absence they fail to do so. After the chordoblast has migrated and assumed its internal position, its organizing functions continue. For one thing, it induces the neuroblast to grow and fold to become the neural tube, and for another, it influences the mesoderm to undergo differentiation into somites. Moreover, it assists the pronephros and the entoderm in their further development. If this organizer is grafted into a second otherwise intact egg, it actually induces the formation of an entire second embryo, not just a second nervous system. Hence it appears clear that, perhaps by means of secretions, one region influences the adjacent ones in the developmental processes.

Tissue-culture methods are also invaluable to the experimental embryologist, and some recent results obtained by their use are significant. When ectoblast and neuroblast are removed (explanted) from an early gastrula and cultured artificially under standard conditions, alone or together, neither gives rise to normal tissue; however, if similar bits are cultured with chordoblast tissue, either ectodermal explant develops into nervous tissue. On the other hand, the German embryologist J. Holtfreter, who performed these studies, subsequently found that by altering the acidity or by freeing the medium of calcium either ectoblast or neuroblast can develop into normal neural material even in the absence of chordoblast. Furthermore, experiments carried out by other scientists the world over (the Belgians have been particularly prominent in the investigations) indicate that factors in addition to an organizer are operative. Position in relation to the animal and vegetal poles appears also to be of importance, and significant changes in the embryo can be produced by inverting the eggs, by removing blastomeres, or by centrifugation.

Cellular Aspects. As the embryo increases in the complexity of its tissues, its cells, too, seem to become more elaborate. For example, electronmicrographs show only a relatively few mitochondria present in gastrular cells, and these few are simple in form, without cristae (Figure 20–15). In the neurula the mitochondria increase in length, number, and complexity and ultimately come to possess the characteristic features of the adult organelle.

Furthermore, changes in the nucleus

Figure 20–15. Development of cellular organelles during embryology. A. An electronmicrograph of an ectoderm cell taken from a frog gastrula. Note the lack of cristae in the mitochondrion. B. Compare the same sort of cell taken from a neurula of the same species (*Rana pipiens*). Both magnified 15,000×. (Electronmicrographs by Dr. S. Karasaki, and courtesy of Dr. T. Yamada, Biology Division, Oak Ridge National Laboratory.)

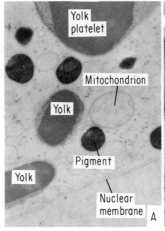
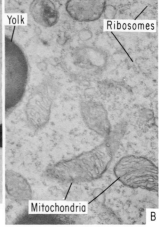

are indicated to occur during the course of embryonic development. This fact has been uncovered by transferring a nucleus of one cell (the donor) to another, from which the nuclear body has been removed, by use of a micromanipulator and the utmost patience. When by these means the nucleus from an embryonic cell is transplanted into an enucleated unfertilized egg, the egg develops normally into a larva, provided that the donor cell has not attained a definitive state. By the same procedures the nucleus can be transferred from a ventral blastomere to a dorsal one, or the other way around, without any abnormal effects in the tissues that eventually ensue. Such nuclear transfers are successful between any two areas or from any portion of an embryo into an egg only until the late gastrula stage has been established. Subsequent to this stage, nuclei from the chordoblast, for instance, will, upon transplantation into an egg cell, permit the zygote to develop to the early gastrula but no further; similarly, failure of growth results if the nucleus is transferred from one tissue to another in more advanced embryos. In short, the nuclei appear to become altered during the course of the embryonic period and may be looked upon as being specialized to the same extent as the tissues in which they occur.

Twin Formation. Generally speaking, twins are of two kinds, *fraternal* and *identical*. In fraternal twins each develops from a separate normal egg, and hence really represents an instance of multiple pregnancy. On the other hand, identical twins develop from a single zygote and appear to be produced in nature by two different processes. In one they arise following the first cleavage by the separation of the two blastomeres; each blastomere then develops as though it

were an entire zygote and produces a young, normal in all respects except for a smaller body size. The second set of twinning processes, which basically involves the production of two organization centers instead of one, is common to fishes and armadillos. For instance, in the Texas armadillo, which always bears quadruplets, the blastula originally forms only one organizer; however, this organizer later spontaneously divides into two, and still later each of these divides again. As a result four young are produced from one zygote, all of which share a single amniotic sac. Which of these procedures is normally followed by humans in the production of identical twins has not yet been established. In all such cases, however, it is clear that either an organizer or the ability to produce an organizer must be present for an embryo to grow from any given portion of an egg (Figure 20–16).

CHANGES AT BIRTH

When by hatching or by being born, a new member of the higher vertebrates leaves the confines of the egg or uterus in which it has developed, an entirely new set of environmental factors is suddenly faced. Particularly is this true in the mammals, for the bird fetus breathes the air within the egg's shell for a short period before hatching, thereby reducing the abruptness of the change to some degree. Consequently, we shall limit our discussion to the first group, employing the human being as the illustration.

Respiratory Changes. Most of the modifications that occur during the birth processes center around the change in mode of respiring. Once the umbilical cord carrying the blood between the embryo and placenta is severed, the placenta

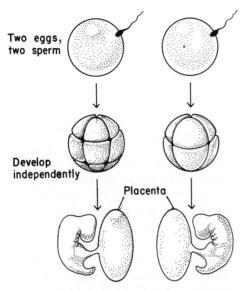

Two eggs, two sperm

Develop independently

Placenta

Have separate placentas, differ as ordinary brothers and sisters

A.   FRATERNAL TWINS

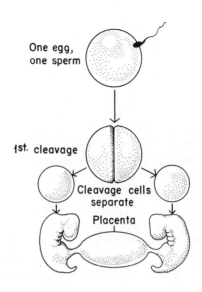

One egg, one sperm

1st. cleavage

Cleavage cells separate

Placenta

B.   IDENTICAL TWINS

Figure 20–16. Known routes by which twins are produced. Fraternal twins always arise from separate eggs (A) but identical twins may be formed either by separation of the blastomeres (B) or, most probably in humans, through the establishment of two organizers on the same zygote.

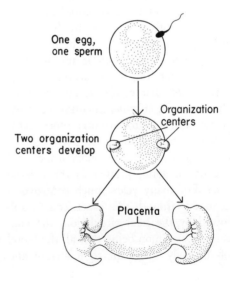

One egg, one sperm

Organization centers

Two organization centers develop

Placenta

C.   IDENTICAL TWINS

can no longer supply the young with oxygen, and the child must immediately begin filling its requirements by means of its own lungs. For years it was assumed that during the fetal period these organs continued in a collapsed state and that the diaphragm and thoracic basket remained idle; only during the last few years has it been accurately determined that respiratory movements do occur in the fetus. Unfortunately, it is still too early to know the extent of inhalation and exhalation or the effects on the condition of the lungs. As far as has been established, the movements are at a slow pace or sporadic; nevertheless, their existence points to the establishment of the respiratory center in the medulla at least two months prior to birth. Upon delivery of the child, it is routine clinical practice to use a stimulant in the form of a mild spank applied to the proper portion of the body to induce a gasping or crying reaction. The intake of air brought about in this manner fills out the lungs and activates normal breathing.

Circulatory Changes. Since the most drastic change in respiratory function involves the shift of the oxygen supply from the placenta to the lungs, the most extreme alterations stem from the termination of the blood flow from the placenta and the augmentation of circulation into the lungs. Throughout the fetal period the principal route of the blood is to the placental region where it loses its waste products and acquires new supplies of oxygen and foodstuffs. Following severance of the umbilical cord, the vessels within the stub attached to the body gradually are resorbed to a large extent.

In the unborn fetus, since the lungs are in large measure functionless, as far as is presently known, a modified pattern of circulation exists in the heart and major blood vessels. In it use is made of an outstanding fetal feature, the *foramen ovale,* that communicates between the two atria, of which mention has been made earlier. Furthermore, there exists a large artery in the unborn young that runs between the pulmonary artery and the dorsal aorta, known as the *arterial duct*. For many years much controversy centered around the exact course followed by the fetal circulation, the consensus of opinion being that all the blood of the body enters the right atrium and immediately passes into the left through the foramen ovale. But by use of X-ray studies and opaque material injected into the blood stream, the details have now been established firmly. Two paths are followed. On the one hand, blood returning from the head and forebody enters the right atrium and is pumped into the right ventricle. Then, after its entrance into the pulmonary artery, a part continues to the lungs, whereas the rest becomes diverted through the arterial duct into the aorta and to the body. However, blood returning from the placenta and hindbody enters the right atrium in such a fashion that about half of it is forced into the right ventricle to follow the same circuit outlined above, and the rest enters the left atrium through the foramen. This blood, along with that received from the lungs, is propelled into the left ventricle, and thence out through the aorta. Therefore, all the chambers of the heart are active but only a small quantity of the blood is circulated through the lungs.

If the child is to survive, this pattern must be altered soon after the lungs take over the respiratory functions. To this end, both the foramen and duct are equipped with sphincter valves. Within four minutes after the cord has been severed, these valves have been found to become tightly closed, so that the adult pattern of heart circulation is established. During the course of time scar tissue forms over the openings and permanently seals them.

Questions for Review and Thought

1. Distinguish between an embryo and a fetus and between a fetus and a larva. What different basic types of egg cell and of eggs are found among vertebrates?

2. List as many factors as you can that are pertinent to the processes of fertilization in the vertebrate.

3. Define the following terms:

(a) corona radiata	(g) archenteron
(b) hyaluronidase	(h) morula
(c) fertilization membrane	(i) somites
(d) invagination	(j) capacitation
(e) cleavage	(k) gastrula
(f) vegetal pole	(l) trophoblast

4. Compare the embryologies of the starfish, frog, and bird, first showing basic resemblances and second the fundamental differences of each. To which is the early portion of mammalian development most similar? To which, the later stages? What unique traits are found in the mammalian embryonic development? What feature of all vertebrates is lacking in the starfish?

5. Name the extraembryonic membranes of higher vertebrates and state the functions of each in birds and mammals. How do you explain the presence of identical membranes in the reptiles, birds, and mammals in view of their absence in frogs and lower forms?

6. Of what does the placenta consist? How does implantation of the egg occur in the human being? By what means are substances exchanged between the parent and the growing young?

7. List three fundamental means employed by the embryo and fetus in developing adult structures. Which one or ones are utilized in formation of the nervous system? Of the skull? Of the heart?

8. Some biologists claim that the human young passes through a fishlike stage during its development. How many traits can you list that seem to justify this point of view?

9. At which stage of development does active specialization appear to occur first? List some factors which appear to aid in determining the fate of the various parts of the growing embryo and give examples.

10. State the differences between the two types of twins and the manner in which each arises.

11. What changes occur in human beings following the embryonic period before birth? At birth?

Supplementary References

Balinsky, B. I. *An Introduction to Embryology*. Philadelphia, Saunders, 1960.

Brachet, J. *The Biochemistry of Development*. New York, Pergamon, 1960.

Corner, G. W. *Ourselves Unborn*. New Haven, Conn., Yale Univ. Press, 1944.

Ebert, J. D. "The First Heartbeats." *Sci. Amer.*, March 1959.

Fischberg, M., and A. W. Blackler. "How Cells Specialize." *Sci. Amer.*, September 1961.

Huettner, A. F. *Fundamentals of Comparative Embryology of the Vertebrates*, rev. ed. New York, Macmillan, 1949.

Puck, T. T. "Single Human Cells *in Vitro*." *Sci. Amer.*, August 1957.

Raven, C. P. *An Outline of Developmental Physiology*, 2nd ed. New York, Pergamon, 1959.

Waddington, C. J. "How Do Cells Differentiate?" *Sci. Amer.*, September 1953.

———. *Principles of Embryology*. London, Macmillan, 1956.

Witschi, E. *Development of Vertebrates*. Philadelphia, Saunders, 1956.

CHAPTER 21

The Basic Principles of Inheritance

IN STUDYING the laws that regulate the passing of individual traits from one generation to another, one of two aspects of the subject may frequently be particularly stressed. One of these is principally concerned with the genetic traits themselves as expressed in various individuals; that is to say, this facet is engaged in studying the individual differences, or *variations,* that exist and the manner in which they are inherited (Figure 21–1). Only by use of these distinctions can an insight be gained as to how the invariable characteristics of a given species may also be transmitted. Were every human being exactly alike in all respects or were all dogs similarly constant, by way of illustration, it would appear that the eggs of the respective species determine the traits of the embryos and resulting individuals, and there would be little else to be learned about the actual processes. Only because hair color differences, ear shape variations,

height distinctions, and the like do exist in each case has it been possible to discern some of the processes actually involved in heredity.

The second point of view often accentuated in the study of genetics centers its focus on the mechanisms whereby the traits are transmitted. Since the parental characteristics are passed to the offspring by way of the fertilized egg, it is obvious that the actual traits themselves are not transferred directly from generation to generation but are somehow represented by factors present within the zygote. These factors, called *genes,* are as a rule generally accepted as being located within the zygote's nucleus on the chromosomes.

Monohybrid Crosses

For many years the earlier biologists and others who had been interested in

Figure 21–1. Inheritable variations in a frog. *A.* The typical pattern of the leopard frog (*Rana pipiens*), a species common throughout eastern temperate North America. *B.* The variant known as mottled (or *kandiyohi*). *C.* A variant called nonspotted (or *burnsi*). Both varieties are dominant over the normal condition. The prime letters indicate corresponding newly metamorphosed young. (Courtesy of Dr. E. Peter Volpe, from "Polymorphism in Anuran Populations" in *Vertebrate Speciation*, W. Frank Blair, ed., University of Texas Press, Austin, 1961.)

the genetic processes worked from the standpoint of the transmission of all the characteristics of each parent to the offspring and, consequently, were unable to obtain any insight into the fundamental processes and laws. Hence, the old concept that had originated with the ancient scholars, that of *blood inheritance,* was generally accepted through the nineteenth century. In this set of ideas, it is held that the young resembles each parent to some extent because its blood is a mixture of that of the mother and father. Even after the discovery that man and other mammals arise from eggs, the blending concept continued in vogue and, in fact, still persists in popular phrases such as "blood relatives" and the like. Not until about a century ago was success experienced in deciphering the basic principles. Then a brilliant Austrian abbot, Gregor Mendel, working in the garden of his monastery, utilized single sets of contrasting traits in his

experiments and succeeded where all others had failed.

However, the results of his experiments and his keen analysis of the principles involved in the processes differed so radically from the then-existing concepts that his colleagues declined to accept them. No attempts were made to disprove his theories nor to test the validity of his experiments; they were merely put to one side while investigations continued along former lines. Consequently, his studies remained neglected from the time of their first publication, 1866, until 1902. Only after the blending concepts early in the twentieth century proved cul-de-sacs was genetics open to new approaches. Then three geneticists, Correns of Germany, Van Tschermak of Austria, and DeVries of the Netherlands, independently of one another rediscovered the basic laws Mendel had revealed 35 years earlier, and his studies and genius finally received the recognition they deserved.

To gain an appreciation of his work, perhaps a brief review of other early theories might be of value.

PREMENDELIAN THEORIES

The above-mentioned blood-blending notions cannot always be dignified by the term "theory," for often they were applied to explain the existence of certain oddities of the animal world. For instance, the ostrich was stated to be the result of a cross between a camel and a sparrow, while a giraffe similarly was conjectured to be the product of the camel and leopard! Although utterly ridiculous, these suggestions permit an insight into the shallow concepts that held through much of historical time. Each of these creations is seen as a blend of the most obvious features, the camel's long neck combined with either the wings and feathers of a bird or the spots of a leopard. But no explanation was ever offered as to why the ostrich never had the legs of the camel and the head of the sparrow, nor, for that matter, as to the manner in which the camel obtained its long neck in the first place.

Like blood blending, a belief in the *inheritance of acquired characteristics* had been in existence from time immemorial and similarly was founded on superficial observation. But this concept finally became formalized as a theory through the efforts of a French paleontologist and invertebrate zoologist named Lamarck, about whom more will be said later. Here it can be mentioned that in the early nineteenth century when this biologist published a theory of evolution, one of his tenets implied that such characteristics could be inherited. For instance, if a man developed powerful muscles in his occupation, his sons could be anticipated to be similarly muscular and thus fitted for the same type of work.

Comparably, those who acquired skill in playing a musical instrument could thus be expected to have musically inclined offspring. Or if an animal gained the ability to climb trees or dig in the soil, its progeny would be equipped for the same activities. One modification of this, in the form of *pangenesis,* was widely accepted until the rediscovery of Mendel's principles. In its most advanced condition, this theory proposes that particles, variously called *pangenes* and *gemmules,* are sent from all the bodily tissues to the reproductive organs, where they enter into the formation of gametes. Hence, unusually developed muscles or acquired musical ability influences the sperm or egg during the formative stages, and as a consequence, the acquired characteristic is transmitted to the next generation. In short, the body determines what traits the gametes carry to the progeny. These ideas were popular with Darwin and since 1940 have had a resurge of acceptance among the followers of the Russian named Lysenko; now, however, in Russia there appears to be a trend toward a reacceptance of the basic laws worked out by Mendel.

SIMPLE DOMINANCE

As pointed out above, Mendel, in using the sweet pea as his subject, employed single sets of contrasting traits, including characteristics such as red flowers and white ones, tall plants bred with dwarf varieties, green-pod and yellow-pod producers—seven sets of variations in all. With each pair of opposites, he conducted separate experiments over four summers and kept detailed notes, so that at the end he had amassed a large quantity of data. It will be noted, too, that he carefully selected sharply marked differences in his breeding stock—that is to say, no intermediate conditions existed between the members of a given pair. By this precaution some of the complexities of inheritance were avoided that had become pitfalls for his predecessors. To illustrate both his procedures and the basic laws of inheritance which his work disclosed, we shall employ an experimental cross of sheep, observing the results of mating black animals to white ones. In genetics, all cases of this sort in which only a single set of alternative traits is under observation are referred to as *monohybrid crosses;* here the black coat versus white form such a set of opposing factors.

A Monohybrid Cross. Almost without exception genetic experiments, following the rediscovery of Mendelian principles, commence with the use of two different lines of animals, each of which breeds true. In our instance the white-coated sheep when bred with others of the same color always bear white-coated young, and similarly the black sheep when crossed with other black-fleeced specimens uniformly give birth to black lambs. These two pure lines are then crossed and the nature of the resulting individuals observed. Here when white sheep are crossed with the black, all the resulting young are found to be white-coated, the factor for black coat apparently disappearing (Figure 21–2). No matter how frequently similar crosses are made, in each instance all the lambs are found to be white-fleeced. In Mendel's work on sweet peas, he obtained comparable results, with one factor entirely suppressing the other. While experimenters of lesser ability may well have stopped at this point and explained that the organisms in each instance had "reverted to type," the Austrian monk was by no means satisfied that such was actually the case. He went the second mile and inbred his hybrid offspring to see what the real situation was. In his test,

as in our illustration, the progeny produced by crossing the two pure-breeding lines are next mated to one another and accurate counts made of the ensuing young. In the coat-color experiment, white sheep are produced in large numbers, but black ones occur, too, in this third generation; however, when a large number of lambs have accumulated and the results have been tallied, approximately three times as many white sheep are found as black. Likewise among his sweet peas Mendel encountered this 3 to 1 ratio; for example, in a study of tall versus dwarf plants, he recorded 787 tall and 277 dwarf specimens in the third generation, which figures approximate 74 and 26 per cent, respectively, of the total.

This series of processes, employed first by Mendel, has established the framework for much of all subsequent experimentation in this field. By use of his procedures, much knowledge has been gained since his time, however, and a new terminology developed; so the plan of the experiment and the results need to be re-examined while modern phraseology is applied. First, three generations are seen to be involved, the original pure-breeding stock and a first and second generation of offspring; these today are referred to as the *parental* (P_1), *first filial* (F_1), and *second filial* (F_2) *generations,* respectively. In any given set of contrasting genes the alternative traits are known as *alleles.* Tallness and dwarfness in Mendel's sweet peas form one set of alleles, black coat and white coat among sheep another, and brown eyes and blue eyes, as well as dark hair and light hair, are well-known sets of alleles in humankind.

Explanation of the Results. As knowledge of chromosomes and their behavior was scanty at the time the genetic principles were being worked out in the Austrian monastery, the formulation of

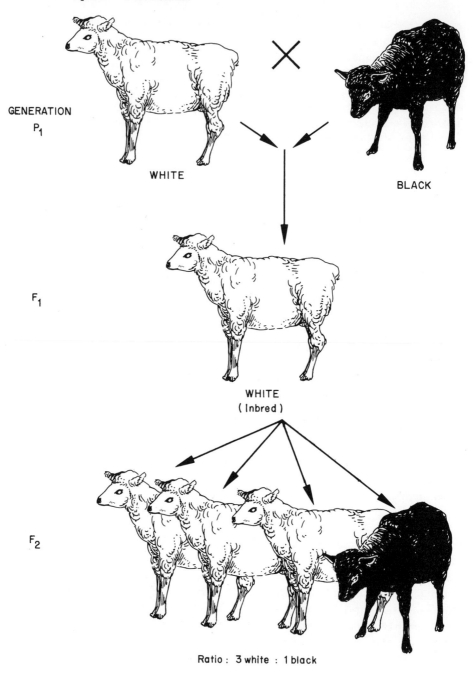

Ratio: 3 white : 1 black

Figure 21–2. A genetical experiment using coat color in sheep.

a workable explanation must have presented an extremely difficult problem to the experimenting abbot; however, he rose to the demands of the occasion. Somehow he deduced that hereditary traits were represented in each individual in pairs and that, during the formation of egg and sperm (or pollen and ovule), each set was reduced to a single representative. Thus the original white-fleeced sheep (P_1 generation), being pure-breeding, contained two white factors, and the black ones, two black factors, but each sperm or egg produced by the former contained only one white factor and by the latter a single black gene. When these two types of gametes were united in fertilization, as in the breeding experiments cited, the resulting F_1 generation was not pure-breeding, for the resulting sheep contained both a white and a black factor. Since the white factor manifested itself in these animals and concealed the black trait also present (Figure 21–2), that trait was said by Mendel to be *dominant* over blackness, which was described as being *recessive*. Today dominant genes are defined as those which entirely conceal the second allele when both are present, while recessive genes are those alleles which become concealed. Further, it is customary to speak of the condition in which both alleles contained in the individual are identical—e.g., white with white or black with black—as *homozygous,* whereas the mixed condition, such as white together with black, is *heterozygous.* These two terms, hence, refer to the actual genes represented in the individual, or the *genotype,* whereas the visible manifestations of a given genotype are referred to as the *phenotype.* Usually in writing problems the dominant gene is assigned the initial letter of its name in capitalized form and the recessive a corresponding lower-case letter; thus whiteness in sheep could be assigned the capital letter W and the black gene, the small letter w. The genotype WW—i.e., homozygosity for the dominant trait— produces a phenotype of white fleece, as does also the heterozygous genotype,

Ww. On the other hand, the phenotype of the homozygous recessive genotype, $ww,$ is black. Although this terminology may be somewhat confusing at first, its usage makes possible both brevity and a greater clarity in dealing with the whole science of genetics.

The Punnett Square. But before we leave this set of experiments, Mendel's results in inbreeding the heterozygous F_1 generation need to be scrutinized. As will be recalled, the progeny approximated three individuals of the dominant phenotype to every one showing the recessive. What explanation can be offered for these data? First, it should be noted, the pure-breeding parental stock, being homozygous, could produce gametes carrying genes of only the corresponding phenotypes; all the eggs and sperm of white sheep uniformly contained only the gene for whiteness, $W,$ and the gametes of the black parents likewise had only $w.$ But this is not true for the heterozygous white sheep of the F_1 generation, which produce eggs and sperm carrying W and others containing w in equal numbers. In other words, half the eggs and sperm carry the white trait, the remainder the recessive allele. As the fertilization of the egg by the sperm nucleus is strictly random, on the average a sperm carrying a white gene has an equal chance of combining with an egg bearing that same gene as with one containing a black, and the same statement is likewise true for sperm carrying the latter allele. The combination of the gametes is most readily worked out by means of the *Punnett square,* in which the types of eggs or ova are written across the top of the checkerboard pattern and those of the sperm on one side, as in Figure 21–3.

There it is seen that because three of the combinations of eggs and sperm

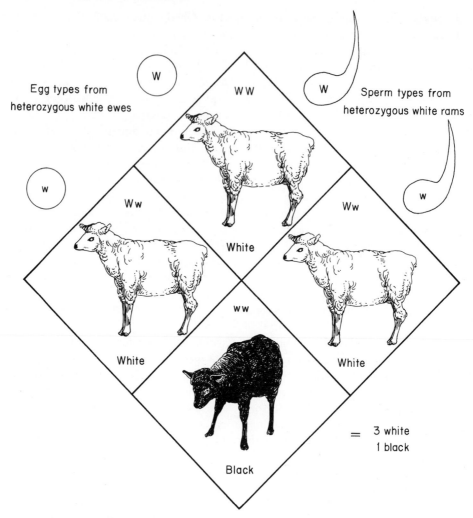

Figure 21–3. The Punnett square based on coat color in sheep. Refer to Figure 21–2.

result in the phenotype white and only one in that of black, a corresponding ratio of 3 to 1 is found when sufficiently large numbers of individuals are produced by interbreeding heterozygotes.

INCOMPLETE DOMINANCE

Through Mendel's deliberate selection of only sharply contrasting sets of alleles, all the traits he utilized similarly showed dominance in one member of each pair; however, there are many instances in which a clear-cut dominant-recessive relationship does not exist between alleles. Frequently in cases of this sort, the heterozygous condition results in a phenotype intermediate between those of the parents.

Incomplete Dominance in Cattle. If pure-breeding cattle are employed as the experimental animal and if coat-color characteristics are observed, results are obtained which differ sharply from those found in sheep. When red shorthorn cattle are crossed with white individuals of the same breed, the resulting offspring are always roan—that is, white mixed with red blotches to a greater or lesser degree. Obviously neither red nor white is dominant in this case, so that the heterozygotes, containing one of each

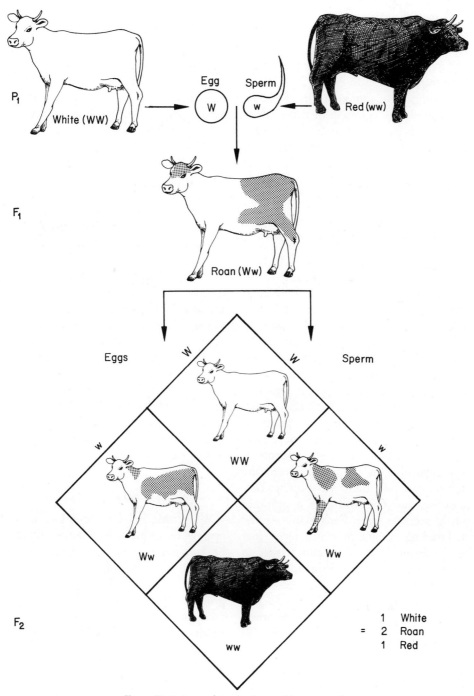

Figure 21–4. Incomplete dominance in a mammal.

allele in all the cells of the body, show a phenotype intermediate between the two homozygous varieties (Figure 21–4). When these F_1 roan individuals are in-bred in sufficient numbers, the F_2 generation is found to include all three coat types, red, roan, and white, in a ratio approximating 1:2:1, respectively. Perhaps this condition in which both alleles are *incompletely dominant* over the other is actually more common in nature than that which displays simple dominance; many instances, however, are concerned with body size differences or other quantitative features and are difficult to isolate into individual allele groups.

The Backcross

When one of the alleles is dominant over the other, it is, of course, impossible to distinguish whether a given individual with the dominant phenotype is homozygous or heterozygous for the trait; only the appearance of the homozygous recessive is distinctive. In order to find out whether a particular animal, possibly desired for breeding purposes for example, will breed true or not, a *backcross*, or *test cross*, is often made. Since the genotype for the trait in question can be clearly recognized in the recessive phenotype, this type of cross is made between the test animal of unknown genetic constitution and one with the appearance of the recessive gene. For instance, if one is breeding rabbits, in which black coat is dominant over white, and wishes to select a new black buck for addition to the permanent stock, more than likely a pure-breeding one would be desired. To determine the genotype of an other-wise favorable individual, crosses would be made with white does, as in Figure 21–5; heterozygous males would tend to sire both black and white offspring in a 1:1 ratio. However, as a rule several

matings would be made with those bucks that failed to produce any white progeny in the first brood to establish beyond doubt their homozygosity for the trait, for sometimes it happens that random-ness of combinations may produce all of one phenotype even in a single brood containing as many as 8 or 10 offspring. Or the same thing may happen in the accumulated family of a single set of parents which produce just one or two young in a litter.

Multiple-Factor Crosses

So far in genetics only a single set of alleles at a time has been under consideration. What happens if a cross is made involving two sets of traits simultaneously? Matings in which two differ-ent pairs of genes are studied together are called *dihybrid crosses,* when three sets are observed concurrently, the breed-ing are said to be *trihybrid,* and so on. While an increased number of pairs makes for greater complexity, as a whole no new principles are displayed in mul-tiple hybrid experiments that are not made clear by the dihybrid cross; hence attention can be largely confined to cases of this simpler type.

Dihybrid Crosses

When Mendel was conducting his original experiments in genetics, although he considered each trait separately, he also noted the behavior of two or more sets of factors combined in the same group of individuals and their descend-ants. From these he established a second fundamental genetic law, one, however, that since has been found not to be uni-versally true. But the exceptions arise only under peculiar circumstances, as will be seen later.

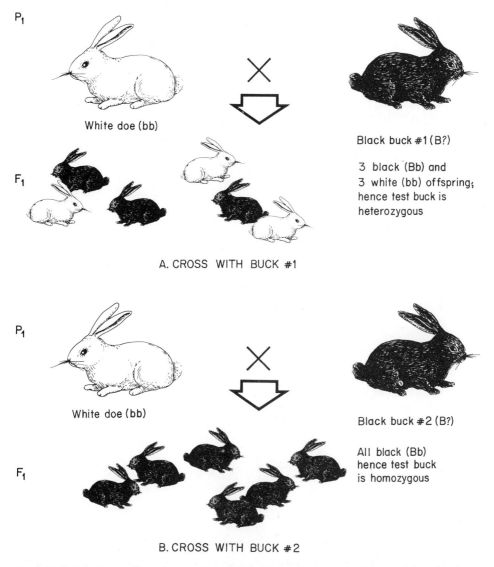

P_1

White doe (bb)

Black buck #1 (B?)

3 black (Bb) and
3 white (bb) offspring;
hence test buck is
heterozygous

F_1

A. CROSS WITH BUCK #1

P_1

White doe (bb)

Black buck #2 (B?)

All black (Bb)
hence test buck
is homozygous

F_1

B. CROSS WITH BUCK #2

Figure 21–5. A backcross. Since the recessive genotype of an animal can be determined from its phenotype, the dominant alone needs to be established by breeding tests. The two sets of figures illustrate the normal results of heterozygosity and homozygosity in the tested animals.

A Dihybrid Cross in Rabbits. As has already been seen, in rabbits black is dominant over white; moreover, short hair has been determined to be dominant over long hair, or Angora. To see how the two sets of alleles interplay with one another, a series of black short-haired rabbits are crossed with white Angora, commencing with stock known to be homozygous in each case. The genotypes of these two parental lines can be designated as *BBSS* and *bbss*, respectively. When gametes are produced in these or any other organism, each set of alleles is represented in the resulting sperm or eggs by one, and only one, of its members. Thus the black short-haired rabbits produce gametes containing one black

P₁ GENERATION

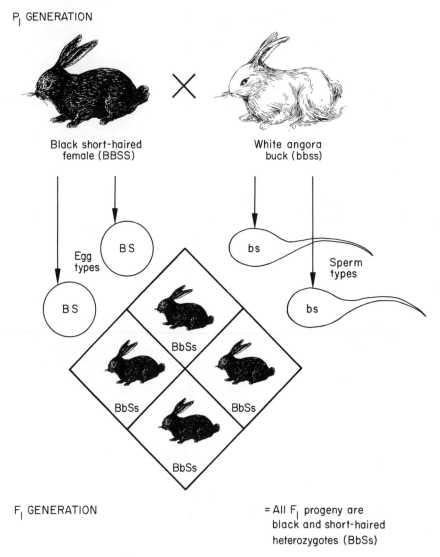

Black short-haired
female (BBSS)   White angora
                                 buck (bbss)

Egg types

BS

BS

bs

Sperm types

bs

BbSs

BbSs   BbSs

BbSs

F₁ GENERATION

= All F₁ progeny are
black and short-haired
heterozygotes (BbSs)

Figure 21–6. A dihybrid cross in rabbits. In dihybrid crosses two sets of alleles are under observation.

and one short-haired gene and can accordingly be symbolized as *BS*, whereas the white Angora form sperm or eggs containing genes for white and long hair, that is *bs* (Figure 21–6). Upon union of these two types of gametes in fertilization, the zygotes, as well as the animals into which each matures, possess the genotype *BbSs*, corresponding alleles usually being written side by side. Because of the existence of simple domi-

nance, this F₁ generation consists entirely of black short-haired individuals. Now when its members are inbred, half of all the gametes produced contain genes for black fur (*B*) and half the factor for white (*b*); but at the same time half also contain the short-haired gene (*S*), and a like number, the Angora allele (*s*). But because the processes of sorting the factors during gamete formation are apparently entirely random, black genes do not necessarily have to be found only with short-haired factors, but are associated in gametes with Angora with the same frequency; similarly the white gene occurs together with short hair just as frequently as it does with Angora. In short, four different types of gametes (i.e., gametes containing four distinct combinations of genes) are produced in equal numbers; these four possible types are

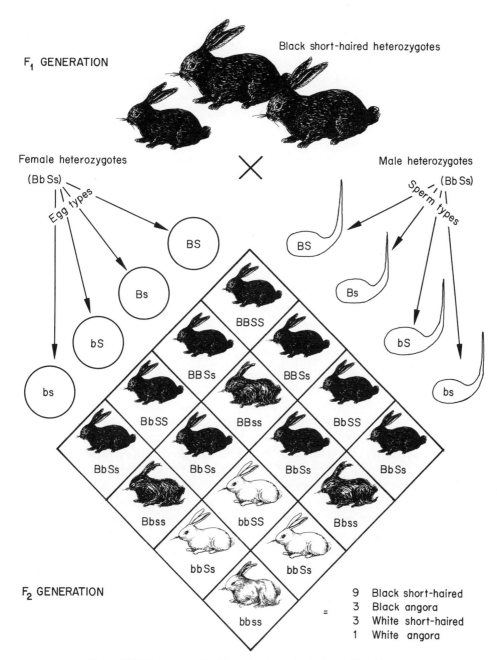

Figure 21–7. Gamete production and a typical ratio in a dihybrid cross.

BS, Bs, bS, and *bs* (Figure 21–7). Now to show all the varieties of genotypes and phenotypes that can result from inbreeding the F₁ generation, a Punnett square must have four subdivisions on each side and contain a total of 16 compartments. When the phenotypic results are summarized from the square, the young rabbits, if produced in sufficient numbers, approximate a ratio of 9 black short-haired, 3 black Angora, 3 white short-haired, and 1 white Angora.

Mendel's Laws of Inheritance. Similar results are obtainable when two sets of alleles are considered together in crosses of many other species of organisms. Wherever simple dominance is involved in both traits under ordinary circumstances, the same 9:3:3:1 ratio is to be anticipated. But the numbers of progeny produced in the above cross need to be examined once more.

If, in this series of matings, one is not concerned with hair length, but only with coat color, on totaling the black- and white-furred varieties of whatever fur length, a total of 12 of the former and 4 of the latter is found—clearly an expression of the 3:1 ratio of a monohybrid dominant mating. Or if the two varieties of hair length are considered by themselves, identical results are obtained; the count shows 12 short- to 4 long-haired animals in the F₂ generation. In other words, it appears that each set of genes behaves as though no other set of alleles were present. This latter statement is a rendering of what Mendel referred to as the *law of independent assortment.* Inheritable factors, in other words, do not behave as one great collection of traits, but each small characteristic is inherited independently of all the rest. In short, an individual is not entirely like its paternal or maternal parent but has resemblances to and differences from each, resulting from the interplay of numerous inheritable factors, each of which behaves as though it alone were being inherited.

A second principle of inheritance brought out by Mendel's experiments is the fact that hereditary traits work as sets, the members of which differ in their ability to express themselves in the heterozygous condition, as was discussed earlier. As frequently one allele dominates completely over the other, Mendel referred to this phenomenon as the *law of dominance*—another "law" we know now not to be universally true. Finally, a third principle, *the law of segregation,* became evident from his studies. When combined by the crossing of two contrasting phenotypes, the genes are themselves unaffected by the close association in the heterozygote but segregate in the gametes in their original condition. A black-haired gene, for instance, does not become diluted or tainted in any way on being combined with a white-haired one but is passed to the next generation through the gametes unaltered from the paternal form.

These principles, almost never questioned today, stood in such sharp contrast to the concept of blood and blending inheritance then generally accepted that Mendel's contemporaries looked upon them as preposterous and accordingly let them pass into oblivion. Through their failure to scrutinize the current theories in light of the new ones, progress in genetics was delayed 35 years, and, as a result, all of biology to some extent. But perhaps, we too on occasion find adherence to old familiar ideas much easier than acceptance of radically different ones, regardless of how well-founded some of the latter may be.

INTERACTION OF GENES

All the cases cited so far have involved single sets of alleles that have governed a given trait by themselves, but in some

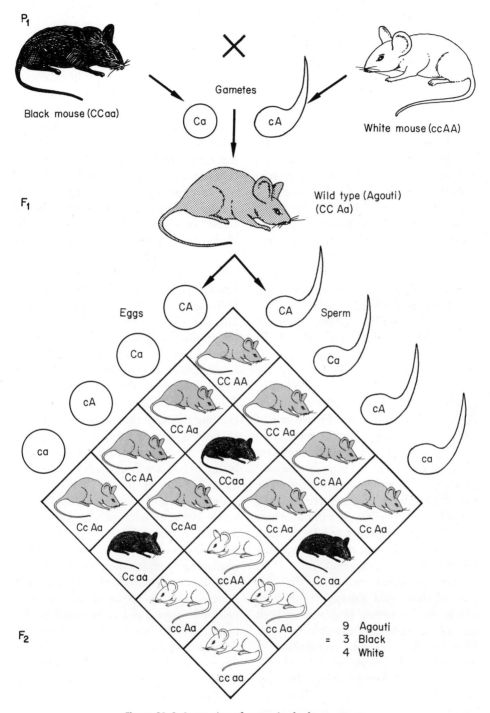

P₁

Black mouse (CCaa)

Gametes

Ca

cA

White mouse (ccAA)

F₁

Wild type (Agouti)
(CC Aa)

Eggs

CA

Ca

cA

ca

CA   Sperm

Ca

cA

ca

CC AA

CC Aa

CC Aa

Cc AA

CCaa

Cc AA

Cc Aa

Cc Aa

Cc Aa

Cc Aa

Cc aa

ccAA

Cc aa

cc Aa

cc Aa

cc aa

F₂

= 9 Agouti
3 Black
4 White

Figure 21–8. Interaction of genes in the house mouse.

instances, two or more sets may influence the same characteristic, some interesting examples of which type of inheritance are cited below.

Coat Color in the House Mouse. The ordinary house mouse is much utilized in the study of genetic phenomena, as it is also in other lines of biological researches, and many varieties have been developed. In investigations of coat color, many instances of multiple factors have been encountered. For example, when certain black-furred mice are bred to albinos, which of course have white hair, the offspring are found to possess neither black nor white fur but a coat identical with that of wild varieties! When hair from a wild mouse is examined carefully, it is found to be varied in color due to the presence of two different pigments. While most of it is black, there is a narrow yellow band near the tip, and under the microscope, traces of yellow can be seen also in the remainder of each hair. The banding produces a grizzled effect on the animal called "agouti," after the large rodent by this name. When the agouti-coated mice resulting from the black-albino cross are inbred, on the average 9 of the progeny are found to be agouti, 3 black, and 4 albino (Figure 21–8). To explain the results two sets of factors are necessary. For the production of any pigment in the fur, the dominant allele for coloration, C, must be present; all animals without it are albinos. The agouti pattern in addition requires the dominant agouti gene, A, without which only the black pigment can be formed, hence the ratio of offspring actually found in the above experiment.

Since, as stated, agouti is the coat color of those wild Eurasian mice from which the laboratory strains have been derived, the foregoing example serves to illustrate the occasional occurrence of throwbacks, or *atavists,* in lines of animals, including human beings. In cases in which two or more sets of alleles are required to produce a given phenotype, separate and distinct hereditary changes in two isolated lines may each result in the loss of a given trait. In the present case the agouti coat was lost, on one hand, by mutation of the allele C to c,

producing albinos, while, on the other, the same characteristic was lost through the change of A to a, with black-coated mice as a consequence. Later when by chance the different lineages recombine, a sudden "reversion to type" occurs.

Comb Shape in Chickens. Among the numerous breeds of chickens, several characteristic varieties of comb are found. The common white leghorn, for instance, is characterized by the *single* type of comb, consisting of a simple upright blade. In Wyandottes there occurs an elongate but low sort, which is covered on the base with papillae and which is known as the *rose* comb. Brahmas and fighting breeds often have a *pea* comb, one that is quite small and bears three longitudinal ridges (Figure 21–9). Both rose and pea are readily established to be dominant over single, but if the attempt is made to determine the relative dominance of the first two types by crossing them, all the offspring are found to possess a new kind of comb, one known as *walnut* because of its resemblance to half a walnut kernel. When this F_1 generation is inbred, not only are walnut, pea, and rose types obtained but single ones in addition, in a ratio of $9:3:3:1$, respectively. To explain the results two sets of alleles are required, each displaying simple dominance. If the dominant member of only a single set is present, rose is produced in one case $(RRpp)$ whereas pea is the result in the other $(rrPP)$; however, if at least one dominant of each set is present, then a phenotype of walnut appears $(RrPp)$. Single comb stems from the lack of any dominant genes $(rrpp)$ (Figure 21–9).

MULTIPLE FACTORS

Multiplicity of factors affecting a given trait may occur in two principal forms— namely, multiple alleles and cumulative

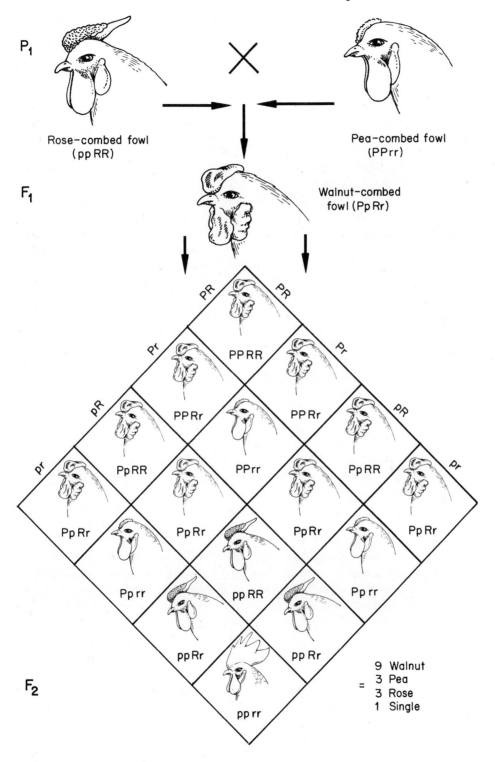

Figure 21–9. Comb shape inheritance in chickens.

(or duplicate) genes. As each of these types has distinctive effects, they need to be described separately.

Multiple Alleles. So far in these discussions, the alleles of any given set have existed as contrasting pairs. This state of affairs is not universal, however, for sometimes three, four, or even more alleles may exist. Nevertheless, no more than a pair of alleles ever are found in the same individual. Perhaps the best-known illustration of this condition is found in the blood groups of man.

As will be recalled, four possible major blood groups occur in human beings, namely, A, B, AB, and O. These four phenotypes are currently suggested to stem from the interplay of three principal alleles, I^A, I^B, and I^O, the last of which is recessive while the first two are equally dominant. Blood group A is produced by both the genotype I^AI^A and I^AI^O, whereas B results from either I^BI^B or I^BI^O. On the other hand, groups of O and AB can arise only from genotypes I^OI^O and I^AI^B, respectively. While the picture is further complicated by the fact that no less than four variations of A exist, three alleles in addition to the set listed, the net results remain unchanged, as dominance is identical in all the A variants. Among other sets of multiple alleles known or suspected to exist are some governing hair color in rabbits and guinea pigs and probably in man also, as well as seed color in corn. As knowledge accumulates, doubtlessly many characteristics now thought to be governed by separate sets of alleles will be discovered in actuality to involve multiple alleles.

Cumulative Genes. On the other hand, there are numerous cases known in which several distinct series of genes influence the same trait in comparable fashions. In some such instances, the action of each dominant allele supplements that of another and thus a stronger effect is produced than by either one alone; expressed in other words, the activities of each dominant gene accumulate in producing the phenotype. Such *cumulative genes* often govern such aspects as size, whether of the whole organism or of certain of its parts, intensity of coloration, or similar quantitative features. A model of this variety of inheritance can be found in one current concept of the genetics of skin pigmentation in human beings.

In this theory three sets of alleles, each of which has a comparable but slightly differing influence on the production of melanin, are supposed to exist. The dominants, which increase melanin formation, are simply referred to as M^1, M^2, and M^3, whereas the corresponding recessives are m^1, m^2, and m^3. If measurements by photoelectric cells are made of various human populations, seven classes of darkness of pigmentation can be distinguished, ranging from the blackest-skinned to white. The greatest amount of melanin is suggested to arise from the genotype $M^1M^1M^2M^2M^3M^3$, while the next lighter shade results from the presence of a single recessive. Thus the phenotypes would be the same regardless of whether the genotype was $M^1m^1M^2M^2M^3M^3$, $M^1M^1M^2m^2M^3M^3$, or $M^1M^1M^2M^2M^3m^3$. Similarly two recessives, regardless of specific kind, result in a slightly paler skin, whereas three produce the shade known as mulatto, four a still lighter one, and so on, until the absence of all factors for this type of pigmentation characterizes the skin in the Caucasian race (Table 21–1).

Quite comparable conditions are found in wheat and in corn. In the former, three sets of genes govern red color of the grain, with cumulative effects, and similarly in corn, yellowness of the fruit

TABLE 21-1

SKIN PIGMENTATION TYPES PRODUCED BY MATINGS BETWEEN TWO MULATTOES

| Gametes Involved | | Number of Dominant Genes in Resulting Combination | Phenotype of Skin | Anticipated Percentages |
First Gamete	Second Gamete			
$M^1M^2M^3$	$M^1M^2M^3$	Six	Darkest brown (black)	1.5
$M^1M^2m^3$ $M^1m^2M^3$ $m^1M^2M^3$	$M^1M^2M^3$	Five	Dark brown	10.0
$M^1M^2m^3$ $M^1m^2M^3$ $m^1M^2M^3$	$M^1M^2m^3$ $M^1m^2M^3$ $m^1M^2M^3$			
$M^1m^2m^3$ $m^1M^2m^3$ $m^1m^2M^3$	$M^1M^2M^3$	Four	Medium dark (brown)	23.0
$M^1m^2m^3$ $m^1M^2m^3$ $m^1m^2M^3$	$M^1M^2m^3$ $M^1m^2M^3$ $m^1M^2M^3$			
$m^1m^2m^3$	$M^1M^2M^3$	Three	Mulatto (medium brown)	31.0
$M^1m^2m^3$ $m^1M^2m^3$ $m^1m^2M^3$	$M^1m^2m^3$ $m^1M^2m^3$ $m^1m^2M^3$			
$M^1M^2m^3$ $M^1m^2M^3$ $m^1M^2M^3$	$m^1m^2m^3$	Two	Light brown	23.0
$M^1m^2m^3$ $m^1M^2m^3$ $m^1m^2M^3$	$m^1m^2m^3$	One	"Yellow" (pale brown)	10.0
$m^1m^2m^3$	$m^1m^2m^3$	None	White	1.5

depends on the activities of three separate sets of alleles. Sometimes, as in coat color among Duroc-Jersey swine, only two sets of genes are involved, while in other cases, such as milk production differences in cattle, no less than 7 or 10 sets have been suggested to exist. In such quantitative distinctions as the body size variations of vertebrates, perhaps dozens of sets are required to produce the total effect.

The Chromosome Theory of Inheritance

Shortly after the rediscovery of Mendel's laws, the American cytologist Sutton suggested that the hereditary factors are located on the chromosomes. According to this view, reasons are at once provided for the principles found by Mendel. For instance, genes occur in pairs because chromosomes do likewise, and one of each allelic set is derived from each of the two parents, a fact that stems from homologous chromosomes being similarly derived. Moreover, when gametes are formed, the number of alleles is halved, just as the chromosome number is reduced in meiosis. Perhaps before entering into the discussion illustrating these correlations, the student will find it helpful to review the appropriate portion of Chapter 4 (page 64), for later some facets of genetics become more deeply dependent on the meiotic processes.

CHROMOSOMES AND GENES

The Chromosomes and Segregation. If hair length in dogs, in which the gene for short hair is dominant over long, is used as an illustration, the cellular processes may be watched together with the genetic to good advantage. Although in actuality the chromosome number in this species is 78 (i.e., 39 pairs), the discussion and the figures alike will assume the presence of only two pairs for the sake of clarity. To assist further in clarification one pair will be treated as being long, the other short; the alleles for coat length will be arbitrarily designated as being situated on the first of these sets (Figure 21–10).

As usual the P_1 stock employed is homozygous respectively for short and long hair; hence, either phenotype can produce gametes of only one genetic type, for each long chromosome in one parent bears a gene for short hair (S), while in the second both homologues possess the long-hair allele (s) (Figure 21–10). After mating and the subsequent union of these two varieties of gametes, a diploid zygote is produced that contains two long chromosomes, one carrying the short-haired gene and the other the long-haired. Because of the dominance of the short-haired genes, the zygotes mature into short-haired dogs, although they are heterozygous for this set of alleles. Now when gametes are produced by this type of dog, or by any other for that matter, the homologous chromosomes, each composed of two chromatids, synapse during prophase of the first meiotic division and line up together on the equatorial plate at metaphase. Hence, when movement of the chromosomes occurs during anaphase, the long chromosome that happens to bear the short-haired gene goes to one pole while its homologue with the long-haired allele moves to the other. During the second division the chromatids of each chromosome are similarly split, so that in the end two of the four resulting gametes contain a short-haired factor while the remainder possess the long-haired gene. Normally whenever sperm are produced these processes are repeated hundreds of times, but regardless of the number, half of the total contains one allele, the rest the second member of the set. Eggs are formed by similar meiotic events, and though the actual number is never nearly so great as that of sperm, the distribution of alleles is always on an equal basis. Consequently at fertilization there is a like opportunity for all combinations of gametes to be made, as expressed in the Punnett square.

Chromosomes and the Dihybrid Cross. The random behavior of genes becomes even clearer when examination is made of the cytological processes involved in a dihybrid cross. As a basis for discussion additional use will be made of the dog, but this time coat color in breeds like the pointer will be the subject. While the actual situation is somewhat more complex than here indicated, for all practical purposes black (B) may be accepted as

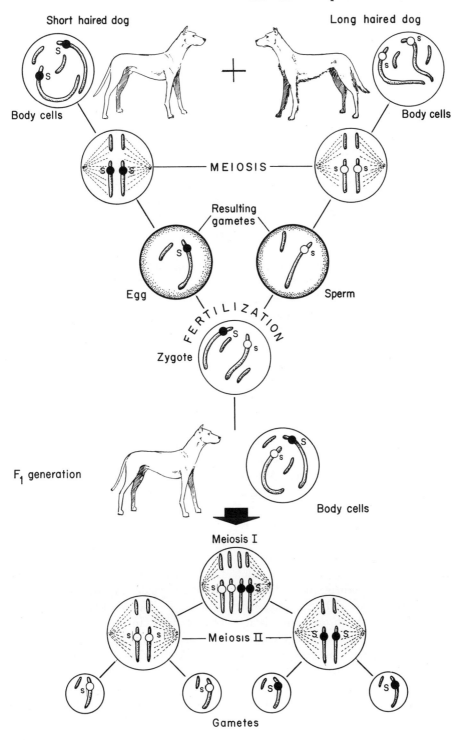

Figure 21–10. The chromosomal basis of gene behavior.

showing simple dominance over brown (*b*), with total color (*T*) displaying the same relationship to the spotted allele (*t*). When crosses involving these two sets of factors are made, the F_1 generation is found to consist entirely of totally black dogs. When these are inbred in sufficient numbers the ensuing F_2 generation may be supposed to include, by way of a concrete illustration, 64 totally black, 23 totally brown, 20 spotted black, and 7 spotted brown individuals. Now what is the cellular basis for these results?

Using just two pairs of chromosomes in the diagram of these cells and suggesting that the total-spotted alleles are placed on the long set, with the black-brown factors on the short pair, we can readily see again that the parental types can each produce only one variety of gamete (Figure 21–11). When these unite in forming the zygote and restore the diploid number, as each set of homologous chromosomes bears opposing alleles, a heterozygous condition for both sets of factors results. Because of the existence of simple dominance in each case, these individuals of *TtBb* genotype display a phenotype of a totally black coat. When these dogs mature and produce gametes, during the meiotic divisions the chromosome number is reduced to haploid as always, and with this reduction, the number of alleles present is likewise halved (Figure 21–11). Insofar as these particular genes are concerned, the reduction can proceed in two different ways. In one procedure, those chromosomes bearing the dominant alleles *T* and *B* happen to line up facing the same pole, whereas those with the recessives are accordingly directed toward the opposite one. Hence, after division has been completed twice, the resulting gametes are *TB* and *tb* in genetic composition. In the second possible combination, each chromosome possessing a recessive gene faces the same pole as a nonhomologous one bearing a dominant; therefore the gametes that ultimately result are *Tb* and *tB* in composition. Since chromosome alignment is seemingly a strictly random set of processes, all four types of both eggs and sperm are produced in respectively equal numbers.

Genes as Points on Chromosomes. According to the chromosome theory, then, a *gene* is a definite particle resting on a chromosome or, according to a more modern concept, a particular portion or *locus* on such an organelle. Therefore alleles, being variations of the same locus, can never be present in a haploid cell in numbers greater than a pair—i.e., one on each homologous chromosome—no matter how many variations in a given set of alleles may exist. Modern terminology also describes genes on a molecular basis, as will be brought out later in connection with a description of the chemical nature of the chromosome. But before those subjects are broached, more needs to be discussed of the behavior of chromosomes and genes in inheritance.

CHROMOSOMES AND SEX

Sex Chromosomes. Among the first discoveries of devices implicated with *sex determination*—i.e., concerned with the formation of sex in an individual—was that made by the American geneticist T. H. Morgan in fruit flies (*Drosophila*). In the science of genetics, this organism has been found to combine a number of traits that make it uniquely valuable. First, it is small and therefore requires a minimum of space to breed; second, its life history is short (10 to 14 days) and its progeny numerous; and third, its chromosome number is small ($2n = 8$) and its variability very high.

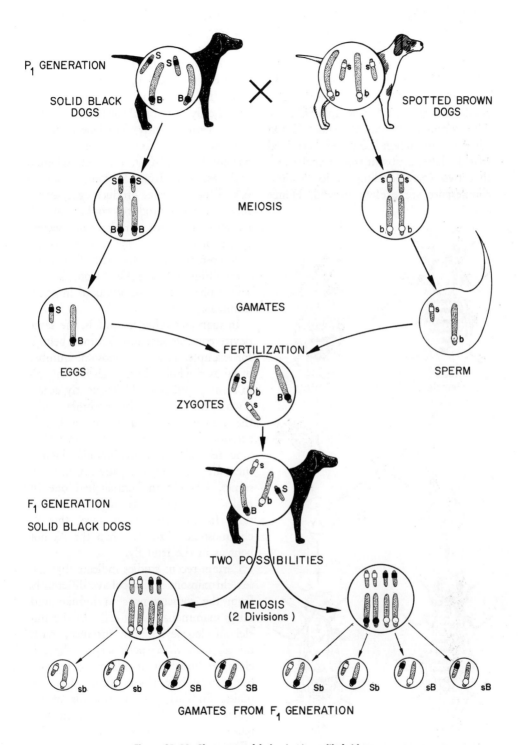

Figure 21–11. Chromosomal behavior in a dihybrid cross.

While the total number of chromosomes in both males and females is the same, all are seen to have homologues in the latter sex when examined under the microscope, whereas the male possesses just three pairs of identical members and two single ones that are not homologous, one being straight and the other hooked. On further examination it can be determined that the latter is absent from females and that two corresponding to its straight counterpart are present instead. Hence it is suggested that these chromosomes are active in controlling the sex of an individual and are therefore called the *sex chromosomes*. Usually the pair with identical members is referred to as the X-chromosomes and the unpaired one found only in the male as the Y-chromosome. Consequently femaleness in the fruit fly results from the existence of chromosomes *XX* in the cell, whereas maleness stems from the combination of *XY*. When females produce eggs, therefore, all their products contain an X-chromosome, but males can secrete sperm of two types, one carrying an X-chromosome, the other the Y-chromosome (Figure 21–12). On union, the two sexual phenotypes are produced in equal numbers.

In man and other mammals, the same device controls sexuality. Human beings, for example, have a chromosome number of 46 as a whole (Figure 21–13) though in some populations 47 frequently occur. Two of these are sex chromosomes, while the remainder are involved in bodily activities and are known as *autosomes*. Since females have matching homologues, these are recognized as paired X-chromosomes, whereas the unmatched one in males is referred to as an *XY* combination. In the present instance, the Y-chromosome is shorter than the X, not bent as in the fruit fly.

Certain recent studies indicate that the sex chromosomes may behave differently from the somatic ones in human and other mammalian body cells. In the nuclei of leucocytes, for instance, dark masses toward the periphery of the nucleus are apparent in cells from females but consistently absent from those of males. Similarly the neutrophils of females show a club or hook on one nuclear lobe that is never seen in those of males (Figure 21–14).

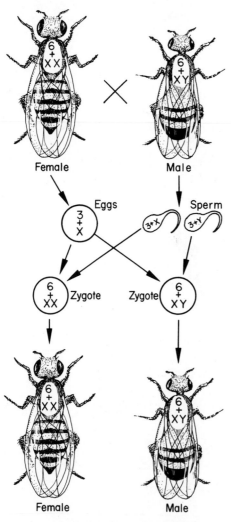

Figure 21–12. Sex inheritance in fruit flies.

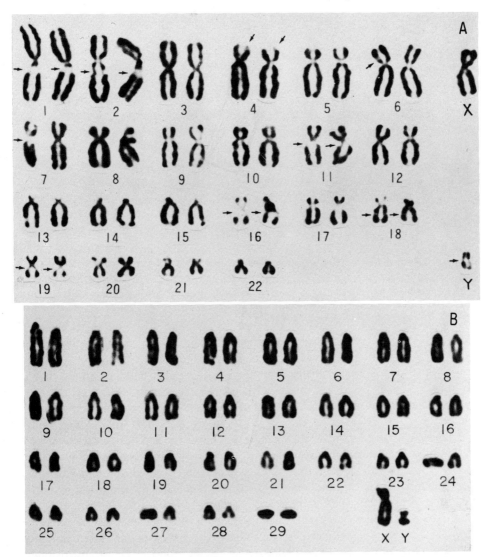

Figure 21–13. Chromosomes from male mammals. All mammals have the X–Y type of sex inheritance. In the human male (A) there are 22 pairs plus an X and a Y, while in domestic bulls (B) there are 29 pairs plus the same combination of sex chromosomes. (Reproduced with permission from Dr. Masao S. Sasaki, Amer. Journ. Human Genetics, Vol. 15, 1963.)

Variations in Sex Determination. A large number of variations on the foregoing basic pattern in sex determination have been found. For instance, in grasshoppers no Y-chomosome exists, only the X variety. In these animals femaleness arises as before by the combination XX, but maleness has only an X, usually expressed XO for clarity's sake. Sometimes the pattern of sexuality is the reverse of the foregoing; in it the males possess the paired sex chromosomes, whereas the females have nonidentical members or only one of the set. Birds,

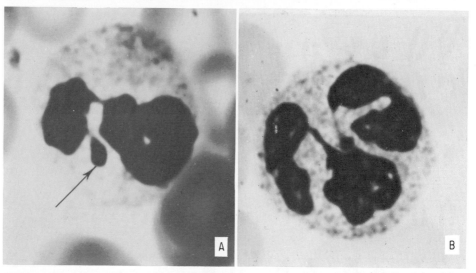

Figure 21–14. Human blood cell differences between the sexes. A large percentage of neutrophils show a hook in the blood from females (A), a feature that usually is absent in blood from males (B). (Courtesy of Dr. John L. Hamerton, *Internat. Rev. Cytol.*, Vol. 12, Academic Press, with permission of the Paediatric Research Unit, Guy's Hospital Medical School.)

including chickens, are one major group of animals known to possess this modification, and moths and butterflies are another.

Among many insects and mites sexuality springs, not from the existence of special chromosomes, but rather from the total number of chromosomes present. Most usually, but not without exception, the difference in number arises from the fact that one sex comes from fertilized, the other from unfertilized eggs. The honeybee is the most noted illustration of this sex-determination device. In this species queens and workers (sterile females) come from fertilized ova and have the diploid number of chromosomes, 32 in all. In contrast, the drones are produced parthenogenetically and therefore have the haploid number, namely 16 (Figure 21–15). Sterility in the workers is induced by nutritional deficiencies during larval growth, not by genetic devices.

SEX-ASSOCIATED INHERITANCE

Along with their role of determining the sex of the individual, the sex chromosomes may show other activities in inheritance, some of which stem from them directly and others indirectly or secondarily.

Sex-Linked Characteristics. Naturally enough, the sex chromosomes may carry genes and, under the varying combinations of X and Y or of X and O, may have a direct effect in heredity. Of particular interest are genes in the first set of combinations borne on that part of the X-chromosome missing in the Y, as in mammals in which the Y-chromosome is shorter than the former. In man hemophilia and common color-blindness (the inability to distinguish red and green) are well-known examples; white-forelock and toothlessness are suspected of being others. Since the characteristics

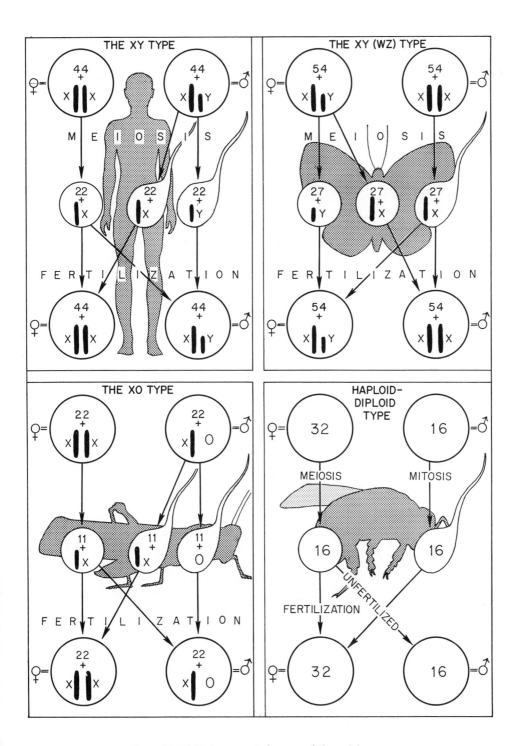

Figure 21–15. Various genetical means of determining sex.

are consequently associated with sexuality, they are referred to as *sex-linked traits*. For our discussion, common color-blindness in man is employed.

In some marriages between persons with normal color vision the children may be found to consist of females with normal vision whereas half of the males may be color-blind. If certain F₁ normal-visioned women marry color-blind men, half of their offspring, both girls and boys, will be color-blind. These data are best explained by the assumptions that normal color vision is dominant over color-blindness and that the alleles are carried on the portion of the X-chromosome that is missing on the Y (Figure 21–16). On this basis, the original normal-visioned mother is heterozygous for color-blindness and is said to be a *carrier* of the trait; she produces eggs of two types, those with an X-chromosome having the dominant factor N and those with an X-chromosome and the recessive gene n. Since the X-chromosome in the sperm required to produce femaleness bears the dominant trait, all female offspring will contain at least one N

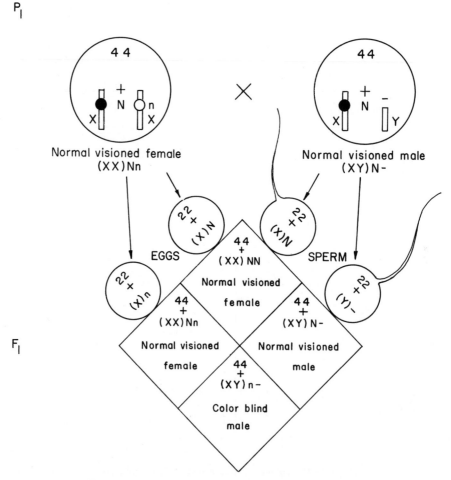

Figure 21–16. Inheritance of color blindness in human beings.

gene, and hence all will have normal vision. On the other hand, the Y-chromosome from the sperm needed for maleness bears no allele, and consequently the gene of the X-chromosome predominates, whether dominant or recessive. The net result is, as stated above, that half of the sons are color-blind.

Sex-Influenced Characteristics. Particularly among mammals, a given gene may behave differently in the two sexes. In most known cases a change in dominance is involved, the trait being dominant in one sex and recessive in the other.

Since the sex of the individual alters the expression of a given genotype, cases of this sort are referred to as *sex-influenced traits*. A common trait of humans is inherited in this fashion. In males baldness is dominant, so that loss of hair with increasing years occurs both in the homozygous and heterozygous conditions; retention of hair in this sex is recessive. In contrast, the gene for baldness is recessive in females, so that hair retention is normal even in the heterozygous genotype; in fact, in this sex as a rule the homozygous condition for baldness most

B. MALE COLOR-BLIND

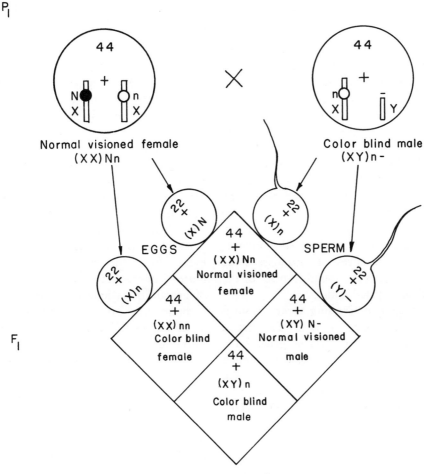

Figure 21-16 (Continued).

frequently expresses itself as thinness of the hair covering of the head rather than its actual loss. Only rarely do women become completely bald. Moreover, if the testes are removed, the baldness factor fails to express itself in males, for androgens must be present for the trait to appear. Other secondary sexual characteristics are similarly sex-influenced. For example, bass voices have the same genotype as sopranos, and tenors the same as altos; in each case, the pitch is influenced by the hormones present in the individual.

CHROMOSOMES AND GENE BEHAVIOR

Mention was made earlier that genes *usually* behave as though no other set were present; exceptions to this Mendelian principle arise when two or more of the contrasting sets of traits are located on the same chromosome. Since the number of chromosomes in any species is small in relation to the infinite number of variations that often exists, it is inevitable that more than one hereditary factor should be found to occupy any one chromosome; in fact, the opposite is the exceptional condition, especially when many traits are involved simultaneously. In instances of this sort some peculiar results are found in place of the usual anticipated ratios.

Linkage and Crossing Over. Instead of the customary ratios of phenotypes, the location of two sets of genes on a single chromosome results in much higher proportions than expected of the original parental combinations, so that the P_1 characteristics appear linked. This failure of two gene sets to act entirely independently is called *linkage*. However, if linkage were complete—that is, if each

chromosome always acted as a unit—whole series of genes would be expected to remain constantly associated with one another; if, for example, the dominant genes A, B, C, D, E, and F were located on a single pair of chromosomes and their recessive alleles a, b, c, d, e, and f correspondingly, only two types of offspring would be produced in the F_2 generation, those with all the dominants and those with all the recessives, as in the original types (Figure 21–17). In actual matings these results are never obtained, for there always occurs a number of new combinations; perhaps a few individuals of phenotypes $ABCDef$ and $abcdEF$ would be found in the example cited. So it appears that some of the parental traits crossed over during gamete formation and produced these new combinations (Figure 21–17).

If the meiotic steps in the formation of gametes are brought to mind, it will be recalled that one of each pair of sister chromatids underwent synapsis with a corresponding chromatid of the homologous chromosome and during these processes the two broke into several segments. At the end these segments were combined so that the originally pure maternal and pure paternal chromatids were then combinations of maternal and paternal members (Figure 4–17). These events form the cytological basis for *crossing over*—that is, the recombination of genetic traits located on homologous chromosomes. To obtain greater clarity, let us employ the same set of genes listed in the foregoing example and follow the events in the F_1 heterozygote during the processes of gametogenesis.

In our illustration here the number of allelic sets is somewhat extended to include dominant genes A through J and recessives a through j; these genes are located on chromosome III, that from

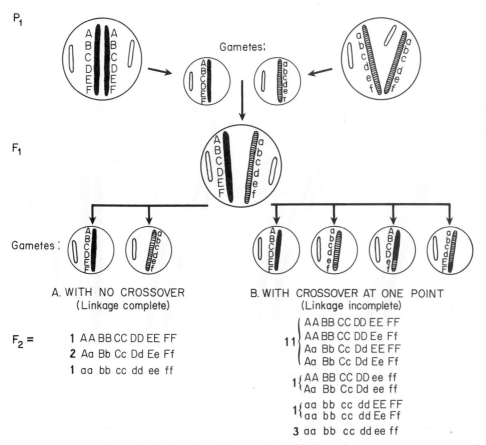

P₁

Gametes:

F₁

Gametes:

A. WITH NO CROSSOVER
(Linkage complete)

B. WITH CROSSOVER AT ONE POINT
(Linkage incomplete)

$F_2 =$

1 AA BB CC DD EE FF
2 Aa Bb Cc Dd Ee Ff
1 aa bb cc dd ee ff

11 {
AA BB CC DD EE FF
AA BB CC DD Ee Ff
Aa Bb Cc Dd EE FF
Aa Bb Cc Dd Ee Ff

1 {
AA BB CC DD ee ff
Aa Bb Cc Dd ee ff

1 {
aa bb cc dd EE FF
aa bb cc dd Ee Ff

3 aa bb cc dd ee ff

Figure 21–17. Complete linkage and simplified crossing over.

the egg being distinguished as III*m*, whereas the homologue from paternal sources is lettered III*p* (Figure 21–18). During the first prophase both sets of chromatids twist around one another, the sister sets held together by the centromeres to which spindle threads eventually attach. Actual contact between the loops of homologous chromatids is in this case suggested to occur between points occupied by the genes *C* and *D* and also between points *H* and *I* (Figure 21–18*A*). After these contacts or *chiasmata* (sing., chiasma) have been established, two unlike (nonsister) chromatids break as in Figure 21–18*B*. Later these segments reunite (Figure 21–18*C*)

to form two chromatids in which recombinations of the original genes exist, while the other two undergo no alterations (Figure 21–18*D*). Hence in this particular example, four different gametes would be produced, one bearing all dominants *A* through *J*, a second containing all recessives *a* through *j*, a third with the genotype *ABCdefghIJ*, and the last with *abcDEFGHij*.

Chromosome Maps. When the genetic activities of any organism are studied intensively over many years, a number of linkage groups will be found to correspond as a rule to the number of chromosomes in the species concerned. To determine the exact sequence of genes

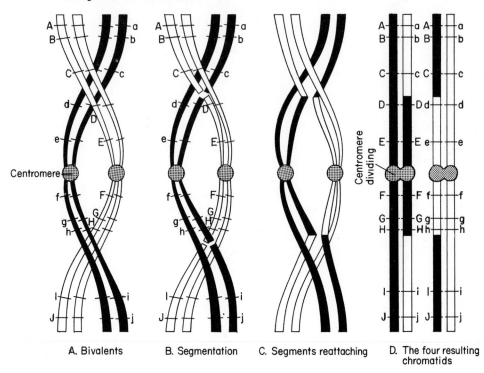

A. Bivalents B. Segmentation C. Segments reattaching D. The four resulting chromatids

Figure 21–18. The chromosomal basis of linkage and crossing over.

in any linkage group, that is, on any chromosome, the relative amount of crossing over between two given points is employed. The theory behind this procedure is based on the assumption that the points of contact between pairing nonsister chromatids are found randomly along their lengths; hence, the greater the distance between two genes, the greater the chance that crossing over will occur between them. In our illustration, for instance, it could occur between points D and E, B and C, and A and B, or any others, as well as between C and D as originally suggested. Hence, if this assumption is correct, it follows that the relative frequency of chiasma formation is correlated to the proportionate distance between the points concerned; the further removed two points are from each other, the greater chance there is that a chiasma will fall between

them. Hence crossing over will on the average occur with greater frequency between C and D, which are shown as rather widely separated, than between A and B, which are approximate. Similarly, still greater crossing over can be expected between A and E than between A and D, whereas recombinations between A and J would occur so frequently that linkage might be completely absent or virtually so. By making large numbers of crosses among various combinations of traits, *chromosome maps* can be drawn for each species. In these processes, which are often quite complex, the whole chromosome is considered to be composed of 100 units, so that the percentage of crossing over thus expresses the number of unit distances between given points. By these means chromosome maps have been drawn for the fruit fly (Figure 21–19), corn, tomato, *Chlamydomonas,* and a number of other experimental plants and animals. Some mapping has been done with human chromosomes, particularly the sex chromosomes, but because of the large number of linkage groups present and the impossibility of running controlled experiments progress along these lines is a time-consuming process.

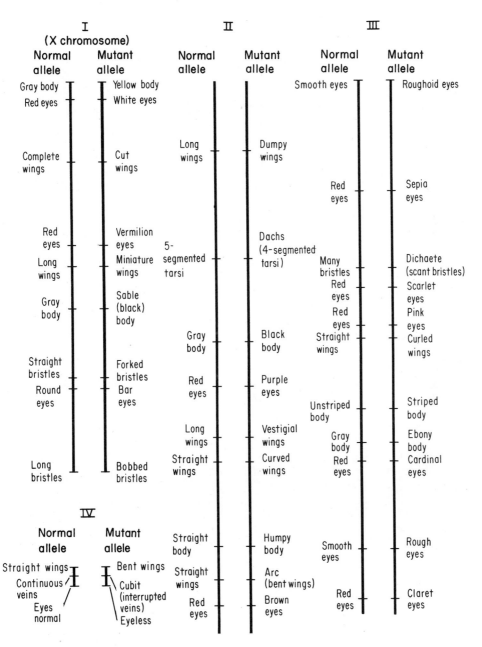

Figure 21–19. A chromosomal map for the fruit fly. The left-hand member of each pair of chromatids bears the normal allele, and the right-hand member bears a corresponding mutant. Many other characters have been located on chromosomes in this species (*Drosophila melanogaster*).

Questions for Review and Thought

1. On what are genetic studies based primarily?
2. Define each of the following terms clearly:

(a) alleles	(g) dihybrid cross
(b) homozygous	(h) linkage
(c) autosomes	(i) recessive
(d) test cross	(j) genotype
(e) sex chromosome	(k) chromosome maps
(f) heterozygote	(l) phenotype

3. List the basic genetic principles worked out originally by Mendel, phrased in your own words. Who rediscovered these principles? What type of experiment most clearly demonstrates each?

4. If M is dominant over m, what ratios of phenotypes would be found in the immediate offspring of matings between (a) $Mm \times mm$; (b) $MM \times Mm$; (c) $Mm \times Mm$; (d) $MM \times mm$? What would the ratios be in each case if M were incompletely dominant?

5. Which of the foregoing is a typical backcross? Why is the backcross used more frequently by animal breeders than by plant geneticists? What substitute measure is available to the latter?

6. In certain breeds of dogs gray is dominant over white and spotted is dominant over solid color. If a solid gray dog is mated to a spotted white, what would the F_1 generation be like? What ratio and types would be found in the F_2 generation if the F_1 offspring are inbred? Now assume that gray is incompletely dominant over white, the heterozygous condition resulting in black, and rework the problem. What are your ratios now in the F_2 generation?

7. What is meant by interaction between genes? List some cases in which this condition probably prevails.

8. Distinguish between sex determination, sex linkage, and sex influence. Cite examples of each. How is sex determined in cattle? In bees? In man? In grasshoppers? In turkeys?

9. What blood types could be expected to be found among the children from a marriage of a woman with type O blood and man of type AB? What could be expected from a marriage between a woman of type A and a man of type B? What from one in which both man and woman are type A?

10. Explain in your own words the difference between linkage and crossing over. How are chromosome maps made?

Supplementary References

Auerbach, C. *The Science of Genetics*. New York, Harper, 1961.

Beadle, G. W. "The Genes of Men and Molds." *Sci. Amer.*, September 1948.

Begg, C. M. M. *Introduction to Genetics*. London, Macmillan, 1959.

Carson, H. L. *Heredity and Human Life*. New York, Columbia Univ. Press, 1963.

Dodson, E. O. *Genetics: The Modern Science of Heredity*. Philadelphia, Saunders, 1956.

Gardner, E. J. *Principles of Genetics*. New York, Wiley, 1960.

Goldschmidt, R. B. *Theoretical Genetics*. Berkeley, Univ. California Press, 1955.

Herskowitz, I. H. *Genetics*. Boston, Little, Brown, 1962.

Hill, J. B., and H. D. Hill. *Genetics and Human Heredity*. New York, McGraw-Hill, 1955.

Horowitz, N. H. "The Gene." *Sci. Amer.,* October 1956.

Jacob, F., and E. L. Wollman. "Viruses and Genes." *Sci. Amer.,* June 1961.

Levine, R. P. *Genetics*. New York, Holt, Rinehart and Winston, 1962.

Moore, J. A. *Heredity and Development*. Oxford, Oxford Univ. Press, 1963.

Penrose, L. S. *Outline of Human Genetics*. New York, Wiley, 1959.

Sager, Ruth, and F. J. Ryan. *Cell Heredity*. New York, Wiley, 1959.

Waddington, C. H. *Strategy of the Genes; A Discussion of Some Aspects of Theoretical Biology*. London, Macmillan, 1958.

Williams, R. J. *Free and Unequal: The Biological Basis of Individual Liberty*. Austin, Univ. Texas Press, 1953.

Other Aspects
of Genetics

WHILE the fundamentals of the science of genetics are covered in the foregoing chapter, there still remain several aspects to be considered. Although these remaining items are a miscellany in that each topic is essentially unrelated directly to the others, they are nonetheless of considerable importance, for some pertain to the real nature of genes, others to the manner of gene expression, and the balance to the influence of extranuclear parts of the cell on heredity and the methods by which variations in genotypes originate.

The Nature of the Gene

In view of the evidence presented earlier, little doubt can remain that the common genes are carried by the chromo-somes; particularly convincing are the facts presented by linkage and crossing-over phenomena and by sex-linked traits. If this point of view is accepted, the first question to be answered concerns the chemicals of which genes may be constructed, and the closely allied second arises as to the methods by means of which the chemical compounds guide the activities of inheritance. Although much remains obscure regarding the answers to the two queries, the currently existing theories on these matters are presented below.

THE CHEMICAL NATURE
OF GENES

While it is known that chromosomes contain between 25 and 48 per cent DNA, a small fraction each of RNA and lipids, and from 50 to 70 per cent proteins, it cannot be stated precisely how these various constituents are combined so as to carry out their cytological and genetical activities. However, in 1953 two biochemists, D. S. Watson and F. H. C. Crick, an American and an Englishman respectively, presented a model that is widely accepted as possibly illustrative both of the chemical nature of the DNA fraction and of a mechanism by which it might duplicate itself exactly. The student should first of all bear in mind that this molecular structure is a model, an intimation of what possibly exists based on many observed facts, yet not a replica of precisely ascertained details. Although it may be basically sound, before this model can approach complete factuality, many fine points must first be clarified, refined, and demonstrated; in short, this proposal is a starting point, though an exciting and thought-provoking one.

In their model, Watson and Crick suggest that DNA consists essentially of two chains of nucleotides (page 25), arranged parallel to one another and twisted into a loose spiral. Each chain fundamentally is composed of a series of pentose sugar molecules linked together by the phosphorus contained in the phosphate radicals, and to every pentose unit is joined either the pyrimidine or purine that completes the nucleotide structure. Greatly abbreviated a single chain appears in simplified fashion as in Figure 22–1. Evidence gathered from X-ray studies of the DNA molecule and other sources suggests that two such chains are compounded into the double condition by links provided by the purine or pyrimidine constituents of nucleotides.

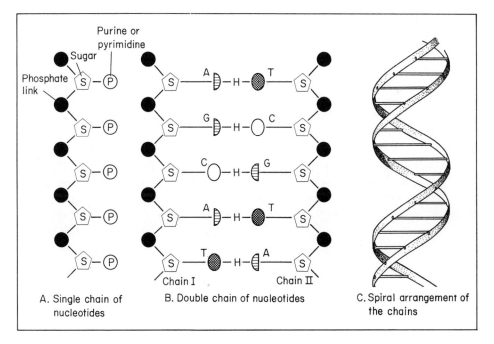

Figure 22–1. Postulated molecular structure of DNA. A. DNA is known to consist of the pentose sugar deoxyribose (S) to which is attached either a purine or a pyrimidine (P), linked together into a chain by phosphate radicals (black circles). B. The actual DNA molecule is believed to consist of two such chains loosely linked together by hydrogen bonds (H). C. The dual chains are spirally twisted according to the Watson-Crick concept.

Also these data indicate that each cross link is composed of one pyrimidine coupled to one purine by a bond provided by a hydrogen atom; such hydrogen bonds are relatively weak and can readily be broken. Furthermore, by precise analytical methods it has been established that each of the two purines which enter into DNA structure constantly occurs in identical proportions as a certain pyrimidine constituent of the molecule. The purine adenine always composes the same proportionate amount of a given DNA molecule as the pyrimidine thymine, and a similar relationship exists between guanine and cytosine; hence, it appears that adenine (*A*) and thymine (*T*) are consistently members of the same cross link and that guanine (*G*) is always paired with cytosine (*C*) (Figure 22–1*B*). Thus the rungs of the spiral-staircaselike molecule may be composed of no other than the four combinations *A-T*, *T-A*, *G-C*, and *C-G*. These combinations then are suggested to be arranged in various sequences to form a "code," one that employs only four letters to form, as shall be seen later, words confined to three letters each. Currently this coding is believed to serve as the actual mechanism employed in heredity; that is to say, a series of code units constitutes what is referred to as a gene. Perhaps the method by which the chemical symbols may act will become clearer as the discussion progresses.

THE DUPLICATION
OF CHROMOSOMES

If this model of DNA is accepted as plausible and is postulated to form the molecular skeleton of a chromosome, it becomes possible to propose a means by which a chromosome may be enabled to form an exact duplicate of itself just preceding mitosis. Substantiating this point of view is the fact that it has been demonstrated many times that the DNA content of the nucleus becomes doubled during the mitotic processes.

Basically the theory commences with the assumption that early in nuclear division, the DNA molecule splits along the hydrogen bonds so that the two long uprights of the spiral are separated. As pointed out above, the hydrogen bonds are very weak, and their separation need not involve a great expenditure of energy. It will be noted that the two chains thus separated are complements of one another; whereas chain I has an *A* or a *T* as a partial rung, chain II has a *T* or an *A*, respectively, and wherever the one has a *C*, the other has a *G* (Figure 22–2). Once separation is completed, each chain, supplied with a sufficient quantity of the necessary purines and pyrimidines, can rebuild a new complement exactly like the partner from which it has just become detached. Under the current concepts, the procedures appear simple enough, for in chain I of the illustration employed above for instance, only an *A* radical can couple to the *T* of the topmost rung, while only *T*'s are able to unite to the next two, a *C* to the *G* of the fourth rung, and so on to the end of the molecule (Figure 22–2*C*, *D*). While all the purines and pyrimidines are attaching by hydrogen bonds to their normal respective opposites, adjacent sugar radicals unite with one another by their phosphate components and eventually build a new assemblage exactly corresponding to the old chain II. In the meanwhile the latter has similarly built an exact replacement for its former chain I by corresponding processes. By these procedures, it is suggested, chromosomes are able to duplicate themselves in a precise manner during mitosis.

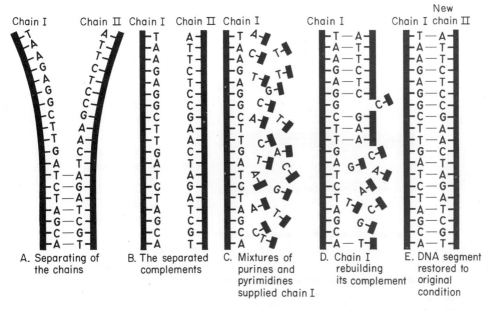

Chain I | Chain II | Chain I | Chain II | Chain I | Chain I | New Chain I chain II

A. Separating of the chains

B. The separated complements

C. Mixtures of purines and pyrimidines supplied chain I

D. Chain I rebuilding its complement

E. DNA segment restored to original condition

Figure 22–2. Molecular means by which chromosomes possibly duplicate themselves. By use of the Watson-Crick model, a manner in which DNA might reconstruct itself can be proposed; each chain duplicates itself in a fashion pre-established by its remaining components. Refer to the text for details.

POSSIBLE MODE OF GENE ACTION

Again it is to be emphasized that, although the foregoing exposition on the structure and duplication of the DNA molecule is plausible enough and fits many of the known data, it is still only a preliminary theory, which as yet fails to explain a number of correlated events and observations. In this connection it should be recalled that the old concept of the earth's being the center of the universe around which all the heavenly bodies rotate is plausible, too, on the surface and satisfactorily explains almost all observable daily phenomena. More accurate data employed with great insight by Copernicus, however, showed how erroneous the obvious explanation was in actuality. In the present case, no explanation, for example, is provided for the duplication of the proteins which constitute half or more of each chromosome. Nevertheless, if the frailty of the present theory of chromosome structure and replication is kept in mind, it is harmless to build upon it and suggest a possible mechanism by means of which genes might carry out their functions in heredity and normal cell activities.

Importance of Proteins. More than likely it will be recalled that in Chapter 2 it was pointed out that proteins are the most distinctive chemical constituent of every given species of organism. Whereas storage carbohydrates are frequently characteristic of large groups of related forms, and lipids vary only slightly in their proportionate contents of fatty acids, proteinaceous substances usually are sharply differentiated among all living things. In fact, in modern studies in systematic zoology, sometimes in attempts to determine relationships, a study of the differences in protein con-

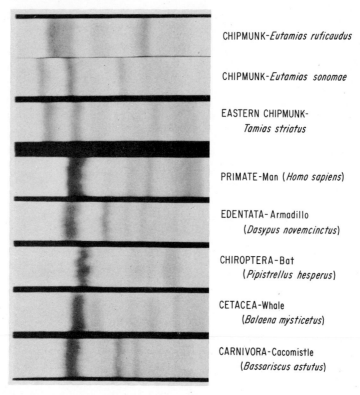

CHIPMUNK-*Eutamias ruticaudus*

CHIPMUNK-*Eutamias sonomae*

EASTERN CHIPMUNK-
Tamias striatus

PRIMATE-Man (*Homo sapiens*)

EDENTATA-Armadillo
(*Dasypus novemcinctus*)

CHIROPTERA-Bat
(*Pipistrellus hesperus*)

CETACEA-Whale
(*Balaena mysticetus*)

CARNIVORA-Cacomistle
(*Bassariscus astutus*)

Figure 22–3. Differences in blood proteins between several mammals. Electrophoresis patterns of blood sera show likenesses as well as differences between members of various orders. At the top, comparisons can be made between two species of the same genus as well as between them and a species of a closely related genus. (Courtesy of Dr. Murray L. Johnson.)

tents of the cells (Figure 22–3) proves of great value. Furthermore, these nitrogen-carrying compounds constitute the great bulk of protoplasm; hence it appears likely that the majority of the genetic processes involves guiding the formation of these basic but highly complex ingredients. Employment of the Watson-Crick model of DNA structure permits some insight into a possible mechanism by means of which the details of protein-building might be transmitted from one generation to the next.

The Formation of Proteins. Primarily, the transmission of hereditary traits is accepted as lying in the "coding" provided by the arrangement of rungs in the spiral DNA molecule, as mentioned earlier,

that purportedly forms a large portion of the chromosomes and all the genes that the latter carries. Under this theory, a gene, then, is a portion of the chromosomal DNA molecule responsible for the synthesis of a particular protein. In carrying out its duty, each gene serves principally as the source of information, in code form; during anabolic processes this hereditary information is first transferred to a molecule of RNA. Unlike the other nucleic acid, RNA is found both inside the nucleus and within the cytoplasm and is believed to migrate between these major subdivisions of the cell in carrying out its normal activities. In the present theory, its role is suggested to be that of messenger, obtaining the coded information from the DNA of the chromosomes and carrying it to the ergastoplasm. In the cytoplasm, then, the latter organelles are conceived as building protein molecules either by superimposing the amino acids directly upon the RNA in template fashion or by otherwise drawing on the information built into the messenger compound. Possibly this role is filled by the "transferring RNA" that constitutes, according to some workers, the major part of the microsomes.

How the coding is translated into terms of amino acids has not as yet been entirely elucidated, although considerable progress has been made. Since in the DNA coding there are four possible radicals at each rung of the ladder, at least three rungs ($4 \times 4 \times 4 = 64$) are needed to supply a clear code combination for each of the 20 basic amino acids. In this scheme, just for illustrative purposes, the sequence G, A, C might be suggested to indicate the amino acid arginine, while G, A, T might be the symbol for tryptophan, A, T, G for valine, T, G, C for glutamine, and so on. Hence, for a simple chainlike protein consisting of, say, 47 amino acid links a total of 141 cross bars in the DNA molecule would compose the gene that controls the formation of the protein in question. While this may seem large, it should be realized that this gene would measure just at 0.05 μ.

While the above code system appears at first to be applicable to proteins and leaves unexplained the specific differences in lipids, steroids, and the like, such is not really the case. Although the proposed system is on a strictly proteinoid basis, the enzymes that govern the formation of the other classes of organic substances are almost without exception composed of the present type of compound, as will be recalled from Chapter 2. So it is not at all unlikely

that by the indirect route of controlling the structure of the enzymes, the molecular patterns of the other protoplasmic materials and hormones are regulated.

Actual Codings in RNA. While the coding according to the current concept is carried from generation to generation by the DNA of the chromosomes, as stated above, the information is made use of through that RNA which serves as messenger. As will be recalled, this nucleic acid differs from the former in having, aside from the difference in pentose sugars, uracil in place of thymine among its nucleotides. During active anabolism RNA becomes applied, this theory conjectures, against the DNA of the genes, and its constituents arrange themselves in a corresponding sequence, with uracil units applying themselves to adenine, the complement of thymine, and the remainder to their respective complementary counterparts. This reconstituted RNA then moves into the cytoplasm, and upon arriving in the ergastoplasm, the transferring RNA of the granules uses the RNA as templates for the sequence of amino acids in the actual synthetic processes.

During the past several years Marshall W. Nirenberg and his co-workers at the National Institutes of Health in Maryland, as well as Crick and others, have made some progress toward determining the genetic code in ribonucleic acid for several of the amino acids, within broad limits. By polymerizing the various nucleotides that compose RNA in either pure states or mixtures and using the resulting "RNA" in incorporating C^{14}-labeled amino acids into proteins, it was possible to measure the differing rates at which the several latter substances were utilized by different combinations of nucleotides. For instance, if the synthetic RNA consists solely of uridylic acid (uracil), chiefly the amino acid phenylalanine becomes built into the protein, suggesting that a code of three or more units of this substance in sequence is the symbol of phenylalanine. Polymers of uridylic and guanylic acids (one or more U's coupled with one or more G's) actively incorporate around seven of the amino acids, suggesting that combinations of these two components may form their respective symbols, and so on. However, out of Crick's latest study (1963) some problems arise. For one thing, RNA appears to be effective as a single chain rather than the double one suggested for DNA; in fact, when made into a double chain, the nucleic acid is completely inactive. Therefore, some revision in the concept of the mechanism by means of which the DNA coding is utilized by messenger RNA appears to be in order. Especially is this so since the complement of a given nucleotide does not code the same amino acid. Hence, if in the double ladder of DNA, the series of A's on one chain serves as the template for the RNA's single-chain sequence of U's, the second chain of DNA consisting of a series of T's should be anticipated to represent the same amino acid. However, such has not proven to be the case, for the complementary set of A's appears to represent lysine, not phenylalanine. Moreover, more than one coding may be the symbol for any given amino acid. For example, some still undetermined sequence of either U, U, and C, or U, U, and G, appears to code leucine, not to mention U, U, U, which also codes phenylalanine! Indeed the latter fact provides evidence that the code, in some cases at least, may be ambiguous as far as knowledge stands today; consequently, considerable modification appears to be in store for the original concept. Nevertheless, while this and many other problems still remain to be solved, it is not unlikely that progress in this area will continue at a rapid pace.

Larger Proteins. More complex proteins would, of course, require a correspondingly longer sequence of symbols, but the actual length appears in practice to be reduced through the fact that proteinaceous compounds are frequently composed of two or more chains tied together by cystine, metallic elements, or other bonding substances. Insulin, it will be remembered, is built in this fashion (page 300), and hemoglobin consists of four long chains, two of one type and two of another, bound together by a complex of iron-containing substances known as "hemes." One of the types of proteins is referred to simply as the alpha-chain and the second as the beta-chain. Among human beings, several different variants of hemoglobin are known to exist; these, like all organic colloids, are capable of

C　S　A

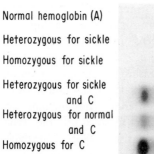

Normal hemoglobin (A)

Heterozygous for sickle

Homozygous for sickle

Heterozygous for sickle
and C

Heterozygous for normal
and C

Homozygous for C

Figure 22–4. Electrophoretic patterns for certain human hemoglobins. In all cases heterozygotes are seen to produce two types of hemoglobin, one for each allele present, whereas homozygotes form but one type. (Courtesy of Dr. Donald L. Rucknagel, Department of Human Genetics, University of Michigan Medical School.)

Figure 22–5. An extreme mutation in the house mouse. In Danforth's short tail mutation, an example of which is shown here, one initial defect brought about by a mutation gives rise to a whole series of secondary and tertiary abnormalities. For instance, in one series of events the first defect becomes apparent during embryology in the notochord; this in turn is followed by early disintegration of the notochord, producing a reduction in the initial states of the vertebrae, then anomalous vertebrae, and finally atypical muscle attachments. (Courtesy of Dr. H. Grüneberg and Discovery, London.)

being carried while in colloidal suspension by electric currents at varying rates of speed, depending on their chemical properties. This fact is frequently made use of by biochemists in a technique called *electrophoresis;* some variations of human hemoglobins thus separated are shown in Figure 22–4. By various means it has in recent years been shown that the alpha-chain is identical in all the varieties of this blood pigment; so only the beta-chain is modified. Thus it would appear that one gene shows no evidence of having mutated. On the other hand, while one gene possibly controls the formation of the second chain, it has undergone changes and now a series of alleles exists. This brings up the question of how genes might undergo changes; one possible answer might well be suggested as our next topic.

CHANGES IN GENES

Mutagens. How genes are induced to change under natural conditions is not known definitely, but it is strongly indicated that many physical and chemical factors may bring about mutations. Under laboratory conditions mutations can be artificially produced by exposing an organism to certain chemicals or to such physical factors as heat, ultraviolet, and cosmic radiation. When these exposed subjects, whether seed plants, microorganisms, or metazoans, are then allowed to produce progeny, altered forms are often found, the traits of which on testing are shown to be hereditary; hence in each case one or more genes are demonstrated to have undergone mutation (Figure 22–5). Radiation and other factors which can induce genetic mutation in organisms are known as *mutagens* and may be just as responsible for naturally occurring mutations as for those in the laboratory.

Changes in Gene Structure. In the currently accepted theory of gene structure, a means by which mutagens possibly instigate mutations may be intimated. If exposure to irradiation, for example, brings about loss in the DNA molecule of one component of a rung, say of thymine, when the chromosome undergoes replication, the incorrect pyrimidine, that is cytosine, or even a purine may occupy the blank space. Suppose in the illustration employed earlier (Figure 22–2) the third rung from the

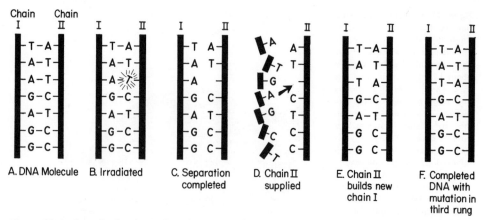

Chain   Chain
I   II

I   II   I   II   II   I   II   I   II   I   II

A. DNA Molecule   B. Irradiated   C. Separation completed   D. Chain II supplied   E. Chain II builds new chain I   F. Completed DNA with mutation in third rung

Figure 22–6. A molecular basis for mutations in genes. By employing the Watson-Crick model, a molecular basis for changes in genes can be proposed. Here the diagram suggests that, under irradiation, the original chain II loses a thymine radical on the third rung; during replication its vacated space becomes filled by an adenine radical, thus changing the code to some extent.

top is affected by removal of the thymine from the pentose base on chain II. Later, as the chromatids prepare to separate after the hydrogen bonds are broken, chain I would reproduce chain II as formerly and remain unchanged. In contrast, on the old chain II any of the four constituents, thymine, guanine, adenine, or cytosine, could couple with the sugar left free by the exposure to the rays. If thymine should happen to become re-

established in this position, as it would in all likelihood in one of four cases, the original molecular structure would be restored. But in the other three cases a new sequence of rungs would be established, and, with it, the genetic information carried would be changed. For instance, the substitution of cytosine would predispose the acquisition of a guanine unit as a mate when chain I is reformed, or if adenine is attached in

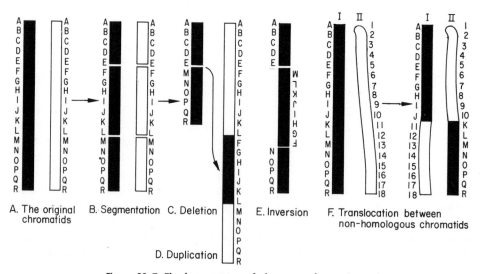

A. The original chromatids   B. Segmentation   C. Deletion   E. Inversion   F. Translocation between non-homologous chromatids

D. Duplication

Figure 22–7. The known types of chromosomal mutations.

thymine's place in chain II thymine would be attached to it on a new chain I (Figure 22–6). In any case, the sequence of rungs would have been altered and the resulting new code would induce a replacement of the usual amino acid with another in the protein molecule whose formation it governs. As a result, the cytoplasmic structure of the organism would become modified to this extent and a mutation might be said to have occurred.

Units of the Gene. By this time the student may have perceived that a gene consists of numerous smaller units, for whereas genes control the formation of whole protein units, above it is indicated that a mutation can alter a unit that codes a single amino acid. To provide greater clarity at the molecular level of genetics, several new terms have been introduced. For the smallest unit of DNA most subject to mutation—that is, for the code of a single amino acid—the name *muton* has been advanced. Second, *cistrons* are small groups of mutons which complement one another; the exact effects of their complementation differ according to whether mutons are on the same chromosome (the *cis* arrangement) or on an opposite one (the *trans* configuration). The term *gene* in a strict sense is reserved for the actual whole bodies which influence a hereditary trait.

CHANGES IN CHROMOSOMES

Genes are not the only cellular object known to be subject to alteration, for chromosomes may mutate, too. Unlike genes, which can undergo mutation at any time of the life cycle, for the greater part the changes in chromosomal structure seem to occur during the processes of synapsis when nonsister chromatids are engaged in an exchange of segments.

Chromosomal Mutations. In order that they may be distinguished from the more usual genal variety, changes in chromosome structure are typically referred to as *chromosomal mutations*. Four variations are possible. Of that number probably the commonest types take place as a pair of events, for while one chromatid loses a segment the nonsister mate gains it (Figure 22–7). Hence, by way of illustration, the chromosome's sequence of genes may be stated to run from *A* to *J*, whereas the mutation involves just the segment *E* to *G*; in one resulting chromatid the series could possibly be altered by its loss to *A, B, C, D, H, I, J*, and by its addition the counterpart could contain *A, B, C, D, E, F, G, E, F, G, H, I, J*. The loss of a part is referred to as a *deletion* or *deficiency* and the gain of one is called a *duplication*. Although the effects of deletions and duplications vary considerably, depending both upon the organism and the part lost or added, quite frequently a loss results in death—that is, it is *lethal*. Since loss of a series of genes renders the organism incapable of forming one or more enzymes or other fundamental proteins, this effect is quite understandable.

Duplications can vary considerably both in effect and in arrangement. Instead of rejoining in the accustomed sequence, occasionally the acquired part may attach to another portion of the chromosome, as for example *A, B, C, D, E, F, G, H, I, J, E, F, G*, often called a "displaced duplication." As a whole, this class of changes is both more frequent and less lethal than deletions, as might be expected. One especially well-investigated instance is that of bar-eye in the fruit fly (*Drosophila melanogaster*), which manifests itself in a change in eye shape. Normally the compound eyes of this fly are oval, but duplication of a certain segment results in a narrow form called bar-eye (Figure 22–8). When such abnormal flies are inbred extensively, an occasional individual is produced in which a second duplication of the same segment occurs. The result in an even narrower eye, referred to as double-bar (Figure 22–8).

A frequently encountered chromosomal mutation is the *inversion,* a condition found in numerous species in both nature and the laboratory. Instead of a part being lost or added, here a segment is merely turned upside down, as it were, so that the sequence of genes is altered. Thus, if the segment *C* to *H* becomes inverted, the series of genes employed is changed to *A, B, H, G, F, E, D, C, I, J*. Among laboratory organisms such a change can be detected through modifications of known linkage groups; in the hypothetical case cited *B* and *H* suddenly become closely linked, and *B* and *C* loosely so. Since all genes are

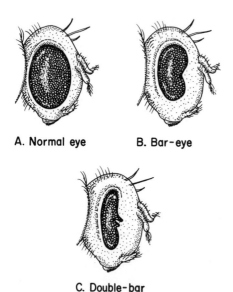

A. Normal eye   B. Bar-eye

C. Double-bar

Figure 22–8. A duplication effect in the fruit fly. A, B. When one segment of a certain chromosome of *Drosophila* becomes duplicated, the eye becomes narrow, instead of rounded as normal. **C.** If the same segment should become reduplicated, an even narrower condition develops called "double-bar."

present, inversions do not always influence the phenotype, but occasional ones behave as single gene mutations—for example, "curly," a wing deformity in *Drosophila*.

Similarly, in the fourth and final variety of chromosomal mutation, lethality and reduction in fertility are usually manifested rather than ordinary phenotypic effects. In this type two nonhomologous chromatids exchange segments during meiosis—for instance, between chromosome I bearing genal sequence *A* to *J* and chromosome II with series *1* to *10*. Following a *translocation,* as this abnormal exchange is called, chromosome I may contain *A, B, C, D, E, 6, 7, 8, 9, 10* and chromosome II, *1, 2, 3, 4, 5, F, G, H, I, J*. As in inversions, lethality and reduction in fertility arise from difficulties experienced in synapsis by the two resulting pairs of freak chromosomes. Translocations, too, are detectable by changes in linkage, but in this case the formation of new linkage associations is involved rather than alterations in cross-over rates; in the foregoing illustration, after translocation, genes *A* to *E* would show linkage with *6* to *10*, whereas *1* to *5* would similarly show linkage with *F* to *J*, patterns that did not previously exist. Occasionally translocations do behave as ordinary mutations, and in some cases alleles that are normally recessive become dominant if a translocation break occurs nearby.

Cytology of Chromosome Mutations. Since many chromosomal mutations are lethal either to the gamete or to the individual, the student may with good reason wonder how their existence has been established. Although, as already indicated, the presence of certain types may be detected by linkage changes, possibly the most reliable method of determining mutations is by cytological studies, particularly of cells undergoing

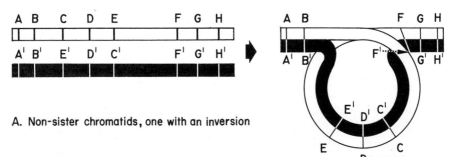

A. Non-sister chromatids, one with an inversion

B. Inverted and normal chromatids in synapsis

Figure 22–9. The cytological basis of some chromosomal mutations. B. Under the microscope pairing chromatids can occasionally be seen to form loops as a result of coiling in opposite directions along portions of their lengths. Such coils are indications of the presence of an inversion in one chromatid.

meiosis. Often, as nonsister chromosomes are undergoing exchange of segments, unusual arrangements of the pairs may be noted. For instance, if one nonsister possesses an inverted segment, it and its counterpart may be seen to coil in opposite directions in the inverted area (Figure 22–9). By this means the chromatids can bring the matching sets of alleles together, despite the differences in sequences.

Much additional light on this and many other phases of cytology and genetics has been thrown by the use of a curious condition found in the fruit fly by the American geneticist, T. S. Painter. Up to the year of this discovery, 1933, *Drosophila* had proven to be extremely valuable in genetics but was disappointing cytologically because of the small size of its chromosomes. Painter, however, found that the chromosomes of the salivary gland cells in this and most flies were gigantic, being perhaps 100 times as long as those of the gametes. After a dye solution has been applied to a preparation, these *giant chromosomes* under the microscope appear to be banded because of the presence of stained and unstainable portions (Figure 22–10).

Since these bands differ in width, intensity, and form and are separated by unstained areas which similarly vary, it is possible to identify the regions of each chromosome by employing the sequence of bands with other chromosomal traits such as swellings, knobs, and constrictions. In many instances in *Drosophila*

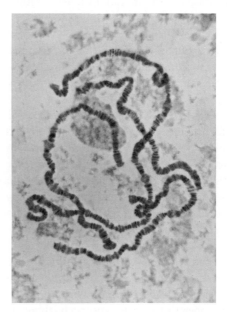

Figure 22–10. The salivary chromosomes of *Drosophila*. Magnified 450×. (Courtesy of General Biological Supply House, Inc., Chicago.)

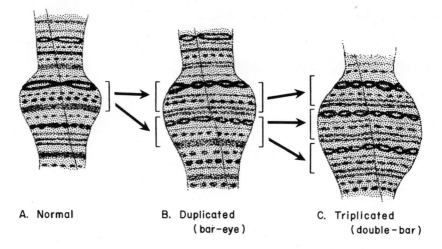

A. Normal	B. Duplicated	C. Triplicated
	(bar-eye)	(double-bar)

Figure 22–11. Duplication and triplication in *Drosophila*. The segment producing bar-eye and double-bar are shown compared to the normal segment in the fruit fly.

chromosomal mutations may thus be directly detected by examination of salivary gland preparations. In this way, bar-eye and double bar have been confirmed as involving duplication and triplication, respectively (Figure 22–11).

Changes in Chromosome Number. In addition to the mutations noted, chromosomes may undergo still another type of change—namely, one in total number. Occasionally an increase in number may result from subdivision of a single chromosome into two or more parts, provided each portion possesses a centromere. Perhaps this process is responsible for the fact that a large number of Japanese people have 47 chromosomes instead of the typical 46. But other processes may also cause increases in number —substantial ones in these cases. Sometimes the cellular mechanism does not operate perfectly, so that, rarely indeed, chromosomes fail to complete the reduction divisions precisely in gamete formation and some of the resulting sperm or eggs contain twice the usual number. That is to say, such abnormal gametes possess the diploid number of chromosomes instead of the haploid. If

these diploid sex cells happen to be successful in fertilization, the resulting zygote, and ultimately the individual into which it matures, will contain the diploid number of chromosomes from one parental cell plus the haploid number from the other; in other words, it would be *triploid* ($3n$), with three times the haploid (n) number of chromosomes in every cell. *Polyploidy* (excess multiples of the haploid) of this sort appears to be especially prevalent among seed plants but is exceedingly uncommon among animals.

Other Aspects of Gene Action

Remaining for discussion are several aspects that amplify or modify the facets of gene action presented above in addition to several that further illuminate the basic concepts of the nature and behavior of the genetic mechanism. So much in the current theories on the DNA molecule and genic control of protein synthesis is convincing that on the surface it all appears to have been thoroughly elucidated, save for minor details. Several genetic problems, however, indicate that such is far from the case. The facts of the matter are that both the theoretical and the practical ends of genetics still need many more capable minds to solve the problems confronting this discipline.

Diverse Gene Attributes

With a background of knowledge that genes are chemical units, whether actually of DNA or otherwise, a better understanding of several facets can be gained, and for this reason they have been reserved for discussion until this late point.

Lethal Genes. As in some types of chromosomal mutations, genes also may be capable of killing their possessors. Among the first *lethal genes* encountered was one that affects the coat color of mice. During the course of genetic studies on these animals it was found that yellow-coated mice never bred true when inbred, although the factor is definitely dominant over wild (or agouti) and other alleles; in short, they behaved uniformly as heterozygotes. When backcrossed to recessives, too, heterozygosity was always demonstrated by the attainment of the 1:1 ratio typical of that type of cross. To determine the reason behind the missing homozygous dominants, crosses were made in a whole series of yellow-coated mice and the progress of the resulting pregnancies was observed by making daily autopsies of females. By these observations it was found that about one fourth of the developing young died early in embryological development and were absorbed by the eighth day of the pregnancy. These were assumed to be the homozygotes. Hence, with a dominant lethal, the expected ratio of young is modified to an extent best illustrated by the details from

this coat-color example. In mice geneticists had earlier established the fact that the gene for the normal fur color (agouti) is dominant over many of the known alleles and is therefore assigned the capital letter A, whereas its allele yellow, being dominant over agouti, is assigned the same capital letter but is distinguished by a superscript Y, as follows:

$$A^Y A \times A^Y A \rightarrow 1 A^Y A^Y : 2 A^Y A : 1 A A$$

Dies   Yellow   Agouti
before birth   mice   mice

Lethal genes are known to exist in a large variety of organisms, exercising their effects in many ways and at any stage of growth. Among the fruit flies, for example, there have been found to be no fewer than 50 lethal genes whose mode of action has been investigated, not to mention perhaps 100 more whose specific effects are still unknown. In man about 20 such genes have been encountered. Among these is a short-fingered dominant (brachydactyly) that in the homozygous condition causes death of the unborn young through skeleton malformations; still another dominant which arises spontaneously in one in every 10,000 births is retinoblastoma, a cancer of the eye that is fatal by the age of five or six years, unless surgically removed.

Influence of Age on Gene Action. In Chapter 21 the sex of an individual was shown to have an influence on the expression of many genes; the chronological age or physiological state of the individual, too, may exert similar control. A familiar instance of this fact is to be found in the graying of hair among human beings; as the student himself has probably observed, in some families graying occurs early in life, in others at a later period, the approximate age being a hereditary characteristic. On the other hand, some individuals do not develop gray hair no matter how old they live to be; this retention, too, is a hereditary trait but does not enter into the present discussion, except in a negative way. The point is that a certain physiological state must be obtained before the graying genes concerned can express themselves, although they have been present in the cells ever since the time of fertilization.

Environmental Influences on Genes. Just as the internal environment in the form of physiology and age influences the phenotypic expression of genes, so do the external surroundings of the in-

A. Himalayan rabbit

B. Same, raised at 30° C

C. Flank maintained below 25°C

Figure 22–12. Environmental influence on genotype expression. *A.* Normal rabbit of the Himalayan breed, raised at room temperatures below 25°C. *B.* When reared at room temperatures above 30°C, the black coloration of the extremities fails to develop. *C.* A normal raised at temperatures below 25°C, but on one flank the skin temperature has been maintained below 25°C by means of ice packs. See text for explanation. (Based on R. Danneel.)

dividual. To illustrate the point, the coat color of some mammals can be cited. One striking example is provided by a certain domestic breed of rabbits called the Himalayan strain (Figure 22–12). Under ordinary conditions the coat of these mammals is white, except that the ears, nose, feet, and tail are black. If these animals are reared in rooms maintained at temperatures above 30°C (86°F), eventually all the fur becomes white; on the contrary, if one area of the skin is cooled artificially below 25°C (77°F) by continued application of ice packs, for instance, the new fur will be black in this limited region. These data are explained by the fact that normally in those body parts in which the skin temperature is 34°C or higher a temperature-sensitive pigmenting factor is unable to operate, so that as a consequence of the interrupted pigment production the incoming fur is white. In contrast, those portions of the body with poorer circulation are relatively more exposed to the cooling effects of the atmosphere, and as the local temperature drops below 34°C the pigmenting factor, then being functional, produces melanin, with black fur as the visible consequence.

Pleiotropic Effects of Genotypes. Since genes, according to modern theory, are principally concerned with the formation of proteins, including virtually all enzymes which secondarily control the synthesis of other classes of chemical compounds, it should be anticipated that every cell of the body will be influenced by the presence or absence of a given gene. Therefore a gene for albinism— that is, the inability to produce the pigment melanin because of the lack of one enzyme—might be expected to manifest itself in all cells by a similar deficiency. Whether such manifold, or *pleiotropic,* effects of genes actually exist consistently or not is a subject on which few geneti-

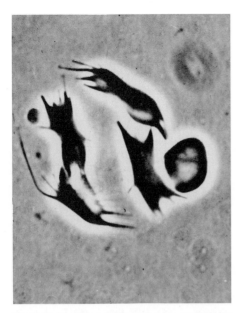

Figure 22–13. Human sickle cells. In an inheritable disease, the erythrocytes become greatly deformed under a reduced oxygen supply as the result of the presence of an unusual hemoglobin. (Courtesy of Dr. Marcel Bessis, *The Cell*, Vol. 5, 1962 and Academic Press.)

cists agree. If influences are actually exerted by a gene on every cell regardless of its location, then brown-haired or brown-eyed persons would be expected to display at least some cytological differences from blond or blue-eyed ones respectively; since demonstrations of comparable effects are lacking, one school of researchers does not believe they exist. On the other hand, at least some examples of influence by a single gene on several distinct aspects of an organism certainly appear to occur, one such instance being that of sickle-cell anemia among human beings, an inheritable disease in which the red blood cells become extremely malformed in the homozygotes when subjected to a reduced oxygen supply (Figure 22–13). This dominant gene, particularly abundant in persons of African extraction, is lethal in the homozygous condition but not in the

heterozygous, in spite of the fact that the cells are subject to considerable deformity. Actually, the shape of the erythrocytes is secondary to the type of hemoglobin that is produced, for the mutant allele (H_s) produces pigment of the variety S instead of the normal A; perhaps the variety S is not efficient enough in its oxygen-carrying powers so that homozygotes die of anemia. On the other hand, heterozygotes produce both kinds of hemoglobins and are to all appearances quite normal. There is strong evidence supporting the point of view now, however, that heterozygotes are resistant to malaria; hence several phenotypic effects are shown to be derived from a single mutant allele. Although the case cited appears sufficiently clearcut, there is still no basis for sweeping generalizations.

CYTOLOGICAL FACTORS IN INHERITANCE

In the early years of the twentieth century, following the rediscovery of the Mendelian principles, it was first believed that traits of the nature demonstrated were probably only secondary phenomena and that the basic factors of genetics still remained to be discovered. Since Mendelian traits were soon shown to be interrelated to chromosome behavior, the supposed undiscovered factors were postulated to be located in the cytoplasm. As more and more activities of the nuclear components came to light, however, cytoplasmic influences assumed rapidly diminishing importance in genetic theory. By the middle of the present century its insignificance in the philosophy of geneticists is reflected by Swanson's statement (1959) that "the cytoplasm can best be viewed as the cellular clay that is molded into shape by the nucleus." Although this attitude remains largely justified by the observed facts, some evidence now indicates that it is not the whole of the truth. These data are derived from two sources, the behavior of cytoplasmic organelles and phenotypic inheritance in which nuclear factors are shown to be absent. In great part the basis for "cytoplasmic inheritance," as nonnuclear factors are together called, lies in a basic difference between eggs and sperm. The sperm, of course, possesses only a minute amount of cytoplasm, whereas the egg contains great quantities of this type of protoplasm; hence virtually all of the cytoplasmic content of the zygote is derived from the female parent.

Inheritance of Cytoplasmic Organelles. Although inheritance of cell organelles has been only very slightly studied because of the difficulties involved, at least two important types, *mitochondria* and *chloroplastids,* have been shown to be self-reproductive bodies. The mitochondria are carried in the cytoplasm of the egg in the form of minute particles called "promitochondria." As may be recalled from the discussion on animal embryology (page 441), these particles gradually develop into definitive mitochondria as the zygote approaches the advanced gastrula or early neurula stage. Thereafter, throughout the whole of the embryological period and, in fact, of the individual's life, the mitochondria grow in size and divide to produce more of the particles. During cellular division approximately equal numbers are distributed to the daughter cells as the result of independent movement on the part of these organelles. The fact that chloroplasts in *Euglena* are self-reproductive bodies has already been mentioned (page 106), for once the organelles have been destroyed by treatment with streptomycin or other agents they are

never reformed. Hence their presence or absence is largely a cytoplasmic function, although sometimes their precise form may be altered by ordinary Mendelian factors in the nucleus. Among the higher seed plants the same state prevails, as indicated by studies on corn. In this and other species which have been tested certain types of albinism result from a lack of chloroplastids in the seedling and, as in the case of albino corn, are lethal in homozygotes. Under laboratory conditions, however, the albino plants can be raised to maturity if glucose is supplied in the culture medium, and these plants can even be employed for breeding purposes. When normal and albino individuals are crossed, the results always depend on the condition of the female gamete. If the egg is normal and the pollen carries the albino factor, the resulting seedlings will contain chloroplasts and readily grow to maturity, so that albinism thus appears to be recessive. Should the cross involve albino ovules, however, even though the pollen may be normal, albinism is produced in all the seedlings, so that the gene now behaves as a dominant. In short, it appears that chloroplastids are self-reproducing bodies and can be derived only from pre-existing chloroplastids. Better still, they are produced at least from forerunners of such bodies, for as in mitochondria the organelles apparently are transmitted in particulate form and develop into the definitive state as embryology proceeds.

Other Expressions of Cytoplasmic Inheritance. Much of the evidence indicative of cytoplasmic inheritance arises from crosses between two distinct species. Often the offspring of such matings differ in appearance, depending on the direction in which the cross occurs. For example, in hybridizations of horses and donkeys, mules are the result when the female is a horse, whereas hinnies are the progeny when the female is of the second species. Since in each case the offspring bears closer resemblances to the female than to the male, the differences between the matings appear to spring from factors carried by the cytoplasm of the egg. These hypothetical factors are often called *plasmogenes*. Hybridization experiments between different species of birds or of seed plants yield comparable results, as do also a number in lower organisms.

Questions for Review and Thought

1. Explain briefly the structure of the DNA molecule according to the Watson-Crick concept and how it has been suggested to duplicate itself. What material is currently accepted as carrying the DNA code to the cytoplasm? How is this feat accomplished? How is the information used?

2. Define mutations in both biological and biochemical terms. By what factors can mutations be induced, in either nature or the laboratory? Describe the various kinds of mutations that are known to exist and give examples or effects.

3. Define the following terms:

      (a) mutagens   (d) triploidy
      (b) pleiotropy   (e) hexaploidy
      (c) giant chromosomes

4. Why do you suppose fruit flies (*Drosophila*) are so extensively employed in genetic researches? Name as many favorable features as you can.

5. What do you think is meant by the term *physiological aging*? What evidence indicates its existence? In what way is this really an aspect of environmental influence on genotype expression?

6. Of what importance is the cytoplasm as a genetic mechanism, and on what evidence is this significance based? Of what additional value is the cytoplasm in the development of the zygote into an individual?

Supplementary References

Asimov, I. *The Genetic Code.* New York, New American Library, 1963.

Begg, C. M. M. *Introduction to Genetics.* New York, Macmillan, 1959.

Benzer, S. "The Fine Structure of the Gene." *Sci. Amer.,* January 1962.

Crick, F. H. C. "The Genetic Code." *Sci. Amer.,* October 1962.

Deering, R. A. "Ultraviolet Radiation and Nucleic Acid." *Sci. Amer.,* December 1962.

Hadorn, E. *Developmental Genetics and Lethal Factors.* New York, Wiley, 1960.

Harris, H. *Human Biochemical Genetics.* Cambridge, Cambridge Univ. Press, 1962.

Herskowitz, I. H. *Genetics.* Boston, Little, Brown, 1962.

King, R. C. *Genetics.* London, Oxford Univ. Press, 1962.

Strauss, B. S. *An Outline of Chemical Genetics.* Philadelphia, Saunders, 1960.

Waddington, C. H. *New Patterns in Genetics and Development.* New York, Columbia Univ. Press, 1962.

PART VI

The Consequences of Genetic Changes

THE FACTS THAT LIVING THINGS undergo changes and that these alterations are of a hereditary nature have been presented in the preceding chapters. In those discussions, too, it was shown that although frequently such mutations, as the variations are called, bring about the death of the individual possessing them, such is by no means always the case. In fact, in several known instances, some that appear on the surface to be deleterious to their possessors may, under certain conditions, actually be advantageous to the species as a whole. Since these genetic mutants, as has already been stated, are inheritable, regardless of whether they are beneficial or otherwise, it might be conjectured that, over many generations, altered genes could tend to accumulate in the organisms and thus produce changes of various degrees of importance in the phenotypes of the descendants. Here both the fact of the accumulation of mutations and the mechanisms involved therein are the topics of chief concern.

The function of the free man and the free mind is, stubbornly and painfully, to try to find truth—truth as it is, not as we hope it to be or prefer it to be.

LEO ROSTEN

The Accumulation of Genetic Changes in Animals

W HILE the mechanisms of inheriting mutations are the concern of the genetic branch of zoology, the study of the consequences of such changes, both those occurring now in organisms and those which have taken place in the past, is centered in the science of *evolution*. At this time the chief objectives are to summarize the major concepts along with the evidence supporting them and to outline the currently accepted theories regarding the processes involved.

Introduction

Unfortunately, not only for biology but for the individuals concerned, even today there persists in many quarters the opinion that evolutionary concepts are basically anti-Christian or sacrilegious and to accept them one must become an atheist—a point of view which survives in spite of the fact that no major religious organization as a body is opposed to the teaching of the subject. In fact, courses in evolution are offered in universities of almost all denominations, for the science is widely recognized as a topic about which educated persons need to be well informed. Although one faith asks that a belief in a single original man be retained and a second that man's soul be considered not a result of evolution but God-given, neither of these subjects is of concern to evolutionists as such; consequently it is evident that no conflict actually exists. As a whole, the trained clergy realize that the Bible is a collection of religious writings, not of scientific facts—as the great astronomer Galileo said, "the Bible's purpose is not to tell how the heavens go, but how to go to Heaven."

And a little thought devoted to the topic shows that this point of view may be entirely valid. Although divinely inspired, the Biblical accounts of creation are nevertheless the products of man's mind and hands. In contrast, the evolutionary principles are founded on observations made upon the earth and the living things that inhabit it, and since almost all thinking people accept these objects as the handiwork of God, is it not really more irreligious to reject the account based on information written into natural objects by their Creator in favor of man-written documents than to do the contrary? Could it not be said that basically evolutionists are attempting to translate the story of creation as written by the original Author? Whether or not all persons can accept this philosophy, at least the facts are worthy of attention. And it is these facts that are in the main presented here.

Theories of Evolution

Some of the earlier concepts of the origins of living things from inanimate matter have already been outlined and the persistence of abiogenesis into the nineteenth century has been indicated. Although many of these beliefs contained hints of the evolutionary principle, it remained for Darwin in 1858 to present to the world a generally acceptable theory of evolution. The concept itself, however, was presented somewhat earlier, in 1802 in fact, by the great French zoologist and paleontologist Jean Baptiste de Lamarck.

Lamarck's Theory of Evolution

Although Lamarck made many notable contributions to invertebrate zoology, his theory of evolution is so weak that often today he is thought of in a contemptuous manner. Actually, he did much to prepare the way for a sound theory by presenting the new concept, that of *changing species,* in the face of the then current notions of *fixed species.* However, the premises of his theory are really philosophically founded on generalities, not scientifically on specific data, and were highly dependent on the concept of inheritance of acquired characteristics. For instance, his own illustration of the processes, that of the acquisition of a long neck by the giraffe, may be cited. This feature, he explained, was acquired by the animal's continually stretching its neck to reach higher leaves. As a result, its progeny had slightly more elongated parts and so on through innumerable generations until this organ finally assumed its present length (Figure 23–1). Since his time countless experiments have been run to test the possibility of inheriting acquired traits but all have uniformly ended in failure.

Darwin's Theory

In contrast to the readily disprovable nature of Lamarck's concept, Charles Darwin's premises appear to be based more solidly on observable fact. His ideas, centering around a concept of *natural selection,* contain six major propositions, which are given here in condensed form.

Variation and Overreproduction. The fact that organisms naturally tend to vary from one individual to another is self-evident and provided the first of his tenets. Although Darwin could not know that these variations arise by genetic mutations, as is common knowledge today, he recognized their universal existence and accepted them as an innate property of life, as has been done on occasion earlier in this text.

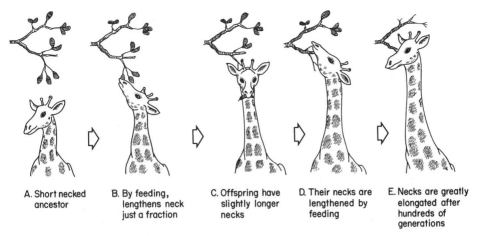

A. Short necked
ancestor

B. By feeding,
lengthens neck
just a fraction

C. Offspring have
slightly longer
necks

D. Their necks are
lengthened by
feeding

E. Necks are greatly
elongated after
hundreds of
generations

Figure 23–1. Lamarck's concept of giraffe evolution. In Lamarck's theory of evolution, the giraffe's neck became elongated from the original short-necked condition through inherited changes brought about by successive generations stretching ever higher for leaves.

Secondly, it is readily observable that living things as species universally tend to overreproduce; that is to say, more offspring frequently are produced than can possibly survive. One need only cite the case of a *Paramecium* to demonstrate the validity of this assumption, the members of which genus undergo fission about once every two hours. By starting with a single specimen on the first day of January and growing these organisms at the maximum rate, according to some calculations, one would have gone only a few days into December of the same year before more paramecia would be on hand than there are electrons in the universe.

The Struggle for Existence. As a consequence of the prodigal rate at which organisms reproduce, Darwin reasoned in this third fundamental premise, competition develops between individuals of both the same and different species for food and space—or as he phrased it, a *struggle for existence* ensues. The "struggle" may include actual combat, as between birds disputing for breeding territory, or it may be entirely of a passive nature, such as that found in an overly densely planted flower bed through each

seedling attempting by growth to obtain sufficient light.

Natural Selection. Because of individual variation, some specimens by chance possess one or more features which give it an advantage over others in the same immediate community. Among the densely planted seedlings, for instance, those plants that happen to grow just a bit more rapidly eventually would overshade and kill off the slower ones, or, under dry conditions, those whose roots penetrated the soil most rapidly or deeply might have a better chance of survival. Individual birds that are just a little larger or whose adrenal glands respond more quickly might tend to be more successful in holding favorable territory and thus would produce offspring where the defeated ones might not. Thus they are *naturally selected,* as Darwin phrased his fourth proposition. However, it need not be supposed that all the excessive population is eliminated by these means and that only the best equipped survive. A bass feeding on a mass of frog eggs might consume all the spawn except for one or two that by accident were overlooked; these remnants could be individuals of any genetic constitution whatever, favorable or otherwise, and in this fashion inferior examples might attain adulthood while better adapted ones may have been killed before hatching. But in the over-all picture perhaps it is not too unreasonable to assume a greater percentage of survival for better-equipped specimens and that natural selection could be an active force.

Inheritance of Variations.   Since the favorable variations stem from genetic mutations, they would be passed along to subsequent generations, and because the better-adapted individuals survive to have progeny more frequently than other variations each succeeding generation will contain a higher percentage of the better adapted individuals. As the term mutation was not then in existence, Darwin, of course, did not express this fifth premise in quite that way; nevertheless, his observed facts of variability and its inheritance are entirely substantiated.

Formation of New Species.   Finally, because of the gradual accumulation of variations over the millennia, Darwin reasoned, new species ultimately come into existence. For a concrete but hypothetical example, let it be assumed that species A occupies a country of grasslands and trees intermingled, of the type known as savannah; this may be imagined as several hundred miles wide, bordered on one side by forest and on the other by treeless prairies. Throughout its breadth some individuals might possess a chance mutation that favors them for survival under more heavily shaded conditions that other examples could not tolerate; perhaps this is accomplished, if a mouse is the subject, by enabling it to breed earlier or by its coat changing in color to blend with the shaded soil. Although this mutation occurs throughout the range, it is effective only along the forest's edge where extensive shaded areas exist. Hence it might be supposed

that after innumerable generations this factor and others could eventually lead to a population of mice capable of growing and reproducing in the wooded area. Ultimately, by continuation of the processes, including further mutations, the individuals better adapted to the particular conditions would become so distinct from the savannah populations that the forest-dwelling ones could be considered a separate species.

Evidences of Evolution

As outlined above, it is readily perceivable that most of Darwin's premises are statements of demonstrable fact; only a few of them are actually theoretical. That even the hypothetical parts might be well founded or valid is indicated by evidences drawn from several sciences and from many biological disciplines. It is helpful to bear in mind that Darwin, trained in the ministry to some extent, as he was, recognized the widespread impact his theory would have on its presentation; accordingly, he exercised the greatest caution in formulating his ideas and supported each with innumerable examples drawn from his broad knowledge of living things. To ensure that he was not wrong, furthermore, he delayed publication for 20 years until the overwhelming accumulation of data compelled him to express them in print. Here only an indication of the type of evidence supplied by each source of natural knowledge can be presented.

GEOLOGICAL EVIDENCE

Since *geology* is the science concerned with the structure and history of the earth, the evidence it presents does not directly support the theory of evolution of living things, for organisms are far removed from the area of its immediate concern. Yet in a broader sense it does uphold the purely biological concepts, at least to the extent that its data indicate early man-written accounts to be in error regarding the earth's own history. Moreover, an acquaintance with this science is extremely helpful in connection with the discussion of fossil life that follows the present one.

The Stratification of the Earth. As a person passes through gaps cut in the hills and mountains or stands beside a great gorge gouged out of the earth's crust by the eroding effects of a river, it is often readily perceived that the earth is built up in layers. Furthermore, closer examination of these *strata* reveals that each consists of a different type of rock. Perhaps the lowermost bed is of granite, and overlying it is one possibly of gneiss; in turn, above this layer may be others of limestone, sandstone, conglomerate, shale, and finally, at the very top, soil derived from a second deposit of limestone. Not only the major types of rock are arranged in layered pattern, but within any one stratum thinner lines of deposition are discernible. Shale, particularly, shows that it is laid down, not all at one time, but by the slow accumulation of silt arranged in thin sheets, one upon another. So it becomes quite evident that the earth was not laid down in a single day but has grown to be what it is now by the gradual wearing down of material in one place, the elevation of mountains in another, and the formation of rocky layers around the borders of the seas. All the events suggested by the rocks need not be considered to have occurred spontaneously, with neither design nor Designer; their details can be made to depict vividly an account of the actual processes of creation.

The Age of the Strata. As taken together from all regions of the world, the many layers of rocks are arranged in corresponding series from bottom to top; each of these major deposits has been provided with a name and is considered to represent a certain period in the development of the earth. These strata are summarized, together with an approximate age and the principal geological events, under the name *geological timetable* (Table 23–1). Frequently, the dates assigned to the respective eras are a source of bewilderment to laymen, who sometimes look on them as wild guesses, whereas actually the figures have been factually arrived at and tend toward conservatism rather than otherwise. Two chief methods are employed in establishing them.

The first and older means is that based on the present rate of silt deposition and the comparative thickness of strata. Assuming that, as a whole, conditions of sedimentation today are fundamentally similar to those of the past, geologists can measure the rate of deposition at the mouths of such great rivers as the Amazon, Mississippi, Nile, and Congo and determine with some degree of precision an average over a period of years. Once these data are in hand, the calculations for a particular rock deposit are a matter of simple arithmetic.

The second means of establishing ages for the various strata involves the use of *radioactive elements*. Such materials break down into other elements at constant rates that have been calculated by physicists. As a rule, these rates of decay are expressed in terms of *half-lives*—that is, the amount of time required for half of a given element to become altered. For instance, uranium[238] has a half-life of 4,510,000,000 years; thus, whether one began with 1 gram, 2 pounds, or 100 molecules of the substance, at the end of the 4,510,000,000 years, either one-half gram, 1 pound, or 50 molecules would remain intact, respectively. For

TABLE 23-1
GEOLOGICAL TIMETABLE

Era	Period or Epoch	Million Years Since Beginning	Geological Events	Animal Events
CENOZOIC	Pleistocene	1 (or 2?)	Ice ages	Development of man
	Pliocene	13	Rocky Mountains continue to rise	Origin of man
	Miocene	27	Sierras formed	First great apes
	Oligocene	37	Continents lowered	First elephants
	Eocene	52		First horses and carnivores
	Paleocene	63		Primitive mammals spread
MESOZOIC	Cretaceous	135	Andes, Alps, Rocky Mountains, and Himalayas form	Dinosaurs reach peak and vanish; first modern birds
	Jurassic	181		First birds; first marsupials; dinosaurs diversify
	Triassic	230	Deserts widespread	First dinosaurs and monotreme mammals
PALEOZOIC	Permian	280	Appalachians form; some ice ages	Wasps and butterflies appear; first mammal-like reptiles
	Pennsylvanian	320	Lands low and swampy	First reptiles; amphibia, beetles, and roaches abundant
	Mississippian	345	Climate warm and moist	Sharks and crinoids abundant
	Devonian	405	Continents become slightly elevated; ice ages	First amphibians; sharks and lungfish abundant
	Silurian	425	Lands low; climate tropical even at poles	First insects (wingless); first bony fish and sharks
	Ordovician	500	Continents extensively submerged	Jawless fishes first appear; mollusks abundant
	Cambrian	600	Climate warm, lands low	Trilobites dominant
PROTEROZOIC		1500?	Some glaciation	First mollusks and worms
ARCHEOZOIC		3500?	Much volcanic activity	Unicellular forms?

half of these remnant portions to decay, a similar period would again be required and so on. Since in decaying each radioactive element forms a known end product, it is possible to determine the age of any rock that contains such elements by measuring the proportional contents of the element and its product. By way of illustration, uranium[238] which decays into lead[208] may be utilized. If a rock specimen upon analysis is found to contain three times as much uranium[238] as lead[208], the uranium obviously is three-quarters intact, or otherwise expressed, one-fourth decayed. In short, one half a half-life has passed since the rock was laid down, that is, the rock is 2,255,000,-000 years of age.

Although uranium[238] was the first element to be used for this purpose, in recent years a number of others have been found to be of great value. Particularly useful is potassium, which decays into argon; since this element, in contrast to the extremely rare uranium, occurs in great abundance, it provides numerous dates, especially for rocks of a granitic nature. Others that are employed, along with their half-lives, are listed in Table 23–2.

One of the listed elements, namely *carbon*[14], is of such importance that it merits fuller discussion. As shown in the chart, the half-life of this material, being comparatively short, provides a useful tool for dating fossils and fairly recent events with reliable accuracy back as far as 50,000 years before the present. Bombardment of ordinary nitrogen (nitrogen[14]) by cosmic rays continually produces in the atmosphere a small but constant supply of carbon[14], which living things incorporate into their bodies at a level that is also a constant. Hence ancient pieces of wood, fragments of bone, or other bits of organisms can be assayed for their carbon[14] content; then, by means of comparisons made against comparable material from living specimens, the age of the fossil can be calculated. Since man has existed as a species during the more recent geological age, anthropologists and archaeologists have found this means of dating specimens an especial asset in their studies, but many events during the last Ice Age, too, have been reliably dated by carbon[14] measurements.

PALEONTOLOGY

Paleontology, the branch of biology concerned with the study of extinct organisms, forms a link between geology and modern biology and draws on both sciences for information. For data concerning the age and sequence of its specimens, the earth science provides a foundation, whereas the probable habits of the fossils it studies are derived from biological researches on comparable species that are still living. The term *fossil* includes anything indicative of the former presence of an organism in the remote past, whether actual body parts, droppings, eggs, footprints, or mere impressions in rock.

Fossilization. Since paleontology can be defined also as the study of fossils, a few words on the formation of its objects may be pertinent. In general, fossilization

TABLE 23–2
RADIOACTIVE ELEMENTS USED IN DATING FOSSILS

Radioactive Element	Product of Breakdown	Half-Life in Years	Remarks
Uranium[238]	Lead[208]	4,500,000,000	Rare, but has provided some significant dates
Thorium[232]	Lead[208]	15,000,000,000	
Rubidium[87]	Strontium[87]	Between 40 and 63 billion	
Potassium[40]	Calcium[40]	1,500,000,000	
Potassium[40]	Argon[40]	14,000,000,000	Abundant; provides dates for events 100,000 years or older
Carbon[14]	Nitrogen[14]	5568 ± 30	For events more recent than 50,000 years

depends on the burial of the dead animal or plant with mud or dust shortly after its death, for any carcass or other remnant that is not almost immediately covered soon undergoes disintegration or is torn to bits by scavengers. As is the case with rock formation, to which fossilization corresponds in many ways, buried remains become more and more heavily covered with silt with the passage of time and therefore the oldest fossils occur in the deepest layers and the most recent ones near the surface.

Following burial, most bodies decay and leave no evidence of their existence; only if conditions are just right do they become preserved as fossils. Most frequently deposition in water and a covering of mud provides the requisite anaerobic situation, so that prehistoric remains are generally found in rocks formed by sedimentation. After burial, although the soft parts typically decay away, harder or more resistant portions remain intact; slowly, over the centuries,

minute particles of the bone or leaf structures break off or are dissolved but the cavities thus vacated are replaced with minerals contained in the wet mud surrounding the specimen, until finally the whole structure has become supplanted by inorganic substances. The processes of replacement are on such a fine scale that it is actually possible to study the cellular structure of fossil leaves, tree trunks, and bones.

Still better fossils are sometimes formed in another manner, one that involves embedding in a gumlike substance. Tar beds, such as those of the noted Rancho La Brea asphalt deposits now included within the city limits of Los Angeles, are often natural traps for ground-dwelling animals. During past ages smaller animals attempting to reach the pools of rain water collected on the asphalt, became mired in the sticky surface. The presence of these hapless creatures attracted larger carnivores, which occasionally likewise found themselves ensnared when at-

Figure 23–2. Mammoth bones in the Rancho La Brea tar pits. Many finds such as these have thrown light on Californian animal life as it existed a million years ago. (Photograph courtesy the Los Angeles County Museum.)

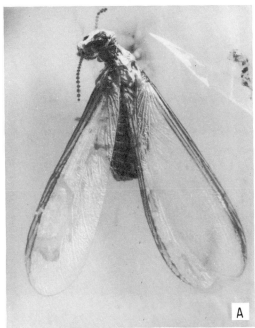

Figure 23–3. Insects embedded in amber. Occasionally insects become entrapped in the sap of trees and may be preserved as fossils under proper conditions. *Kalotermes snyderi* Snyder, a termite (A) and *Agriotes succiniferus* Becker, a click beetle (B), both from the late Oligocene of Chiapas, Mexico, are shown. A film of air partially conceals the latter's head and thorax. Note the fine state of preservation as indicated by the hairs on the beetle's wing covers. (Courtesy of Dr. Paul D. Hurd, Jr., and the Department of Entomology and Parasitology, University of California, Berkeley.)

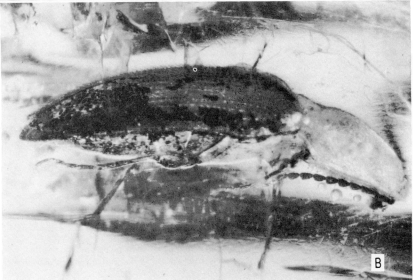

tempting to feed on the others. In turn, as they slowly sank in the gummy bed, their dead carcasses lured vultures and other scavengers to a similar fate. Over a million years or more this bed became one of the richest depositories for well-preserved skeletons of Pleistocene (Table 23–1) birds and mammals (Figure 23–2).

By similar methods, but on a much smaller scale, insects may become embedded in sap oozing from trees and eventually are preserved intact in amber, as fossilized resin is called (Figure 23–3).

Incompleteness of the Fossil Record. Because of the peculiar requirements of fossilization, it is obvious that only a

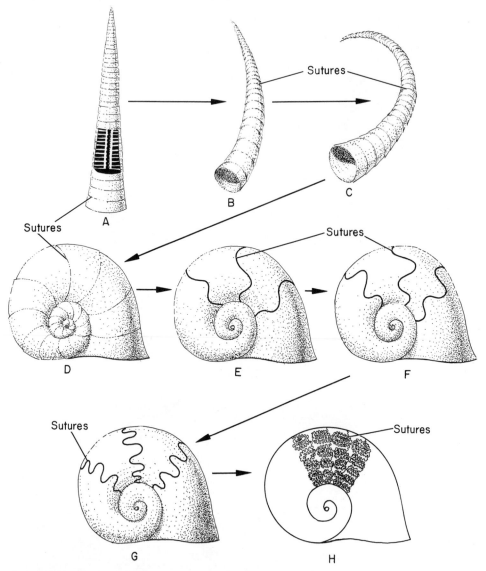

Figure 23–4. Evolution of the nautiloids. The straight cone first gives way step-by-step to coiled species; still later, the straight suture of early forms is replaced by increasingly complexly folded sutures.

small fraction, indeed, of things living at a particular time have opportunity for preservation as fossils. Especially is this true of organisms which, like slugs, jellyfish, hydra, and protozoans, have no hard parts within their bodies. Moreover, after fossils have been formed, the stratum in which they lie may become elevated and eventually completely eroded away by wind and water action or may be destroyed by heat of compression or by volcanic activities. In final analysis, to be of value in paleontology, a fossil must be exposed to the surface, encountered by an interested person, and safely deposited in a well-maintained collection. Consequently, there is little wonder that the fossil record is fragmentary and that gaps in knowledge are of frequent occurrence.

The Evolution of the Nautiloids. Like the Protozoa, most of the metazoans that arose in pre-Cambrian times were too soft-bodied to leave clear evidence of their origin, although it is true that during the close of the Proterozoic some mollusk shells and many worm burrows are to be found. Following the Cambrian a number of invertebrates, especially those like Mollusca and Echinodermata, which possess resistant shells and skeletons, have left remarkably complete records of their origin, ascendancy, and often, extinction. Perhaps one of the most clear-cut and interesting is that of the mollusks that led to the modern nautili. These surviving representatives, it will be recalled (page 203), possess coiled shells divided by septa into chambers, with elaborate sutures on the surface marking the internal location of the septa. Although during their history several important side-branches develop, including one that leads to the squids and octopi and another to a now extinct group known as ammonites, for simplicity's sake, all are referred to as *nautiloids*.

Although there is little doubt that ancestral forms developed no later than late Cambrian, the first clear-cut nautiloids are found in the next higher period, the Ordovician. These earliest fossil representatives had straight conical shells (Figure 23–4); internally, however, these simple hard coverings demonstrate their nautiloid nature by the presence of chambers formed by transverse septa through which runs the characteristic siphon. Externally, too, the relationships are indicated by the presence of sutures, but

Figure 23–5. Complex suturing in a nautiloid. In this ammonite, one of the nautiloids, can be gathered some idea of the complexity that eventually developed in the suturing of the shell. (Courtesy of Dr. J. Dan Powell, *Journ. Paleon.*, Vol. 37, 1963.)

unlike higher species the sutures in these early forms are simply straight lines. That this chambered gas-filled shell was a highly favorable adaptation for its possessors is indicated by the fact that certain species attained a length of 15 feet and thus were by far the largest animal of Ordovician times. Although the straight shell was successful, it was not the ultimate, for it later became supplanted by slightly coiled varieties and these, in turn, by more strongly spiral types, until quite tight coils were established. Thus one feature of modern nautili, a tightly spiraled shell containing chambers, was brought to perfection, but the sutures were still quite simple.

It was not until the Devonian, 100 million years later, that the sutures began to lose their simplicity. In some of the species extant during that period the lines first became broadly waved and then gradually increasingly undulant (Figure 23–4) but still gave no real indication of the intricacies to come. From this period on the shell of the several groups of nautiloids increased steadily in complexity and by the Mesozoic the suturing was highly intricate (Figure 23–5).

Throughout the 170 million years of this era these animals dominated the seas; more than 6,000 different species have so far been described from Mesozoic deposits, some of which exceed 10 feet in diameter. Then, when the era drew to a close, all except a handful of species entirely disappeared.

The Evolution of the Horse. One of the first historical sequences to be worked out for a mammal, but by no means the last, was that of the horse. Its account opens with the earliest creature that possessed any recognizable equine qualities, the small species of eohippus (*Hyracotherium*), found during the Eocene, about the size of a large terrier. As forests were then more abundant than grasslands, it is not surprising to find that these early forebears of the modern horse had teeth suited for browsing on low shrubs rather than for grazing. Nor did they possess the long muzzle of the present-day form; the anterior region of the skull was so short, in fact, that the eyes were located about halfway between the base and the tip of the nose. Moreover, the feet were quite different, the hind pair having three toes, the front set four;

Figure 23–6. A restored skeleton of *Mesohippus*. While the feet still possess three functional toes and the neck is short, the legs are somewhat elongated and a prolonged muzzle is present. From Big Badlands, South Dakota (Oligocene). (Courtesy of the Museum of Geology, South Dakota School of Mines and Technology, Rapid City.)

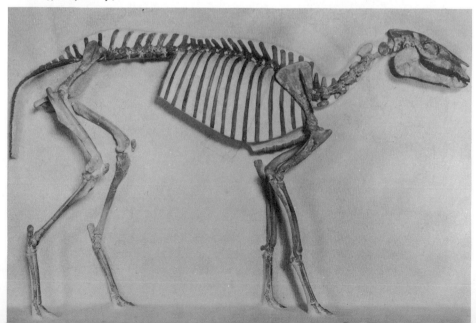

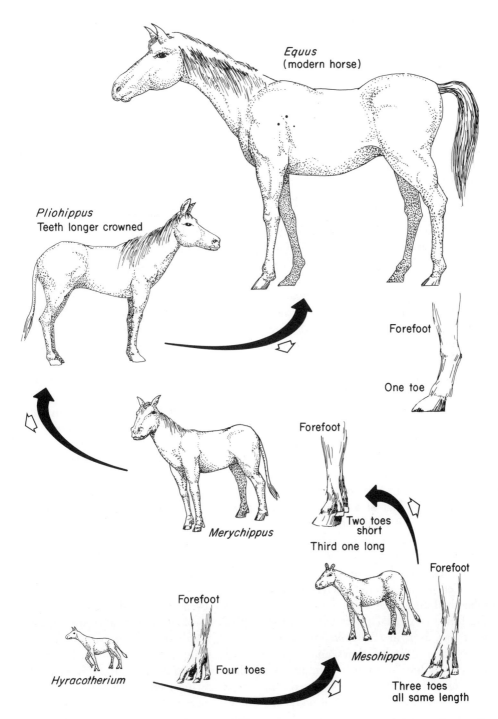

Figure 23–7. The evolutionary history of the horse. Only a few of the numerous changes undergone by the members of this group are shown in this diagram.

yet each toe bore a hoof, and the foot otherwise shared many structural similarities with modern descendants. Later in the Eocene and in the Oligocene many lines of development are found in the Old World, several of which, including *Mesohippus,* show changes leading toward present-day structures. In *Meso-*

hippus, for instance, the muzzle elongated somewhat (Figure 23–6), so that the eyes were located well behind the middle of the length, and the dentition became modified when the canines were lost and the premolars enlarged to approach molars in size. Moreover, the legs lengthened to some extent, while the forefeet lost the fourth toe, so that they like the hind ones, had three toes, all of which were sufficiently long to reach the ground and be functional. In the late Oligocene and early Miocene, *Miohippus* and others show these processes carried still further (Figure 23–7). The structure of the feet, especially, was more advanced, for the lateral toes had become so shortened as to be useless remnants. Although a number of quite horselike genera of this period persisted in browsing, others, including *Merychippus,* as the grasslands spread, became adapted to this newly abundant source of food. In particular, this genus shows the final steps in the conversion of the premolars into molarlike teeth and the early stages in the loss of distinct roots on all of the grinding types of teeth. In stature now a body size similar to that of a burro had been attained, and, all in all, one would have had little difficulty in identifying these creatures as some type of horse had they been encountered in the flesh. The remainder of the account merely finishes what had thus been well initiated. On the feet all external traces of extra toes were lost, even in *Pliohippus,* the dominant form of Pliocene times, and reduced to mere "splints" on the remaining middle digit, while the legs elongated still more strongly and the over-all body size increased. Furthermore, the muzzle became longer and the roots of the grinding teeth were displaced entirely. As these developments reached their culmination, the modern genus *Equus* finally appeared in the Pleistocene to continue by a series of representatives until the present.

COMPARATIVE MORPHOLOGY

The biological discipline in which the structure of one species is compared with that of another, namely *comparative morphology,* has so much evidence to present that only a few examples of its major categories can be outlined. In many studies the various fossil representatives are also considered with extant varieties, for the principles are of universal application.

Homologous and Analogous Structures. When comparisons of closely related forms are made, it is to be anticipated that the various organs and appendages, although differing in finer details, should correspond to one another in their major aspects, and such is found to be the case in actuality. For example, the legs and feet of an owl are essentially of the same construction as those of a heron, even though they are used in different ways, whereas the wings of both types are basically identical to those of all other birds. When less similar species, such as members of different vertebrate classes, are compared (e.g., a bird with a mammal), however, it is somewhat amazing to find comparable similarities in fundamental structures. Not only are corresponding bones found in the legs and toes of the two diverse types, for example, but likenesses even in musculature, nerve supply, and blood supply also are encountered. Furthermore, comparisons of the bird's wing with the mammal's foreleg show similitudes, and indeed comparable facts are uncovered no matter what system or organs are examined, whether the digestive tract, reproductive system, or skull. That these data cannot be explained on the assumption that there is only one way to form a leg, digestive system, or other part becomes obvious when basically dissimilar species, such as a vertebrate and an arthropod, are

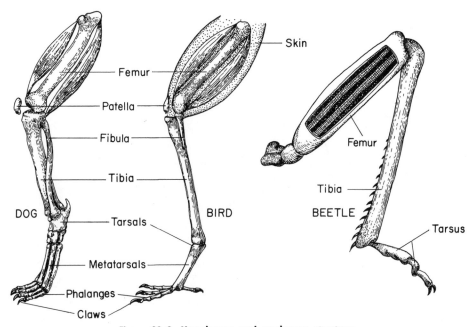

Figure 23–8. Homologous and analogous structures.

studied together. Insects, for example, are ·found to have well-developed legs, but the skeleton is of chitin, not of bone as in a bird or mammal, and the muscles are enclosed within the skeletal elements, whereas the vertebrates have the opposite arrangement. Nor can correspondences be found in musculature, nerve supply, or blood vessels—veins and arteries are in fact completely lacking in the insect leg. Hence, although an insect has legs, in the sense of appendages employed in walking, no fundamental similarities to bird or mammal legs exist in morphology. Therefore these appendages, as are all organs that correspond in function but not in structure, are said to be *analogous,* whereas parts that closely approach one another on a morphological basis are referred to as being *homologous* (Figure 23–8).

If comparisons of a vertebrate and an insect are made system by system, only analogies can be found, whether skeletal, digestive, nervous, or any other is considered. In contrast, insects share nu-

merous homologies with spiders, crayfish, and other arthropods, just as birds, fish, and the other vertebrates have many homologues in common. To explain these and innumerable other data, biologists suggest that such homologies are indicative of actual relationships—that is to say, their possessors are diverse descendants of common ancestry—whereas analogies are suggested to result from unlike structures being put to similar uses. Often, when basically dissimilar parts become adapted for the same function, the term *convergence* is applied (e.g., the wings of flying insects and flying vertebrates), whereas *divergence* pertains to differing adaptations made of one basic organ, such as the various specializations of the forelimb of mammals (Figure 23–9).

Vestigial Structures. As the morphology of any species is studied, parts are encountered for which no use can be found and which seem to be remnants of some former functional organ. Possibly the most noted example of such

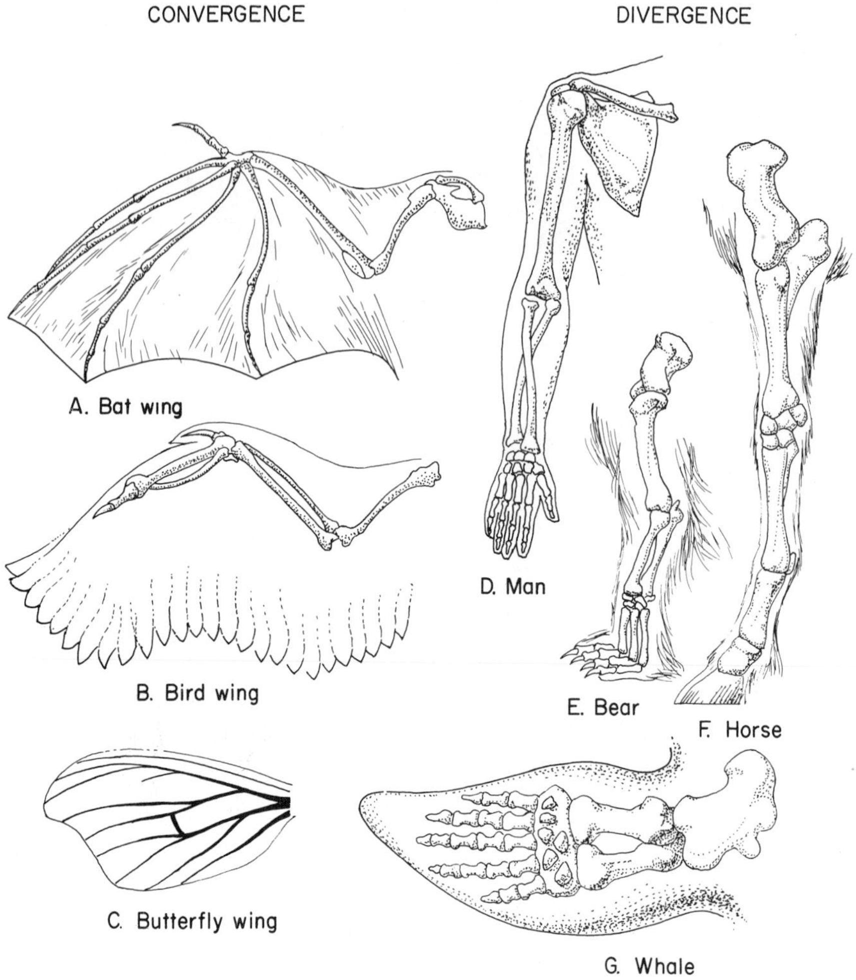

CONVERGENCE   DIVERGENCE

A. Bat wing

B. Bird wing

C. Butterfly wing

D. Man

E. Bear

F. Horse

G. Whale

Figure 23–9. Convergent and divergent evolution. On one hand, basically different body parts may become superficially similar through adaptation for like functions, and, on the other, fundamentally identical structures may become highly differentiated through adaptation to diversified usages.

vestigial structures is the vermiform appendix of man and other higher primates. As pointed out before (page 335), this is all that apparently remains of a once large and useful caecum that earlier primates employed in digesting bits of nutshells or other resistant vegetable matter. A biologist might explain the degeneracy of the caecum into an appendix on the basis that the higher primates, having undergone alteration in their food habits, would be unaffected when a chance mu-

tation reduced the size of the caecum somewhat or even after a series of many similar genetic changes further reduced it to its present vermiform state. In contrast, if a comparable mutation occurred in an individual among the more primitive forms, which still pursue the earlier modes of feeding, the progeny, being unable to digest their natural food, would perish, and hence would leave no descendants to pass on the deformity.

Many comparable vestiges are found

in numerous types of animals. To mention only a few, whales, for instance, possess a pelvis but no hind appendages, and similarly the boa constrictor, alone of the modern snakes, has remnants of pelvic bones. In man one anatomist found and listed close to 100 characters that have no function, including the coccyx, the vestige of a former tail, wisdom teeth, which are rarely serviceable, canines, which are far too weak to serve for tearing flesh, and a complete but functionless set of muscles to move the ears. Furthermore, in connection with the coccyx, it might also be pointed out that an occasional human is born with an external tail which often is 4 inches or more in length. Although as a rule such tails consist solely of cartilage and skin, more than one has contained a bone or two.

COMPARATIVE EMBRYOLOGY

During its embryological development, the individual frequently undergoes a series of changes which have no visible bearing on the attainment of the definitive form. Often characteristics are acquired which so strikingly resemble simpler species that one famous biologist, named Ernst Haeckel, during the late nineteenth century, felt impelled to announce his *biogenetic law*, which succinctly states that "ontogeny recapitulates phylogeny"—that is, the "history of the development of the individual repeats the salient features of the history of its race." Although Haeckel thus conceived of embryos as representing actual adult ancestral stages, generally today they are more usually accepted as portraying the embryonic or immature states of a former antecedent. Illustrations of the type of evidence presented by embryology is confined to those groups with which the student has a deeper acquaintance.

The Larvae of Certain Crustacea. One of the puzzles that faced early systematists working with invertebrates involved the placing of certain oddities that resembled the then-known phyla very little, if at all. Among the enigmatic groups was that comprised of the barnacles. On the basis of the hard valves that cover

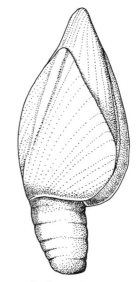

A. Barnacle

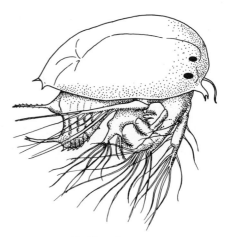

B. Nauplius

Figure 23–10. A barnacle and larva. Whereas the adult barnacle shows almost no resemblance to other crustaceans, the larva is quite similar to forms such as shown in Figure 11–4.

the body, some zoologists classed these animals as mollusks, whereas others found the remnants of appendages enclosed beneath the valves as suggestive of arthropod affinities. But until clear-cut evidence was encountered, the various proposals remained solely matters of opinion. Once the life cycle of the barnacle had been worked out, however, doubt could remain no longer, for the egg was found to hatch into a typical nauplius (page 189), which larval type is found in the life cycle of many well-known crustaceans (Figure 23–10). Although the adults of these aquatic arthropods bear no resemblances to other members of this class, the existence of similar larvae, characterized by the presence of only three pairs of appendages in each case, suggests that the two diverse groups at one time shared a common ancestral type, and hence are related.

The Embryos of Vertebrates. Perhaps the most striking evidence of embryology is found in the series of embryos derived from the various vertebrate classes. Not only do they provide eye-catching similarities externally (Figure 23–11), but many others exist internally. Without doubt the student will recall the notochord characteristic of all chordates, which exists in every stage in the lower forms but is confined to the developmental stages of the higher members except as vestiges. Embryonic vertebrates without exception possess a set of gill slits too, which become functional only in the simpler classes, although in

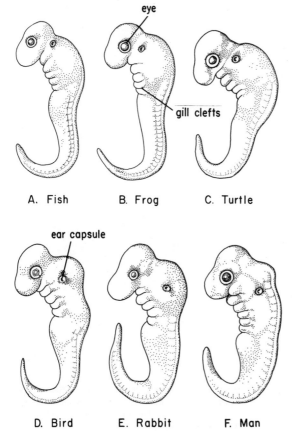

A. Fish   B. Frog   C. Turtle

D. Bird   E. Rabbit   F. Man

Figure 23–11. A series of vertebrate embryos. Embryos of the major vertebrate classes are illustrated at corresponding stages of development.

each case, whether fish, snake, bird, or mammal is the subject, arteries, veins, supportive cartilages, and other basic parts are universally present. But the account of how the original gill arches became modified to form jaws, the trachea, ear ossicles, and so on, need not be repeated here. Even in species that are tailless in the adult well-marked tails are found in the developing young. In addition, many other items of resemblances in the embryo can be listed briefly, some of which are confined to the higher vertebrates, including the reptiles proper, birds, and mammals. Among the more pertinent of these features are the extraembryonic membranes, all four of which are found in these three groups, in spite of the great differences that exist in the immediate environments in which the embryos grow, especially in the inter-uterine development provided by mammals. Even among the mammalian forms, it will be remembered, a well-developed yolk sac exists, although it is utterly devoid of yolk, and hence is a completely useless vestige. Finally, the fact that higher mammals undergo gastrulation and other processes in manners closely resembling the corresponding steps in birds can have meaning only if it is assumed that the placental mammalians descended from ancestors that laid eggs rich in yolk, like those of the avians and monotremes.

COMPARATIVE PHYSIOLOGY AND BIOCHEMISTRY

Since modern comparative physiology and biochemistry alike are concerned with the chemistry of living things, they frequently overlap both in their approaches and discoveries. Although actually they differ somewhat in point of view and interest, the two are treated here as though they were one and the same science.

Comparative Serology. In the comparative serological aspects of physiology, use is made of the animal's ability to secrete antibodies in counteracting the presence of foreign proteins. Each antibody, it will be remembered, is, as a rule, specific against only one kind of protein, and, in turn, each of these antigens is characteristic of one species of organism. Here this statement must be qualified somewhat, for every species produces some proteins shared by its close relatives, but each also forms a number of compounds confined to itself alone (Figure 23–12). As a result the more closely related species are, the more proteins they have in common, whereas the distantly related forms have few or none.

To test the relationships on this series of assumptions, comparative serology employs standard immunization procedures up to a certain point. If species A is to be tested against species B, blood serum taken from either test species is injected into a third form, often a guinea pig or sheep. In the following hypothetical experiment the sheep shall be employed, for it produces a larger quantity of test material, and species A will supply the blood proteins. When injected into the sheep, species A's serum behaves as an antigen and induces antibody formation in the treated species. After a couple of weeks some of the antibody-containing serum can be prepared from a small quantity of the sheep's blood and used as an *antiserum,* in this case anti-A serum. Procedures beyond this point vary considerably, but one frequently employed technique utilizes two series of glass test tubes, in each of which a carefully measured quantity of undiluted antiserum is placed. Then, using fresh blood serum from species A, a standard amount of this material is added above the anti-

serum of one series but at steadily increasing dilutions. In the first test tube
a dilution of 1 part serum to 100 parts
water might be employed, and in other
tubes 1 to 500, 1 to 1,000, 1,500, 2,000,
and so on. At the heavier concentrations

distinct rings of precipitates form on the
interfaces between the two liquids as
the anti-A serum reacts with the proteins of A, but as dilution increases the
layer becomes successively thinner, until
a point is reached at which no reaction

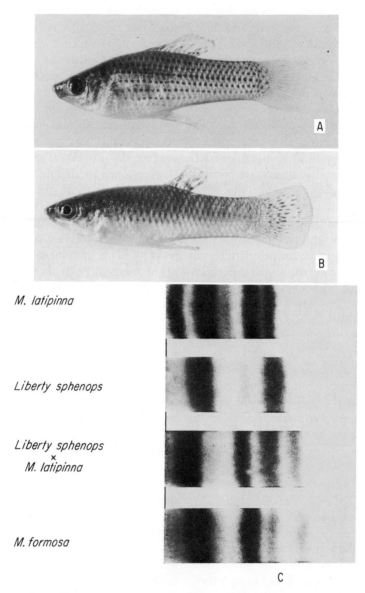

M. latipinna

Liberty sphenops

Liberty sphenops
×
M. latipinna

M. formosa

C

Figure 23–12. Protein differences between species. In these two species of tropical fish, commonly called
"mollies," striking differences in proteins are found by electrophoretic studies.   A. Male *Mollienesia
latipinna,* collected near Brownsville, Texas.   B. Male *M. sphenops,* from near Tamazunchale, Mexico.
C. Electrophoresis patterns of muscle proteins from these two species. (Courtesy of Dr. Richard E. Hewitt
and the Carnegie Institution of Washington.)

can be detected. This first series gives a measure of the *titer,* or strength, of the antiserum, and its end point is considered to represent 100 per cent interactability between the two sera. In the second set of tubes serum from species B is then tested similarly against anti-A serum. Reaction in this second set, the actual test, is always lighter and reaches an end point at a greater concentration than the serum of A, perhaps at 75 per cent as dilute or maybe only at 10 per cent. To be more concrete, let it be assumed that species A shows a reaction up to, but not beyond, 1 part in 10,000, whereas species B fails to react at greater dilutions than 1 in 6,000; by dividing the first end point into the second, species B may be said to be

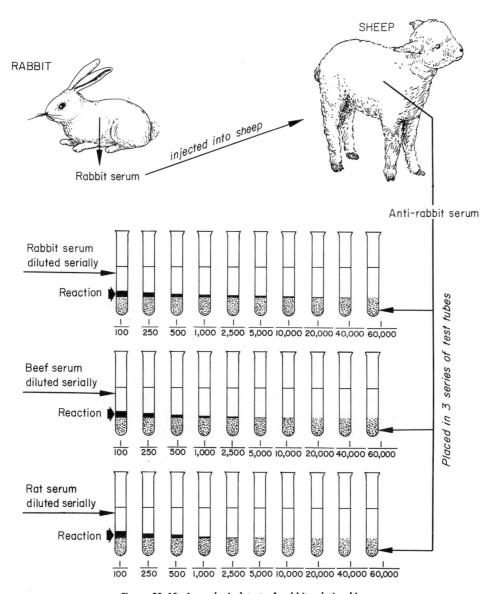

Figure 23–13. A serological test of rabbit relationships.

"60 per cent" related to species A—that is, it shares 60 per cent of the same proteins (Figure 23–13).

By these means the relationships of large numbers of animals have been tested, often with striking results. One interesting set of experiments attempts to determine the relationships of the rabbits with other mammals. On the basis of dentition, earlier mammalogists had placed these animals with the rodents, but subsequent studies of the teeth, as well as other aspects of morphology, show that many points of difference exist, so for several decades they have been removed to an order called Lagomorpha. Serological tests indicate a similar isolation of the rabbits from the rodents, to which animals they are found to be no more closely related chemically than is man; in fact, closer kinship to cattle is shown than to any other species tested. Similarly, when serological tests are applied to human beings, close ties to the chimpanzee are found on this basis, less strong ones to baboons, and only remote relationships to dogs. Here, too, agreement with morphological and systematic findings is observed.

Cellular Physiology. Whereas serology tests the differences in molecular structure of blood plasma proteins to show varying degrees of absence and correspondence, *cellular physiology* strongly suggests the common ancestry of all living things because of fundamental similarities in cell chemistry. Whether the organism studied is a blue-green alga, bacterium, yeast, worm, or human, many identical physiological and biochemical processes are found in all cases. In each and every one energy is derived from glucose, first of all, by way of phosphorylation and glycolysis, and second, in the processes occur identical sets of enzymes and coenzymes, ATP, DPN, FM, the cytochrome series, and others already familiar to the student. Moreover, the chemical constituents of protoplasm itself show a similar catholicity. Although minor fluctuations in the proportions of the elements are encountered from species to species, basically the same sorts of compounds are found in each, and many of these besides the coenzymes cited above share chemical identity. And, finally, the RNA codings for amino acids appear to be the same, insofar as current knowledge indicates, in all the diverse forms of life.

OTHER SOURCES OF EVIDENCE

Although all the branches of biology have overwhelming quantities of data bearing on evolution, space considerations too must be borne in mind. Consequently the remaining biological disciplines with contributions to make are only briefly outlined, although some of them testify in a most convincing fashion.

Systematics. Before knowledge of the number and variety of organisms had become very extensive, it was commonly expected that each species would be found clear-cut and sharply delineated from all others on the premise that each had been individually created. However, as the New World and other extra-European portions of the globe were opened up and became explored biologically, the numbers and variations of known forms increased with great rapidity. Furthermore, as museum collections grew in size and were studied in detail, difficulty was often experienced in separating one species from another. Frequently, what had been believed to be two different forms were found to represent mere extreme variations or subspecies, as intergrades between the extremes came to hand from intervening territories. Consequently the variants have come to be accepted as stemming from adaptations acquired by the same species to local dissimilarities in environment. In other words, the several subspecies have evolved from a common ancestral stock in response to respective differences in ecology.

Furthermore, the scheme of classification itself is set up to reflect the differing levels of relationships between organisms. The fact that species of living things are so similarly constructed as to permit their arrangement into genera might be taken as indicative of common descent; likewise, the assignment of genera into families, families into orders, and so on, is suggestive of differing levels of common ancestry.

Biogeography. The importance of evidence presented by biogeography is well indicated by the fact that under its influence Darwin first conceived his theory. On the voyage of the *Beagle* around the world in search of biological information, the ship had put into port in Peru, where this famous biologist, then still a young man, became acquainted with the animal and plant life. Next the ship headed for the Galapagos Islands, located about 600 miles out to sea; here Darwin became so impressed with the biota that he was inspired with the evolutionary concept. In the first place, a number of organisms, including a huge terrestrial turtle, were quite distinct from anything found on the mainland, whereas others closely resembled, yet possessed marked differences from, species he had just encountered in Peru. These data he found most readily explained if it were assumed that the islands had been at one time connected with the continent but long since had become isolated. Since connection with the mainland had been broken, some of the inhabitants of the continental land masses became extinct, leaving surviving remnants such as the tortoises on the islands, as well as the other way around. Furthermore, the presence of similar yet distinct forms could be explained on a basis that the insular and mainland forms in each case had originally been one species but that on either the islands or continent, or on both, mutations occurred subsequent to their separation, which because of the barrier that existed between them could no longer be transmitted from one population to another.

Evidence from Genetics. Basically, this science presents three principal types of evidence, the first of which is derived from breeding tests between species. When two totally dissimilar species (i.e., systematically unrelated) are crossed—for example, if pollen from plum is applied to a fig blossom—no offspring result and the two are said to be *intersterile*. Only matings between closely similar and systematically related species ever produce progeny; even then in some cases when the mating is successful the resulting hybrid may be sterile. The mule is an example of this fact and shows that horses and donkeys are *interfertile* to some degree. As a whole, matings between these two species reflect the treatment generally accorded them by systematists. Their partial interfertility corresponds to a degree of relationship expressed by the fact that formerly both were considered members of the same genus *Equus;* simultaneously, the sterility of the progeny indicates that the kinship is not extremely close, as signified by the current removal of the donkey in systematic treatments to a separate genus or subgenus on structural considerations. Like serology, interfertility provides a gauge to measure relationships, but, for the most part, it is useful only among close relatives.

The second kind of genetic evidence is quite different in its nature from the foregoing and concerns the existence of *homologous genes.* In two different species of fruit flies, *Drosophila melanogaster* and *D. simulans,* normally the eyes are red, but sometimes white eyes arise by mutation. By the usual techniques it has been found that the two alleles for eye color in the common laboratory species (*melanogaster*) are located on the X-chromosome, and more recently the same location has been established for the corresponding genes in the second form. By crossing the two species, it has now been determined that the white-eye gene of each is also the allele of red in the other, and hence, the two sets of genes are homologous. In fact, by using a whole series of such interbreeding tests an investigator has determined that no gene of one species is without a homologue in the other. Hence

the resemblances of the two fruit flies could be stated in genetic terms as resulting from the presence of innumerable homologous genes and the differences similarly from lack of homologous sets perhaps or the presence of distinctive alleles.

Moreover, the most recent work on the chemical nature of genes indicates that in the majority, if not all, of the organisms the same coding is employed for the various amino acids. $U, U, U,$ for example, is the symbol of phenylalanine and leucine whether one is concerned with yeast, bacteria, seed plants, or vertebrates, and the same is true for each coding studied to date. So it is evident that the chemistry of inheritance itself is universally shared, a fact difficult of explanation on any grounds except that of genuine relationship.

Questions for Review and Thought

1. Summarize Darwin's theory of evolution. Which of his premises are observable facts and which are strictly theoretical?

2. Prepare a bare but complete outline of the sciences (including biological branches) that in one way or another contribute to an understanding of the history of living things. Give the basic types of evidence presented in each case.

3. Define geology and paleontology. Show how these two sciences differ and how they might be of mutual assistance. How does the earth's crust seem to have been formed? State the means by which rocks are dated.

4. From a textbook of paleontology, or other source, outline the evolutionary changes that have occurred in the following groups of animals, giving names of geological periods and dates:

    (a) elephants   (c) Arthropoda
    (b) reptiles   (d) fishlike vertebrates

5. In each instance state whether the sets of structures are completely homologous, entirely analogous, or a combination of the two and the reasons for your answers:

    (a) the bony structure of bat and bird wings
    (b) the entire wings of bats and birds
    (c) the eyes of insects and man
    (d) the gills of crayfish and squids
    (e) the flame-cells of flatworms and rotifers
    (f) the pinchers of crabs and scorpions
    (g) the prehensile hands of squirrels and monkeys

6. List all the major features of vertebrate embryos, class by class, to show the likenesses and differences, tying in the changes in the urinary and reproductive systems outlined in appropriate chapters.

7. Outline in detail the procedures employed in comparative serology.

8. What evidence can you give that suggests that certain genes may be homologous in different species?

Supplementary References

Abelson, P. H. "Paleobiochemistry." *Sci. Amer.,* July 1956.

Blechschmidt, E. *Stages of Human Development before Birth.* Philadelphia, Saunders, 1961.

Cain, A. J. *Animal Species and Their Evolution.* New York, Harper, 1960.

Colbert, E. H. *Dinosaurs: Their Discovery and Their World.* New York, Dutton, 1961.

Crow, J. F. "Ionizing Radiation and Evolution." *Sci. Amer.,* September 1959.

Darwin, C. *On the Origin of Species.* New York, Philosophical Libr., 1951.

Dodson, E. O. *Evolution: Process and Product.* New York, Reinhold, 1960.

Eiseley, L. C. "Charles Darwin." *Sci. Amer.,* February 1956.

Glass, B., *et al. Forerunners of Darwin* (1745–1859). Baltimore, Johns Hopkins Press, 1959.

Huxley, J. S. *Evolution as a Process.* London, Macmillan, 1954.

Moore, R. *Man, Time, and Fossils: The Story of Evolution,* 2nd ed. New York, Knopf, 1961.

Ross, H. H. *A Synthesis of Evolutionary History.* Englewood Cliffs, N. J., Prentice-Hall, 1962.

Sanderson, I. T. *The Dynasty of Abu: A History and Natural History of the Elephants, Past and Present.* New York, Knopf, 1962.

Sheppard, P. M. *Natural Selection and Heredity,* rev. ed. New York, Harper, 1959.

Simpson, G. G. *Life of the Past.* New Haven, Conn., Yale Univ. Press, 1953.

Tinbergen, N. "The Evolution of Behavior in Gulls." *Sci. Amer.,* December 1960.

The Mechanical
Basis for
Changing Species

Now THAT the concept of evolution and the evidence showing the existence of this natural phenomenon have been outlined, questions arise regarding the possible mechanisms by means of which the evolutionary processes might be brought about. While obviously the changes in species basically arise from the inheritable mutations among individuals, problems center around theoretical considerations as to how these can possibly effect alterations at the species level. In other words, is it possible for scattered genetic variants to become accumulated within populations to such a degree as to induce the creation of a new species?

Population Genetics

In studying the genetic events within natural species, normally it is assumed that the major populations composing each are *panmictic*—that is, every individual within the population has an equal opportunity of mating with any other of the opposite sex, regardless of its genotype. In other words, no bias exists against any specimen because of its genetic constitution; consequently, each gene can, over a period of years, be transmitted freely throughout the entire population. As far as any given gene is concerned, each panmictic population containing it represents a *gene pool*.

The Hardy-Weinberg Law. Since the evolutionary concept is one that depends on changes in species, a basic question arises as to how such changes can be brought about from a genetic standpoint. To test the feasibility of developing extensive alterations, it might be well to employ a hypothetical species of bird, in which a crest of feathers (*n*) on the head is recessive to the absence of this feature, called normal (N). Further, it is assumed that the two alleles are represented in such proportions in the population as a whole that about 70 per cent of the gametes produced carry a normal gene and the remainder, the recessive one. If these gametes unite randomly, what change in genetic constituency can be anticipated for the gametes engendered by the next generation and eventually alter the species' genetic makeup?

When the next generation is initiated at breeding season, the gametes may be expected to unite and produce the various genotypes in the proportions indicated by the following Punnett square:

Egg Types

	0.70 N	0.30 n
0.70 N	0.49 NN normal	0.21 Nn normal
0.30 n	0.21 Nn normal	0.09 nn crested

Sperm Types

Thus 49 per cent of the second generation are homozygous normal birds, 42 per cent are normal but heterozygous, and only the remaining 9 per cent are crested; hence on the surface it appears that a great reduction in the crested allele has occurred. However, when it is recalled that half the gametes produced by the heterozygotes will carry the recessive gene and if this amount (21 per cent) is added to the homozygous recessive gametes (9 per cent), it becomes evident that no genetic change has really taken place within the population. Consequently, each generation on mathematical considerations can be anticipated only to generate sperm and eggs containing normal and crested genes at a uniform ratio of 70 to 30, no matter how many times the processes are repeated. This constancy in proportions of contrasting genes in panmictic populations is an expression of the *Hardy-Weinberg law;* this, in effect, states that all other factors being equal, evolution is an impossibility from a strictly genetical standpoint.

Changes within Populations. But the very fact that the numerous panmictic populations which constitute every species do not always possess identical ratios of genes indicates that the Hardy-Weinberg law does not operate constantly in nature and that some external factors exist which tend to counteract the mathematical probability of constancy. For example, in the human species the Nordics are characteristically blue-eyed and blond-haired, many Mediterranean people have brown eyes and black hair, and numerous other populations, not to mention races, similarly possess representative combinations of traits. Therefore some forces were operative at one time or another that upset the Hardy-Weinberg expectations, else these differing ratios of alleles could not have arisen.

Among the more obvious factors that may induce changes in the ratio of genes are *migration* and *mutation.* If the bearers respectively of alleles A and a were to migrate out of a gene pool in proportions equaling the existing ratio, of course, the over-all constitution would remain unaltered, but it can logically be anticipated that proportionally more A than a might leave a few populations, whereas in several others the opposite could occur. So, although the mean rate of migration of the two alleles in the sum of the species' numerous gene pools might correspond to the original proportions, a certain number could be altered in one direction or the other by these processes.

Similarly, if gene a mutates back to

its allele *A* and if the opposite simultaneously happens at the same rate, the net result is nil, for one change cancels the other. However, if the first mutation occurs with greater frequency than the second, a net gain may be envisioned to occur and a change in their ratios instigated. Nor is there any reason to suppose that either allele could not mutate to a third one, say *a'* or *A'*, such as is known to exist for the human blood groups and hair color (dark, blond, red). In general, the net difference between the rate of mutation of one allele to another is referred to as *mutation pressure.* Even a fairly low mutation pressure can eventually produce a population almost entirely homozygous for one allele or the other, and, if the direction of change is not reversible, then complete homozygosity for the mutant can be produced in a relatively short expanse of time.

When the mutation results in a phenotype either more or less favorable to the organism for its survival or for the opportunity of reproducing itself, *selection* can exercise a decided influence on the existing proportions of alleles. Lethality in the homozygous condition, for one illustration, could certainly tend continually to reduce the proportional rate of occurrence of the allele concerned. In a preceding discussion one lethal of many African tribes, sickle-cell anemia (*S*), has already been mentioned. On the basis of the fact that one third of some populations are heterozygotes, with normal recessive homozygotes (*s*) constituting the remainder, a drop of 7 per cent in the frequency of *S* should be noted in each generation, due to the 100 per cent negative selection of homozygous dominants. Although this is the normally expected fate of lethal dominants, in actual experience no change in ratio occurs, for other selective forces are operative in the area, in this case principally malaria. With the

relative lack of modern medical facilities in the region, this disease has a high rate of fatality and normal (*ss*) individuals have been found less resistant to its ravages than those who carry the sickle-cell trait (*Ss*). Hence, in spite of its lethality in the homozygous condition, the sickle-cell allele is subject to a positive selective action that counterbalances the unfavorable one, so that constancy in the ratio of genes is preserved.

Not always is the rate of selection, often referred to as *selection pressure,* so strong as in the foregoing example. Yet it is not at all unlikely that many mutations either improve or worsen the individual's ability to perpetuate its genotype by way of progeny, whether its actual survival is directly concerned or just its longevity, reproductivity, or rate of growth. However, it should always be borne in mind that favorableness can vary in accordance with the environment of the period, and as geological times advance what may have at one time been a highly successful adaptation may prove a strong handicap under new conditions. There can be little doubt that the dinosaurs, which thrived and dominated the lands for more than 100 million years, must have possessed many extremely advantageous genes and the group enjoyed positive selective activity for these long eons. But during the world-wide climatic revolutions that marked the close of the Mesozoic, with its tremendous impact on the character of the vegetation, what previously had proven to be of survival value now became detrimental, with consequences that are well known to the student.

The fourth and final known factor that can operate to effect alterations in the genetic constitution of the species is highly efficient in small populations but absent in large panmictic ones. However, as shown in a preceding discussion, the geographical range of species is the generalized sum of innumerable small populations, each separated by minor geographical or ecological barriers, yet united by the wanderings of occasional individuals or by physical changes wrought by geological time. In these demes chance combinations of gametes may accidentally favor one gene or the other; for instance, in any given hospital or community mostly girl babies will be born one month, while in another boys may be dominant temporarily among the newborn. Or perhaps providing a better illustration in the human species are the occasional newspaper accounts of a family with a "football team" for progeny, eleven sons but no daughters, whereas others may have eight or more girls but not a single male offspring. Although each time an egg is fertilized there is an equal chance for either an X- or a Y-chromosome-carrying sperm to unite with the egg, only when large numbers of progeny are summarized is equality in number of the sexes attained. Whereas in large populations or in the over-all aspects of a species such chance variations from normality, distinguished by the term *genetic drift,* tend to cancel one another, in small ones they may exert strong influences here and there, just as migrations do.

POSSIBLE STEPS IN SPECIES CHANGES

Since the observed facts clearly indicate that many populations of diverse organisms under natural conditions do undergo genetic changes, despite the Hardy-Weinberg law, a question next arises as to the manner in which mutations may accumulate and possibly influence the creation of a new species. Perhaps the most lucid approach to an understanding of the existing theories is

that of breaking the topic into two basic steps, the first one to propose the processes involved in the formation of subspecies, followed by a second that considers the conversion of these to full species rank. Moreover, use of a hypothetical case rather than the abstract processes may further simplify matters. To this end an imaginary species of frog may be utilized, in which the eyes have, among other features, a typical golden-yellow iris and the sides of the body are whitish. This nonexistent frog species occupies a theoretical range that is roughly rectangular in outline, with its long axis running east and west; although its conjectural geographical locality matters little, for ease of discussion it might be convenient to suppose it lies just north of the equatorial belt.

A Possible Manner of Origin of Subspecies. To start the processes of change within this species, a series of spontaneous mutations may be assumed to occur in the northeastern quarter of the species range so as to produce a proportion of 1 mutant to 100,000 normal. If the population density is, in the interest of simplicity, taken to be approximately uniform throughout the territory, this new allele in which perhaps the iris is white instead of golden is thus present in a ratio of $1:400,000$ individuals when the inhabitants of the four quarters are considered. Assuming all else to be equal, over a period of years wandering white-eyed specimens could disseminate that gene throughout the whole of the species. Because of the existence of this *gene flow,* although genetic drift and differential migrations may effect local changes in proportionate quantities of the alleles, those of the entire species can be envisioned only as remaining constant at $1:400,000$, according to the Hardy-Weinberg law. Similarly, if a second mutation should arise, this time one that alters the white flanks to yellow and is confined originally to the southwestern quarter, it, too, given sufficient time, could be expected to spread throughout the entire range. So all that has been accomplished by these mutations is the production of rare individual variants, some with white eyes instead of golden, some with yellow flanks in place of white, and a very few representatives with both new traits (Figure 24–1).

But the foregoing is the end product

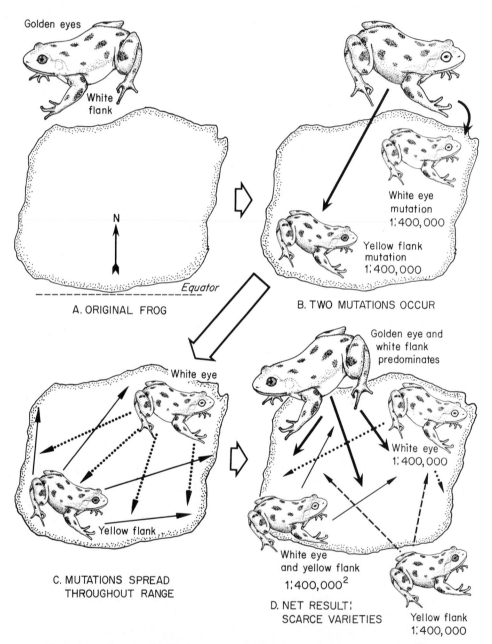

Figure 24–1. The eventual distribution of mutations in the absence of natural selection.

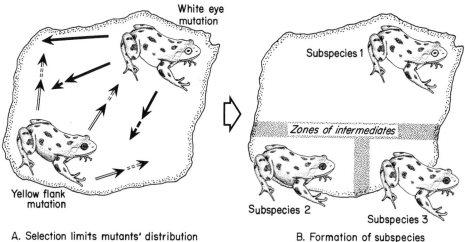

A. Selection limits mutants' distribution

B. Formation of subspecies

Figure 24–2. Natural selection and the origin of new subspecies.

only when all else is equal; let us now propose that each trait possesses a *selective value*—that is, makes its possessor somewhat more capable of surviving certain conditions than the normal. If the white-eyed gene in the foregoing illustration is conjectured to produce a side effect that delays egg laying by several weeks, then in the north, especially during years in which exceptionally late cold spells occur, golden-eyed normals might have a large percentage of their progeny killed by the freeze, whereas the white-eyed mutants would produce their usual numbers. Thus it is conceivable, that over a few centuries of time white-eyed frogs could become the dominant form and might even replace the golden-eyed type entirely. However, this displacement would occur only in colder regions, for the delay in breeding in the warmer belt might result in the failure of the white-eyed tadpoles to reach maturity before the ponds and small streams go dry for the summer. Hence in the south the gene, being in this sense lethal, would be excluded from entering this area (Figure 24–2).

Now a selective value may similarly

be assumed for the second mutation that arose within the southwestern area; possibly an assumption can be made that the yellow-flank mutation shortens the hibernation period, so that the adults initiate breeding in late winter. Because eggs are deposited early, perhaps they can be imagined as surviving only in situations exposed to the sun, and, hence are confined to open grasslands of southern locations. Consequently, since the normal white-flanked specimens mate later than the new variant, their larvae tend to survive less successfully in such localities, for they are at a disadvantage in competition with the further developed and larger yellow-flanked variants. If the southwestern quarter is assumed to be largely open grasslands whereas the southeastern is forested, eventually most of the individuals in the southwest would become almost exclusively yellow-flanked, while retaining the golden eyes as suggested above. Those in the southeast, however, would retain both sets of primitive conditions and would remain golden-eyed and white-flanked, and the northern half would be largely occupied by white-eyed and white-flanked specimens. As several distinctive traits are now distributed on a geographical basis, a systematist might feel justified in treating each as distinct major subspecies. This category rather than that of species would be selected because in all likelihood zones of intergradation containing forms intermediate to the distinctive types would exist between each of these large groups.

The Origin of New Species. And as long as the climate fluctuated somewhat from year to year and as long as intermediate conditions otherwise made it possible for regions of intergradation to persist, the existence of gene flow between the several major populations is evidenced. In its presence these subspecies could never be expected to attain the species level of distinction, for whenever a new gene came into existence in any portion of the range, barring strong selective pressures, it would sooner or later be transmitted throughout all populations. Thus it is apparent that creation of new species can occur only after major populations become segregated from the rest by some mechanism that prevents gene flow; in other words, *reproductive isolation* must come into existence. As an illustration the foregoing hypothetical case may be continued a

bit further. Typically, the male frogs during the mating seasons float in the water or stand on the bank of the pond and call to attract females. Each species has its own song, and females respond only to males that produce the right pattern of notes. In western Australia, for example, there are three species of frog that are so similar in appearance that it is extremely difficult to identify specimens by examination; however, their calls are so distinctive that they can be distinguished at a distance. If the hypothetical yellow-flanked gene of the southwest grasslands is considered also to influence the voice of the male and the response of the female, the entire population would be as effectively isolated reproductively from the northern and southeastern forms as though a wall were built between them, and that population would soon acquire a degree of distinctiveness that would warrant its recognition as a full fledged species, for intergrades normally could not occur (Figure 24–3).

In birds and most other vertebrates and invertebrates as well such *behavioristic* changes can be equally efficacious. Moreover, *physiological* alterations, especially in regard to reproductive func-

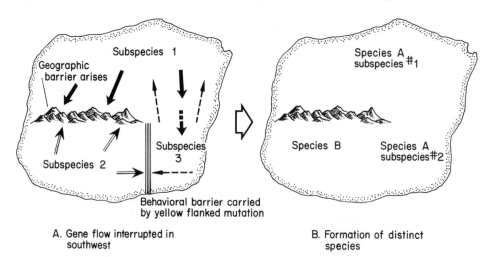

A. Gene flow interrupted in southwest

B. Formation of distinct species

Figure 24–3. Reproductive isolation and the formation of new species.

tion, can induce reproductive isolation; for instance, if in a bird that normally breeds in May a mutation in some individuals delays mating until July, it can be readily understood that the two populations would be thoroughly isolated. Among other isolating mechanisms that can be named are *geographical* features such as mountains, rivers, and oceans, *ecological* and *climatic* conditions such as forests, grasslands, temperature, and rainfall, and *morphological* barriers, which are especially frequent among invertebrates and quite commonly involve inability of mating be-

cause of changes in shape of the external genital organs. Finally, *cytological* factors frequently result in intersterility through the inability of chromosomes to undergo synapsis, so that inviable gametes are produced, or through an incompatibility of the egg and sperm.

To summarize, in order to produce subspecies, aside from mutations and random-chance factors, natural selection is required, whereas to form new species gene flow must be interrupted by reproductive isolation to eliminate the intergradation that typically ties subspecies together.

Questions for Review and Thought

1. What law suggests that evolution cannot occur? On what is this based? By what four means are the effects of this law suggested to be overcome?

2. What do you suppose would happen in a village of Africans possessing the stated ratio of sickle trait if malaria was completely eliminated from the area? What might conceivably happen if the disease should mutate and become so frequent and severe that all normal-celled individuals die whereas only 10 per cent of the heterozygotes do?

3. Define the following terms:

(a) mutation pressure (d) gene flow
(b) selection pressure (e) gene pool
(c) reproductive isolation (f) panmictic

4. What would you suggest to be the main fundamental ingredient involved in all evolutionary changes in species?

5. Starting with a species of green lizards, whose heads bear a red crest and which breed in May, prepare an imaginary account of how this species could be developed into four distinct subspecies. List with examples all factors that might be involved in converting these into full species.

Supplementary References

Carter, G. S. *A Hundred Years of Evolution*. London, Macmillan, 1957.

Dobzhansky, T. *Evolution, Genetics and Man*. New York, Wiley, 1955.

Dodson, E. O. *Evolution: Process and Product*. New York, Reinhold, 1960.

Dowdeswell, W. H. *The Mechanism of Evolution*. New York, Harper, 1960.

Greene, J. C. *The Death of Adam: Evolution and Its Impact on Western Thought*. Ames, Iowa State Univ. Press, 1959.

Lerner, I. M. *Genetical Basis of Selection*. New York, Wiley, 1958.

Li, C. C. *Population Genetics*. Chicago, Univ. Chicago Press, 1955.

Mayr, E. *Animal Species and Evolution*. Cambridge, Mass., Harvard Univ. Press, 1963.

Patterson, J. T. *Isolating Mechanisms*. Austin, Univ. Texas Press, 1947.

The History of Mankind

With the facts of evolution in hand, as well as a theoretical basis for the processes, it is pertinent now to examine our own possible origins and changes in the light of this knowledge. Although so far as the science of biology is concerned, man's history is not one whit more important than that of any other animal, it nevertheless is of particular interest to each of us as members of that species. Frequently speculation on our origins or on events in our descendancy are of considerable appeal, whether these pertain to just immediate families, to the whole of our nation, or to all of mankind.

held no notion at all of evolution and was a strict adherent to the concept of the species' fixity, he nevertheless classified man along with apes, monkeys, and other similar forms in the order of mammals he named the Primates. This relationship he based, of course, strictly on the structural resemblances that all these animals share. And these similarities must be appreciated, along with their possible mode of origin, before man's history in a more restricted sense can be fully comprehended. Perhaps the origin of the whole group provides the most logical point with which to begin this discussion.

The Lower Primates

Even though Carl Linné, the author of the binomial scheme of classification,

PRIMATE CHARACTERISTICS

Among the modern representatives of the order *Primates,* are included the large-eyed lemurs, loris, and tarsiers in addition to the various monkeys, apes, and man, but these are definitely primate in all their traits and hence too advanced to be considered ancestral. However, to these are often added the tree shrews, peculiar squirrel-like, arboreal forms of Oriental forests that possess an over-all simplicity of structure that makes them ideal subjects for the role of the progenitor type. Although some points of their anatomy demonstrate that their relationships are strictly with the order Insectivora, to which the insect-eating mammals like moles and typical shrews are also relegated, they display an over-all primitiveness that here will be employed, in lieu of the still-unknown actual ancestral prototype of the Primates, as suggestive of the latter's characteristics.

Possible Ancestral Primate Traits. As indicated by the tree shrews, among the most likely characteristics of the primitive mammalian stock that gave rise to the Primates is that of a multiplicity of teeth, for many marsupials, bats, insectivores, and other simpler forms similarly have 56 or even larger numbers of teeth. Moreover, the dentition was probably of a generalized type—that is, without specialization for any particular function—and included incisors, canines, premolars, and molars on both jaws. Like the other simpler mammals cited, the progenitor more than likely had five digits on each leg, every one of which was provided with a claw. Furthermore, it undoubtedly was small in body size and had a mouselike low skull, ending in a long muzzle. As to whether or not the distant stock was ground-dwelling or arboreal is not clear, but regardless of this background, there can be little doubt that it took to the trees before recognizable Primates ever came into existence. In short, this hypothetical form possessed all the characteristics that today are found in the tree shrew except those which make the latter

a definitive member of the Insectivora—features of the skull, brain, scapula, and other organs that are beyond present consideration.

The Characteristics of the Order Primates. Beyond this possible point of origin, the rest of the evolutionary account, or *phylogeny,* of the apes and their kin depends on a comprehension of the structural traits shared by the higher members of the order. Aside from those that characterize mammals in general, the most common feature is the presence of nails on the digits in place of claws; as no other mammal possesses this modification of the claw, this trait becomes an absolute indicator of membership in this taxon (Figure 25–1). Perhaps this sentence should read *"the* absolute indicator," for it alone is entirely unique to the group. For instance, although the restriction of mammary glands to the thoracic region is distinctive in the sense that most mammals have at least several sets on the abdomen, the dugongs have an arrangement similar to the present group. Prehensile hands and feet, with the thumb or great toe opposable to the rest, are a feature shared by all members of this order, but they are possessed also by squirrels and several other unrelated arboreal types. Stereoscopic vision, which provides for an improved ability in perceiving depth and thus judging distance, has been developed by carnivores as well as by those under discussion. And perhaps the only other really distinctive trait, a generalized pattern of dentition including 32 to 36 teeth, while found in most members of the order, is absent in a few like the aye-aye, which lacks canines. Nonetheless, it can be noted that no other type of mammal possesses an identical combination of structural features, and it is primarily on such constellations of distinctions that this, like any taxon of living things, is established.

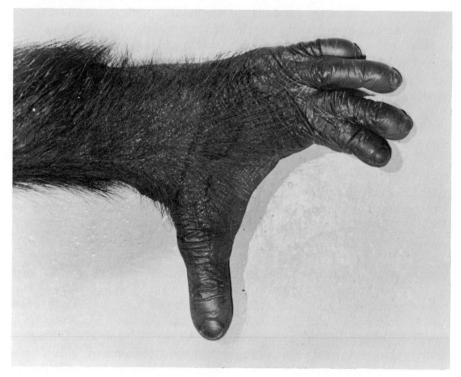

Figure 25–1. Distinctive features of the Primates. This foot of the pigmy champanzee, or bonobo (*Pan paniscus*), shows both its prehensile nature and the nails on the digits that form two of the more unusual traits of these members of this order. (San Diego Zoo photo.)

In addition to these several general trends, certain comparative conditions and physiological processes are also generally true of the Primates. Color vision, for one thing, is probably better developed in the higher members of the group than in any vertebrate, but lower forms like tarsiers and lemurs are color-blind, for, since they are strictly nocturnal, their eyes accordingly lack cones in the retina. Second, the central nervous system is highly developed in the more advanced species, particularly the cerebral cortex and cerebellum, but in the primitive forms no especial enlargement can be noted. Then, too, sweat glands of the eccrine type are more abundant than apocrine, whereas the reverse is true in other mammals, and menstruation instead of the usual estrous cycle is found in many monkeys and all apes as well as human beings, but in no other order.

THE EARLY PRIMATES

It should not be supposed that changes from the hypothetical ancestor to a recognizable definitive primate came about abruptly; each trait and trend that characterizes the group today was acquired over millions of years by the long, slow processes of species formation, repeated untold numbers of times. For instance, the progenitor did not at any time produce young that had nails in place of claws. More likely, to judge from the condition among the lemurs and tarsiers, in which only one digit on each hand or foot is provided with a nail, one species possibly underwent a mutation in which

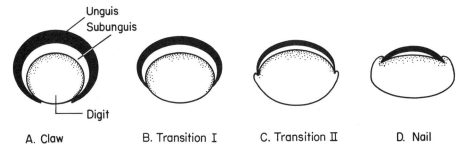

Figure 25–2. **Hypothetical stages in the transition of a claw into a nail.** Although only two intermediate steps are shown in the diagram, many more doubtlessly were required to change the claw into a nail by evolutionary processes.

Figure 25–3. **A modern lemur.** Photographed in the forests of Madagascar. (Courtesy of Dr. J. J. Petter.)

the claw of one finger on each hand was flattened a bit and perhaps not entirely closed on the lower surface. Later a second mutation in the descendants of that species carried the flattening and opening slightly further, and still later, a third genetic change added to these trends, until finally, a recognizable nail was brought into existence (Figure 25–2). In the animals mentioned, which range from the size of a rat to as large as a cat, many other typical primate features are similarly poorly developed. The cerebrum is not especially enlarged; so the braincase is relatively low, particularly in lemurs, and the muzzle is long. While in lemurs

(Figure 25–3) the eyes are set at an angle so that vision is not entirely stereoscopic, the modern species of loris and the tarsier have this primate characteristic fully developed (Figure 25–4); hence, the acquirement of this trait may be perceived to have involved a series of gradual steps. Although a few other features of the order, such as opposable thumbs and great toes and thoracic nipples, are fully developed at this lower level, many, including abundant eccrine sweat glands and menstruation, either have not been carried to completion as yet or are entirely lacking.

Between these lower relatively simple

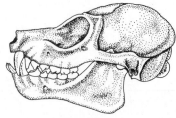

Figure 25–4. The slow loris. *A.* In this photograph of a specimen captured in east Africa can be seen the forward-directed eyes, the nails, and the opposable thumbs typical of most Primates. (Courtesy of *Pacific Discovery.*) *B.* The skull is considerably lower than that of more advanced members of the order, indicative of a relatively smaller brain and less intelligence.

forms and the next level in primate history is a large gap so far as extant species are concerned, nor is this breach extensively filled by the fossil record. As a whole, members of the order are not good subjects for fossilization, for their arboreal habitats militate against the animals' becoming buried with any high degree of frequency, and moreover, their general level of intelligence enables them as a group to avoid tar pits or similar natural traps that have led to mass preservation of less-shrewd species. Furthermore the animals are largely confined to the tropics, in which regions fossils are both less abundant and more difficult to uncover.

The Higher Primates

In all the existing primates other than the foregoing, the typical features are well-developed. Nails are found on every digit, the eyes are directed forward and provide stereoscopic vision, the brain has become enlarged, and this enlargement has been accompanied by a correlated elevation of the cranium. The dentition, too, has assumed its definitive characteristics, having become reduced to 32 teeth in the adult set while remaining generalized in retaining teeth of all types. Hence, the changes beyond the lowest *anthropoids,* as all higher primates are called, concern relative development of body and skull for the most part, aside from the rather sudden appearance of menstruation among the highest types.

NONHOMINOIDS

Customarily two separate superfamilies of monkeys are recognized, one of which is confined to the New World and provided with prehensile tails; as this is generally considered the more primitive, it is typically arranged as the lowest branch of the anthropoids. Above these forms, the old-world monkeys, found throughout tropical regions of Eurasia and Africa, along with a sprinkling of South American forms, are treated as representing the next higher branch (Figure 25–5). Among these the tail is not capable of grasping objects and is, in fact, frequently reduced in length, sometimes to a mere stub, as in the mandrill and macaque. In addition in many larger species of old-world monkeys, often referred to as the lesser apes, menstruation, sometimes of a simple nature, has largely replaced the primitive estrous cycle, so that an approach to the condition in the highest forms is made.

Besides man, only a few of the most advanced anthropoid types exist today, uniformly regarded as representing two different families. In one, the *Pongidae,* are placed the great apes, while in the second, the *Hominidae,* modern man and his fossil predecessors are included. Each of these branches is currently suggested to have descended from a fossil form that lacked the definitive characteristics both of man and of the great apes. From this common point each has gone on a completely different line of development, so that the modern Pongidae no more resemble the common progenitor than do the various races of men. Before the discussion of the immediate fossil ancestry of the latter, the changes that have occurred in the former should be examined first.

The Great Apes. Prerequisite to an appreciation of the changes that have taken place is a knowledge of the peculiar traits possessed by the end products of the branch, the existing members of the Pongidae. Among the most outstanding features is the unusual length and strength of the forearms, adaptations that permit *brachiation*—i.e., the ability

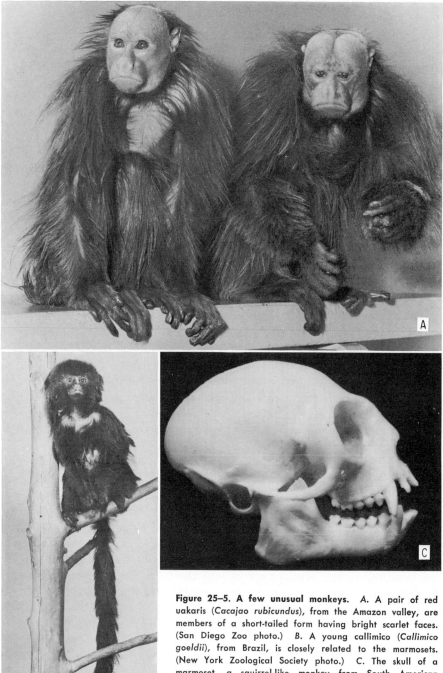

Figure 25–5. A few unusual monkeys. *A.* A pair of red uakaris (*Cacajao rubicundus*), from the Amazon valley, are members of a short-tailed form having bright scarlet faces. (San Diego Zoo photo.) *B.* A young callimico (*Callimico goeldii*), from Brazil, is closely related to the marmosets. (New York Zoological Society photo.) *C.* The skull of a marmoset, a squirrel-like monkey from South American jungles.

Figure 25–6. A lowland gorilla. Gorillas, like Albert from the San Diego Zoo, are the largest of all primates, for males frequently attain a weight of 500 pounds. (San Diego Z ɔ photo.)

to progress through the trees by means of the arms largely unassisted by the body or legs. Particularly striking is this development in many species of gibbons that live in southeastern Asia, with the orangutan of tropical portions of that same continent ranking second. The gorillas (Figure 25–6) and chimpanzees of African jungles have shorter arms and cannot brachiate to the same degree as the foregoing; consequently these species are confined to the ground to a greater extent, although their nests are built in trees. In this respect they are more similar to the fossil "apes" of the Miocene period, the oldest apelike forms so far encountered, which do not have the arms elongated at all and therefore are considered to have lacked the ability to brachiate. Generally, a fossil form of the genus *Proconsul* is accepted as being similar to the actual progenitor of modern apes as well as of man. On the basis of these characteristics, then the gibbons and orangutan can well be looked upon as the most highly developed pongids, with the gorilla and chimpanzee less advanced, a degree of relationship that also receives confirmation from serological studies (Figure 25–7).

MAN'S HISTORY

The Fossil Record of Man's Development. In common with the other primates, man's earlier stages were passed in tropical regions, and hence, well-preserved fossils are similarly scarce. Nevertheless, during the last several decades a number of important finds have been made that contribute to both the numbers and particulars of man's ancestral types. Only cranial portions, fragments of jaws, or isolated teeth, unfortunately, are characteristically found as fossils, although a number of more or less complete skeletons have been encountered in recent years. Since only fragmentary remains are typically all that provides the fossil basis of man's ancestry, the question may arise as to how anthropologists can be certain as to the identity of their specimens. To answer this inquiry ref-

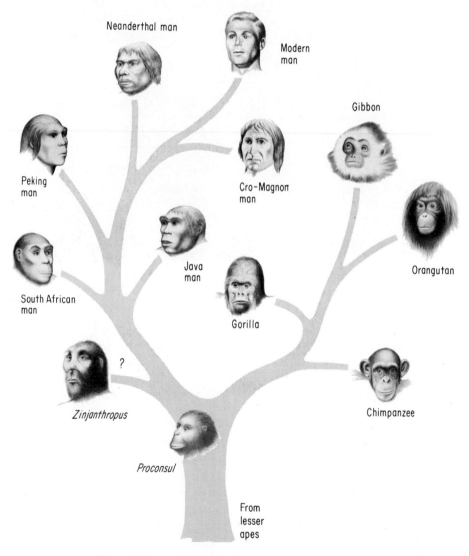

Figure 25–7. A phylogenetic tree of the higher primates.

erence to the chief points of difference between man and the modern apes needs to be made.

Aside from the absence of hair on the body, which characteristic can scarcely be expected to fossilize, distinctive features of mankind are confined to his upright carriage, his lack of prehensibility in the feet, his higher skull, flatter face, lower orbital ridge, his use of fire and other tools, and especially the shape of the dental arch. Since the last-named trait is both among the most distinctive and most frequently fossilized body part, it is of particular value in establishing hominoid relationships. If the dental arch of any of the great apes is examined, it is found to resemble closely the same structure in monkeys. In all the anthropoids, save man, the molars on each jaw form rows that parallel one another (Figure 25–8), so that the dental arch resembles a capital letter U. That of man, on the other hand, is found to be broadly rounded, more like the outline of a bowl than U-shaped; furthermore, the teeth are more closely set so the whole arch is proportionately shorter. This trait, then, can serve as an absolute measure of human relationship, for no ape or monkey, past or present, possessed anything resembling its condition. However, it is logical to suppose that this trait too evolved gradually; so at the earliest stages, conditions intermediate between the pongid's and mankind's might be anticipated, but thus far few fossils representing this early level have been encountered. Nevertheless, fossil forms with definitive human dental arches have been found that show either primitive or intermediate stages in the development of other peculiarities of modern man.

Early Fossil Forms. Perhaps the oldest, geologically speaking, fossil form (Figure 25–9) that possesses the typical

dental arch is the *South African Man* (*Australopithecus prometheus*), which is from the earliest part of Pleistocene deposits in South Africa. This is antedated, however, by a still earlier form, from the same general area, called *Plesianthropus* (meaning "nearly a man"), or *Giant South African Apeman*. As the names imply, the latter has characteristics of both man and apes, with skull and dental arch characteristics somewhat intermediate between the two but possessing pelvic bones closer to those of man. No general agreement has as yet been

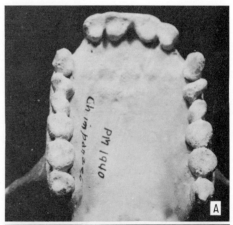

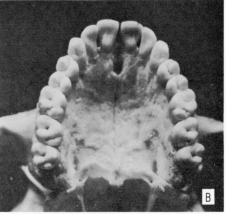

Figure 25–8. The dental arches of the pongids and hominids. In the great apes, as well as in the lower anthropoids, the dental arch is parallel-sided (A), whereas that of modern man is shorter and broadly rounded (B).

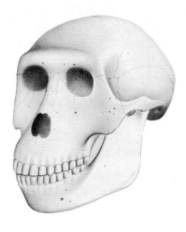

Figure 25–9. A skull and restoration of the South African man (Australopithecus prometheus).

reached by anthropologists as to the proper disposition of this form—i.e., whether it should be considered to belong to the pongid or hominoid line of ascent. Even less is known about an exciting find made in 1959 in Tanganyika. Although *Zinjanthropus boisi* (Figure 25–10), as this form is called, appears definitely to be human as very primitive

tools are associated with it, the date of its occurrence (1,750,000 years) is far older than that of any other hominoid fossil. This date, obtained by refined potassium-argon techniques, establishes the Pleistocene as being nearly 2 million years in duration, twice as long as previously believed. However, as already stated, the South African Man is definitely along the human line, although low in the scale. As a whole in this fossil man, the cranium is flat, not rising high above the scarcely evident orbital ridges, and the braincase's capacity of around 615 ml lies within the same range as that of the gorilla. But since the latter's body mass is about three times greater than this man's, the proportionate increase in brain size attained here is evident (Figure 25–6). In addition to *Australopithecus,* other fossil men have been found in Africa, so many in fact that Africa is often accepted as being the site of man's origin, but for the most part these others are only scantily known.

On another continent an important fossil (Figure 25–11) was found late in the nineteenth century that is relatively early in the history of humanity, namely that of the *Java Man* (*Pithecanthropus erec-*

Figure 25–10. A restoration of Zinjanthropus boisi.

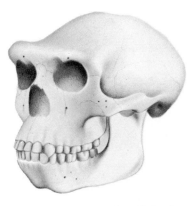

Figure 25–11. A restoration of the Java man (*Pithecanthropus erectus*) and the skull on which it is based.

tus). For many decades the proper affinities of this form have been the subject of much debate, not always of a cool and objective nature, but since so many other fossil species have now been encountered, anthropologists currently for the greater part agree that it represents a man somewhat higher than the South African Man in the scale of evolution. Closely allied to this (Figure 25–12) is the *Peking Man* of China (*Sinanthropus pekinensis*), which had a considerably greater brain capacity, 900 to 1,200 ml compared with 750 to 900 ml for the former—that of modern man averages 1,350 ml. As the limb bones of both species are similar in shape to ours, it is certain that these fossil forms had an upright carriage. While only three specimens of the Java Man so far have been found, all from early Pleistocene about three-quarters of a million years ago, fragments of nearly 40 individuals of Peking Man have now been uncovered, which in age are closer to a half million years.

Recent Fossils. Between the above early men and more recent times, a scattering of extinct species occurs, but as

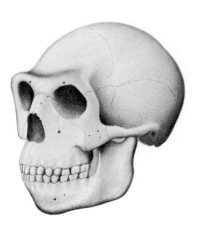

Figure 25–12. The Peking woman's skull and possible appearance (*Sinanthropus pekinensis*).

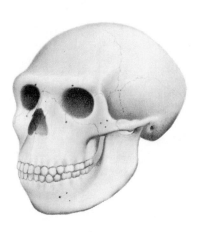

Figure 25–13. The Neanderthal man (*Homo neanderthalensis*) is a close relative of modern man that preceded him to Europe.

these are almost entirely represented by single fragments, they shall be passed by without further comment. However, around 150,000 years ago, there arose a form that persisted well into the last Ice Age, no less than 50,000 B.P.—a man that occupied much of Europe and North Africa and some parts of southern Asia. While a chin is lacking (Figure 25–13) and the head is thrust forward in "stoop-shoulder" fashion, the level of intelligence of *Neanderthal Man* (*Homo neanderthalensis*) must have been high, for he possessed a brain of unusual dimensions, approaching an average of 1,450 ml. And this cranial capacity does not take into account his relatively shorter stature, close to a mean of 5 ft. In build, too, these human beings were exceptionally rugged, with broad shoulders and powerful neck muscles. As a whole, the skull bones are thick and the orbital ridges rather pronounced, although less prominent than those of the Java Man, while the forehead is low and retreating, but again superior to that of *Pithecanthropus*.

Culturally Neanderthal Man had made immense progress, for although his stone implements were of the primitive Old Stone Age (Paleolithic) type, he had a strong social organization that enabled him to hunt successfully such huge beasts as the mammoth and woolly rhinoceros that then occupied much of the western Eurasian continent. While, in common with primitive man as a whole, cannibalism seems to have been practiced, there is much evidence to intimate that religions were followed, for in a Swiss cave occupied by *H. neanderthalensis* an altar has been found on which a bear skull was placed. This supposition is further strengthened by the fact that skeletons are often encountered arranged in a manner implying ceremonial burial.

The Advent of Modern Man. Early in the last continental glaciation while Neanderthal Man still existed, the first known remains of modern man were laid down in caves of southern France. These direct ancestral forms, *Cro-Magnon* by name, are considered to be a subspecies of *Homo sapiens,* to which species we ourselves belong. In body form, Cro-Magnon was tall, averaging close to 6 ft, and possessed unusually large brains, up to 1,650 ml in volume; the skull bore low

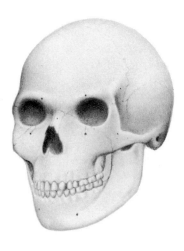

Figure 25–14. A skull and restoration of Cro-magnon man.

orbital ridges, and the chin was quite evident. Their stone tools also are advanced in form over those possessed by Neanderthal.

There is little doubt that this Cro-Magnon man (Figure 25–14) did not come into existence in such a dramatic fashion as suggested by his sudden appearance in France; it seems more likely that he invaded Europe from another land, probably killing off the neanderthal inhabitants in the process. Recent evidence points to a possible origin of *H. sapiens* in Africa, for in Palestine where the range of *neanderthalensis* ended in later times, a curious mixture of bones is found, grading from typical *neanderthalensis* to forms more closely approaching *sapiens*. This fact suggests that for many eons, the Near East provided a boundary between the two species, which fought and killed one another on one hand and occasionally interbred on the other. Finally, after *sapiens* had attained

Figure 25–15. An Australian aboriginal and his dingo pup. Among modern races of men, the Australian aboriginal is often rated as the most primitive. The deep-set eyes and low, broad nose are among his especially distinctive features. The dingos, or native wild dogs, can be used for hunting only until they become around 18 months of age; after that they revert to their wild state. (Courtesy of the Australian News and Information Bureau.)

its definitive structure and increased in numbers, it invaded and ultimately completely occupied the former land of the neanderthals (Figure 25–15).

Man—An Animal and More. Although the story is fragmentary with large gaps in knowledge of particulars, sufficient details now exist to leave room for little doubt as to the fact of man's common origin with lower forms. That he is one with the rest of the living world is, first of all, indicated by his cells sharing identical processes and enzymes possessed by all other organisms. His oneness with the Metazoa is undeniably indicated by the astral rays the animals alone, save for the brown seaweeds, display during mitosis. The presence of a notochord, gill slits, and hollow dorsal nerve cord can suggest nothing less than actual relationship with the Chordata; his hairy coat, though scant, his skeletal features, milk glands, diaphragm, heart, and brain structure uniformly attest to his common derivation from a mammalian stock. And finally, his internal and external morphology, including many unusual features shared by all species concerned and no other, as well as functional and chemical traits, too, shows that an apelike form was the common progenitor of both modern apes and man. So man is thoroughly and completely an animal in all his physical aspects.

However, we should not think for a moment that man is *just* an animal, for he is not. He possesses innumerable qualities not found in any other living thing on earth, even over and above the cultural objects his great brain has produced. An appreciation of beauty, his search for truth, and desire for mercy and justice are attributes no mere animal ever displays. Nor does any other organism strive to make the world better for posterity or show evidence of possessing a belief in things divine or a spiritual life to come, other than man.

Questions for Review and Thought

1. Characterize the order Primates. What are among the possible traits possessed by the ancestral stock? Why is a tree shrew often suggested to be ancestral to this mammalian order? Do all primate traits apply to mankind? If not, which are exceptions?

2. On what basis are the lemur and loris placed in the Primates? In what ways are they not primate in comparison to higher members? Why might the tarsier be considered more typical of the order than the lemur?

3. Outline the nonhuman history of the primates above the lemur-tarsier branch or branches. Suggest the changes that occurred in the ancestral stock at each level.

4. List the principal types of great apes. Which are the largest and the smallest of the species? Which two are found in Africa and which in Asia? Why are the gibbons often treated as the most advanced of the apes?

5. Prepare a list of the important types of fossil humankind, and give the characteristics of each as far as you are able. By what means can a fossil be clearly established as human? On what basis is Africa often proposed as the original home of man?

6. Outline the principal changes that have occurred both to man and to the great apes since their common ancestor lived back in Miocene times.

Supplementary References

Bacon, A. *Man's Next Billion Years.* New York, Exposition Press, 1959.
Clymer, E. *The Case of the Missing Link.* New York, Basic Books, 1962.

Dart, R. A., and C. Dennis. *Adventures with the Missing Link,* 2nd ed. New York, Viking, 1961.

Dobzhansky, T. *Mankind Evolving: The Evolution of the Human Species.* New Haven, Conn., Yale Univ. Press, 1962.

Lasker, G. W. *Evolution of Man.* New York, Holt, Rinehart and Winston, 1961.

LeGros-Clark, W. E. *Antecedents of Man.* Chicago, Quadrangle Books, 1960.

Lehrman, R. L. *The Long Road to Man.* New York, Basic Books, 1961.

Napier, J. "The Evolution of the Hand." *Sci. Amer.,* December 1962.

Schenk, G. *The History of Man.* Philadelphia, Chilton, 1961.

Von Koenigswald, G. H. R. *Evolution of Man.* Ann Arbor, Univ. Michigan Press, 1962.

Walker, E. P. *The Monkey Book.* New York, Macmillan, 1954.

Washburn, S. L. "Tools and Human Evolution." *Sci. Amer.,* September 1960.

Index

In place of a glossary this index serves to guide the reader to definitions of terms, where they may be seen in proper context. References to definitions are shown in **boldface**; illustrations are indicated by means of an asterisk (*).

DATE DUE

MAR 28 '72			
RESERVE			
MAY 8 '74			
MAY 1 4 '74			
Reserve			
JAN 27 '75			
OCT 1 5 '76			
GAYLORD			PRINTED IN U.S.A.